Student Solutions Manual

Bob Martin
Tarrant County College

D1507298

John Tobey Jeffrey Slater

Intermediate Algebra

Fifth Edition

PEARSON

Prentice
Hall

Upper Saddle River, NJ 07458

Editor-in-Chief: Chris Hoag
Executive Editor: Paul Murphy
Supplements Editor: Christina Simoneau
Executive Managing Editor: Kathleen Schiaparelli
Assistant Managing Editor: Becca Richter
Production Editor: Allyson Kloss
Supplement Cover Manager: Paul Gourhan
Supplement Cover Designer: Joanne Alexandris
Manufacturing Buyer: Ilene Kahn

© 2006 Pearson Education, Inc.
Pearson Prentice Hall
Pearson Education, Inc.
Upper Saddle River, NJ 07458

All rights reserved. No part of this book may be reproduced in any form or by any means, without permission in writing from the publisher.

Pearson Prentice Hall™ is a trademark of Pearson Education, Inc.

The author and publisher of this book have used their best efforts in preparing this book. These efforts include the development, research, and testing of the theories and programs to determine their effectiveness. The author and publisher make no warranty of any kind, expressed or implied, with regard to these programs or the documentation contained in this book. The author and publisher shall not be liable in any event for incidental or consequential damages in connection with, or arising out of, the furnishing, performance, or use of these programs.

This work is protected by United States copyright laws and is provided solely for teaching courses and assessing student learning. Dissemination or sale of any part of this work (including on the World Wide Web) will destroy the integrity of the work and is not permitted. The work and materials from it should never be made available except by instructors using the accompanying text in their classes. All recipients of this work are expected to abide by these restrictions and to honor the intended pedagogical purposes and the needs of other instructors who rely on these materials.

Printed in the United States of America

10 9 8 7 6 5 4 3 2

ISBN 0-13-149090-7 Standalone
      0-13-185761-4 Student Study Pack Component

Pearson Education Ltd., *London*
Pearson Education Australia Pty. Ltd., *Sydney*
Pearson Education Singapore, Pte. Ltd.
Pearson Education North Asia Ltd., *Hong Kong*
Pearson Education Canada, Inc., *Toronto*
Pearson Educación de Mexico, S.A. de C.V.
Pearson Education—Japan, *Tokyo*
Pearson Education Malaysia, Pte. Ltd.

Table of Contents

Chapter 1

1.1 Exercises

1. Integers include negative numbers. Whole numbers are nonnegative integers.

3. A terminating decimal is a decimal that comes to an end.

5. 13,001: Natural, Whole, Integer, Rational, Real

7. -42: Integer, Rational, Real

9. -6.1313: Rational, Real

11. $-\dfrac{8}{7}$: Rational, Real

13. $\dfrac{\pi}{5}$: Irrational, Real

15. 0.79: Rational, Real

17. 7.040040004L : Irrational, Real

19. $-25, -\dfrac{28}{7}$

21. $-\dfrac{28}{7}, -25, -\dfrac{18}{5}, -\pi -0.763, -0.333$L

23. $\dfrac{1}{10}, \dfrac{2}{7}, 9, \dfrac{283}{5}, 52.8$

25. $-\dfrac{18}{5}, -0.763, -0.333$L

27. 1,2,3,4,5,6,7

29. Commutative property of addition.

31. Inverse property of multiplication.

33. Identity property of addition.

35. Commutative property of multiplication.

37. Identity property of multiplication.

39. Distributive property of multiplication over addition.

41. Associative property of addition.

43. Associative property of multiplication.

45. Associative property of multiplication.

47. 12 is the additive inverse of -12.

49. $-\dfrac{3}{5}$ is the multiplicative inverse of $-\dfrac{5}{3}$.

51. (a) $\dfrac{3}{8} = 0.375 = 37.5\%$

    (b) $\dfrac{5}{8} = 0.625 = 62.5\%$

    (c) None

53. There are several possibilities. The second and third numbers increase by $100. $500 does not follow this pattern. The fourth through the eleventh numbers follow a doubling pattern. $125,000 does not follow this pattern.

55. No. When the winnings reach $15,625

1

© 2006 Pearson Education, Inc., Upper Saddle River, NJ. All rights reserved. This material is protected under all copyright laws as they currently exist. No portion of this material may be reproduced, in any form or by any means, without permission in writing from the publisher.

the next amount would be $7812.50 which is not a whole number.

57. $154(0.4) = 61.6$, about 62 people

1.2 Exercises

1. To add two real numbers with the same sign, add their absolute values. The sum takes the common sign. To add two real numbers with different signs, find the difference of their absolute values. The answer takes the sign of the number with the larger absolute value.

3. $\left|-\dfrac{2}{3}\right| = -\left(-\dfrac{2}{3}\right) = \dfrac{2}{3}$

5. $|8.3| = 8.3$

7. $|9-14| = |-5| = 5$

9. $|-b| = -(-b) = b$

11. $-6 + (-12) = -18$

13. $-3 + (-5) = -3 + (-(-5)) = -3 + 5 = 2$

15. $5\left(-\dfrac{1}{3}\right) = -\dfrac{5}{3} = -1\dfrac{2}{3}$

17. $\dfrac{-18}{-2} = 9$

19. $(-0.3)(0.1) = -0.03$

21. $-4.9 + 10.5 = 5.6$

23. $-\dfrac{5}{12} + \dfrac{7}{18} = -\dfrac{15}{36} + \dfrac{14}{36} = -\dfrac{1}{36}$

25. $(-2.4) \div (6) = \dfrac{-2.4}{6} = -0.4$

27. $\left(-\dfrac{2}{3}\right)\left(-\dfrac{7}{4}\right) = \dfrac{2 \cdot 7}{3 \cdot 4} = \dfrac{7}{3 \cdot 2} = \dfrac{7}{6} = 1\dfrac{1}{6}$

29. $(-4)\left(\dfrac{1}{2}\right) + (-7)(-3) = -2 + 21 = 19$

31. $12 + (-12) = 0$

33. $\dfrac{-5}{0}$ Undefined

35. $\dfrac{0}{-3} = 0$

37. $\dfrac{3-3}{-8} = \dfrac{0}{-8} = 0$

39. $\dfrac{-7 + (-7)}{-14} = \dfrac{-14}{-14} = 1$

41. $\dfrac{17}{18} + \left(-\dfrac{5}{6}\right) = \dfrac{17}{18} - \dfrac{15}{18} = \dfrac{2}{18} = \dfrac{1}{9}$

43. $\dfrac{5}{6} \div \left(-\dfrac{3}{4}\right) = -\dfrac{5}{6} \cdot \dfrac{4}{3} = -\dfrac{5 \cdot 2}{3 \cdot 3} = -\dfrac{10}{9} = -1\dfrac{1}{9}$

45. $5 + 6 - (-3) - 8 + 4 - 3$
$= 11 + 3 - 8 + 1$
$= 14 + (-8) + 1$
$= 6 + 1 = 7$

2

© 2006 Pearson Education, Inc., Upper Saddle River, NJ. All rights reserved. This material is protected under all copyright laws as they currently exist. No portion of this material may be reproduced, in any form or by any means, without permission in writing from the publisher.

47. $\dfrac{12-4(3)}{2-6} = \dfrac{12-12}{-4} = \dfrac{0}{-4} = 0$

49. $6(-2)+3-5(-3)-4$

$= -12+3-(-15)-4$

$= -9+15+(-4)$

$= 6+(-4)$

$= 2$

51. $15+20\div 2-4(3)$

$= 15+10-12$

$= 24-12$

$= 13$

53. $\dfrac{6-2(7)}{5-6} = \dfrac{6-14}{-1} = \dfrac{-8}{-1} = 8$

55. $\dfrac{1+49\div(-7)-(-3)}{-1-2}$

$= \dfrac{1+(-7)+3}{-3}$

$= \dfrac{-6+3}{-3}$

$= \dfrac{-3}{-3}$

$= 1$

57. $4\left(-\dfrac{1}{2}\right)+\left(\dfrac{2}{3}\right)9 = -2+6 = 4$

59. $\dfrac{1.63482-2.48561}{(16.05436)(0.07814)}$

$= \dfrac{-0.85079}{1.25448769}$

≈ -0.678197169

61. One or three of the quantities a,b,c must be negative. In other words, when multiplying an odd number of negative numbers, the answer will be negative.

Cumulative Review

63. Commutative property of addition.

65. $-\dfrac{1}{2}\pi, \sqrt{3}$

67. $0.125+2(0.06)+5(0.1875)$

$+7(0.10)+3(0.25) = \$2.63\dfrac{1}{4}$

69. $1,300,000(0.75) = 975,000$

1.3 Exercises

1. The base is a and the exponent is 3.

3. Positive

5. -11 and 11, $(-11)(-11) = 121$

$(11)(11) = 121$

7. $9\cdot 9\cdot 9\cdot 9 = 9^4$

9. $(-6)(-6)(-6)(-6)(-6) = (-6)^5$

11. $x\cdot x\cdot x\cdot x\cdot y\cdot y\cdot y = x^4 y^3$

13. $2^5 = 2\cdot 2\cdot 2\cdot 2\cdot 2 = 32$

15. $(-5)^2 = (-5)(-5) = 25$

17. $-6^2 = -(6)(6) = -36$

3

© 2006 Pearson Education, Inc., Upper Saddle River, NJ. All rights reserved. This material is protected under all copyright laws as they currently exist. No portion of this material may be reproduced, in any form or by any means, without permission in writing from the publisher.

19. $-1^4 = -(1)(1)(1)(1) = -1$

21. $\left(\dfrac{2}{3}\right)^2 = \left(\dfrac{2}{3}\right)\left(\dfrac{2}{3}\right) = \dfrac{4}{9}$

23. $\left(-\dfrac{1}{4}\right)^4 = \left(-\dfrac{1}{4}\right)\left(-\dfrac{1}{4}\right)\left(-\dfrac{1}{4}\right)\left(-\dfrac{1}{4}\right) = \dfrac{1}{256}$

25. $(0.8)^2 = (0.8)(0.8) = 0.64$

27. $(0.04)^3 = (0.04)(0.04)(0.04)$
$\qquad\qquad = 0.000064$

29. $\sqrt{81} = 9$

31. $-\sqrt{16} = -4$

33. $\sqrt{\dfrac{4}{9}} = \dfrac{2}{3}$

35. $\sqrt{0.09} = 0.3$

37. $\sqrt{4+12} = \sqrt{16} = 4$

39. $\sqrt{4901-1} = \sqrt{4900} = 70$

41. $\sqrt{\dfrac{5}{36}+\dfrac{31}{36}} = \sqrt{\dfrac{36}{36}} = \sqrt{1} = 1$

43. $\sqrt{-36}$ not a real number

45. $-\sqrt{-0.36}$ not a real number

47. $5(3-9)+7 = 5(-6)+7$
$\qquad\qquad = -30+7$
$\qquad\qquad = -23$

49. $-12 \div (4) + 8(-3) = -3 + (-24) = -27$

51. $(-2)(-10) + (-4)^2 = 20 + 16 = 36$

53. $(5+2-8)^3 - (-7) = (7-8)^3 + 7$
$\qquad\qquad = (-1)^3 + 7 = -1 + 7$
$\qquad\qquad = 6$

55. $(-2)^3 + (-4)^2 - 3 = -8 + 16 - 3$
$\qquad\qquad\qquad = 8 - 3 = 5$

57. $-3^2 + 2(4-7) = -9 + 2(-3)$
$\qquad\qquad\qquad = -9 + (-6) = -15$

59. $5\big[(1.2 - 0.4) - 0.8\big] = 5(0.8 - 0.8)$
$\qquad\qquad\qquad\qquad = 5(0) = 0$

61. $4(-6) - 3^2 + \sqrt{25} = -24 - 9 + 5$
$\qquad\qquad\qquad\qquad = -33 + 5 = -28$

63. $\dfrac{7 + 2(-4) + 5}{8 - 6} = \dfrac{7 + (-8) + 5}{2}$
$\qquad\qquad\qquad = \dfrac{-1 + 5}{2} = \dfrac{4}{2} = 2$

65. $\dfrac{-3(2^3 - 1)}{3 - 10} = \dfrac{-3(8 - 1)}{-7} = \dfrac{-3(7)}{-7}$
$\qquad\qquad\qquad = \dfrac{-21}{-7} = 3$

67. $\dfrac{\left|2^2 - 5\right| - 3^2}{-5 + 3} = \dfrac{\left|4 - 5\right| - 9}{-2} = \dfrac{\left|-1\right| - 9}{-2}$
$\qquad\qquad = \dfrac{1 + (-9)}{-2}$
$\qquad\qquad = \dfrac{-8}{-2} = 4$

4

© 2006 Pearson Education, Inc., Upper Saddle River, NJ. All rights reserved. This material is protected under all copyright laws as they currently exist. No portion of this material may be reproduced, in any form or by any means, without permission in writing from the publisher.

69. $\dfrac{\sqrt{(-5)^2-3+14}}{|19-6+3-25|} = \dfrac{\sqrt{25+11}}{|13-22|}$

$\qquad\qquad = \dfrac{\sqrt{36}}{|-9|} = \dfrac{6}{9} = \dfrac{2}{3}$

71. $\dfrac{\sqrt{6^2-3^2-2}}{(-3)^2-4} = \dfrac{\sqrt{36-9-2}}{9-4}$

$\qquad\qquad = \dfrac{\sqrt{36-11}}{5} = \dfrac{\sqrt{25}}{5}$

$\qquad\qquad = \dfrac{5}{5} = 1$

73. $(5.986)^5 \approx 7685.702373$

75. $2^{11} - 2^9 = 2048 - 512 = 1536$

Cumulative Review

77. Inverse property of multiplication.

79. $\dfrac{40,000-5000}{5000} = \dfrac{35,000}{5000} = 7$
An increase of 700%

81. $1 + 0.1 + 1.1(0.1) = 1.21$
An increase of 21%.

How Am I Doing? Sections 1.1-1.3

1. $\pi, \sqrt{7}$

2. $\sqrt{9}, 3, \dfrac{6}{2}, 0$

3. $\sqrt{3}$ belongs to the real number set and the irrational number set.

4. The associative property of addition.

5. The inverse property of multiplication.

6. $30 \div (-6) + 3 - 2(-5) = -5 + 3 + 10$
$\qquad\qquad\qquad = -2 + 10 = 8$

7. $8\left(\dfrac{-3}{4}\right) + (-6)(-3) = -6 + 18 = 12$

8. $\dfrac{15-4(3)}{2-8} = \dfrac{15-12}{-6} = \dfrac{3}{-6} = -\dfrac{1}{2}$

9. $\dfrac{-5+(-5)}{-15} = \dfrac{-10}{-15} = \dfrac{2}{3}$

10. $-9 + 6(-2) - (-3) = -9 - 12 + 3 = -18$

11. $\sqrt{\dfrac{25}{36}} = \dfrac{5}{6}$

12. $\sqrt{0.81} = 0.9$

13. $4^4 = 4 \cdot 4 \cdot 4 \cdot 4 = 256$

14. $3^3 - \sqrt{4(-5)+29} = 27 - \sqrt{-20+29}$
$\qquad\qquad\qquad\qquad = 27 - \sqrt{9}$
$\qquad\qquad\qquad\qquad = 27 - 3 = 24$

15. $(-4)^3 + 2(3^2 - 2^2) = -64 + 2(9-4)$
$\qquad\qquad\qquad\qquad = -64 + 2(5)$
$\qquad\qquad\qquad\qquad = -64 + 10 = -54$

16. $\dfrac{4-6^2}{3+\sqrt{16+9}} = \dfrac{4-36}{3+\sqrt{25}} = \dfrac{-32}{3+5}$
$\qquad\qquad\qquad = \dfrac{-32}{8} = -4$

5

© 2006 Pearson Education, Inc., Upper Saddle River, NJ. All rights reserved. This material is protected under all copyright laws as they currently exist. No portion of this material may be reproduced, in any form or by any means, without permission in writing from the publisher.

17. $\left|2^2 - 5 - 6\right| = \left|4 - 11\right| = \left|-7\right| = 7$

18. $\dfrac{\sqrt{(-2)^2 + 5}}{\left|12 - 15\right|} = \dfrac{\sqrt{4 + 5}}{\left|-3\right|}$

$$= \dfrac{\sqrt{9}}{3} = \dfrac{3}{3} = 1$$

1.4 Exercises

1. $3^{-2} = \dfrac{1}{3^2} = \dfrac{1}{9}$

3. $x^{-5} = \dfrac{1}{x^5}$

5. $(-7)^{-2} = \dfrac{1}{7^2} = \dfrac{1}{49}$

7. $\left(-\dfrac{1}{9}\right)^{-1} = \left(-\dfrac{9}{1}\right)^1 = -9$

9. $x^4 \cdot x^8 = x^{4+8} = x^{12}$

11. $17^4 \cdot 17 = 17^{4+1} = 17^5$

13. $(3x)\left(-2x^5\right) = -6x^{1+5} = -6x^6$

15. $\left(-12x^3 y\right)\left(-3x^5 y^2\right) = 36x^8 y^3$

17. $4x^0 y = 4 \cdot 1 \cdot y = 4y$

19. $(3xy)^0 (7xy) = 1(7xy) = 7xy$

21. $\left(2x^0 y^5 z\right)\left(-5xy^0 z^8\right) = -10xy^5 z^9$

23. $\left(-\dfrac{3}{5} m^{-2} n^4\right)(5m^2 n^{-5}) = -\dfrac{3(5)m^{-2+2} n^{4-5}}{5}$

$$= -\dfrac{3m^0 n^{-1}}{1} = -\dfrac{3}{n}$$

25. $\dfrac{x^{16}}{x^5} = x^{16-5} = x^{11}$

27. $\dfrac{a^{20}}{a^{25}} = a^{20-25} = a^{-5} = \dfrac{1}{a^5}$

29. $\dfrac{2^8}{2^5} = 2^{8-5} = 2^3 = 8$

31. $\dfrac{2x^3}{x^8} = 2x^{3-8} = 2x^{-5} = \dfrac{2}{x^5}$

33. $\dfrac{10ab^5 c}{-2ab^2} = -5b^3 c$

35. $\dfrac{-20a^{-3} b^{-8}}{14a^{-5} b^{-12}} = -\dfrac{10}{7} a^{-3-(-5)} b^{-8-(-12)}$

$$= -\dfrac{10}{7} a^2 b^4$$

37. $\left(x^2\right)^8 = x^{2 \cdot 8} = x^{16}$

39. $\left(3a^5 b\right)^4 = 3^4 a^{5 \cdot 4} b^4 = 81a^{20} b^4$

41. $\left(\dfrac{x^2 y^3}{z}\right)^6 = \dfrac{x^{2 \cdot 6} y^{3 \cdot 6}}{z^6} = \dfrac{x^{12} y^{18}}{z^6}$

43. $\left(\dfrac{3ab^{-2}}{4a^0 b^4}\right)^2 = \left(\dfrac{3a}{4b^6}\right)^2 = \dfrac{3^2 a^2}{4^2 b^{6 \cdot 2}}$

$$= \dfrac{9a^2}{16b^{12}}$$

6

© 2006 Pearson Education, Inc., Upper Saddle River, NJ. All rights reserved. This material is protected under all copyright laws as they currently exist.
No portion of this material may be reproduced, in any form or by any means, without permission in writing from the publisher.

45. $\left(\dfrac{2xy^2}{x^{-3}y^{-4}}\right)^{-3} = \left(2x^4y^6\right)^{-3}$

$= \dfrac{1}{\left(2x^4y^6\right)^3}$

$= \dfrac{1}{2^3 x^{4\cdot 3} y^{6\cdot 3}}$

$= \dfrac{1}{8x^{12}y^{18}}$

47. $(x^{-1}y^3)^{-2}(2x)^2 = x^2 y^{-6}(4x^2) = \dfrac{4x^4}{y^6}$

49. $\dfrac{\left(-3m^5 n^{-1}\right)^3}{\left(-mn\right)^2} = \dfrac{\left(-3\right)^3 m^{5\cdot 3} n^{-1(3)}}{\left(-m\right)^2 n^2}$

$= \dfrac{-27 m^{15} n^{-3}}{m^2 n^2}$

$= \dfrac{-27 m^{13}}{n^5} = -\dfrac{27 m^{13}}{n^5}$

51. $\dfrac{2^{-3} a^2}{2^{-4} a^{-2}} = 2^{-3-(-4)} a^{2-(-2)} = 2a^4$

53. $\left(\dfrac{1}{2}y\right)^{-3} = \dfrac{1}{2^{-3}} y^{-3} = \dfrac{2^3}{y^3} = \dfrac{8}{y^3}$

55. $\left(\dfrac{y^{-3}}{x}\right)^{-3} = \dfrac{y^{-3(-3)}}{x^{-3}} = x^3 y^9$

57. $\dfrac{a^{-2} b^0}{ab^{-5}} = a^{-2-1} b^{0-(-5)} = a^{-3} b^5 = \dfrac{b^5}{a^3}$

59. $\left(\dfrac{14 x^{-3} y^{-3}}{7 x^{-4} y^{-3}}\right)^{-2} = \left(2x\right)^{-2} = \dfrac{1}{\left(2x\right)^2} = \dfrac{1}{4x^2}$

61. $\dfrac{7^{-8}\cdot 5^{-6}}{7^{-9}\cdot 5^{-5}\cdot 6^0} = 7^{-8-(-9)} 5^{-6-(-5)} = 7^1 5^{-1} = \dfrac{7}{5}$

63. $\left(9x^{-2}y\right)\left(-\dfrac{2}{3}x^3 y^{-2}\right) = -6xy^{-1} = -\dfrac{6x}{y}$

65. $\left(-3.6982 x^3 y^4\right)^7 = \left(-3.6982\right)^7 x^{3\cdot 7} y^{4\cdot 7}$

$\approx -9460.906704 x^{21} y^{28}$

67. $38 = 3.8 \times 10^1$

69. $1,730,000 = 1.73 \times 10^6$

71. $0.83 = 8.3 \times 10^{-1}$

73. $0.0000529 = 5.29 \times 10^{-5}$

75. $7.13 \times 10^5 = 713,000$

77. $3.07 \times 10^{-1} = 0.307$

79. $9.01 \times 10^{-7} = 0.000000901$

81. $(3.1 \times 10^{-4})(1.5 \times 10^{-2}) = 4.65 \times 10^{-6}$

83. $\dfrac{3.6 \times 10^{-5}}{1.2 \times 10^{-6}} = 3 \times 10^{-5-(-6)} = 3 \times 10^1$

85. $7,200,000\,\dfrac{\text{ft}^3}{\text{s}} \cdot \dfrac{0.305^3 \text{m}^3}{\text{ft}^3}$

$= 204,282.9\,\dfrac{\text{m}^3}{\text{s}}$

87. $\left(\dfrac{5.1 \times 10^4 \text{ cycles}}{\text{sec}}\right)\left(1.5 \times 10^2 \text{ sec}\right)$

$= 7.65 \times 10^6 \text{ cycles}$

© 2006 Pearson Education, Inc., Upper Saddle River, NJ. All rights reserved. This material is protected under all copyright laws as they currently exist. No portion of this material may be reproduced, in any form or by any means, without permission in writing from the publisher.

89. $\left(\dfrac{5.3 \times 10^{-23} \, \text{gram}}{\text{molecule}} \right)\left(2 \times 10^4 \, \text{molecule} \right)$

$= 10.6 \times 10^{-19} = 1.06 \times 10^{-18} \, \text{gram}$

Cumulative Review

91. $\dfrac{\text{mass of earth}}{\text{mass of moon}} = \dfrac{3.79 \times 10^{24} \, \text{metric tons}}{7.34 \times 10^{19} \, \text{metric tons}}$

$\dfrac{\text{mass of earth}}{\text{mass of moon}} = 51,635$

mass of earth $= 51,635 \times$ mass of moon

93. $5 + 2(-3) + 12 \div (-6)$

$= 5 + (-6) + (-2)$

$= -1 + (-2)$

$= -3$

95. $\dfrac{5 + 3 - 4}{32 \div (-8)} = \dfrac{8 - 4}{-4} = \dfrac{4}{-4} = -1$

1.5 Exercises

1. It is $-5x^2$ since y is multiplied by $-5x^2$.

3. $5x^3, -6x^2, 4x, 8$

5. $1, -3, -8$

7. $5, -3, 1$

9. $6.5, -0.02, 3.05$

11. $3ab + 8ab = 11ab$

13. $4y - 7x + 2x - 6y = -2y - 5x$

15. $x^2 - 3x - 4x^2 + 2x = -3x^2 - x$

17. $4ab - 3b^2 - 5ab + 3b^2 = -ab$

19. $0.1x^2 + 3x - 0.5x^2 = -0.4x^2 + 3x$

21. $\dfrac{2}{3}m + \dfrac{5}{6}n - \dfrac{1}{3}m + \dfrac{1}{3}n$

$= \dfrac{1}{3}m + \dfrac{7}{6}n$

23. $\dfrac{3}{4}a^2 - 4b + \dfrac{1}{4}a^2 + 5b$

$= a^2\left(\dfrac{3}{4} + \dfrac{1}{4} \right) + 5b - 4b$

$= a^2 + b$

25. $1.2x^2 - 5.6x - 8.9x^2 + 2x$

$= -7.7x^2 - 3.6x$

27. $6x(3x + y) = (6x)(3x) + (6x)(y)$

$= 18x^2 + 6xy$

29. $-x\left(-x^3 + 3x^2 + 5x \right)$

$= (-x)(-x^3) + (-x)(3x^2) + (-x)(5x)$

$= x^4 - 3x^3 - 5x^2$

31. $-2a^2(a - 3a^2 + 2ab)$

$= -2a^3 + 6a^4 - 4a^3b$

33. $2xy\left(x^2 - 3xy + 4y^2 \right)$

$= 2x^3y - 6x^2y^2 + 8xy^3$

35. $\dfrac{3}{4}\left(8x^2 - 4x + 2 \right) = 6x^2 - 3x + \dfrac{3}{2}$

37. $\dfrac{x}{2}\left(7x^2 - 4x + 1 \right) = \dfrac{7}{2}x^3 - 2x^2 + \dfrac{1}{2}x$

© 2006 Pearson Education, Inc., Upper Saddle River, NJ. All rights reserved. This material is protected under all copyright laws as they currently exist. No portion of this material may be reproduced, in any form or by any means, without permission in writing from the publisher.

39. $3ab\left(a^4b - 3a^2 + a - b\right)$

$\qquad = 3a^5b^2 - 9a^3b + 3a^2b - 3ab^2$

41. $1.5x^2\left(x - 2y + 3y^2\right)$

$\qquad = 1.5x^3 - 3x^2y + 4.5x^2y^2$

43. $2(x-1) - x(x+1) + 3\left(x^2 + 2\right)$

$\qquad = 2x - 2 - x^2 - x + 3x^2 + 6$

$\qquad = 2x^2 + x + 4$

45. $4\left[x + \left(\dfrac{1}{2}x - y\right)\right] - 3\left[\dfrac{2}{3}x - (x - y)\right]$

$\qquad = 4\left[x + \dfrac{1}{2}x - y\right] - 3\left[\dfrac{2}{3}x - x + y\right]$

$\qquad = 4\left[\dfrac{3}{2}x - y\right] - 3\left[-\dfrac{1}{3}x + y\right]$

$\qquad = 6x - 4y + x - 3y$

$\qquad = 7x - 7y$

47. $2\left\{3x - 2\left[x - 4(x+1)\right]\right\}$

$\qquad = 2\left\{3x - 2\left[x - 4x - 4\right]\right\}$

$\qquad = 2\left\{3x - 2\left[-3x - 4\right]\right\}$

$\qquad = 2\left\{3x + 6x + 8\right\}$

$\qquad = 2\left\{9x + 8\right\}$

$\qquad = 18x + 16$

49. $7x(x+4) - (x^2 - 2y)$

$\qquad = 7x^2 + 28x - x^2 + 2y$

$\qquad = 6x^2 + 28x + 2y$

51. $6x^3 - 2x^2 - 9x^3 - 12x^2 = -3x^3 - 14x^2$

53. $2\left[-3(2x+4) + 8(2x-4)\right]$

$\qquad = 2\left[-6x - 12 + 16x - 32\right]$

$\qquad = 2\left[10x - 44\right]$

$\qquad = 20x - 88$

55. $3y\left[y - (x-5)\right] = 3y\left[y - x + 5\right]$

$\qquad\qquad\qquad\quad = 3y^2 - 3xy + 15y$

Cumulative Review

57. $2(-3)^2 + 4(-2)$

$\qquad = 2(9) - 8$

$\qquad = 18 - 8$

$\qquad = 10$

59. $\dfrac{5(-2) - 8}{3 + 4 - (-3)} = \dfrac{-10 - 8}{7 + 3}$

$\qquad\qquad\qquad = \dfrac{-18}{10}$

$\qquad\qquad\qquad = \dfrac{-9}{5}$

$\qquad\qquad\qquad = -1.8$

61. $\dfrac{1,893,500 \text{ organisms}}{\text{inch}} \cdot \dfrac{1 \text{ inch}}{0.0254 \text{ meters}}$

$\qquad = \dfrac{1,893,500 \text{ organisms}}{0.0254 \text{ meters}} \cdot \dfrac{1000 \text{ meter}}{\text{kilometer}}$

$\qquad \approx \dfrac{7.4547 \times 10^{10} \text{ organisms}}{\text{kilometer}}$

63. $35,861 \cdot \dfrac{1}{7} = 5123$

1.6 Exercises

1. $14 + 6x = 14 + 6(-2) = 14 - 12 = 2$

© 2006 Pearson Education, Inc., Upper Saddle River, NJ. All rights reserved. This material is protected under all copyright laws as they currently exist. No portion of this material may be reproduced, in any form or by any means, without permission in writing from the publisher.

3. $x^2 + 7x + 12 = (-2)^2 + 7(-2) + 12$

$\qquad = 4 + (-14) + 12$

$\qquad = -10 + 12$

$\qquad = 2$

5. $3 + 7x - x^2 = 3 + 7(1) - 1^2 = 3 + 7 - 1$

$\qquad = 10 - 1$

$\qquad = 9$

7. $-2x^2 + 5x - 3 = -2(-4)^2 + 5(-4) - 3$

$\qquad = -2(16) + (-20) - 3$

$\qquad = -32 + (-20) - 3$

$\qquad = -52 - 3$

$\qquad = -55$

9. $(-3y)^4 = (-3(-1))^4$

$\qquad = (3)^4$

$\qquad = 81$

11. $-3y^4 = -3(-1)^4 - 3(1)$

$\qquad = -3$

13. $2ax - by - a = 2(1)\left(\dfrac{1}{2}\right) - (-2)(3) - 1$

$\qquad = 1 + 6 - 1$

$\qquad = 6$

15. $\sqrt{b^2 - 4ac} = \sqrt{5^2 - 4(1)(-14)}$

$\qquad = \sqrt{24 + 56}$

$\qquad = \sqrt{81}$

$\qquad = 9$

17. $2x^2 - 5x + 6$

$\qquad = 2(-3.52176)^2 - 5(-3.52176) + 6$

$\qquad = 48.41439$ to five decimal places

19. $F = \dfrac{9}{5}(-60) + 32 = -76°F$

21. $C = \dfrac{5(122) - 160}{9} = 50°C$

23. $T = 2\pi\sqrt{L/g}$

$\qquad T = 2(3.14)\sqrt{32/32}$

$\qquad T = 6.28$ seconds

25. $A = \$4800\left[1 + (0.12)(1.5)\right]$

$\qquad A = \$5664$

27. $A = \$1900\left[1 + (0.06)(3)\right] = \$2242$

29. $S = \dfrac{1}{2}(32)(3)^2 = 144$ feet

31. $S = \dfrac{1}{2}(32)(7)^2 = 784$ feet

33. $z = \dfrac{(36)(4)}{36 + 4} = \dfrac{144}{40} = \dfrac{18}{5} = 3\dfrac{3}{5}$

35. $m = \dfrac{9 \cdot 150}{9 + 12} = \dfrac{1350}{21} = 64$ milligrams

37. $A = \pi r^2 = 3.14 \cdot 0.5^2 = 0.785$ sq in.

39. $A = \dfrac{1}{2}ab = \dfrac{1}{2} \cdot 16 \cdot 7 = 56$ sq cm

© 2006 Pearson Education, Inc., Upper Saddle River, NJ. All rights reserved. This material is protected under all copyright laws as they currently exist.
No portion of this material may be reproduced, in any form or by any means, without permission in writing from the publisher.

41. $A = ab = 4\left(\dfrac{7}{8}\right) = \dfrac{7}{2}$ sq yards

43. $A = lw = (6.1)(4.05)$
$A = 24.705$ sq centimeters

45. $A = \dfrac{1}{2}a(b+c) = \dfrac{1}{2} \cdot 6(5+7)$
$A = \dfrac{1}{2} \cdot 6(12) = 3(12)$
$A = 36$ sq centimeters

47. (a) $V = \pi r^2 h = 3.14(4)^2(11)$
$V = 552.64$ cubic centimeters
(b) $S = 2\pi rh + 2\pi r^2$
$S = 2(3.14)(4)(11) + 2(3.14)(4)^2$
$S = 376.8$ square centimeters

49. $A = \pi r^2 = 3.14(8)^2 = 200.96$ sq cm
$C = \pi(16) = 3.14(16) = 50.24$ cm

51. (a) $\dfrac{45,032 \text{ cal}}{\text{hr}} \dfrac{120 \text{ watt}}{104 \dfrac{\text{cal}}{\text{hr}}} = 51,960$ watt

(b) $\dfrac{104 \text{ cal}}{\text{hr} \cdot \text{person}} 433$ persons
$= \dfrac{45,032 \text{ cal}}{\text{hr}}$

Cumulative Review Problems

53. $\left(\dfrac{-5x^2}{2y^3}\right)^2 = \dfrac{(-5)^2 \left(x^2\right)^2}{(2)^2 \left(y^3\right)^2}$
$= \dfrac{25x^4}{4y^6}$

55. $2\{5 - 2[x - 3(2x+1)]\}$
$= 2\{5 - 2[x - 6x - 3]\}$
$= 2\{5 - 2[-5x - 3]\}$
$= 2\{5 + 10x + 6\}$
$= 2\{11 + 10x\}$
$= 22 + 20x$
$= 20x + 22$

57. $12,000,000 - 0.30(19,000,000)$
$= 6,300,000$ people

Putting Your Skills To Work

1. $C = \dfrac{5}{9}(F - 32) = \dfrac{5}{9}(68 - 32)$
$C = 20°C$
$K = C + 273 = 20 + 273$
$K = 293$ degrees Kelvin

2. $C = K - 273 = 195 - 273 = -78°C$
$F = \dfrac{9}{5}C + 32 = \dfrac{9}{5}(-78) + 32 = -108°F$

3. $C = K - 273 = 185 - 273 = -88°C$

4. $K = C + 273$
$K = \dfrac{5}{9}(F - 32) + 273$
$K = \dfrac{5}{9}(32 - 32) + 273$
$K = 273$ degrees Kelvin

5. 1 nanodegree Kelvin
$= 1 \times 10^{-9}$ degrees Kelvin

© 2006 Pearson Education, Inc., Upper Saddle River, NJ. All rights reserved. This material is protected under all copyright laws as they currently exist. No portion of this material may be reproduced, in any form or by any means, without permission in writing from the publisher.

6. 240 nanodegrees Kelvin

$= 240 \times 10^{-9} = 2.4 \times 10^{-7}$ degrees Kelvin

40 nanodegrees Kelvin

$= 40 \times 10^{-9} = 4.0 \times 10^{-8}$ degrees Kelvin

7. 22.5 million degrees Kelvin

$= 22.5 \times 10^{6}$ degrees Kelvin

$= 2.25 \times 10^{7}$ degrees Kelvin

8. $\dfrac{\text{sun's core}}{\text{lowest temp}} = \dfrac{2.25 \times 10^{7}}{4 \times 10^{-8}}$

$\dfrac{\text{sun's core}}{\text{lowest temp}} = 5.625 \times 10^{14}$

sun's core $= 5.625 \times 10^{14} \cdot$ lowest temp

Chapter 1 Review Problems

1. -5 : Integer, Rational, Real

2. $\dfrac{7}{8}$: Rational, Real

3. 3: Natural, Whole, Integer, Rational, Real

4. $0.\overline{3}$: Rational, Real

5. 2.1652384L : Irrational, Real

6. Commutative property of addition

7. Associative property of multiplication

8. Yes, all rational numbers are real numbers.

9. $-15 - (-20) = -15 + 20 = 5$

10. $-7.3 + (-16.2) = -23.5$

11. $-8(-6) = 48$

12. $-12 \div 3 = -4$

13. $-\dfrac{5}{7} \div \left(-\dfrac{5}{13}\right) = \dfrac{5}{7} \cdot \dfrac{13}{5}$

$= \dfrac{13}{7} = 1\dfrac{6}{7}$

14. $-\dfrac{3}{5}\left(\dfrac{2}{3}\right) = -\dfrac{2}{5}$

15. $4(-3)(-10) = -12(-10)$

$= 120$

16. $5 + 6 - 2 - 5$

$= 11 - 2 - 5$

$= 9 - 5$

$= 4$

17. $-3.6(-1.5) = 5.4$

18. $0 \div (-14) = 0$

19. $7 \div 0$ undefined

20. $-17 + (+17) = 0$

21. $17 - 3(6) = 17 - 18 = -1$

22. $\dfrac{5-8}{2-7-(-2)} = \dfrac{-3}{-5+2}$

$= \dfrac{-3}{-3}$

$= 1$

12

© 2006 Pearson Education, Inc., Upper Saddle River, NJ. All rights reserved. This material is protected under all copyright laws as they currently exist. No portion of this material may be reproduced, in any form or by any means, without permission in writing from the publisher.

23. $4\sqrt{16} + 2^3 - 6 = 4 \cdot 4 + 8 - 6$
$$= 16 + 2$$
$$= 18$$

24. $2(5) - |-2| + (-1)^3 = 10 - 2 + (-1)$
$$= 8 + (-1)$$
$$= 7$$

25. $4 - 2 + 6\left(-\dfrac{1}{3}\right) = 2 + (-2) = 0$

26. $\sqrt{(-1)^2 + 6(4)} + 8 \div (-2) = \sqrt{1 + 24} + (-4)$
$$= \sqrt{25} + (-4)$$
$$= 5 + (-4)$$
$$= 1$$

27. $\sqrt{\dfrac{25}{36}} - 2\left(\dfrac{1}{12}\right) = \dfrac{5}{6} - \left(\dfrac{1}{6}\right)$
$$= \dfrac{4}{6} = \dfrac{2}{3}$$

28. $6|-3-1| + 5(-3)(0) - 4^2 = 6|-4| - 16$
$$= 6(4) - 16$$
$$= 24 - 16$$
$$= 8$$

29. $(-0.4)^3 = -0.064$

30. $(3xy^2)(-2x^{0y})(4x^3y^3) = -24x^{1+0+3}y^{2+1+3}$
$$= -24x^4y^6$$

31. $(5a^4bc^2)(-6ab^2) = -30a^{4+1}b^{1+2}c^2$
$$= -30a^5b^3c^2$$

32. $\dfrac{42x^6y}{36xy^7} = \dfrac{7x^{6-1}}{6y^{7-1}} = \dfrac{7x^5}{6y^6}$

33. $\dfrac{27ab^3c}{81a^5bc^0} = \dfrac{b^2c}{3a^4}$

34. $\left(\dfrac{-3x^3y}{2x^4z^2}\right)^4 = \dfrac{(-3)^4(x^3)^4y^4}{2^4(x^4)^4(z^2)^4}$
$$= \dfrac{81x^{12}y^4}{16x^{16}z^8}$$
$$= \dfrac{81y^4}{16x^4z^8}$$

35. $(-2xy^6z^0)^3 = (-2)^3x^3y^{6(3)}(1)^3$
$$= -8x^3y^{18}$$

36. $(2x^2y^{-4})(-5x^{-1}y) = -10x^{2-1}y^{-4+1}$
$$= -10xy^{-3}$$
$$= -\dfrac{10x}{y^3}$$

37. $\dfrac{3x^5y^{-6}}{12x^{-2}y} = \dfrac{x^{5-(-2)}}{4y \cdot y^6} = \dfrac{x^7}{4y^{1+6}} = \dfrac{x^7}{4y^7}$

38. $\dfrac{\left(3^{-1}y\right)^{-2}}{\left(4^{-1}y^{-2}\right)^{-1}} = \dfrac{3^{-1(-2)}y^{-2}}{4^{-1(-1)}y^{-2(-1)}}$
$$= \dfrac{3^2y^{-2}}{4y^2}$$
$$= \dfrac{9}{4y^{2+2}}$$
$$= \dfrac{9}{4y^4}$$

© 2006 Pearson Education, Inc., Upper Saddle River, NJ. All rights reserved. This material is protected under all copyright laws as they currently exist. No portion of this material may be reproduced, in any form or by any means, without permission in writing from the publisher.

39. $\dfrac{(2b)^{-3}}{(3a^{-3})^{-1}} = \dfrac{2^{-3}b^{-3}}{3^{-1}a^{-3(-1)}}$

$\qquad = \dfrac{3^1}{2^3a^3b^3}$

$\qquad = \dfrac{3}{8a^3b^3}$

40. $\left(\dfrac{a^5b^2}{3^{-1}a^{-5}b^{-4}}\right)^3 = \left(\dfrac{3a^{5-(-5)}b^{2-(-4)}}{1}\right)^3$

$\qquad = \left(3a^{10}b^6\right)^3 = 3^3a^{10\cdot3}b^{6\cdot3} = 27a^{30}b^{18}$

41. $\left(\dfrac{x^3y^4}{5x^6y^8}\right)^3 = \dfrac{x^9y^{12}}{5^3x^{18}y^{24}} = \dfrac{1}{125x^9y^{12}}$

42. $0.00721 = 7.21\times10^{-3}$

43. $(5,300,000)(2,000,000,000)$

$\qquad = 5.3\times10^6\left(2.0\times10^9\right)$

$\qquad = 10.6\times10^{15} = 1.06\times10^{16}$

44. $3.4\times10^{-7} = 0.000000348$

45. $5.82\times10^{13} = 58,200,000,000,000$

46. $-x+8+6x^2+7x-4$

$\qquad = 6x^2+(7-1)x+8-4$

$\qquad = 6x^2+6x+4$

47. $-5ab^2\left(a^3+2a^2b-3b-4\right)$

$\qquad = -5a^4b^2-10a^3b^3+15ab^3+20ab^2$

48. $3x(x-7)-(x^2+1) = 3x^2-21x-x^2-1$

$\qquad\qquad\qquad\qquad = 2x^2-21x-1$

49. $2x^2-\left\{2+x\left[3-2(x-1)\right]\right\}$

$\qquad = 2x^2-\left\{2+x\left[3-2x+2\right]\right\}$

$\qquad = 2x^2-\left\{2+x\left[5-2x\right]\right\}$

$\qquad = 2x^2-\left\{2+5x-2x^2\right\}$

$\qquad = 2x^2-2-5x+2x^2$

$\qquad = 4x^2-5x-2$

50. $5(2)^2-3(2)(-1)-2(-1)^3$

$\qquad = 5(4)-6(-1)-2(-1)$

$\qquad = 20+6+2 = 28$

51. $V = \pi r^2h$

$\qquad V = 3.14(3)^2(2)$

$\qquad V = 56.52$ cubic meters

52. $A = \dfrac{1}{2}bh$

$\qquad A = \dfrac{1}{2}(46)(58)$

$\qquad A = 1334$ square yards

53. $A = \dfrac{1}{2}(b_1+b_2)h$

$\qquad A = \dfrac{1}{2}(26+34)14$

$\qquad A = 420$ square inches

54. $(-20\div4)^3+12(-3)-2$

$\qquad = (-5)^3+(-36)-2$

$\qquad = -125+(-38)$

$\qquad = -163$

55. $\sqrt{19-3}-15(3)\div5 = \sqrt{16}-45\div5$

$\qquad\qquad\qquad\qquad = 4-9$

$\qquad\qquad\qquad\qquad = -5$

© 2006 Pearson Education, Inc., Upper Saddle River, NJ. All rights reserved. This material is protected under all copyright laws as they currently exist. No portion of this material may be reproduced, in any form or by any means, without permission in writing from the publisher.

56. $(-7a^2b)(-2a^0b^3c^2) = 14a^{2+0}b^{1+3}c^2$
$$= 14a^2b^4c^2$$

57. $\dfrac{(3x^{-1}y^2)^3}{(4x^2y^{-2})^2} = \dfrac{3^3 x^{-1(3)}y^{2(3)}}{4^2 x^{2(2)}y^{-2(2)}}$
$$= \dfrac{27x^{-3}y^6}{16x^4y^{-4}}$$
$$= \dfrac{27y^{6-(-4)}}{16x^{4-(-3)}}$$
$$= \dfrac{27y^{10}}{16x^7}$$

58. $\dfrac{4x^{-3}y^2}{-16x^2y^{-3}} = -\dfrac{x^{3-2}y^{2-(-3)}}{4}$
$$= -\dfrac{xy^5}{4}$$

59. $\left(\dfrac{3a^{-5}b^0}{2a^{-2}b^3}\right)^2 = \dfrac{3^2 a^{-5(2)}(1)^2}{2^2 a^{-2(2)}b^{3(2)}}$
$$= \dfrac{9a^{-10-(-4)}}{4b^6}$$
$$= \dfrac{9a^{-6}}{4b^6}$$
$$= \dfrac{9}{4a^6b^6}$$

60. $0.000058 = 5.8 \times 10^{-5}$

61. $8.95 \times 10^7 = 89,500,000$

62. $3x + 5x^2 - 2x^3 - 6x - 8x^3$
$$= (-2-8)x^3 + 5x^2 + (3-6)x$$
$$= -10x^3 + 5x^2 - 3x$$

63. $3ab^2(-2a + 3ab - 1)$
$$= -6a^2b^2 + 9a^2b^3 - 3ab^2$$

64. $-2\{x + 3[y - 5(x+y)]\}$
$$= -2\{x + 3[y - 5x - 5y]\}$$
$$= -2\{x + 3[-4y - 5x]\}$$
$$= -2\{x - 12y - 15x\}$$
$$= -2\{-14x - 12y\}$$
$$= 28x + 24y$$

65. $5a^2 - 3ab + 4b$
$$= 5(-3)^2 - 3(-3)(-2) + 4(-2)$$
$$= 5(9) - 3(6) + (-8)$$
$$= 45 - 18 - 8$$
$$= 19$$

66. $A = \pi r^2$
$$A = 3.14(4)^2$$
$$A = 50.24 \text{ m}^2$$

67. $T = 2\pi\sqrt{\dfrac{L}{g}} = 2(3.14)\sqrt{\dfrac{512}{32}}$
$$T = 25.12 \text{ seconds}$$

68. $\dfrac{2}{3}(6x - 9y) - (x - 2y) = 4x - 6y - x + 2y$
$$= 3x - 4y$$

How Am I Doing? Chapter 1 Test

1. $\pi, 2\sqrt{5}$

2. $-2, 12, \dfrac{9}{3}, \dfrac{25}{25}, 0, \sqrt{4}$

3. Commutative property of multiplication.

15

© 2006 Pearson Education, Inc., Upper Saddle River, NJ. All rights reserved. This material is protected under all copyright laws as they currently exist. No portion of this material may be reproduced, in any form or by any means, without permission in writing from the publisher.

4. $(7-5)^3 - 18 \div (-3) + \sqrt{10+6}$

$\quad = 2^3 + (-18) \div (-3) + \sqrt{16}$

$\quad = 8 + (-18) \div (-3) + 4$

$\quad = 8 + 6 + 4 = 14 + 4$

$\quad = 18$

5. $(4-5)^2 - 3(-2) \div 3 = (-1)^2 - (-6) \div 3$

$\qquad\qquad\qquad\qquad = 1 - (-2)$

$\qquad\qquad\qquad\qquad = 3$

6. $\dfrac{16x^3 y}{20x^{-1}y^5} = \dfrac{4x^{3-(-1)}}{5y^{5-1}}$

$\qquad\quad = \dfrac{4x^4}{5y^4}$

7. $\left(5x^{-3}y^{-5}\right)\left(-2x^3 y^0\right) = -10x^{-3+3}y^{-5+0}$

$\qquad\qquad\qquad\qquad = -10x^0 y^{-5}$

$\qquad\qquad\qquad\qquad = -\dfrac{10}{y^5}$

8. $\left(\dfrac{5a^{-2}b}{a}\right)^2 = \dfrac{5^2 a^{-2(2)}b^2}{a^2}$

$\qquad\quad = \dfrac{25a^{-4}b^2}{a^2}$

$\qquad\quad = \dfrac{25b^2}{a^{2-(-4)}}$

$\qquad\quad = \dfrac{25b^2}{a^6}$

9. $7x - 9x^2 - 12x - 8x^2 + 5x = -17x^2$

10. $5a + 4b - 6a^2 + b - 7a - 2a^2$

$\quad = -8a^2 - 2a + 5b$

11. $3xy^2 \left(4x - 3y + 2x^2\right)$

$\quad = 12x^2 y^2 - 9xy^3 + 6x^3 y^2$

12. $0.000002186 = 2.186 \times 10^{-6}$

13. $2.158 \times 10^9 = 2{,}158{,}000{,}000$

14. $\left(3.8 \times 10^{-5}\right)\left(4 \times 10^{-2}\right) = 15.2 \times 10^{-7}$

$\qquad\qquad\qquad\qquad\quad = 1.52 \times 10^{-6}$

15. $2x^2(x - 3y) - x(4 - 8x^2)$

$\quad = 2x^3 - 6x^2 y - 4x + 8x^3$

$\quad = 10x^3 - 6x^2 y - 4x$

16. $2\left[-3(2x+4) + 8(3x-2)\right]$

$\quad = 2\left[-6x - 12 + 24x - 16\right]$

$\quad = 2\left[18x - 28\right]$

$\quad = 36x - 56$

17. $2(-4)^2 - 3(-4) - 6$

$\quad = 2(16) + (-3)(-4) - 6$

$\quad = 32 + 12 - 6 = 44 - 6$

$\quad = 38$

18. $5(3)^2 + 3(3)(-3) - (-3)^2$

$\quad = 5(9) + (-27) - 9$

$\quad = 45 - 27 - 9$

$\quad = 18 - 9$

$\quad = 9$

19. $A = \dfrac{1}{2}\left(b_1 + b_2\right)$

$\quad A = \dfrac{1}{2}(6+7)(12) = 78 \text{ sq m}$

© 2006 Pearson Education, Inc., Upper Saddle River, NJ. All rights reserved. This material is protected under all copyright laws as they currently exist. No portion of this material may be reproduced, in any form or by any means, without permission in writing from the publisher.

20. $A = \pi r^2 = 3.14(6)^2 = 113.04$ sq m

21. $A = p(1 + rt)$

$A = \$8000(1 + 0.05(3))$

$A = \$9200$

© 2006 Pearson Education, Inc., Upper Saddle River, NJ. All rights reserved. This material is protected under all copyright laws as they currently exist. No portion of this material may be reproduced, in any form or by any means, without permission in writing from the publisher.

Chapter 2

2.1 Exercises

1. $3x - 15 = 3(-20) - 15 = -75 \neq 45$

No: when you replace x by -20 in the equation, you do not get a true statement.

3. $7x - 8 = 7 \cdot \dfrac{2}{7} - 8 = 2 - 8 = -6$

Yes. When you replace x with $\dfrac{2}{7}$ in the equation, you get a true statement.

5. Multiply each term of the equation by the LCD, 12, to clear the fractions.

7. No; it would be easier to subtract 3.6 from both sides of the equation since the coefficient of x is 1.

9. $-11 + x = -3$

$\qquad x = -3 + 11$

$\qquad x = 8$

check: $-11 + 8 \overset{?}{=} -3$

$\qquad\qquad -3 = -3$

11. $-9x = 45$

$\qquad x = -5$

check: $-9(-5) \overset{?}{=} 45$

$\qquad\qquad 45 = 45$

13. $-14x = -70$

$\qquad x = \dfrac{-70}{-14}$

$\qquad x = 5$

check: $-14(5) \overset{?}{=} -70$

$\qquad\qquad -70 = -70$

15. $8x - 1 = 11$

$\qquad 8x = 12$

$\qquad x = \dfrac{12}{8} = \dfrac{3}{2}$

$\qquad x = 1\dfrac{1}{2}$

$\qquad x = 1.5$

check: $8\left(\dfrac{3}{2}\right) - 1 \overset{?}{=} 11$

$\qquad\qquad 11 = 11$

17. $9x + 3 = 5x - 9$

$\qquad 9x - 5x + 3 = 5x - 5x - 9$

$\qquad 4x + 3 = -9 \Rightarrow 4x + 3 - 3 = -9 - 3$

$\qquad 4x = -12 \Rightarrow x = -3$

check: $9(-3) + 3 \overset{?}{=} 5(-3) - 9$

$\qquad -27 + 3 \overset{?}{=} -15 - 9$

$\qquad\qquad -24 = -24$

19. $16 - 2x = 5x - 5$

$\qquad -7x = -21$

$\qquad x = 3$

check: $16 - 2(3) \overset{?}{=} 5(3) - 3$

$\qquad\qquad 10 = 10$

21. $3a - 5 - 2a = 2a - 3$

$\qquad a - 5 = 2a - 3$

$\qquad -a = 2$

$\qquad a = -2$

check: $3(-2) - 5 - 2(-2) \overset{?}{=} 2(-2) - 3$

$\qquad -6 - 5 + 4 \overset{?}{=} -4 - 3$

$\qquad -11 - 4 \overset{?}{=} -7$

$\qquad\qquad -7 = -7$

18

© 2006 Pearson Education, Inc., Upper Saddle River, NJ. All rights reserved. This material is protected under all copyright laws as they currently exist. No portion of this material may be reproduced, in any form or by any means, without permission in writing from the publisher.

23. $4(y-1) = -2(3+y)$

$$4y - 4 = -6 - 2y$$
$$6y = -2$$
$$y = -\frac{1}{3}$$

check: $4\left(-\frac{1}{3}-1\right) \overset{?}{=} -2\left(3+\left(-\frac{1}{3}\right)\right)$

$$4\left(\frac{-4}{3}\right) \overset{?}{=} -2\left(\frac{8}{3}\right)$$
$$-\frac{16}{3} = -\frac{16}{3}$$

25. $6-(y+4) = 5-2(y-1)$

$$6 - y - 4 = 5 - 2y + 2$$
$$2 - y = 7 - 2y$$
$$y = 5$$

check: $6-(5+4) \overset{?}{=} 5-2(5-1)$

$$6-9 \overset{?}{=} 5-2(4)$$
$$-3 \overset{?}{=} 5-8$$
$$-3 = -3$$

27. $\frac{2}{3}x = 8$

$$x = \frac{3}{2} \cdot 8$$
$$x = 12$$

29. $\frac{y}{2} + 4 = \frac{1}{6}$

$$3y + 24 = 1$$
$$3y = -23$$
$$y = -\frac{23}{3} \text{ or } -7\frac{2}{3}$$

31. $6 \cdot \left(\frac{2}{3} - \frac{x}{6}\right) = 1 \cdot 6 \Rightarrow 6 \cdot \frac{2}{3} - 6 \cdot \frac{x}{6} = 6$

$$(-1)(4-x) = 6(-1)$$
$$-4 + x + 4 = -6 + 4$$
$$x = -2$$

33. $2 \cdot \left(\frac{1}{2}(x+3) - 2\right) = 2 \cdot 1$

$$x + 3 - 4 = 2$$
$$x - 1 + 1 = 2 + 1$$
$$x = 3$$

35. $5 - \frac{2x}{7} = 1 - (x-4)$

$$35 - 2x = 7 - 7x + 28$$
$$35 - 2x = 35 - 7x$$
$$5x = 0$$
$$x = 0$$

37. $10 \cdot (0.3x + 0.4) = 10 \cdot (0.5x - 0.8)$

$$3x + 4 - 5x - 4 = 5x - 8 - 5x - 4$$
$$-2x = -12$$
$$x = 6$$

39. $0.6 - 0.02x = 0.4x - 0.03$

$$60 - 2x = 40x - 3$$
$$42x = 63$$
$$x = 1.5$$

41. $0.2(x-4) = 3$

$$2(x-4) = 30$$
$$2x - 8 = 30$$
$$2x = 38$$
$$x = 19$$

19

© 2006 Pearson Education, Inc., Upper Saddle River, NJ. All rights reserved. This material is protected under all copyright laws as they currently exist. No portion of this material may be reproduced, in any form or by any means, without permission in writing from the publisher.

43. $0.05x - 2 = 0.3(x - 5)$

$0.05x - 2 = 0.3x - 1.5$

$5x - 200 = 30x - 150$

$-25x = 50$

$x = -2$

45. $2x + 12 = 3 + 4x - 7 \Rightarrow -2x = -4 - 12$

$-2x = -16 \Rightarrow x = 8$

47. $\dfrac{x-2}{7} + \dfrac{5}{2} = \dfrac{9}{2} \Rightarrow 2(x-2) + 35 = 63$

$2x - 4 = 28 \Rightarrow 2x = 32 \Rightarrow x = 16$

49. $15 \cdot \left(\dfrac{1}{3} - \dfrac{x+1}{5} \right) = 15 \cdot \dfrac{x}{3}$

$15 \cdot \dfrac{1}{3} - 15 \cdot \dfrac{x+1}{5} = 5x \Rightarrow 5 - 3(x+1) = 5x$

$5 - 3x - 3 = 5x \Rightarrow 2 - 3x = 5x \Rightarrow 2 = 8x$

$x = \dfrac{2}{8} = \dfrac{1}{4}$

51. $2 + 0.1(5 - x) = 1.3x - (0.4x - 2.5)$

$2 + 0.5 - 0.1x = 1.3x - 0.4x + 2.5$

$2.5 - 0.1x = 0.9x + 2.5$

$2.5 - 2.5 = 0.9x + 0.1x \Rightarrow 0 = x$

$x = 0$

53. $12 \cdot \left(\dfrac{1}{2}(x+2) \right) = 12 \cdot \left(\dfrac{2}{3}(x-1) - \dfrac{3}{4} \right)$

$6(x+2) = 8(x-1) - 9$

$6x + 12 = 8x - 8 - 7 = 8x - 17$

$29 = 2x \Rightarrow x = \dfrac{29}{2}$

55. $7x + 4 = 3x - 8 - 7x + 1$

$7x + 4 = -4x - 7$

$11x = -11$

$x = -1$

57. $2x - 4(x+1) = -2x + 14$

$2x - 4x - 4 = -2x + 14$

$-2x - 4 = -2x + 14$

$-4 = 14$, since $-4 \neq 14$, no solution

59. $7(x+1) - 4 = 10x + 3(1-x)$

$7x + 7 - 4 = 10x + 3 - 3x$

$7x + 3 = 7x + 3$, identical so

any real number is a solution.

61. $6 + 8(x-2) = 10x - 2(x+4)$

$6 + 8x - 16 = 10x - 2x - 8$

$8x - 10 = 8x - 8$

$-10 = -8, \; -10 \neq -8, \quad$ no solution

63. $x - 2 + \dfrac{2x}{5} = -2 + \dfrac{7x}{5}$

$5x - 10 + 2x = -10 + 7x$

$7x - 10 = 7x - 10$, identical so

any real number is a solution.

Cumulative Review Problems

65. $5 - (4-2)^2 + 3(-2) = 5 - (2)^2 + (-6)$

$= 5 - 4 + (-6)$

$= 1 + (-6) = -5$

67. $(-2)^4 - 12 - 6(-2) = 16 - 12 + (-6)(-2)$

$= 4 + 12$

$= 16$

© 2006 Pearson Education, Inc., Upper Saddle River, NJ. All rights reserved. This material is protected under all copyright laws as they currently exist. No portion of this material may be reproduced, in any form or by any means, without permission in writing from the publisher.

65. (a) $\dfrac{27,000,000}{4000} = 6750$

    (b) $\dfrac{6200 + 8420 + 12,065}{3} = 8895$

2.2 Exercises

1. $6x + 5y = 3$

$$6x = 3 - 5y$$

$$x = \dfrac{3 - 5y}{6}$$

3. $2x + 3y = 24 - 6x$

$$8x = 24 - 3y$$

$$x = \dfrac{24 - 3y}{8}$$

5. $y = \dfrac{2}{3}x - 4$

$$3y = 2x - 12 \Rightarrow 2x - 12 = 3y$$

$$2x = 3y + 12$$

$$x = \dfrac{3y + 12}{2}$$

7. $x = -\dfrac{3}{4}y + \dfrac{2}{3}$

$$12x = -9y + 8$$

$$9y = -12x + 8$$

$$y = \dfrac{-12x + 8}{9}$$

9. $A = lw$

$$l = \dfrac{A}{w}$$

11. $A = \dfrac{h}{2}(B + b) \Rightarrow 2A = hB + hb$

$$hB + hb = 2A \Rightarrow hB = 2A - hb$$

$$B = \dfrac{2A - hb}{h}$$

13. $A = 2\pi rh$

$$r = \dfrac{A}{2\pi h}$$

15. $H = \dfrac{2}{3}(a + 2b)$

$$3H = 2a + 4b$$

$$4b = 3H - 2a$$

$$b = \dfrac{3H - 2a}{4}$$

17. $2(2ax + y) = 3ax - 4y$

$$4ax + 2y = 3ax - 4y$$

$$ax = -6y$$

$$x = -\dfrac{6y}{a}$$

19. (a) $A = \dfrac{1}{2}ab$

$$2A = ab$$

$$a = \dfrac{2A}{b}$$

    (b) $a = \dfrac{2(20)}{2.5}$

$$a = 16$$

21

© 2006 Pearson Education, Inc., Upper Saddle River, NJ. All rights reserved. This material is protected under all copyright laws as they currently exist. No portion of this material may be reproduced, in any form or by any means, without permission in writing from the publisher.

21. (a) $A = a + d(n-1) \Rightarrow A = a + dn - d$

$A - a + d = dn \Rightarrow dn = A - a + d$

$n = \dfrac{A - a + d}{d}$

(b) $n = \dfrac{A - a + d}{d}$

$n = \dfrac{28 - 3 + 15}{15} = \dfrac{8}{3}$

23. $t = -0.7x + 160$

$10t = -7x + 1600$

$7x = 1600 - 10t$

$x = \dfrac{1600 - 10t}{7}$

$x = \dfrac{1600 - 10(139)}{7}$

$x = 30$

$1975 + 30 = 2005$

25. (a) $\dfrac{m}{1.15} = k$

$m = 1.15k$

(b) $m = 1.15(29)$

$m = 33.35$ miles per hour

27. (a) $C = 0.6547D + 5.8263$

$C - 5.8263 = 0.6547D$

$0.6547D = C - 5.8263$

$D = \dfrac{C - 5.8263}{0.6547}$

(b) $D = \dfrac{9.56 - 5.8263}{0.6547}$

$D = \$5.7$ billion

Cumulative Review

29. $(2x^{-3}y)^{-2} = 2^{-2}x^{6}y^{-2} = \dfrac{x^6}{2^2 y^2} = \dfrac{x^6}{4y^2}$

31. $7 + 6 \div 2 - (5-2)^2 = 7 + 3 - 3^2$

$\qquad\qquad = 10 - 9 = 1$

33. $\$5000(1.05) + \$4000(1.09) = \$9610$

2.3 Exercises

1. $|x| = b,\ b > 0$ will always have two solutions, $x = b$ and $x = -b.$ Since $b > 0,\ b$ and $-b$ are different.

3. The first step in solving $|x-7| - 2 = 8$ is isolating the absolute value, $|x-7| = 10,$ from which

$x + 7 = 10 \qquad$ or $\quad x + 7 = -10$

$\qquad x = 10 - 7 \qquad\qquad x = -10 - 7$

$\qquad x = 3 \qquad\qquad\qquad x = -17$

5. $|x| = 30$

$\quad x = -30$ or $x = 30$

check: $|30| \overset{?}{=} 30 \qquad |-30| \overset{?}{=} 30$

$\qquad\quad 30 = 30 \qquad\qquad 30 = 30$

7. $|x - 6| = 16$

$\quad x - 6 = 16$ or $x - 6 = -16$

$\qquad x = 22 \qquad\qquad x = -10$

check: $|22 - 6| \overset{?}{=} 16 \qquad |-10 - 6| \overset{?}{=} 16$

$\qquad\quad |16| \overset{?}{=} 16 \qquad\qquad |16| \overset{?}{=} 16$

$\qquad\quad 16 = 16 \qquad\qquad\quad 16 = 16$

© 2006 Pearson Education, Inc., Upper Saddle River, NJ. All rights reserved. This material is protected under all copyright laws as they currently exist. No portion of this material may be reproduced, in any form or by any means, without permission in writing from the publisher.

9. $|2x-5|=13$

$2x-5=13$ or $2x-5=-13$

$2x=18 \qquad\qquad 2x=-8$

$x=9 \qquad\qquad\quad x=-4$

check: $|2\cdot9-5|\overset{?}{=}13 \quad |2(-4)-5|\overset{?}{=}13$

$\qquad\quad |18-5|\overset{?}{=}13 \qquad |-8-5|\overset{?}{=}13$

$\qquad\qquad |13|\overset{?}{=}13 \qquad\quad |-13|\overset{?}{=}13$

$\qquad\qquad\quad 13=13 \qquad\qquad 13=13$

11. $|5-4x|=11$

$5-4x=11$ or $5-4x=-11$

$-4x=6 \qquad\qquad -4x=-16$

$x=-\dfrac{3}{2} \qquad\qquad x=4$

check: $\left|5-4\left(-\dfrac{3}{2}\right)\right|\overset{?}{=}11 \quad |5-4(4)|\overset{?}{=}11$

$\qquad\qquad |5+6|\overset{?}{=}11 \qquad |5-16|\overset{?}{=}11$

$\qquad\qquad |11|\overset{?}{=}11 \qquad\quad |-11|\overset{?}{=}11$

$\qquad\qquad\quad 11=11 \qquad\qquad 11=11$

13. $\left|\dfrac{1}{2}x-3\right|=2$

$\dfrac{1}{2}x-3=2$ or $\dfrac{1}{2}x-3=-2$

$x-6=4 \qquad\qquad x-6=-4$

$x=10 \qquad\qquad\quad x=2$

check: $\left|\dfrac{1}{2}\cdot10-3\right|\overset{?}{=}2 \quad \left|\dfrac{1}{2}\cdot2-3\right|\overset{?}{=}2$

$\qquad\quad |5-3|\overset{?}{=}2 \qquad |1-3|\overset{?}{=}2$

$\qquad\quad |-2|\overset{?}{=}2 \qquad |1-3|\overset{?}{=}2$

$\qquad\qquad 2=2 \qquad\qquad 2=2$

15. $|2.3-0.3x|=1$

$2.3-0.3x=1$ or $2.3-0.3x=-1$

$23-3x=10 \qquad\qquad 23-3x=-10$

$-3x=-13 \qquad\qquad -3x=-33$

$x=\dfrac{13}{3} \qquad\qquad\qquad x=11$

check: $\left|2.3-0.3\left(\dfrac{13}{3}\right)\right|\overset{?}{=}1 \quad |2.3-0.3(11)|\overset{?}{=}1$

$\qquad\quad |2.3-1.3|\overset{?}{=}1 \qquad |2.3-3.3|\overset{?}{=}1$

$\qquad\qquad |1|\overset{?}{=}1 \qquad\qquad |-1|\overset{?}{=}1$

$\qquad\qquad\quad 1=1 \qquad\qquad\qquad 1=1$

17. $|x+2|-1=7$

$|x+2|=8$

$x+2=8$ or $x+2=-8$

$x=6 \qquad\quad x=-10$

check: $|6+2|-1\overset{?}{=}7 \qquad |-10+2|-1\overset{?}{=}7$

$\qquad\quad |8|-1\overset{?}{=}7 \qquad\qquad |-8|-1\overset{?}{=}7$

$\qquad\qquad 8-1\overset{?}{=}7 \qquad\qquad\quad 8-1\overset{?}{=}7$

$\qquad\qquad\quad 7=7 \qquad\qquad\qquad\quad 7=7$

19. $\left|\dfrac{1}{2}-\dfrac{3}{4}x\right|+1=3 \Rightarrow \left|\dfrac{1}{2}-\dfrac{3}{4}x\right|=2$

$\dfrac{1}{2}-\dfrac{3}{4}x=2$ or $\dfrac{1}{2}-\dfrac{3}{4}x=-2$

$-\dfrac{3}{4}x=\dfrac{3}{2} \qquad\qquad -\dfrac{3}{4}x=-\dfrac{5}{2}$

$x=-2 \qquad\qquad\qquad x=\dfrac{10}{3}$

check: $\left|\dfrac{1}{2}-\dfrac{3}{4}(-2)\right|+1\overset{?}{=}3, \ 3=3$

$\left|\dfrac{1}{2}-\dfrac{3}{4}\cdot\dfrac{10}{3}\right|+1\overset{?}{=}3, \ 3=3$

© 2006 Pearson Education, Inc., Upper Saddle River, NJ. All rights reserved. This material is protected under all copyright laws as they currently exist. No portion of this material may be reproduced, in any form or by any means, without permission in writing from the publisher.

21. $\left|1-\dfrac{3}{4}x\right|+4=7 \Rightarrow \left|1-\dfrac{3}{4}x\right|=3$

$$1-\dfrac{3}{4}x=3 \quad \text{or} \quad 1-\dfrac{3}{4}x=-3$$

$$4-3x=12 \qquad 4-3x=-12$$

$$-3x=8 \qquad\quad -3x=-16$$

$$x=-\dfrac{8}{3} \qquad\quad x=\dfrac{16}{3}$$

check: $\left|1-\dfrac{3}{4}\cdot\dfrac{-8}{3}\right|+4\overset{?}{=}7 \quad \left|1-\dfrac{3}{4}\cdot\dfrac{16}{3}\right|+4\overset{?}{=}7$

$$|1+2|+4\overset{?}{=}7 \qquad |1-4|+4\overset{?}{=}7$$

$$|3|+4\overset{?}{=}7 \qquad |-3|+4\overset{?}{=}7$$

$$3+4\overset{?}{=}7 \qquad 3+4\overset{?}{=}7$$

$$7=7 \qquad 7=7$$

23. $\left|\dfrac{1-3x}{2}\right|=\dfrac{4}{5}$

$$\dfrac{1-3x}{2}=\dfrac{4}{5} \quad \text{or} \quad \dfrac{1-3x}{2}=-\dfrac{4}{5}$$

$$5-15x=8 \qquad 5-15x=-8$$

$$-15x=3 \qquad\quad -15x=-13$$

$$x=-\dfrac{1}{5} \qquad\quad x=\dfrac{13}{15}$$

check: $\left|\dfrac{1-3\left(-\dfrac{1}{5}\right)}{2}\right|\overset{?}{=}\dfrac{4}{5},\ \dfrac{4}{5}=\dfrac{4}{5}$

$$\left|\dfrac{1-3\left(\dfrac{13}{15}\right)}{2}\right|\overset{?}{=}\dfrac{4}{5},\ \dfrac{4}{5}=\dfrac{4}{5}$$

25. $|x+6|=|2x-3|$

$$x+6=2x-3 \quad \text{or} \quad x+6=-(2x-3)$$

$$-x=-9 \qquad\quad x+6=-2x+3 \Rightarrow 3x=-3$$

$$x=9 \qquad\qquad\quad x=-1$$

27. $\left|\dfrac{x-1}{2}\right|=|2x+3|$

$$\dfrac{x-1}{2}=2x+3 \quad \text{or} \quad \dfrac{x-1}{2}=-(2x+3)=-2x-3$$

$$x-1=4x+6 \qquad x-1=-4x-6$$

$$-3x=7 \qquad\qquad 5x=-5$$

$$x=-\dfrac{7}{3} \qquad\qquad x=-1$$

29. $|1.5x-2|=|x-0.5|$

$$1.5x-2=x-0.5 \quad \text{or} \quad 1.5x-2=-(x-0.5)$$

$$15x-20=10x-5 \qquad 15x-20=-10x+5$$

$$5x=15 \qquad\qquad 25x=25$$

$$x=3 \qquad\qquad x=1$$

31. $|3-x|=\left|\dfrac{x}{2}+3\right|$

$$3-x=\dfrac{x}{2}+3 \quad \text{or} \quad 3-x=-\left(\dfrac{x}{2}+3\right)=-\dfrac{x}{2}-3$$

$$6-2x=x+6 \qquad 6-2x=-x-6$$

$$-3x=0 \qquad\qquad -x=-12$$

$$x=0 \qquad\qquad x=12$$

33. $|1.62x+3.14|=2.19$

$$1.62x+3.14=2.19$$

$$1.62x=-0.95$$

$$x=-0.59$$

$$\text{or } 1.62x+3.14=-2.19$$

$$1.62x=-5.33$$

$$x=-3.29$$

24

© 2006 Pearson Education, Inc., Upper Saddle River, NJ. All rights reserved. This material is protected under all copyright laws as they currently exist. No portion of this material may be reproduced, in any form or by any means, without permission in writing from the publisher.

35. $|3(x+4)| + 2 = 14$

$$|3x+12| = 12$$

$$3x+12 = 12 \text{ or } 3x+12 = -12$$

$$4x = 0 \qquad\qquad 3x = -24$$

$$x = 0 \qquad\qquad x = -8$$

check: $|3(0+4)| + 2 \overset{?}{=} 14$

$$14 = 14$$

$$|3(-8+4)| + 2 \overset{?}{=} 14$$

$$14 = 14$$

37. $\left|\dfrac{5x}{3} - 1\right| = 0 \Rightarrow \dfrac{5x}{3} - 1 = 0$

$$5x = 3 \Rightarrow x = \frac{3}{5}$$

check: $\left|\dfrac{5 \cdot \dfrac{3}{5}}{3} - 1\right| \overset{?}{=} 0, \ 0 = 0$

39. $\left|\dfrac{4}{3}x - \dfrac{1}{8}\right| = -5.$ No solution, since absolute value is nonnegative.

41. $\left|\dfrac{2x-1}{3}\right| = \dfrac{5}{6}$

$$\frac{2x-1}{3} = \frac{5}{6} \quad \text{or} \quad \frac{2x-1}{3} = -\frac{5}{6}$$

$$12x - 6 = 15 \qquad\quad 12x - 6 = -15$$

$$12x = 21 \qquad\qquad 12x = -9$$

$$x = \frac{7}{4} \qquad\qquad\quad x = -\frac{3}{4}$$

41. check: $\left|\dfrac{2 \cdot \dfrac{7}{4} - 1}{3}\right| \overset{?}{=} \dfrac{5}{6}, \ \dfrac{5}{6} = \dfrac{5}{6}$

$$\left|\dfrac{2\left(-\dfrac{3}{4}\right) - 1}{3}\right| \overset{?}{=} \dfrac{5}{6}, \ \dfrac{5}{6} = \dfrac{5}{6}$$

43. $|1.5x - 2.5| = |x+3|$

$$1.5x - 2.5 = x+3 \text{ or } 1.5x - 2.5 = -x - 3$$

$$0.5x = 5.5 \qquad\qquad 2.5x = -0.5$$

$$x = 11 \qquad\qquad\quad x = -0.2$$

check: $|1.5(11) - 2.5| \overset{?}{=} |11+3|$

$$14 = 14$$

$$|1.5(-0.2) - 2.5| \overset{?}{=} |-0.2 + 3|$$

$$-2.8 = -2.8$$

Cumulative Review

45. $(3x^{-3}yz^0)\left(\dfrac{5}{3}x^4y^2\right) = 5x^{-3+4}y^{1+2} \cdot 1$

$$= 5xy^3$$

47. $5(\text{cost of beaker}) = 975 - 825 = 150$

$$\text{cost of beaker} = \$30$$

$$3(\text{cost of Bunsen burner}) + 25(30) = 975$$

$$3(\text{cost of Bunsen burner}) = 225$$

$$(\text{cost of Bunsen burner}) = \$75$$

© 2006 Pearson Education, Inc., Upper Saddle River, NJ. All rights reserved. This material is protected under all copyright laws as they currently exist. No portion of this material may be reproduced, in any form or by any means, without permission in writing from the publisher.

2.4 Exercises

1. Let $x =$ the number.
$$\frac{3}{5}x = -54$$
$$3x = -270$$
$$x = -90$$
The number is -90.

3. Let $x =$ the monthly membership fee
$$12x - 50 = 526$$
$$12x = 576$$
$$x = 48$$
The monthly membership is $48.

5. Let $x =$ the weight of the package.
$$3 + 0.8x = 17.40$$
$$0.8x = 14.4$$
$$x = 18$$
The package weighed 18 pounds.

7. Let $x =$ the number of weeks for the laundromat cost to equal the cost of a new washer and dryer.
$$11.75x = 846$$
$$x = 72$$
It would take 72 weeks.

9. Profit = Revenue − Cost.
For one year the profit must be $129,000.

The revenue for one week is
$(2000 \cdot 8 \cdot 15) = 240,000$.

The cost for one week is
$14,000 \cdot 8 + 85,000 = 197,000$.

The profit for one week is
$240,000 - 197,000 = 43,000$.

9. Let $x =$ the number of weeks of travel,
then $43,000x = 129,000 \Rightarrow x = 3$

Let $x =$ the number of weeks of travel,
then $43,000x = 129,000 \Rightarrow x = 3$

He needs to travel three weeks each year.

11. Let $x =$ miles Melissa drives each day.
$0.5x =$ miles Marcia drives each day.
$x + 17 =$ miles John drives each day.
$$x + 0.5x + x + 17 = 112$$
$$2.5x = 95$$
$$x = 38$$
$$0.5x = 19$$
$$x + 17 = 55$$
Each day Melissa drives 38 miles, Marcia drives 19 miles, and John drives 55 miles.

13. Let $x =$ the width of the field.
$$P = 2W + 2L$$
$$2x + 2(3x - 6) = 340$$
$$2x + 6x - 12 = 340$$
$$8x = 352$$
$$x = 44$$
$$3x - 6 = 126$$
The width of the field is 44 yards and the length of the field is 126 yards.

© 2006 Pearson Education, Inc., Upper Saddle River, NJ. All rights reserved. This material is protected under all copyright laws as they currently exist.
No portion of this material may be reproduced, in any form or by any means, without permission in writing from the publisher.

15. Let $x =$ the length of the shortest side

$2x - 7 =$ the length of the longest side

$x + 6 =$ the length of the third side

$2x - 7 + x + 6 + x = 59$

$4x = 60$

$x = 15$ ft, short side

$2x - 7 = 23$ ft, longest side

$x + 6 = 21$ ft, third side

17. Let $x =$ yearly phone bill for Saugus.

$2x - 610 =$ yearly phone bill for Salem

Saugus + Salem = Total

$x + 2x - 610 = 2504$

$3x = 2664$

$x = \$888$ for Saugus

$2x - 610 = \$1166$ for Salem

19. (a)

Let $x =$ number of Clear Call free min

$2(x - 50) = x + 300 + \dfrac{1}{3}x$

$\dfrac{2}{3}x = 400$

$x = 600$, Clear Call free min

$x - 50 = 550$, Reliable free min

$\dfrac{1}{3}x + 300 = 500$, Nationwide free min

(b)

$\dfrac{\$71.50}{550 \text{ min}} = \dfrac{\$0.13}{1 \text{ min}}$, Reliable

$\dfrac{\$90}{600 \text{ min}} = \dfrac{\$0.15}{1 \text{ min}}$, Clear Call

$\dfrac{\$70}{500 \text{ min}} = \dfrac{\$0.14}{1 \text{ min}}$, Nationwide

Reliable has the lowest cost per min.

Cumulative Review Problems

21. Identity property of addition.

23. $7(-2) \div 7(-3) - 3 = -14 \div 7(-3) - 3$

$= (-2)(-3) - 3$

$= 6 - 3$

$= 3$

How Am I Doing? Sections 2.1-2.4

1. $2x - 1 = 12x + 36$

$-10x = 37$

$x = -3.7$

2. $\dfrac{x - 2}{4} = \dfrac{1}{2}x + 4$

$x - 2 = 2x + 16$

$-x = 18$

$x = -18$

3. $4(x - 3) = x + 2(5x - 1)$

$4x - 12 = x + 10x - 2$

$-7x = 10$

$x = -\dfrac{10}{7} = -1\dfrac{3}{7}$

4. $0.6x + 3 = 0.5x - 7$

$6x + 30 = 5x - 70$

$x = -100$

5. $5x - 8y = 15$

$-8y = 15 - 5x$

$8y = 5x - 15$

$y = \dfrac{5x - 15}{8}$

27

© 2006 Pearson Education, Inc., Upper Saddle River, NJ. All rights reserved. This material is protected under all copyright laws as they currently exist. No portion of this material may be reproduced, in any form or by any means, without permission in writing from the publisher.

6. $5ab - 2b = 16ab - 3(8 + b)$

$5ab - 2b = 16ab - 24 - 3b$

$-11ab = -b - 24$

$11ab = b + 24$

$a = \dfrac{b + 24}{11b}$

7. $A = P + Prt$

$Prt = A - P$

$r = \dfrac{A - P}{Pt}$

8. $r = \dfrac{A - P}{Pt}$

$r = \dfrac{118 - 100}{(100)3}$

$r = \dfrac{18}{300}$

$r = \dfrac{3}{50}$

$r = 0.06$

9. $|3x - 2| = 7$

$3x - 2 = 7$ or $3x - 2 = -7$

$3x = 9$ $3x = -5$

$x = 3$ $x = -\dfrac{5}{3}$

10. $|8 - x| - 3 = 1$

$|8 - x| = 4$

$8 - x = 4$ or $8 - x = -4$

$-x = -4$ $-x = -12$

$x = 4$ $x = 12$

11. $\left| \dfrac{2x + 3}{4} \right| = 2$

$\dfrac{2x + 3}{4} = 2$ or $\dfrac{2x + 3}{4} = -2$

$2x + 3 = 8$ $2x + 3 = -8$

$2x = -5$ $x = -11$

$x = -\dfrac{5}{2} = -2.5$ $x = -\dfrac{11}{2} = -5.5$

12. $|5x - 8| = |3x + 2|$

$5x - 8 = 3x + 2$ or $5x - 8 = -3x - 2$

$2x = 10$ $8x = 6$

$x = 5$ $x = \dfrac{6}{8} = 0.75$

13. $P = 2L + 2W$

$64 = 2(3W - 4) + 2W$

$32 = 3W - 4 + W$

$4W = 36$

$W = 9$

$3W - 4 = 23$

The dimensions are 9 cm × 23 cm.

14. $\$6 + \$01.2n = 9.12$

$0.12n = 3.12$

$n = 26$ checks

15. Let $x =$ number of lb Cindi picked up

$x + \dfrac{x}{2} + 80 = 455$

$2x + x + 160 = 910$

$3x = 750$

$x = 250$ pounds for Cindi

$\dfrac{x}{2} + 80 = 205$ pounds for Alan

28

© 2006 Pearson Education, Inc., Upper Saddle River, NJ. All rights reserved. This material is protected under all copyright laws as they currently exist. No portion of this material may be reproduced, in any form or by any means, without permission in writing from the publisher.

16. Let x = length of short side

$$2x - 5 + x + 9 + x = 62$$
$$4x = 58$$
$$x = 14.5 \text{ ft, short side}$$
$$x + 9 = 23.5 \text{ ft, third side}$$
$$2x - 5 = 24 \text{ ft, long side}$$

2.5 Exercises

1. Let x = population in 1969.

$$x + 0.34x = 273.1$$
$$1.34x = 273.1$$
$$x = 203.8059701$$
$$x \approx 203.8$$

The population in 1969 was approximately 203.8 million people.

3. Let x = the original price.
sale price = 80% of original price

$$0.80x = 340$$
$$x = \$425 \text{ original price}$$

5. Let x = number of unemployed

$$x - 0.15x = 969$$
$$0.85x = 969$$
$$x = 1140$$

1140 residents were unemployed in the previous month.

7. Let x = the number of hemlocks.

$$x + 2x + 3x + 20 = 1400$$
$$6x = 1380$$
$$x = 230$$
$$2x = 460$$
$$3x + 20 = 710$$

230 hemlocks, 460 spruces, and 710 balsams were planted.

9. Let x = Walker's salary 25 yrs ago

$$3x + 4(500 - x) = 1740$$
$$3x + 2000 - 4x = 1740$$
$$-x = -260$$
$$x = 260$$
$$500 - x = 240$$

Walker earned \$260 a week 25 years ago. Angela earned \$240 a week 25 years ago.

11. Let x = number of mg in packet A

$$17x + 14(8 - x) = 127$$
$$17x + 112 - 14x = 127$$
$$3x = 15$$
$$x = 5$$
$$8 - x = 3$$

5 mg are contained in packet A. 3 mg are contained in packet B.

13. $I = prt$

$$I = 600(0.12)(3)$$
$$I = \$216$$

15. $I = prt$

$$I = 5000(0.031)(1.5)$$
$$I = \$232.50$$

17. Let x = amount invested at 5%.

$$0.05x + 0.08(6400 - x) = 395$$
$$0.05x + 512 - 0.08x = 395$$
$$-0.03x = -117$$
$$x = 3900$$
$$6400 - x = 2500$$

She invested \$3900 at 5% and \$2500 at 8%.

© 2006 Pearson Education, Inc., Upper Saddle River, NJ. All rights reserved. This material is protected under all copyright laws as they currently exist. No portion of this material may be reproduced, in any form or by any means, without permission in writing from the publisher.

19. Let $x =$ amount invested at 3.5%.

$$0.035x + 0.022(18,000 - x) = 552$$
$$0.035x + 396 - 0.022x = 552$$
$$0.013x = 156$$
$$x = 12,000$$
$$18,000 - x = 6000$$

He invested $12,000 in the certificate of deposit and $6000 in the fixed interest account.

21. Let $x =$ number of grams with 45% fat.

$$0.45x + 0.20(30 - x) = 0.30(30)$$
$$0.45x + 6 - 0.2x = 9$$
$$0.25x = 3$$
$$x = 12$$
$$30 - x = 18$$

She should use 12 grams of the 45% fat cheese and 18 grams of the 20% fat cheese.

23. Let $x =$ number of pounds with 30% fat.

$$0.30x + 0.10(100 - x) = 0.25(100)$$
$$0.3x + 10 - 0.1x = 25$$
$$0.2x = 15$$
$$x = 75$$
$$100 - 75 = 25$$

She should use 75 pounds of the 30% fat hamburger and 25 pounds of the 10% fat hamburger.

25. Let $x =$ number of gal of 25% fertilizer

$$0.25x + 0.15(150 - x) = 0.18(150)$$
$$0.25x + 22.5 - 0.15x = 27$$
$$0.1x = 4.5$$
$$x = 45$$
$$150 - x = 105$$

25. They should mix 45 gal of 25% fertilizer with 105 gal of 15% fertilizer.

27. Let $x =$ speed on secondary roads.

$$4x + 2(x + 20) = 250$$
$$4x + 2x + 40 = 250$$
$$6x = 210$$
$$x = 35$$

Speed on the secondary roads was 35 miles per hour.

29. Let $x =$ time they walked on treadmill.

$$5x = 4.2x + 0.6$$
$$0.8x = 0.6$$
$$x = \frac{3}{4}$$

They each walked $\frac{3}{4}$ of an hour.

31. Let $x =$ profit two years ago.

$$x + 0.65x = 1.65x = \text{ profit last year.}$$
$$(0.6)(1.65x) = \text{ profit this year.}$$
$$0.6(1.65x) = 17,820,000$$
$$x = 18,000,000$$

Profit was $18,000,000 two years ago.

33.
$$A_{\text{triangle}} = \frac{1}{2}bh \Rightarrow 6 = \frac{1}{2}(3)h$$
$$2(6) = 3h \Rightarrow 3h = 12$$
$$h = 4$$
$$A_{\text{parallelogram}} = bh = 8 \cdot 4 = 32 \text{ cm}^2$$

Cumulative Review Problems

35. $5a - 2b + c = 5(1) - 2(-3) + (-4)$
$$= 5 + 6 - 4$$
$$= 11 - 4 = 7$$

© 2006 Pearson Education, Inc., Upper Saddle River, NJ. All rights reserved. This material is protected under all copyright laws as they currently exist. No portion of this material may be reproduced, in any form or by any means, without permission in writing from the publisher.

37. $\dfrac{2-6(-1)+5^2}{|4-7|} = \dfrac{2+6+25}{|-3|}$

$= \dfrac{8+25}{3}$

$= \dfrac{33}{3}$

$= 11$

2.6 Exercises

1. True, $6 < 8$ and $8 > 6$ convey the same information.

3. True, dividing both sides of an inequality by -4 reverses the direction of the inequality.

5. False, the graph of $x \leq 6$ does include the point at 6 on the number line.

7. $6 > -3$

9. $-7 < -2$

11. $\dfrac{3}{4} > \dfrac{2}{3}$

13. $-\dfrac{2}{9} = -0.\overline{2} < -0.2\overline{142857} = -\dfrac{3}{14}$

15. $-3.4 > -3.41$

17. $|3-7| = |-4| = 4 < 7 = |7| = |9-2|$

19. $x \geq -2$

21. $x < 15$

23. $2x - 7 \leq -5$

$2x \leq 2$

$x \leq 1$

25. $3x - 7 > 9x + 5$

$-6x > 12$

$x < -2$

27. $0.5x + 0.1 < 1.1x + 0.7$

$5x + 1 < 11x + 7$

$-6x < 6$

$x > -1$

29. $4x - 1 > 15$

$4x > 16$

$x > 4$

31. $7x + 2 \leq 2x - 8$

$5x \leq -10$

$x \leq -2$

33. $2x + \dfrac{5}{3} > \dfrac{2}{5}x - 1$

$30x + 25 > 6x - 15$

$24x > -40$

$x > -\dfrac{5}{3}$

35. $3x - 11 + 4(x+8) < 0$

$3x - 11 + 4x + 32 < 0$

$7x < -21$

$x < -3$

31

© 2006 Pearson Education, Inc., Upper Saddle River, NJ. All rights reserved. This material is protected under all copyright laws as they currently exist. No portion of this material may be reproduced, in any form or by any means, without permission in writing from the publisher.

37. $3\left(\dfrac{2}{3}x-(x-2)\right)\ge 3(4)$

$2x-3(x-2)\ge 12$

$2x-3x+6\ge 12$

$-x\le 6\Rightarrow x\ge -6$

39. $0.6x+1\le 2.8$

$0.6x\le 1.8$

$x\le 3$

41. $0.1(x-2)\ge 0.5x-0.2$

$0.1x-0.2\ge 0.5x-0.2$

$-0.4x\ge 0$

$x\le 0$

43. $2-\dfrac{1}{5}(x-1)\ge \dfrac{2}{3}(2x+1)$

$30-3(x-1)\ge 10(2x+1)$

$30-3x+3\ge 20x+10$

$-23x\ge -23$

$x\le 1$

45. $\dfrac{2x-3}{5}+1\ge \dfrac{1}{2}x+3$

$2(2x-3)+10\ge 5x+30$

$4x-6+10\ge 5x+30$

$-x\ge 26$

$x\le -26$

47. Let x = number of tables.

$4\cdot 3+4x>52$

$12+4x>52$

$4x>40$

$x>10$

She would have to serve more than ten tables.

49. Let x = the number of minutes he talks after the first minute.

$3.95+0.55x\le 13.30$

$0.55x\le 9.35$

$x\le 17$

He can talk for a maximum of $17+1=18$ minutes.

51. Let x = number of computers

$130+155+59x\le 1100$

$59x\le 815$

$x\le 13.81355932$

A maximum of 13 computers can be taken up.

53. Let x = the number of time-shares sold each month.

$12,000-\left(500,000+6000x\right)\ge 100,000$

$12,000x-500,000-6000x\ge 100,000$

$6000x\ge 600,000$

$x\ge 100$

At least 100 time-shares must be sold each month.

47. Let n = the number of visits

$115<36n$

$n>3.19\overline{4}$

They would need to visit at least four times.

Cumulative Review

57. $3xy(x+2)-4x^2(y-1)$

$=3x^2y+6xy-4x^2y+4x^2$

$=6xy-x^2y+4x^2$

59. $\left(\dfrac{3x}{2y^2w^{-4}}\right)^3=\dfrac{3^3x^3}{2^3y^6w^{-12}}=\dfrac{27x^3w^{12}}{8y^6}$

© 2006 Pearson Education, Inc., Upper Saddle River, NJ. All rights reserved. This material is protected under all copyright laws as they currently exist. No portion of this material may be reproduced, in any form or by any means, without permission in writing from the publisher.

2.7 Exercises

1. $3 < x \ and \ x < 8$

3. $-4 < x \ and \ x < 2$

5. $7 < x < 9$

7. $-2 < x \le \dfrac{1}{2}$

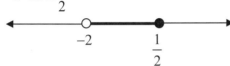

9. $x > 8 \ or \ x < 2$

11. $x \le -\dfrac{5}{2} \ or \ x > 4$

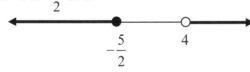

13. $x \le -10 \ or \ x \ge 40$

15. $2x + 3 \le 5 \ or \ x + 1 \ge -2$
$$2x \le 2 \qquad x \ge -3$$
$$x \le 1$$
$$-3 \le x \le 1$$

17. $2x - 3 > 0 \ or \ x - 2 < -7$
$$2x > 3 \qquad\quad x < -5$$
$$x > \dfrac{3}{2}$$

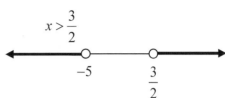

19. $x < 8 \ and \ x > 10$ do not overlap.
No solution.

21. $t < 10.9 \ or \ t > 11.2$

23. $5000 \le c \le 12,000$

25. $-20 \le C \le 11$
$$-20 \le \dfrac{5}{9}\left(F - 32\right) \le 11$$
$$-180 \le 5F - 160 \le 99$$
$$-20 \le 5F \le 259$$
$$-4° \le F \le 51.8°$$

27. $18,000 \le Y \le 33,000$
$$18,000 \le 129\left(d - 4\right) \le 33,000$$
$$\dfrac{18,000}{129} \le d - 4 \le \dfrac{33,000}{129}$$
$$\dfrac{18,000}{129} + 4 \le d \le \dfrac{33,000}{129} + 4$$
$$\$143.53 \le d \le \$259.81$$

29. $x - 3 > -5 \ and \ 2x + 4 < 8$
$$x > -2 \qquad\quad 2x < 4$$
$$-2 < x \qquad\quad x < 2$$
$$-2 < x < 2 \text{ is the solution.}$$

33

© 2006 Pearson Education, Inc., Upper Saddle River, NJ. All rights reserved. This material is protected under all copyright laws as they currently exist. No portion of this material may be reproduced, in any form or by any means, without permission in writing from the publisher.

31. $-3x + 2 \geq -1$ *and* $4 - x \leq 6$

$\qquad -3x \geq -3 \qquad\quad -x \leq 2$

$\qquad\quad x \leq 1 \qquad\qquad x \geq -2$

$\qquad -2 \leq x \leq 1$ is the solution.

33. $2x - 5 < -11$ *or* $5x + 1 \geq 6$

$\qquad 2x < -6 \qquad\quad 5x \geq 5$

$\qquad x < -3 \qquad\qquad x \geq 1$

$\qquad x < -3$ *or* $x \geq 1$ is the solution.

35. $-0.3x + 1 \geq 0.2x$ *or* $-0.2x + 0.5 > 0.7$

$\qquad -3x + 10 \geq 2x \qquad\qquad -2x + 5 > 7$

$\qquad\quad -5x \geq -10 \qquad\qquad\quad -2x > -2$

$\qquad\qquad x \leq 2 \qquad\qquad\qquad\quad x < 1$

$\qquad x \leq 2$ contains $x < 1$

$\qquad x \leq 2$ is the solution.

37. $\dfrac{5x}{2} + 1 \geq 3$ *and* $x - \dfrac{2}{3} \geq \dfrac{4}{3}$

$\qquad 5x + 2 \geq 6 \qquad\quad 3x - 2 \geq 4$

$\qquad\quad 5x \geq 4 \qquad\qquad 3x \geq 6$

$\qquad\quad x \geq \dfrac{4}{5} \qquad\qquad\quad x \geq 2$

$\qquad x \geq 2$ is the solution.

39. $2x + 5 < 3$ *and* $3x - 1 > -1$

$\qquad 2x < -2 \qquad\quad 3x > 0$

$\qquad x < -1 \qquad\qquad x > 0$

$\qquad x < -1$ *and* $x > 0$ do not overlap

No solution.

41. $3x - 1 \geq -10$ *and* $4x + 7 \leq 2x + 1$

$\qquad 3x \geq -9 \qquad\qquad 2x \leq -6$

$\qquad x \geq -3 \qquad\qquad\quad x \leq -3$

$\qquad x = -3$ is the solution.

43. $\dfrac{2 + 3x}{4} \leq -2$ *or* $\dfrac{2x - 7}{3} < 1$

$\qquad 2 + 3x \leq -8 \qquad\quad 2x - 7 < 3$

$\qquad\quad 3x \leq -10 \qquad\qquad 2x < 10$

$\qquad\quad x \leq -\dfrac{10}{3} \qquad\qquad\quad x < 5$

$\qquad x < 5$ is the solution since

$\qquad x < 5$ contains $x \leq -\dfrac{10}{3}$.

45. $2(x + 1) - 5 > -7$ *or* $4 - (x + 3) < 5 - 2x$

$\qquad 2x + 2 - 5 > -7 \qquad\quad 4 - x - 3 < 5 - 2x$

$\qquad\quad 2x - 3 > -7 \qquad\qquad -x + 1 < 5 - 2x$

$\qquad\qquad 2x > 4 \qquad\qquad\qquad 2x - x < 4$

$\qquad\qquad\quad x > 2 \qquad\qquad\qquad\quad x < 4$

The solution is all real numbers.

47.

$\dfrac{1}{4}(x + 2) + \dfrac{1}{8}(x - 3) \leq 1$ *and* $\dfrac{3}{4}(x - 1) > -\dfrac{1}{4}$

$\qquad 2x + 4 + x - 3 \leq 8 \qquad\qquad 3x - 3 > -1$

$\qquad\qquad 3x + 1 \leq 8 \qquad\qquad\qquad 3x > 2$

$\qquad\qquad 3x \leq 7 \qquad\qquad\qquad\quad x > \dfrac{2}{3}$

$\dfrac{2}{3} < x \leq \dfrac{7}{3}$ is the solution.

Cumulative Review

49. $\quad 3y - 5x = 8$

$\qquad\quad -5x = 8 - 3y$

$\qquad (-1)(-5x) = (-1)(8 - 3y) = -8 + 3y$

$\qquad\qquad 5x = 3y - 8$

$\qquad\qquad x = \dfrac{3y - 8}{5}$

34

© 2006 Pearson Education, Inc., Upper Saddle River, NJ. All rights reserved. This material is protected under all copyright laws as they currently exist. No portion of this material may be reproduced, in any form or by any means, without permission in writing from the publisher.

51. $|x+4|-x^2+3x$

$$=|-1+4|-(-1)^2+3(-1)$$
$$=|-3|-1-3$$
$$=3-4$$
$$=-1$$

53. $40 to $50 is an increase of $10. $50 to $120 is an increase of $70. $120 to $190 is an increase of $70. $190 to $230 is an increase of $40. The next four bids will be:
1) $230 + $10 = $240
2) $240 + $70 = $310
3) $310 + $70 = $380
4) $380 + $40 = $420

2.8 Exercises

1. $|x|\le 8$
$$-8\le x\le 8$$

-8 8

3. $|x+4.5|<5$
$$-5<x+4.5<5$$
$$-9.5<x<0.5$$

-9.5 0.5

5. $|x-3|\le 5$
$$-5\le x-3\le 5$$
$$-2\le x\le 8$$

7. $|2x-5|\le 7$
$$-7\le 2x-5\le 7$$
$$-2\le 2x\le 12$$
$$-1\le x\le 6$$

9. $|5x-2|\le 4$
$$-4\le 5x-2\le 4$$
$$-2\le 5x\le 6$$
$$-\frac{2}{5}\le x\le \frac{6}{5}$$

11. $|0.5-0.1x|<1$
$$-1<0.5-0.1x<1$$
$$-1.5<-0.1x<0.5$$
$$15>x>-5$$
$$-5<x<15$$

13. $\left|\frac{1}{4}x+2\right|<6$
$$-6<\frac{1}{4}x+2<6$$
$$-24<x+8<24$$
$$-32<x<16$$

15. $\left|\frac{3}{4}(x-1)\right|<6$
$$-6<\frac{3}{4}(x-1)<6$$
$$-24<3x-3<24$$
$$-21<3x<27$$
$$-7<x<9$$

17. $\left|\frac{3x-2}{4}\right|<3$
$$-3<\frac{3x-2}{4}<3$$
$$-12<3x-2<12$$
$$-10<3x<14$$
$$-\frac{10}{3}<x<\frac{14}{3}$$

35

© 2006 Pearson Education, Inc., Upper Saddle River, NJ. All rights reserved. This material is protected under all copyright laws as they currently exist. No portion of this material may be reproduced, in any form or by any means, without permission in writing from the publisher.

19. $|x| > 5$

$x > 5 \text{ or } x < -5$

21. $|x + 2| > 5$

$x + 2 < -5 \text{ or } x + 2 > 5$

$x < -7 \qquad x > 3$

23. $|x - 1| \geq 2$

$x - 1 \leq -2 \text{ or } x - 1 \geq 2$

$x \leq -1 \qquad x \geq 3$

25. $|3x - 8| \geq 7$

$3x - 8 \leq -7 \text{ or } 3x - 8 \geq 7$

$3x \leq 1 \qquad\qquad 3x \geq 15$

$x \leq \dfrac{1}{3} \qquad\qquad x \geq 5$

27. $|6 - 0.1x| > 5$

$6 - 0.1x > 5 \qquad or \qquad 6 - 0.1x < -5$

$-0.1x > -1 \qquad\qquad -0.1x < -11$

$x < -10 \qquad\qquad\qquad x > 110$

29. $\left| \dfrac{1}{5}x - \dfrac{1}{10} \right| > 2$

$\dfrac{1}{5}x - \dfrac{1}{10} < -2 \quad or \quad \dfrac{1}{5}x - \dfrac{1}{10} > 2$

$2x - 1 < -20 \qquad\qquad 2x - 1 > 20$

$2x < -19 \qquad\qquad\quad 2x > 21$

$x < -\dfrac{19}{2} \qquad\qquad\quad x > \dfrac{21}{2}$

31. $\left| \dfrac{1}{3}(x - 2) \right| < 5$

$-5 < \dfrac{1}{3}(x - 2) < 5$

$-15 < x - 2 < 15$

$-13 < x < 17$

33. $|3x + 5| < 17$

$-17 < 3x + 5 < 17$

$-22 < 3x < 12$

$-\dfrac{22}{3} < x < 4$

35. $|2 - 9x| > 20$

$2 - 9x > 20 \qquad or \quad 2 - 9x < -20$

$-9x > 18 \qquad\qquad\quad -9x < -22$

$x < -2 \qquad\qquad\qquad x > \dfrac{22}{9}$

37. $\qquad |m - s| \leq 0.12$

$|m - 18.65| \leq 0.12$

$-0.12 \leq m - 18.65 \leq 0.12$

$18.53 \leq m \leq 18.77$

39. $\qquad |n - p| \leq 0.05$

$|n - 9.68| \leq 0.05$

$-0.05 \leq n - 9.68 \leq 0.05$

$9.63 \leq n \leq 9.73$

41. $12 < 4x - 8 < -12$ implies $12 < -12$ which is a false statement.

Cumulative Review

43. $(6 - 4)^3 \div (-4) + 2^2 = 2^3 \div (-4) + 2^2$

$= 8 \div (-4) + 4$

$= -2 + 4 = 2$

© 2006 Pearson Education, Inc., Upper Saddle River, NJ. All rights reserved. This material is protected under all copyright laws as they currently exist.
No portion of this material may be reproduced, in any form or by any means, without permission in writing from the publisher.

45.

$$\text{distance} = \text{rate} \cdot \text{time}$$

$$2\left[\frac{1}{8}\text{circumference}\right] = \text{rate} \cdot \text{time}$$

$$2\left[\frac{1}{8}(2\pi \cdot \text{radius})\right] = \text{rate} \cdot \text{time}$$

$$2\left[\frac{1}{3}(2 \cdot 3.14 \cdot 19)\right] = 3 \cdot t$$

$$t = 9.94 \text{ seconds}$$

47. First rack:
cost per CD
$$= \frac{39.95 + 6.50}{160} = \$0.29 = 29 \text{ cents}$$

Second rack:
cost per CD
$$= \frac{24.95 + 5.95}{120} = \$0.2575 = 26 \text{ cents}$$

Third rack:
cost per CD
$$= \frac{18.95 + 4.75}{75} = \$0.316 = 32 \text{ cents}$$

The second rack is the least expensive per CD space.

Putting Your Skills to Work

1. (a) $\dfrac{23 \text{ mi}}{\text{gal}} \cdot 18.5 \text{ gal} = 425.5 \text{ mi}$

    (b) $\dfrac{51 \text{ mi}}{\text{gal}} \cdot 11.9 \text{ gal} = 606.9 \text{ mi}$

2. $20 \text{ day} \cdot \dfrac{70 \text{ mi}}{\text{day}} = 1400 \text{ mi}$

$$1400 \text{ mi} \cdot \frac{\text{gal}}{32 \text{ mi}} = 43.8 \text{ gal}$$

$$1400 \text{ mi} \cdot \frac{\text{gal}}{60 \text{ mi}} = 23.3 \text{ gal}$$

3. $C = x \text{ mi} \cdot \dfrac{\text{gal}}{32 \text{ mi}} \cdot \dfrac{\$2.10}{\text{gal}}$

$$C = 0.065625x$$

4. $C = x \text{ mi} \cdot \dfrac{\text{gal}}{60 \text{ mi}} \cdot \dfrac{\$2.10}{\text{gal}}$

$$C = 0.035x$$

5.

$$C = 0.065625(1400) = \frac{\$91.875}{\text{month}}$$

$$C = 0.035(1400) = \frac{\$49}{\text{month}}$$

$$\left(\frac{\$91.875}{\text{month}} - \frac{\$49}{\text{month}}\right)n = \$20,510 - \$19,875$$

$$\left(\frac{\$91.875}{\text{month}} - \frac{\$49}{\text{month}}\right)n = \$635$$

$n = 14.8 \text{ month}$
George would need to commute to work for 15 months before it would be worth buying the Prius over the Camry.

6. $\left(\dfrac{\$91.875}{\text{month}} - \dfrac{\$49}{\text{month}}\right)n = \$635 + \$1000$

$$n = 38.1 \text{ month}$$

George would need to commute to work for 39 months before it would be $1000 less expensive to have bought the Prius rather than the Camry.

© 2006 Pearson Education, Inc., Upper Saddle River, NJ. All rights reserved. This material is protected under all copyright laws as they currently exist.
No portion of this material may be reproduced, in any form or by any means, without permission in writing from the publisher.

Chapter 2 Review Problems

1. $7x - 3 = -5x - 18$
   $12x = -15$
   $$x = -\frac{5}{4}$$
   $x = -1.25$

2. $8 - 2(x + 3) = 24 - (x - 6)$
   $8 - 2x - 6 = 24 - x + 6$
   $2 - 2x = 30 - x$
   $-x = 28$
   $x = -28$

3. $4(x - 1) + 2 = 3x + 8 - 2x$
   $4x - 4 + 2 = x + 8$
   $4x - 2 = x + 8$
   $3x = 10$
   $$x = \frac{10}{3}$$
   $$x = 3\frac{1}{3}$$

4. $x - \dfrac{7}{5} = \dfrac{1}{3}x + \dfrac{7}{15}$
   $15x - 21 = 5x + 7$
   $10x = 28$
   $$x = \frac{14}{5}$$
   $$x = 2\frac{2}{5}$$

5. $\dfrac{1}{9}x - 1 = \dfrac{1}{2}\left(x + \dfrac{1}{3}\right)$
   $2x - 18 = 9x + 3$
   $-7x = 21$
   $x = -3$

6. $\dfrac{x - 4}{2} - \dfrac{1}{5} = \dfrac{7x + 1}{20}$
   $10x - 40 - 4 = 7x + 1$
   $10x - 44 = 7x + 1$
   $3x = 45$
   $x = 15$

7. $5x = 3(1.6x - 4.2)$
   $5x = 4.8x - 12.6$
   $0.2x = -12.6$
   $x = -63$

8. $1.2x - 1 = 2(1.6x + 1.5)$
   $1.2x - 1 = 3.2x + 3$
   $-2x = 4$
   $x = -2$

9. $4x - 8y = 5$
   $-8y = 5 - 4x$
   $8y = 4x - 5$
   $$y = \frac{4x - 5}{8}$$

10. $R = \dfrac{1}{3}mn$
    $3R = mn$
    $$m = \frac{3R}{n}$$

11. $2(3ax - 2y) - 6ax = -3(ax + 2y)$
    $6ax - 4y - 6ax = -3ax - 6y$
    $3ax = -2y$
    $$a = -\frac{2y}{3x}$$

38

© 2006 Pearson Education, Inc., Upper Saddle River, NJ. All rights reserved. This material is protected under all copyright laws as they currently exist.
No portion of this material may be reproduced, in any form or by any means, without permission in writing from the publisher.

12. $\frac{1}{2}a + 3b = \frac{2}{3}(2b - 1)$

$3a + 18b = 8b - 4$

$10b = -3a - 4$

$b = \frac{-3a - 4}{10}$

13. (a) $C = \frac{5F - 160}{9}$

$9C = 5F - 160 \Rightarrow 5F - 160 = 9C$

$5F = 9C + 160$

$F = \frac{9C + 160}{5}$

(b) $F = \frac{9(10) + 160}{5}$

$F = 50°$ when $C = 10°$.

14. (a) $P = 2W + 2L \Rightarrow P - 2L = 2W$

$2W = P - 2L$

$W = \frac{P - 2L}{2}$

(b) $W = \frac{100 - 2(20.5)}{2} = 29.5$ m

15. $|4x - 5| = 7$

$4x - 5 = 7$ or $4x - 5 = -7$

$4x = 12 \qquad 4x = -2$

$x = 3 \qquad x = -\frac{1}{2}$

16. $|3x + 2| = 20$

$3x + 2 = 20$ or $3x + 2 = -20$

$3x = 18 \qquad 3x = -22$

$x = 6 \qquad x = -\frac{22}{3}$

17. $|3 - x| = |5 - 2x|$

$3 - x = 5 - 2x$ or $3 - x = -(5 - 2x)$

$x = 2 \qquad 3 - x = -5 + 2x$

$-3x = -8$

$x = \frac{8}{3}$

18. $|x + 8| = |2x - 4|$

$x + 8 = 2x - 4$ or $x + 8 = -2x + 4$

$-x = -12 \qquad 3x = -4$

$x = 12 \qquad x = -\frac{4}{3}$

19. $\left|\frac{1}{4}x - 3\right| = 8$

$\frac{1}{4}x - 3 = 8$ or $\frac{1}{4}x - 3 = -8$

$x - 12 = 32 \qquad x - 12 = -32$

$x = 44 \qquad x = -20$

20. $|4 - 7x| = 25$

$4 - 7x = 25$ or $4 - 7x = -25$

$-7x = 21 \qquad -7x = -29$

$x = -3 \qquad x = \frac{29}{7}$

21. $|2x - 8| + 7 = 12$

$|2x - 8| = 5$

$2x - 8 = 5$ or $2x - 8 = -5$

$2x = 13 \qquad 2x = 3$

$x = \frac{13}{2} \qquad x = \frac{3}{2}$

© 2006 Pearson Education, Inc., Upper Saddle River, NJ. All rights reserved. This material is protected under all copyright laws as they currently exist.
No portion of this material may be reproduced, in any form or by any means, without permission in writing from the publisher.

22. $|0.2x - 1| + 1.2 = 2.3$

$\qquad |0.2x - 1| = 1.1$

$\qquad 0.2x - 1 = 1.1 \text{ or } 0.2x - 1 = -1.1$

$\qquad 0.2x = 2.1 \qquad\qquad 0.2x = -0.1$

$\qquad x = \dfrac{21}{2} \qquad\qquad x = -\dfrac{1}{2}$

23. $\qquad P = 2L + 2W$

$\qquad 42 = 2(2W + 3) + 2W$

$\qquad 21 = 2W + 3 + W$

$\qquad 3W = 18$

$\qquad W = 6 \text{ ft, width}$

$\qquad 2W + 3 = 15 \text{ ft, length}$

24. Let $x =$ the number of women.

$\qquad 2x - 200 + x = 280$

$\qquad 3x - 200 = 280$

$\qquad 3x = 480$

$\qquad x = 160$

$\qquad 2x - 200 = 120$

There are 160 women and 120 men attending Western Tech.

25. Let $x =$ how many miles she drove.

$\qquad 30(2) + 0.12x = 102$

$\qquad 60 + 0.12x = 102$

$\qquad 0.12x = 42$

$\qquad x = 350$

She drove 350 miles.

26. Let $x =$ number of miles from airport to hotel.

$$\$2.50 + \dfrac{\$0.35}{\frac{1}{5}\text{ mile}}\left(x - \dfrac{1}{5}\right)\text{ mile} = \$14.75$$

$\qquad 0.5 + 0.35\left(x - \dfrac{1}{5}\right) = 2.95$

$\qquad 0.35x - 0.07 = 2.45$

$\qquad 0.35x = 2.52$

$\qquad x = 7.2$

It is 7.2 miles from the airport to the hotel.

27. Let $x =$ the amount withheld for retirement.

$\qquad x + x + 13 + 3(x + 13) = 102$

$\qquad 2x + 13 + 3x + 39 = 102$

$\qquad 5x + 52 = 102$

$\qquad 5x = 50$

$\qquad x = 10$

$\qquad x + 13 = 23$

$\qquad 3(x + 13) = 69$

$10 is withheld for retirement, $23 for state tax, and $69 for federal tax.

28. Let $x =$ the number of tickets Nicholas sold

$\qquad x + 2x - 5 + 2x + 10 = 180$

$\qquad 5x = 175$

$\qquad x = 35$

$\qquad 2x - 5 = 65$

$\qquad 2x + 10 = 80$

Nicholas sold 35 tickets, Emma sold 65 tickets, and Jackson sold 80 tickets.

© 2006 Pearson Education, Inc., Upper Saddle River, NJ. All rights reserved. This material is protected under all copyright laws as they currently exist. No portion of this material may be reproduced, in any form or by any means, without permission in writing from the publisher.

29. Let $x =$ the number of students enrolled last year.
$$0.88x = 2332$$
$$x = 2650$$
2650 students were enrolled last year.

30. Let $x =$ the number of two-door sedans
$$3x + x = 260,000$$
$$4x = 260,000$$
$$x = 65,000$$
$$3x = 195,000$$
They should manufacture 65,000 two-door sedans and 195,000 four-door sedans.

31. Let $x =$ amount invested at 12%.
$$0.08x + 0.12(7000 - x) = 740$$
$$0.08x + 840 - 0.12x = 740$$
$$-0.04x = -100$$
$$x = 2500$$
$$7000 - x = 4500$$
She should invest $2500 at 8% and $4500 at 12%.

32. Let $x =$ the number of liters of 2% acid.
$$0.02x + 0.05(24 - x) = 0.04(24)$$
$$0.02x + 1.2 - 0.05x = 0.96$$
$$-0.03x = -0.24$$
$$x = 8$$
$$24 - x = 16$$
He should use 8 liters of the 2% acid and 16 liters of the 5% acid.

33. Let $x =$ the number of pounds of the $4.25 a pound coffee.
$$4.25x + 4.50(30 - x) = 4.40(30)$$
$$4.25x + 135 - 4.5x = 132$$
$$-0.25x = -3$$
$$x = 12$$
$$30 - x = 18$$
12 pounds at $4.25 and 18 pounds at $4.50 should be used.

34. Let $x =$ current full-time students.
$$\frac{1}{2}x + \frac{1}{3}(890 - x) = 380$$
$$3x + 1780 - 2x = 2280$$
$$x = 500$$
$$890 - 500 = 390$$
The present number of students is 500 full-time and 390 part-time.

35. $7x + 8 < 5x$
$$2x < -8$$
$$x < -4$$

36. $9x + 3 < 12x$
$$-3x < -3$$
$$x > 1$$

37. $4x - 1 < 3(x + 2)$
$$4x - 1 < 3x + 6$$
$$x < 7$$

38. $3(3x - 2) < 4x - 16$
$$9x - 6 < 4x - 16$$
$$5x < -10$$
$$x < -2$$

© 2006 Pearson Education, Inc., Upper Saddle River, NJ. All rights reserved. This material is protected under all copyright laws as they currently exist. No portion of this material may be reproduced, in any form or by any means, without permission in writing from the publisher.

39. $\dfrac{1}{9}x + \dfrac{2}{9} > \dfrac{1}{3}$

$x + 2 > 3$

$x > 1$

40. $\dfrac{7}{4} - 2x \geq -\dfrac{3}{2}x - \dfrac{5}{4}$

$7 - 8x \geq -6x - 5$

$-2x \geq -12$

$x \leq 6$

41. $\dfrac{1}{3}(x-2) < \dfrac{1}{4}(x+5) - \dfrac{5}{3}$

$4x - 8 < 3x + 15 - 20$

$x < 3$

42. $\dfrac{1}{3}(x+2) > 3x - 5(x-2)$

$x + 2 > 9x - 15x + 30$

$7x > 28$

$x > 4$

43. $7x - 6 \leq \dfrac{1}{3}(-2x + 5)$

$21x - 18 \leq -2x + 5$

$23x \leq 23$

$x \leq 1$

44. $-3 \leq x < 2$

45. $-4 < x \leq 5$

46. $-8 \leq x \leq -4$

47. $-9 \leq x \leq -6$

48. $x < -2 \ \ or \ \ x \geq 5$

49. $x < -3 \ or \ x \geq 6$

50. $x > -5 \ and \ x < -1$

51. $x > -8 \ and \ x < -3$

52. $x + 3 > 8 \ or \ x + 2 < 6$

$x > 5 \qquad\qquad x < 4$

53. $x - 2 > 7 \ or \ x + 3 < 2$

$x > 9 \qquad\qquad x < -1$

54. $x + 3 > 8 \ and \ x - 4 < -2$

$x > 5 \qquad\qquad x < 2$

No solution.

55. $-1 < x + 5 < 8$

$-6 < x < 3$

56. $0 \leq 5 - 3x \leq 17$

$-5 \leq -3x \leq 12$

$\dfrac{5}{3} \geq x \geq -4$

$-4 \leq x \leq \dfrac{5}{3}$

42

© 2006 Pearson Education, Inc., Upper Saddle River, NJ. All rights reserved. This material is protected under all copyright laws as they currently exist. No portion of this material may be reproduced, in any form or by any means, without permission in writing from the publisher.

57. $2x - 7 < 3$ *and* $5x - 1 \geq 8$

$\qquad 2x < 10 \qquad\qquad 5x \geq 9$

$\qquad\quad x < 5 \qquad\qquad\quad x \geq \dfrac{9}{5}$

$\qquad \dfrac{9}{5} \leq x < 5$

58. $4x - 2 < 8$ *or* $3x + 1 > 4$

$\qquad 4x < 10 \qquad\qquad 3x > 3$

$\qquad\quad x < \dfrac{5}{2} \qquad\qquad\quad x > 1$

The solution is all real numbers.

59. $|x + 7| < 15$

$\qquad -15 < x + 7 < 15$

$\qquad -22 < x < 8$

60. $|x + 9| < 18$

$\qquad -18 < x + 9 < 18$

$\qquad -27 < x < 9$

61. $\left| \dfrac{1}{2}x + 2 \right| < \dfrac{7}{4}$

$\qquad -\dfrac{7}{4} < \dfrac{1}{2}x + 2 < \dfrac{7}{4}$

$\qquad -7 < 2x + 8 < 7$

$\qquad -15 < 2x < -1$

$\qquad -\dfrac{15}{2} < x < -\dfrac{1}{2}$

62. $\left| \dfrac{1}{5}x + 3 \right| < \dfrac{11}{5}$

$\qquad -\dfrac{11}{5} < \dfrac{1}{5}x + 3 < \dfrac{11}{5}$

$\qquad -11 < x + 15 < 11$

$\qquad -26 < x < -4$

63. $|2x - 1| \geq 9$

$\qquad 2x - 1 \leq -9 \ or \ 2x - 1 \geq 9$

$\qquad 2x \leq -8 \qquad\qquad 2x \geq 10$

$\qquad\ x \leq -4 \qquad\qquad\ x \geq 5$

64. $|3x - 1| \geq 2$

$\qquad 3x - 1 \leq -2 \ or \ 3x - 1 \geq 2$

$\qquad 3x \leq -1 \qquad\qquad 3x \geq 3$

$\qquad\ x \leq -\dfrac{1}{3} \qquad\qquad x \geq 1$

65. $|3(x - 1)| \geq 5$

$\qquad 3(x - 1) \leq -5 \ or \ 3(x - 1) \geq 5$

$\qquad 3x - 3 \leq -5 \qquad\quad 3x - 3 \geq 5$

$\qquad 3x \leq -2 \qquad\qquad 3x \geq 8$

$\qquad\ x \leq -\dfrac{2}{3} \qquad\qquad x \geq \dfrac{8}{3}$

66. $|2(x - 3)| \geq 4$

$\qquad 2(x - 3) \leq -4 \ or \ 2(x - 3) \geq 4$

$\qquad 2x - 6 \leq -4 \qquad\quad 2x - 6 \geq 4$

$\qquad 2x \leq 2 \qquad\qquad\ 2x \geq 10$

$\qquad\ x \leq 1 \qquad\qquad\quad\ x \geq 5$

67. Let $x =$ the number of minutes he talks.

$\qquad 3.95 + 0.64(x - 1) \leq 13.05$

$\qquad 3.95 + 0.64x - 0.64 \leq 13.05$

$\qquad\qquad\quad 0.64x \leq 9.74$

$\qquad\qquad\qquad\ x \leq 15.21875$

He can talk for a maximum of 15 minutes.

© 2006 Pearson Education, Inc., Upper Saddle River, NJ. All rights reserved. This material is protected under all copyright laws as they currently exist.
No portion of this material may be reproduced, in any form or by any means, without permission in writing from the publisher.

68. Let $x =$ the number of packages.
$$170 + 200 + 77.5x \le 1765$$
$$77.5x \le 1395$$
$$x \le 18$$
A maximum of eighteen packages can be carried.

69. Let $n =$ number of cubic yards
$$\$20 + \$25.50n \le \$224$$
$$\$25.50n \le \$204$$
$$n \le 8$$
He can order a maximum of 8 cubic yards.

70. Let $x =$ the weight of the package.
$$0.33 + 0.22(x - 1) \le 3.50$$
$$0.22x - 0.22 \le 3.17$$
$$0.22x \le 3.39$$
$$x \le 15.4\overline{09}$$
The package could weigh a maximum of 15 ounces.

71. Let $n =$ number of bolts per box
$$1.5 + 2.5n < 14$$
$$2.5n < 12.5$$
$$n < 5$$
5 is the maximum number of bolts per box.

72. $1.04(2,312,000) \le x \le 1.06(2,854,000)$
$$2,404,480 \le x \le 3,025,240$$

73. $4 - 7x = 3(x + 3)$
$$4 - 7x = 3x + 9$$
$$-10x = 5$$
$$x = -\frac{1}{2}$$

74. $H = \frac{3}{4}B - 16$
$$\frac{3}{4}B = H + 16$$
$$B = \frac{4H + 64}{3}$$

75. Let $x =$ number of gm of 77% copper
$$0.77x + 0.92(100 - x) = 0.80(100)$$
$$0.77x + 92 - 0.92x = 80$$
$$-0.15x = -12$$
$$x = 80$$
$$100 - x = 20$$
She should use 80 gm of 77% copper and 20 gm of 92% copper.

76. $7x + 12 < 9x$
$$-2x < -12$$
$$x > 6$$

77. $\frac{2}{3}x - \frac{5}{6}x - 3 \le \frac{1}{2}x - 5$
$$8x - 10x - 36 \le 6x - 60$$
$$-8x \le -24$$
$$x \ge 3$$

78. $-2 \le x + 1 \le 4$
$$-3 \le x \le 3$$

79. $2x + 3 < -5 \quad$ or $\quad x - 2 > 1$
$$2x < -8 \qquad\qquad x > 3$$
$$x < -4$$

© 2006 Pearson Education, Inc., Upper Saddle River, NJ. All rights reserved. This material is protected under all copyright laws as they currently exist. No portion of this material may be reproduced, in any form or by any means, without permission in writing from the publisher.

80. $|2x-7|+4=5$

$$|2x-7|=1$$

$2x-7=-1$ or $2x-7=1$

    $2x=6$ $2x=8$

     $x=3$ $x=4$

81. $\left|\dfrac{2}{3}x-\dfrac{1}{2}\right|\le 3$

$$-3\le \dfrac{2}{3}x-\dfrac{1}{2}\le 3$$

$$-18\le 4x-3\le 18$$

$$-15\le 4x\le 21$$

$$-\dfrac{15}{4}\le x\le \dfrac{21}{4}$$

82. $|2-5x-4|>13$

$2-5x-4>13$ or $2-5x-4<-13$

    $-5x>15$ $-5x<-11$

      $x<-3$ $x>\dfrac{11}{5}$

How Am I Doing? Chapter 2 Test

1. $5x-8=-6x-10$

   $11x=-2$

      $x=-\dfrac{2}{11}$

2. $3(7-2x)=14-8(x-1)$

   $21-6x=14-8x+8$

      $2x=1$

       $x=\dfrac{1}{2}$

3. $\dfrac{1}{3}(-x+1)+4=4(3x-2)$

   $-x+1+12=36x-24$

      $-37x=-37$

         $x=1$

4. $100(0.5x+1.2)=100(4x-3.05)$

   $50x+120=400x-305$

     $425=350x\Rightarrow 350x=425$

        $x=\dfrac{425}{350}=\dfrac{17(25)}{14(25)}=\dfrac{17}{14}$

        $x=1\dfrac{3}{14}$

5. $L=a+d(n-1)$

   $L=a+dn-d$

 $L-a+d=dn$

       $n=\dfrac{L-a+d}{d}$

6. $A=\dfrac{1}{2}bh\Rightarrow 2A=bh\Rightarrow bh=2A$

   $b=\dfrac{2A}{h}$

7. $b=\dfrac{2A}{h}$

   $b=\dfrac{2(15)\text{ cm}^2}{10\text{ cm}}$

   $b=3\text{ cm}$

8. $H=\dfrac{1}{2}r+3b-\dfrac{1}{4}$

  $4H=2r+12b-1$

  $2r=4H-12b+1$

    $r=\dfrac{4H-12b+1}{2}$

© 2006 Pearson Education, Inc., Upper Saddle River, NJ. All rights reserved. This material is protected under all copyright laws as they currently exist. No portion of this material may be reproduced, in any form or by any means, without permission in writing from the publisher.

9. $|5x - 2| = 37$

$$5x - 2 = 37 \text{ or } 5x - 2 = -37$$
$$5x = 39 \qquad\qquad 5x = -35$$
$$x = \frac{39}{5} \qquad\qquad x = -7$$

10. $\left|\frac{1}{2}x + 3\right| - 2 = 4$

$$\left|\frac{1}{2}x + 3\right| = 6$$

$$\frac{1}{2}x + 3 = 6 \text{ or } \frac{1}{2}x + 3 = -6$$
$$x + 6 = 12 \qquad x + 6 = -12$$
$$x = 6 \qquad\qquad x = -18$$

11. Let x = the length of first side

$$x + 2x + x + 5 = 69$$
$$4x = 64$$
$$x = 16$$
$$2x = 32$$
$$x + 5 = 21$$

The first side is 16 meters, the second side is 32 meters, and the third side is 21 meters.

12. $0.95x = \$2489$

$$x = \$2620, \text{ August electric bill}$$

13. Let x = gallons of 50% antifreeze

$$0.50x + 0.90(10 - x) = 0.60(10)$$
$$0.5x + 9 - 0.9x = 6$$
$$-0.4x = -3$$
$$x = 7.5$$
$$10 - 7.5 = 2.5$$

She should use 2.5 gallons of 90% and 7.5 gallons of 50%.

14. Let x = amount invested at 6%.

$$0.06x + 0.10(5000 - x) = 428$$
$$0.06x + 500 - 0.1x = 428$$
$$-0.04x = -72$$
$$x = 1800$$
$$5000 - x = 3200$$

$1800 was invested at 6% and $3200 was invested at 10%.

15. $5 - 6x < 2x + 21$

$$-8x < 16$$
$$x > -2$$

16. $-\frac{1}{2} + \frac{1}{3}(2 - 3x) \geq \frac{1}{2}x + \frac{5}{3}$

$$-3 + 4 - 6x \geq 3x + 10$$
$$-9x \geq 9$$
$$x \leq -1$$

17. $-11 < 2x - 1 \leq -3$

$$-10 < 2x \leq -2$$
$$-5 < x \leq -1$$

18. $x - 4 \leq -6 \text{ or } 2x + 1 \geq 3$

$$x \leq -2 \qquad\qquad 2x \geq 2$$
$$x \geq 1$$

19. $|7x - 3| \leq 18$

$$-18 \leq 7x - 3 \leq 18$$
$$-15 \leq 7x \leq 21$$
$$-\frac{15}{7} \leq x \leq 3$$

46

© 2006 Pearson Education, Inc., Upper Saddle River, NJ. All rights reserved. This material is protected under all copyright laws as they currently exist. No portion of this material may be reproduced, in any form or by any means, without permission in writing from the publisher.

20. $|3x+1| > 7$

$$3x+1 < -7 \text{ or } 3x+1 > 7$$
$$3x < -8 \qquad\quad 3x > 6$$
$$x < -\frac{8}{3} \qquad\quad x > 2$$

Cumulative Test for Chapters 1-2

1. $-12, -3, 0, \frac{1}{4}, 2.16, 2.333\text{L}, -\frac{5}{8}, 3$

2. Associative property of addition.

3. $\sqrt{49} + 3(2-6)^2 - (-3)$
$$= 7 + 3(-4)^2 + 3$$
$$= 7 + 3(16) + 3$$
$$= 7 + 48 + 3$$
$$= 55 + 3$$
$$= 58$$

4. $\left(-\frac{2}{3}x^4y^{-2}z^0\right)(6x^{-1}y^6z^2)$
$$= -4x^{4-1}y^{-2+6}z^{0+2}$$
$$= -4x^3y^4z^2$$

5. $\dfrac{7ab^3}{-14a^5b^{-2}} = \dfrac{b^5}{-2a^4}$

6. $2x^2 + 3xy - y^2 = 2(-2)^2 + 3(-2)(1) - 1^2$
$$= 2(4) - 6 - 1$$
$$= 8 - 7$$
$$= 1$$

7. $A = \pi r^2 = 3.14(7)^2 = 153.86$ sq in.

8. $2x - [6x - 3(x+5y)]$
$$= 2x - [6x - 3x - 15y]$$
$$= 2x - [3x - 15y]$$
$$= 2x - 3x + 15y$$
$$= -x + 15y$$

9. $\dfrac{1}{4}(x+5) - \dfrac{5}{3} = \dfrac{1}{3}(x-2)$
$$3x + 15 - 20 = 4x - 8$$
$$-x = -3$$
$$x = 3$$

10. $h = \dfrac{2}{3}(b+d)$
$$3h = 2b + 2d$$
$$2b = 3h - 2d$$
$$b = \dfrac{3h - 2d}{2}$$

11. Let $x =$ length of first side.
$$x + x + 10 + 2x - 5 = 105$$
$$4x + 5 = 105$$
$$4x = 100$$
$$x = 25$$
$$x + 10 = 35$$
$$2x - 5 = 45$$
The first side is 25 meters, the second side is 35 meters, and the third side is 45 meters.

12. $0.85x = \$68$
$$x = \$80, \text{ original price of saw}$$

47

© 2006 Pearson Education, Inc., Upper Saddle River, NJ. All rights reserved. This material is protected under all copyright laws as they currently exist. No portion of this material may be reproduced, in any form or by any means, without permission in writing from the publisher.

13. Let x = the number of gallons at 50%.

$$0.50x + 0.80(9-x) = 0.70(9)$$

$$0.5x + 7.2 - 0.8x = 6.3$$

$$-0.3x = -0.9$$

$$x = 3$$

$$9 - x = 6$$

He should use 3 gallons at 50% and 6 gallons at 80%.

14. Let x = amount invested at 12%.

$$0.12x + 0.10(6500 - x) = 690$$

$$0.12x + 650 - 0.1x = 690$$

$$0.02x = 40$$

$$x = 2000$$

$$6500 - x = 4500$$

She invested $2000 at 12% and $4500 at 10%.

15. $-4 - 3x < -2x + 6$

$$-x < 10$$

$$x > -10$$

$$-10$$

16. $\frac{1}{3}(x+2) \le \frac{1}{5}(x+6)$

$$5x + 10 \le 3x + 18$$

$$2x \le 8$$

$$x \le 4$$

$$4$$

17. $-7 < 5x + 3 < 18$

$$-10 < 5x < 15$$

$$-2 < x < 3$$

18. $x + 5 \le -4$ or $2 - 7x \le 16$

$$x \le -9 \qquad -7x \le 14$$

$$x \ge -2$$

19. $\left| \frac{1}{2}x + 2 \right| \le 8$

$$-8 \le \frac{1}{2}x + 2 \le 8$$

$$-16 \le x + 4 \le 16$$

$$-20 \le x \le 12$$

20. $|3x - 4| > 11$

$$3x - 4 < -11 \text{ or } 3x - 4 > 11$$

$$3x < -7 \qquad 3x > 15$$

$$x < -\frac{7}{3} \qquad x > 5$$

48

© 2006 Pearson Education, Inc., Upper Saddle River, NJ. All rights reserved. This material is protected under all copyright laws as they currently exist. No portion of this material may be reproduced, in any form or by any means, without permission in writing from the publisher.

Chapter 3

3.1 Exercises

1. Graphs are used to show the relationships among the <u>variables</u> in an equation.

3. To locate the point (a,b), assuming that $a,b > 0$, we move a units to the right and b units up. To locate the point (b,a) we move b units right and a units up. If $a \neq b$ the graphs of the points will be different. Thus, the order of the numbers in (a,b) matters. $(1,3)$ is not the same as $(3,1)$.

5. $y = 3x - 7$

   $y = 3(-2) - 7 = -6 - 7 = -13$

   $(-2,13)$ is a solution of $y = 3x - 7$.

7. $7x + 14y = -21$

   $7x + 14\left(\dfrac{1}{2}\right) = -21$

   $14x + 14 = -42$

   $14x = -56$

   $x = -4$

   $\left(-4, \dfrac{1}{2}\right)$ is a solution of $7x + 14y = -21$.

9. $y = 2x - 3$

x	y
0	3
2	1
4	5

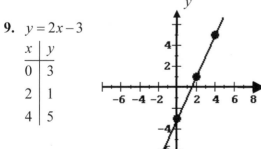

11. $y = 4 - 2x$

x	y
-1	6
0	4
1	2

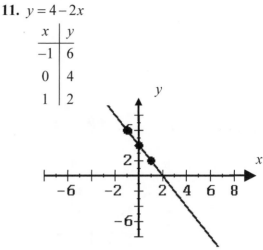

13. $y = \dfrac{2}{3}x - 4$

x	y
-3	-6
0	-4
3	-2

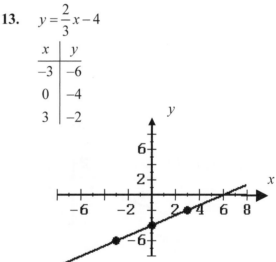

15. $2y - 3x = 6$

x	y
-2	0
0	3
2	6

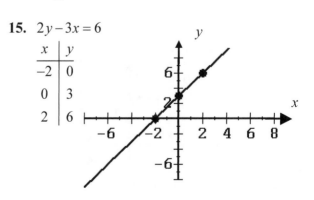

49

© 2006 Pearson Education, Inc., Upper Saddle River, NJ. All rights reserved. This material is protected under all copyright laws as they currently exist. No portion of this material may be reproduced, in any form or by any means, without permission in writing from the publisher.

17. $2x - y = 6$

x	y
0	−6
2	−2
3	0

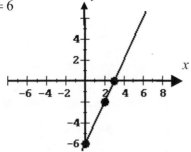

19. $-3x - 4y = 8$

x	y
4	−5
0	−2
$-2\frac{2}{3}$	0

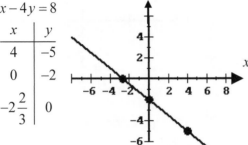

21. $5y - 4 = 3x - 4$

$3x - 5y = 0$

x	y
0	0
−5	−3
5	3

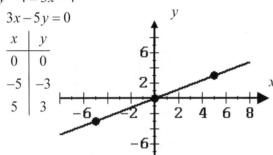

23. $x = -5$, vertical line

x	y
−5	3
−5	0
−5	−2

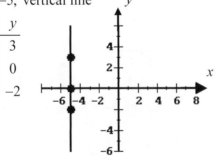

25. $3x - 18 = 0$

$3x = 18$

$x = 6$, vertical line

x	y
6	0
6	1
6	2

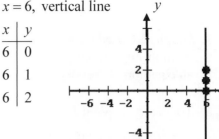

27. $2y + 8 = 0$, $2y = -8$, $y = -4$

The graph is a horizontal line.

x	y
0	−4
1	−4
2	−4

29. $y = -1.5x + 2$

x	y
−2	5
0	2
2	−1

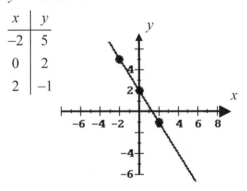

50

© 2006 Pearson Education, Inc., Upper Saddle River, NJ. All rights reserved. This material is protected under all copyright laws as they currently exist. No portion of this material may be reproduced, in any form or by any means, without permission in writing from the publisher.

31. $2x + 5y = -5$

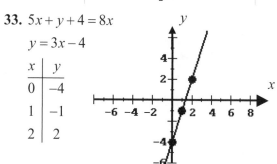

x	y
-5	1
0	-1
5	-3

33. $5x + y + 4 = 8x$

$y = 3x - 4$

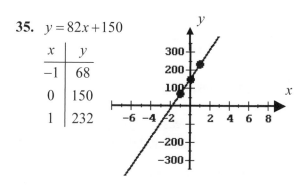

x	y
0	-4
1	-1
2	2

35. $y = 82x + 150$

x	y
-1	68
0	150
1	232

37. From the table the greatest increase in median weekly earnings of men occurred between 1995 and 2000.

5 year period	increase
1980 to 1985	$406 - 380 = 26$
1985 to 1990	$481 - 406 = 75$
1990 to 1995	$538 - 481 = 57$
1995 to 2000	$627 - 538 = 89$
2000 to 2005	$637 - 627 = 10$

39. From the table the median weekly earnings of men and women had the largest difference in 1990.

year	difference
1980	$380 - 269 = 111$
1985	$406 - 277 = 129$
1990	$481 - 346 = 135$
1995	$538 - 406 = 132$
2000	$627 - 537 = 90$
2005	$637 - 542 = 95$

41. $(542 - 269) \div (269) = 1.015 = 101.5\%$

43. (a) $V(T) = 120 - 32T$

T	$V(T) = 120 - 32T$
0	$120 - 32(0) = 120$
1	$120 - 32(1) = 88$
2	$120 - 32(2) = 56$
3	$120 - 32(3) = 24$
4	$120 - 32(4) = -8$

(b)

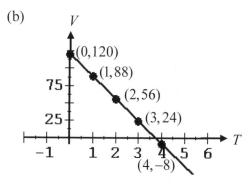

(c) The baseball is moving downward instead of upward at $T = 4$ seconds.

51

© 2006 Pearson Education, Inc., Upper Saddle River, NJ. All rights reserved. This material is protected under all copyright laws as they currently exist. No portion of this material may be reproduced, in any form or by any means, without permission in writing from the publisher.

45. $P = 14.7 - 0.0005d$

d	$P = 14.7 - 0.0005d$
0	14.7
1000	14.2
2000	13.7
3000	13.2
9000	10.2
15,000	7.2

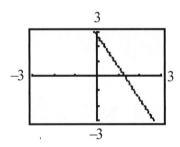

47. $y = -2.15x + 2.73$

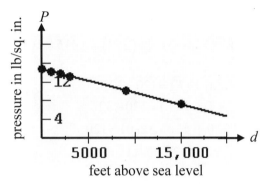

49. $y = 0.713x + 25.82$

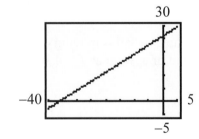

Cumulative Review

51. $36 \div (8-6)^2 + 3(-4)$
$= 36 \div 2^2 + (-12)$
$= 36 \div 4 + (-12)$
$= 9 + (-12)$
$= -3$

53. $R = 2G$
$B = 3R$
$2W = Y$
$2Y = R$
$W = 130$
$Y = 2W = 260$
$R = 2Y = 520$
$G = \dfrac{1}{2}R = 260$
$B = 3R = 1560$

3.2 Exercises

1. Slope measures <u>vertical</u> change (rise) versus <u>horizontal</u> change (run).

3. The slope of a horizontal line is 0.

5. $m = \dfrac{y_2 - y_1}{x_2 - x_1} = \dfrac{-7-5}{-3-(-3)} = \dfrac{-12}{0}$. The line passing through $(-3, -7)$ and $(-3, 5)$ does not have a slope because division by 0 is undefined.

7. $m = \dfrac{y_2 - y_1}{x_2 - x_1}$

$m = \dfrac{2 - (-6)}{2 - 6} = \dfrac{8}{-4} = -2$

52

© 2006 Pearson Education, Inc., Upper Saddle River, NJ. All rights reserved. This material is protected under all copyright laws as they currently exist.
No portion of this material may be reproduced, in any form or by any means, without permission in writing from the publisher.

9. $m = \dfrac{y_2 - y_1}{x_2 - x_1} = \dfrac{4 - 0}{\dfrac{3}{2} - (-2)} = \dfrac{8}{7}$

11. $m = \dfrac{y_2 - y_1}{x_2 - x_1} = \dfrac{-1.5 - (-2.3)}{6.8 - 5.6} = \dfrac{2}{3}$

13. $m = \dfrac{y_2 - y_1}{x_2 - x_1} = \dfrac{-2 - \dfrac{1}{4}}{\dfrac{3}{2} - \dfrac{3}{2}} = \dfrac{-\dfrac{9}{4}}{0}$ no slope

15. $m = \dfrac{y_2 - y_1}{x_2 - x_1} = \dfrac{-3 - (-3)}{-7 - 10}$

$m = \dfrac{0}{-17} = 0$

17. $m = \dfrac{y_2 - y_1}{x_2 - x_1} = \dfrac{\dfrac{3}{2} - 1}{6 - 2} = \dfrac{\dfrac{1}{2}}{4} = \dfrac{1}{8}$

19. $m = \dfrac{\text{rise}}{\text{run}} = \dfrac{48 \text{ ft}}{80 \text{ ft}} = 0.6$

21. $m = \dfrac{\text{rise}}{\text{run}} = \dfrac{35.7}{142.8} = 0.25$

23. $m = \dfrac{\text{rise}}{\text{run}}$

$0.16 = \dfrac{\text{rise}}{500}$

$\text{rise(fall)} = 80 \text{ ft}$

25. $m = \dfrac{y_2 - y_1}{x_2 - x_1} = \dfrac{7 - 3}{6 - 24} = -\dfrac{2}{9}$

$m_{\text{p}} = -\dfrac{2}{9}$

27. $m = \dfrac{y_2 - y_1}{x_2 - x_1}$

$m = \dfrac{1 - 2}{7 - 6.5} = -2$

$m_{\text{p}} = -2$

29. $m = \dfrac{y_2 - y_1}{x_2 - x_1}$

$m = \dfrac{\dfrac{1}{2} - 5}{-9 - (-6)} = \dfrac{3}{2}$

$m_{\text{p}} = \dfrac{3}{2}$

31. $m = \dfrac{y_2 - y_1}{x_2 - x_1}$

$m = \dfrac{12 - 9}{8 - 3} = \dfrac{3}{5}$

$m_{\perp} = -\dfrac{5}{3}$

33. $m = \dfrac{y_2 - y_1}{x_2 - x_1} = \dfrac{-\dfrac{1}{2} - \dfrac{5}{2}}{2 - 1} = -3$

$m_{\perp} = \dfrac{1}{3}$

35. $m = \dfrac{y_2 - y_1}{x_2 - x_1}$

$m = \dfrac{0 - 4.2}{-8.4 - 0} = \dfrac{1}{2}$

$m_{\perp} = -2$

37. $m_k = \dfrac{-9 - 11}{-3 - 1} = 5$

$m_h = \dfrac{-13 - 7}{-2 - 2} = 5.$

© 2006 Pearson Education, Inc., Upper Saddle River, NJ. All rights reserved. This material is protected under all copyright laws as they currently exist. No portion of this material may be reproduced, in any form or by any means, without permission in writing from the publisher.

39. To be a parallelogram, AD must be parallel to BC and AB must be parallel to DC.

$$m_{AD} = \frac{1-2}{2-(-4)} = -\frac{1}{6}$$

$$m_{BC} = \frac{-2-(-1)}{-1-(-7)} = -\frac{1}{6}$$

$$m_{AB} = \frac{1-(-2)}{2-(-1)} = 1$$

$$m_{CD} = \frac{-1-2}{-7-(-4)} = 1.$$

Since $m_{AD} = m_{BC}$ and $m_{AB} = m_{CD}$ the opposite sides are parallel and $ABCD$ is a parallelogram.

41. (a) $m = \dfrac{\text{rise}}{\text{run}} = \dfrac{5}{60} = \dfrac{1}{12}$

(b) $\dfrac{1}{12} = \dfrac{\text{rise}}{24}$, $24 = 12 \cdot \text{rise}$

$$12 \cdot \text{rise} = 24 \Rightarrow \text{rise} = \frac{24}{2} = 2 \text{ ft}$$

(c) $\dfrac{1}{12} = \dfrac{1.7}{\text{run}}$, run $= 20.4$ ft

The ramp will have a horizontal distance of 20.4 ft.

Cumulative Review

43. $\dfrac{5 + 3\sqrt{9}}{|2-9|} = \dfrac{5+3(3)}{|-7|}$

$$= \frac{5+9}{7}$$

$$= \frac{14}{7}$$

$$= 2$$

45. $\dfrac{-15x^6 y^3}{-3x^{-4}y^6} = \dfrac{5x^{6+4}}{y^{6-3}}$

$$= \frac{5x^{10}}{y^3}$$

3.3 Exercises

1. First determine the slope from the coordinates of the points. Then substitute the slope and the coordinates of one of the points into the point-slope form of the equation of a line. This may be rewritten in standard form or slope-intercept form.

3. $y = mx + b$, $y = \dfrac{3}{4}x - 9$

5. $y = mx + b \Rightarrow y = \dfrac{3}{4}x + \dfrac{1}{2}$

$$4y = 3x + 2 \Rightarrow 3x + 2 = 4y \Rightarrow 3x = 4y - 2$$

$$3x - 4y = -2$$

7. From the graph, $m = \dfrac{1}{2}$, $b = 3$.

$$y = \frac{1}{2}x + 3$$

9. From the graph, $m = -1$, $b = 3$.

$$y = -x + 3$$

11. From the graph, $m = 3$, $b = 0$.

$$y = 3x$$

13. From the graph, $m = -\dfrac{3}{2}$, $b = 0$.

$$y = -\frac{3}{2}x$$

© 2006 Pearson Education, Inc., Upper Saddle River, NJ. All rights reserved. This material is protected under all copyright laws as they currently exist. No portion of this material may be reproduced, in any form or by any means, without permission in writing from the publisher.

15. From the graph, $m = \dfrac{3}{4}$, $b = -4$.

$$y = \dfrac{3}{4}x - 4$$

17. $x - y = 5$

$$y = x - 5, \ m = 1, \ b = -5$$

19. $5x - 4y = -20$

$$4y = 5x + 20$$

$$y = \dfrac{5}{4}x + 5, \ m = \dfrac{5}{4}, \ b = 5$$

21. $3x + \dfrac{2}{3}y = -2$

$$9x + 2y = -6$$

$$2y = -9x - 6$$

$$y = -\dfrac{9}{2}x - 3, \ m = -\dfrac{9}{2}, \ b = -3$$

23. $y = \dfrac{1}{2}x - 3, \ m = \dfrac{1}{2}, \ b = -3$

x	y
0	-3
2	-2

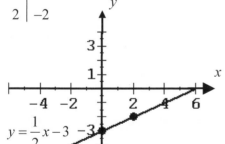

25. $5x + 3y = 18$.

x	y
0	6
3	1

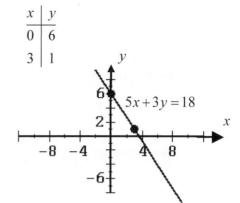

27. $m = \dfrac{y_2 - y_1}{x_2 - x_1}$

$$m = \dfrac{4 - 2}{6 - 9} = -\dfrac{2}{3}$$

$$y - y_1 = m(x - x_1)$$

$$y - 4 = -\dfrac{2}{3}(x - 6)$$

$$y - 4 = -\dfrac{2}{3}x + 4$$

$$y = -\dfrac{2}{3}x + 8$$

29. $y - y_1 = m(x - x_1)$

$$y - (-2) = 5(x - (-7))$$

$$y + 2 = 5x + 35$$

$$y = 5x + 33$$

31. $y - y_1 = m(x - x_1)$

$$y - 0 = -\dfrac{1}{5}(x - 6)$$

$$y = -\dfrac{1}{5}x + \dfrac{6}{5}$$

55

© 2006 Pearson Education, Inc., Upper Saddle River, NJ. All rights reserved. This material is protected under all copyright laws as they currently exist. No portion of this material may be reproduced, in any form or by any means, without permission in writing from the publisher.

33. $m = \dfrac{y_2 - y_1}{x_2 - x_1}$

$m = \dfrac{4+1}{3+4} = \dfrac{5}{7}$

$y - y_1 = m(x - x_1)$

$y - 4 = \dfrac{5}{7}(x - 3)$

$y - 4 = \dfrac{5}{7}x - \dfrac{15}{7}$

$y = \dfrac{5}{7}x + \dfrac{13}{7}$

35. $m = \dfrac{y_2 - y_1}{x_2 - x_1}$

$m = \dfrac{-3 - (-5)}{\dfrac{1}{2} - \dfrac{7}{2}} = -\dfrac{2}{3}$

$y - y_1 = m(x - x_1)$

$y + 3 = -\dfrac{2}{3}\left(x - \dfrac{1}{2}\right)$

$y + 3 = -\dfrac{2}{3}x + \dfrac{1}{3}$

$y = -\dfrac{2}{3}x - \dfrac{8}{3}$

37. $m = \dfrac{y_2 - y_1}{x_2 - x_1}$

$m = \dfrac{-3 - (-3)}{12 - 7} = 0$

$y - y_1 = m(x - x_1)$

$y - (-3) = 0(x - 12)$

$y + 3 = 0$

$y = -3$

39. $5x - y = 4$

$y = 5x - 5, \ m = 5$

$m(\text{Pline}) = 5$

$y - y_1 = m(x - x_1)$

$y - 0 = 5(x - (-2))$

$y = 5x + 10$

$5x - y = -10$

41. $x = 3y - 8$

$3y = x + 8, \ y = \dfrac{1}{3}x + \dfrac{8}{3}, \ m = \dfrac{1}{3}$

$m(\text{Pline}) = \dfrac{1}{3}$

$y - (-1) = \dfrac{1}{3}(x - 5)$

$3y + 3 = x - 5$

$x - 3y = 8$

43. $2y = -3x, \ y = -\dfrac{3}{2}, m = -\dfrac{3}{2}$

$m(\perp \text{line}) = \dfrac{2}{3}$

$y - (-1) = \dfrac{2}{3}(x - 6)$

$3y + 3 = 2x - 12$

$2x - 3y = 15$

45. $x + 7y = -12, \ y = -\dfrac{1}{7}x - \dfrac{12}{7}, \ m = -\dfrac{1}{7}$

$m(\perp \text{line}) = 7$

$y - (-1) = 7(x + 4)$

$y + 1 = 7x + 28$

$7x - y = -27$

56

© 2006 Pearson Education, Inc., Upper Saddle River, NJ. All rights reserved. This material is protected under all copyright laws as they currently exist. No portion of this material may be reproduced, in any form or by any means, without permission in writing from the publisher.

47. $-3x + 5y = 40$, $y = \dfrac{3}{5}x + 8$, $m_1 = \dfrac{3}{5}$

$5y + 3x = 17$, $y = -\dfrac{3}{5}x + \dfrac{17}{3}$, $m_2 = -\dfrac{3}{5}$

$m_1 m_2 = \dfrac{3}{5}\left(-\dfrac{3}{5}\right) = -\dfrac{9}{25}$

The lines are neither P or $\perp$.

49. $y = -\dfrac{3}{4}x - 2$, $m_1 = -\dfrac{3}{4}$

$6x + 8y = -5$, $8y = -6x - 5$

$y = -\dfrac{3}{4}x - \dfrac{5}{8}$, $m_2 = -\dfrac{3}{4}$

$m_1 = m_2 \Rightarrow$ lines are parallel

51. $y = \dfrac{5}{6}x - \dfrac{1}{3}$, $m_1 = \dfrac{5}{6}$

$6x + 5y = -12$, $5y = -6x - 12$

$y = -\dfrac{6}{5}x - \dfrac{12}{5}$, $m_2 = -\dfrac{6}{5}$

$m_1 \neq m_2$

$m_1 m_2 = \dfrac{5}{6}\left(-\dfrac{6}{5}\right) = -1$

The lines are perpendicular.

53. $y = 1.43x - 2.17$, $y = 1.43x + 0.39$

Lines appear parallel.

55. $y = 5.51x + 68.7$

$y = 5.51(36) + 68.7 = 267.06$

The cost of a new home in 2016 will be $267,060.

57. From the graph, the median cost of a home in 2007 will be approximately $217,000. Answers may vary.

59. $y = 1.64x + 87.7$

$y = 1.64(36) + 87.7 = 146.74$

The number of housing units in the year 2016 will be 146,740,000.

61. From the graph, the number of housing units in 2007 will be approximately 131,980,000. Answers may vary.

Cumulative Review

63. $0.3x + 0.1 = 0.27x - 0.02$

$30x + 10 = 27x - 2$

$3x = -12$

$x = -4$

65. $\dfrac{5}{4} - \dfrac{3}{4}(2x + 1) = x - 2$

$4 - 3(2x + 1) = 4x - 8$

$4 - 6x - 3 = 4x - 8$

$10x = 10$

$x = 1$

How Am I Doing? Sections 3.1-3.3

1. $5x + 2y = -12$

$5a + 2(6) = -12$

$5a + 12 = -12$

$5a = -24$

$a = -\dfrac{24}{5} = -4.8$

57

© 2006 Pearson Education, Inc., Upper Saddle River, NJ. All rights reserved. This material is protected under all copyright laws as they currently exist. No portion of this material may be reproduced, in any form or by any means, without permission in writing from the publisher.

2. $y = -\dfrac{1}{2}x + 5$

x	y
0	5
2	4
4	3

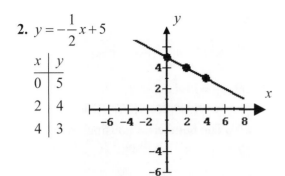

6. $m = \dfrac{y_2 - y_1}{x_2 - x_1}$

$m = \dfrac{4 - (-2)}{\dfrac{2}{3} - \dfrac{5}{6}}$

$m = -36$

$m_{\text{Pline}} = -36$

3. $5x + 3y = -15$

x	y
-6	5
-3	0
0	-5

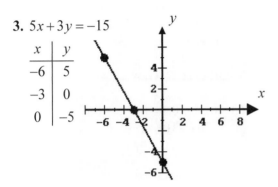

7. $m = \dfrac{y_2 - y_1}{x_2 - x_1}$

$m = \dfrac{0 - (-4)}{5 - (-13)}$

$m = \dfrac{2}{9}$

$m_{\perp\text{line}} = -\dfrac{9}{2}$

4. $4y + 6x = -8 + 9x$

$4y = 3x - 8$

$y = \dfrac{3}{4}x - 2$

x	y
-4	-5
0	-2
4	1

8. $m = 0.13 = \dfrac{\text{rise}}{\text{run}}$

$0.13 = \dfrac{\text{rise}}{500 \text{ ft}}$

$\text{rise} = 0.13(500)$

$\text{rise} = 65 \text{ ft}$

9. $6x + 7y = 14$

$7y = -6x + 14$

$y = -\dfrac{6}{7}x + 2$

$m = -\dfrac{6}{7}, \ b = 2$

5. $m = \dfrac{y_2 - y_1}{x_2 - x_1}$

$m = \dfrac{3 - (-6)}{-2 - (-1)}$

$m = -9$

10. $y - y_1 = m(x - x_1)$

$y - (-3) = -2(x - 7)$

$y + 3 = -2x + 14$

$y = -2x + 11$

58

© 2006 Pearson Education, Inc., Upper Saddle River, NJ. All rights reserved. This material is protected under all copyright laws as they currently exist. No portion of this material may be reproduced, in any form or by any means, without permission in writing from the publisher.

11. $3x - 5y = 10$

$$5y = 3x - 10$$

$$y = \frac{3}{5}x - 2, m = \frac{3}{5}, m_\perp = -\frac{5}{3}$$

$$y - y_1 = m(x - x_1)$$

$$y - (-2) = -\frac{5}{3}(x - (-1))$$

$$3y + 6 = -5x - 5$$

$$3y = -5x - 11$$

$$y = -\frac{5}{3}x - \frac{11}{3}$$

12. $m = \dfrac{y_2 - y_1}{x_2 - x_1}$

$$m = \frac{-8 - 7}{-1 - 2}$$

$$m = 5$$

$$y - y_1 = m(x - x_1 \, 0$$

$$y - (-8) = 5(x - (-1))$$

$$y + 8 = 5x + 5$$

$$y = 5x - 3$$

3.4 Exercises

1. You need to use a dashed line when graphing a linear inequality that contains the $>$ or $<$ symbols.

3. To graph the region $x > 5$ you should shade the region to the right of the line $x = 5$.

5. When graphing $3x - 2y \geq 0$ the point $(0, 0)$ cannot be used as a test point because it is on the line. Using $(-4, 2)$ as a test point gives
$3x - 2y = 3(-4) - 2(2) = -16 \geq 0$
which is a false statement.

7. $y > -2x + 4$, Test point: $0, 0$

$$0 > -2(0) + 4, \ 0 > 4 \text{ False}$$

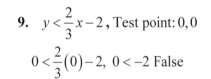

9. $y < \dfrac{2}{3}x - 2$, Test point: $0, 0$

$$0 < \frac{2}{3}(0) - 2, \ 0 < -2 \text{ False}$$

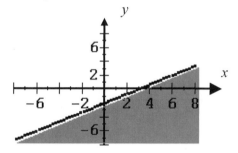

11. $y \geq -\dfrac{5}{3}x + 3$

Test point: $(0, 0)$

$$0 \geq -\frac{5}{3}(0) + 3$$

$$0 \geq 3 \text{ False}$$

59

© 2006 Pearson Education, Inc., Upper Saddle River, NJ. All rights reserved. This material is protected under all copyright laws as they currently exist. No portion of this material may be reproduced, in any form or by any means, without permission in writing from the publisher.

13. $5y - x \le 15$

Test point: $(0,0)$

$5(0) - 0 \le 15$

$0 \le 15$ True

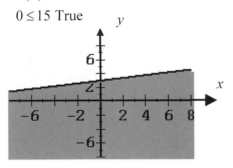

15. $2x + y > 0$

Test point: $(1,1)$

$2(1) + 1 > 0$

$3 > 0$ True

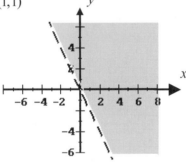

17. $5x - 2y \ge 0$

Test point: $(1,1)$

$5(1) - 2(1) \ge 0$

$3 \ge 0$ True

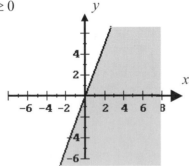

19. $x > -4$

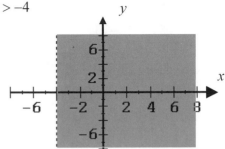

21. $y \le -1$

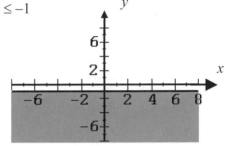

23. $-8x \le -12$, $x \ge \dfrac{3}{2}$

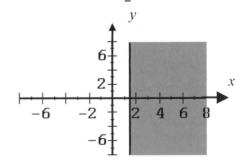

25. $4y \ge 2$, $y \ge \dfrac{1}{2}$

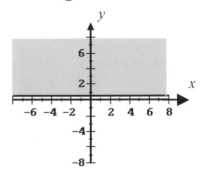

© 2006 Pearson Education, Inc., Upper Saddle River, NJ. All rights reserved. This material is protected under all copyright laws as they currently exist.
No portion of this material may be reproduced, in any form or by any means, without permission in writing from the publisher.

27. $x \geq 0$, $y \geq 0$ is QI.

$x + y \leq 3$ is region below line. The shaded triangular region in the graph will satisfy all three inequalities.

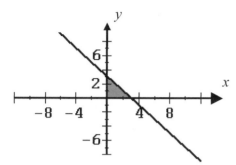

29. $75x + 175y \leq 2100$

$75(0) + 175(0) \leq 2100$

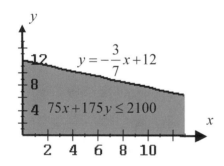

Cumulative Review

31. $3x^2 + 6x - 2\big|_{x=-2} = 3(-2)^2 + 6(-2) - 2$

$\qquad\qquad\qquad = 3(4) - 12 - 2$

$\qquad\qquad\qquad = -2$

33. $\dfrac{12(18)}{24} = 9$ packages

3.5 Exercises

1. A relation is any set of ordered pairs. A function is a set of ordered pairs in which no two different ordered pairs have the same first coordinate.

3. A function may be described as a set of ordered pairs, as an equation, and as a graph.

5. Domain $= \{0, 5, 7\}$

Range $= \{0, 11, 13\}$

Relation is *not* a function.

7. Domain $= \{85, 16, -102, 62\}$

Range $= \{-12, 4, 48\}$

Relation is a function.

9. Domain $= \{6, 8, 10, 12, 14\}$

Range $= \{38, 40, 42, 44, 46\}$

Relation is a function.

11. Domain $= \{$Jan., Feb., Mar., April,

$\qquad\qquad\qquad$ May, June, July, Aug.,

$\qquad\qquad\qquad$ Sept., Oct., Nov., Dec.$\}$

Range $= \{81, 80, 79\}$

Relation is a function.

13. Domain $= \{$Chicago, New York$\}$

Range $= \{1454, 1350, 1250$

$\qquad\qquad\qquad\quad 1136, 1127, 1046\}$

Relation is *not* a function.

15. Domain $= \{10, 20, 30, 40, 50\}$

Range $=$

$\{11.51, 23.02, 34.53, 46.04, 57.55\}$

Relation is a function.

17. Function

19. Not a function

21. Function

61

© 2006 Pearson Education, Inc., Upper Saddle River, NJ. All rights reserved. This material is protected under all copyright laws as they currently exist. No portion of this material may be reproduced, in any form or by any means, without permission in writing from the publisher.

23. Not a function

25. Function

27. $g(x) = 2x - 5$

$g(-2.4) = 2(-2.4) - 5 = -9.8$

29. $g(x) = 2x - 5$

$g\left(\dfrac{1}{2}\right) = 2\left(\dfrac{1}{2}\right) - 5 = -4$

31. $h(x) = \dfrac{2}{3}x + 2$

$h(-6) = \dfrac{2}{3}(-6) + 2 = -2$

33. $h(x) = \dfrac{2}{3}x + 2$

$h(2) = \dfrac{2}{3}(2) + 2 = 3\dfrac{1}{3}$

35. $r(x) = 2x^2 - 4x + 1$

$r(-1) = 2(-1)^2 - 4(-1) + 1 = 7$

37. $r(x) = 2x^2 - 4x + 1$

$r(-0.1) = 2(-0.1)^2 - 4(-0.1) + 1$

$r(-0.1) = 1.42$

39. $b(x) = -x^2 + 2x - 1$

$b(0) = -0^2 + 2(0) - 1$

$b(0) = -1$

41. $b(x) = -x^2 + 2x - 1$

$b(5) = -5^2 + 2(5) - 1$

$b(5) = -25 + 10 - 1$

$b(5) = -16$

43. $t(x) = x^3 - 3x^2 + 2x - 3$

$t(4) = 4^3 - 3(4)^2 + 2(4) - 3$

$t(4) = 64 - 48 + 8 - 3$

$t(4) = 21$

45. $t(x) = x^3 - 3x^2 + 2x - 3$

$t(-2) = (-2)^3 - 3(-2)^2 + 2(-2) - 3$

$t(-2) = -8 - 3(4) - 4 - 3$

$t(-2) = -8 - 12 - 7$

$t(-2) = -27$

47. $f(x) = \sqrt{2 - x}$

$f(-2) = \sqrt{2 - (-2)}$

$f(-2) = \sqrt{4}$

$f(-2) = 2$

49. $g(x) = \left|6 - x^2\right|$

$g(2) = \left|6 - 2^2\right|$

$g(2) = \left|6 - 4\right|$

$g(2) = \left|2\right| = 2$

51. $g(x) = x^2 + 3$

Substitute given domain values for x to find y.

x	$g(x) = x^2 + 3$
-2	7
-1	4
0	3
1	4
2	7

Range $= \{3, 4, 7\}$

62

© 2006 Pearson Education, Inc., Upper Saddle River, NJ. All rights reserved. This material is protected under all copyright laws as they currently exist.
No portion of this material may be reproduced, in any form or by any means, without permission in writing from the publisher.

53. $d(x) = 3 - \frac{1}{4}x,\ d(x) \to y$

$$y = 3 - \frac{1}{4}x \Rightarrow x = 12 - 4y$$

Substitute given range values for y to find x.

$x = 12 - 4y$	y
12	0
11	1/4
9	3/4
−4	4

Domain $= \{12, 11, 9, -4\}$

Cumulative Review

55. $|x + 3| \le 2$

$$-2 \le x + 3 \le 2$$
$$-5 \le x \le -1$$

57. $81(20) + 76(20) = 3140$ tons

3.6 Exercises

1. $f(x) = \frac{3}{4}x + 2$

x	$f(x)$
−4	−1
0	2
4	5

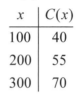

3. $f(x) = -3x - 1$

x	$f(x)$
−1	2
0	−1
1	−4

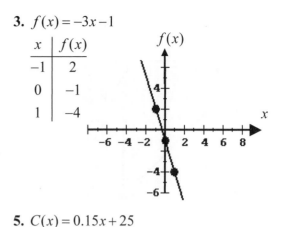

5. $C(x) = 0.15x + 25$

x	$C(x)$
100	40
200	55
300	70

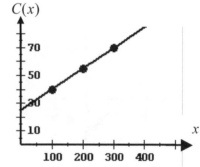

7. $P(x) = -1500x + 45,000$

x	$P(x)$
0	45,000
10	30,000
30	0

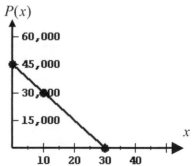

© 2006 Pearson Education, Inc., Upper Saddle River, NJ. All rights reserved. This material is protected under all copyright laws as they currently exist. No portion of this material may be reproduced, in any form or by any means, without permission in writing from the publisher.

9. $f(x) = |x-1|$

x	-1	0	1	2	3	4
$f(x)$	2	1	0	1	2	3

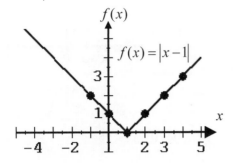

11. $g(x) = |x| - 5$

x	-2	-1	0	1	2
$g(x)$	-3	-4	-5	-4	-3

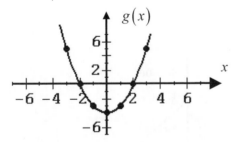

13. $g(x) = x^2 - 4$

x	-3	-2	-1	0	1	2	3
$g(x)$	5	0	-3	-4	-3	0	5

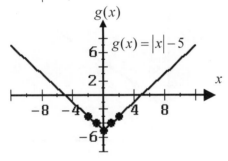

15. $g(x) = (x+1)^2$

x	-3	-2	-1	0	1
$g(x)$	4	1	0	1	4

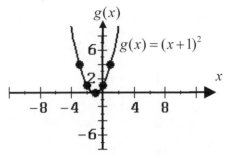

17. $g(x) = x^3 - 3$

x	$g(x)$
-1	-4
0	-3
1	-2

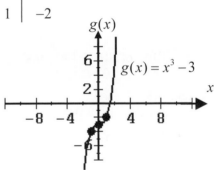

19. $p(x) = -x^3$

x	$p(x)$
-1	1
0	0
1	-1

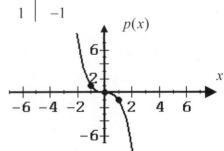

64

© 2006 Pearson Education, Inc., Upper Saddle River, NJ. All rights reserved. This material is protected under all copyright laws as they currently exist.
No portion of this material may be reproduced, in any form or by any means, without permission in writing from the publisher.

21. $f(x) = \dfrac{2}{x}$

x	-4	-2	-1	$-\dfrac{1}{2}$	$\dfrac{1}{2}$	1	2	4
$f(x)$	$-\dfrac{1}{2}$	-1	-2	-4	4	2	1	$\dfrac{1}{2}$

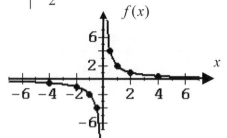

23.

$h(x) = -\dfrac{6}{x}$

x	-6	-3	-2	-1	1	2	3	6
$h(x)$	1	2	3	6	-6	-3	-2	-1

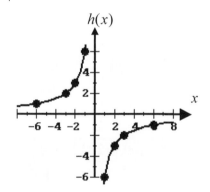

25. $y_1 = x^2$, $y_2 = 0.4x^2$, $y_3 = 2.6x^2$

From the graphs in we see that the larger the coefficient of x^2 the faster the graph rises.

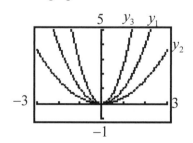

27. From the graph $f(2) = 1\dfrac{1}{2}$.

x	$f(x)$
-5	-2
3	2
5	3

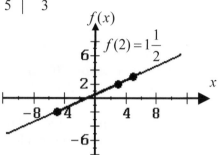

29. From the graph $f(2) = 2.4$

x	$f(x)$
0	3
1	2.5
3	2.2
-1	4
-2	6

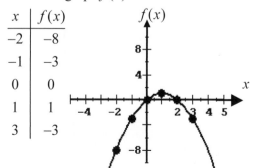

31. From the graph $f(2) = 0$

x	$f(x)$
-2	-8
-1	-3
0	0
1	1
3	-3

65

© 2006 Pearson Education, Inc., Upper Saddle River, NJ. All rights reserved. This material is protected under all copyright laws as they currently exist. No portion of this material may be reproduced, in any form or by any means, without permission in writing from the publisher.

33. (a)

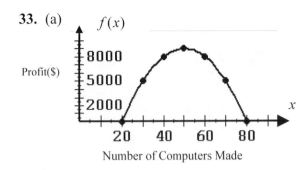

Number of Computers Made

(b) From the graph, 50 computers should be made each day for maximum profit.
(c) To earn a profit of $8000 or more each day the company should manufacture between 40 and 60 computers.
(d) If the company manufactures 82 computers per day they will operate at a loss.
(e) If the company manufactures forty five computers per day the profit will be approximately $8700.

Cumulative Review

35. $2(3ax - 4y) = 5(ax + 3)$

$6ax - 8y = 5ax + 15$

$ax = 8y + 15$

$x = \dfrac{8y + 15}{a}$

37. $\dfrac{1}{2}(x + 2) - 5 = x - \dfrac{3}{4}(x + 4)$

$\dfrac{1}{2}x + 1 - 5 = x - \dfrac{3}{4}x - 3$

$\dfrac{1}{2}x - 4 = \dfrac{1}{4}x - 3$

$\dfrac{1}{4}x = 1$

$x = 4$

39. $\dfrac{10 \text{ times}}{\text{hour}} \cdot \dfrac{24 \text{ hours}}{\text{day}} (31 + 31 + 29) \text{ days}$

$= 21{,}840 \text{ times}$

Putting Your Skills to Work

1.

D	30	31	32	33
Y	50	49	48	47

D	34	35	40	45
Y	46	45	40	35

2. An increase of 10 more trees will produce a decrease of 10 lb down to 25 lb.

3. Substitution of the D values from the table into the formula $Y = 50 - (D - 30)$ gives the Y values in the table.

4. $Y = 50 - (D - 30)$

$Y = 50 - D + 30$

$Y = 80 - D$

5. $H = DY$

$H = D(80 - D)$

$H = 80D - D^2$

6.

D	0	10	20	30
H	0	700	1200	1500

D	40	50	60	70	80
H	1600	1500	1200	700	0

7.

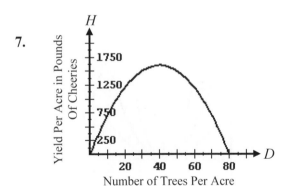

Number of Trees Per Acre

© 2006 Pearson Education, Inc., Upper Saddle River, NJ. All rights reserved. This material is protected under all copyright laws as they currently exist. No portion of this material may be reproduced, in any form or by any means, without permission in writing from the publisher.

7. From the graph 40 trees should be planted per acre to achieve the highest yield.

8. $\dfrac{40 \text{ trees}}{\text{acre}} \cdot \dfrac{40 \text{ lb}}{\text{tree}} \cdot \dfrac{\$0.47}{\text{lb}} = \dfrac{\$752}{\text{acre}}$

4. $7x = x + 2y$

x	y
−2	−6
0	0
2	6

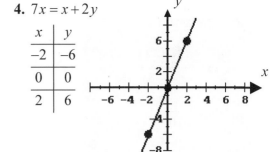

Chapter 3 Review Problems

1. $y = -\dfrac{1}{4}x - 1$

x	y
−4	0
0	−1
4	−2

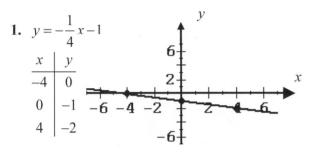

5. $-3y + 2 = -8y - 13$

$5y = -15$

$y = -3$

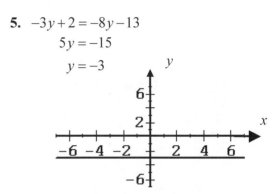

2. $y = -\dfrac{3}{2}x + 5$

x	y
0	5
2	2
4	−1

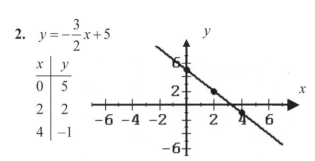

6. $5x - 6 = -2x + 8$

$7x = 14$

$x = 2$

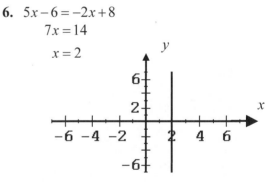

3. $y - 2x + 4 = 0$

x	y
0	−4
2	0
4	4

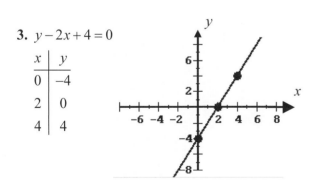

7. $m = \dfrac{y_2 - y_1}{x_2 - x_1}$

$m = \dfrac{3 - 1}{\dfrac{1}{2} - \dfrac{3}{2}}$

$m = -2$

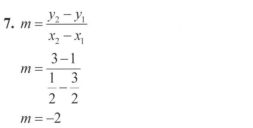

67

© 2006 Pearson Education, Inc., Upper Saddle River, NJ. All rights reserved. This material is protected under all copyright laws as they currently exist. No portion of this material may be reproduced, in any form or by any means, without permission in writing from the publisher.

8. $m = \dfrac{y_2 - y_1}{x_2 - x_1}$

$m = \dfrac{-5 - (-4)}{2 - (-8)}$

$m = -\dfrac{1}{10}$

9. $m = \dfrac{y_2 - y_1}{x_2 - x_1}$

$m = \dfrac{6 - 1.8}{-3 - (-3)}$

$m = \dfrac{4.2}{0}$ slope is undefined

10. $m = \dfrac{y_2 - y_1}{x_2 - x_1}$

$m = \dfrac{-1 - (-1)}{7.5 - 0.3}$

$m = \dfrac{0}{7.2} = 0$

11. $m = \dfrac{y_2 - y_1}{x_2 - x_1}$

$m = \dfrac{-4 - (-3)}{-8 - 2}$

$m = \dfrac{1}{10}$

12. $m = \dfrac{y_2 - y_1}{x_2 - x_1} = \dfrac{\frac{1}{3} - 2}{\frac{2}{3} - 4} = \dfrac{1}{2}$

$m_{\perp} = -\dfrac{1}{m}$

$m_{\perp} = -\dfrac{1}{\frac{1}{2}} = -2$

13. $y = mx + b$

$y = \dfrac{2}{3}x + (-4)$

$3y = 2x - 12$

$2x - 3y = 12$

14. $y - y_1 = m(x - x_1)$

$y - (-2) = -4\left(x - \dfrac{1}{2}\right)$

$y + 2 = -4x + 2$

$4x + y = 0$

15. $y - y_1 = m(x - x_1)$

$y - 1 = 0(x - (-3)) = 0$

$y - 1 = 0$

$y = 1$

16. (a) $P = 140x - 2000$ has $m = 140$

(b) $P = 140x - 2000 = 0$

$140x = 2000$

$x = 14\dfrac{2}{7}$

The company must sell at least 15 microcomputers each day to make a profit.

17. $m = \dfrac{y_2 - y_1}{x_2 - x_1} = \dfrac{6 - \frac{-1}{2}}{5 - (-1)} = \dfrac{13}{12}$

$y - y_1 = m(x - x_1)$

$y - 6 = \dfrac{13}{12}(x - 5)$

$12y - 72 = 13x - 65$

$13x - 12y = -7$

© 2006 Pearson Education, Inc., Upper Saddle River, NJ. All rights reserved. This material is protected under all copyright laws as they currently exist. No portion of this material may be reproduced, in any form or by any means, without permission in writing from the publisher.

18. A line with undefined slope is a vertical line, $x = -6$.

19. $7x + 8y - 12 = 0$
$$8y = -7x + 12$$
$$y = -\frac{7}{8}x + \frac{3}{2}$$
$$m = -\frac{7}{8}, \ m_\perp = -\frac{1}{m} = -\frac{1}{-\frac{7}{8}} = \frac{8}{7}$$
$$y - y_1 = m_\perp (x - x_1)$$
$$y - 5 = \frac{8}{7}(x - (-2))$$
$$7y - 35 = 8x + 16$$
$$8x - 7y = -51$$

20. $3x - 2y = 8$
$$2y = 3x - 8$$
$$y = \frac{3}{2}x - 4$$
$$m = \frac{3}{2} \Rightarrow m_p = \frac{3}{2}$$
$$y - y_1 = m_p (x - x_1)$$
$$y - 1 = \frac{3}{2}(x - 5)$$
$$2y - 2 = 3x - 15$$
$$3x - 2y = 13$$

21. From the graph $m = \frac{3}{4}$ and $b = -4$.
$$y = mx + b$$
$$y = \frac{3}{4}x - 4$$

22. From the graph $m = -3$ and $b = 5$.
$$y = mx + b$$
$$y = -3x + 5$$

23. From the graph $m = 0$ and $b = 2$.
$$y = mx + b$$
$$y = 2$$

24. $y < 2x + 4$, Test point: $(0,0)$
$$0 < 2(0) + 4, \ 0 < 4 \text{ True}$$

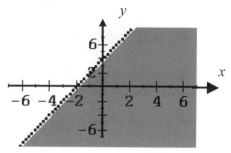

25. $y < 3x + 1$
Test point: $(0,0)$, $0 < 3(0) + 1$,
$0 < 1$, True

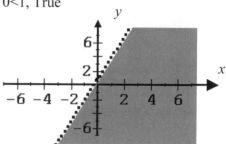

26. $y > -\frac{1}{2}x + 3$
Test point: $(0,0)$
$$0 > -\frac{1}{2}(0,0) + 3$$
$0 > 3$ False

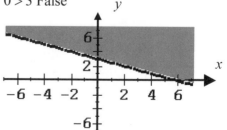

69

© 2006 Pearson Education, Inc., Upper Saddle River, NJ. All rights reserved. This material is protected under all copyright laws as they currently exist. No portion of this material may be reproduced, in any form or by any means, without permission in writing from the publisher.

27. $y > -\dfrac{2}{3}x + 1$

Test point: $(0,0)$

$0 > -\dfrac{2}{3}(0) + 1$

$0 > 1$ False

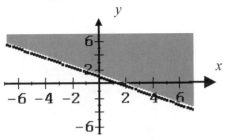

28. $3x + 4y \le -12$

Test point: $(0,0)$

$3(0) + 4(0) \le -12$

$0 \le -12$ False

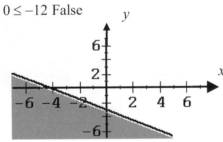

29. $x \le 3y$

Test point: $(0,3)$

$0 \le 3(3)$

$0 \le 9$ True

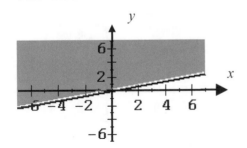

30. $5x + 3y \le -15$

Test point: $(0,0)$

$5(0) + 3(0) \le -15$

$0 \le -15$ False

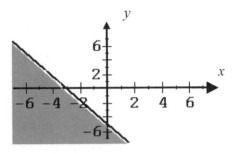

31. $3x - 5 < 7$

$3x < 12$

$x < 4$

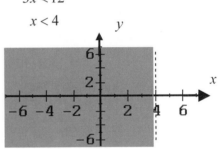

32. $5y - 2 > 3y - 10$

$2y > -8$

$y > -4$

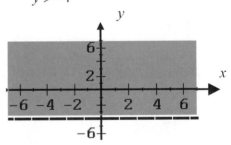

33. Domain $= \{-20, -18, -16, -12\}$

Range $= \{14, 16, 18\}$

Relation is a function.

70

© 2006 Pearson Education, Inc., Upper Saddle River, NJ. All rights reserved. This material is protected under all copyright laws as they currently exist. No portion of this material may be reproduced, in any form or by any means, without permission in writing from the publisher.

34. Domain: $\{0,1,2,3\}$

Range: $\{0,1,4,9,16\}$

Relation is not a function.

35. Function, no two ordered pairs have the same first coordinate by VLT.

36. Function, no two ordered pairs have the same first coordinate by VLT.

37. Not a function, from VLT at least two ordered pairs have the same first coordinate.

38. $f(x) = 3x - 8$

$f(-2) = 3(-2) - 8$

$f(-2) = -6 - 8$

$f(-2) = -14$

$f(-3) = 3(-3) - 8$

$f(-3) = -9 - 8$

$f(-3) = -17$

39. $g(x) = 2x^2 - 3x - 5$

$g(-3) = 2(-3)^2 - 3(-3) - 5 = 22$

$g(2) = 2(2)^2 - 3(2) - 5 = -3$

40. $h(x) = x^3 + 2x^2 - 5x + 8$

$h(-1) = (-1)^3 + 2(-1)^2 - 5(-1) + 8$

$h(-1) = -1 + 2 + 5 + 8$

$h(-1) = 14$

41. $p(x) = |-6x - 3|$

$p(3) = |-6(3) - 3|$

$p(3) = |-21|$

$p(3) = 21$

42. $f(x) = 2|x - 1|$

x	$f(x) = 2|x-1|$
-2	4
0	2
1	0
2	2
3	4

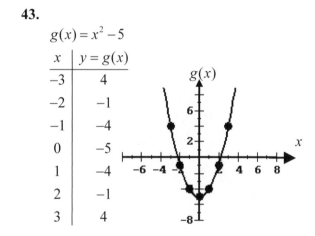

43.

$g(x) = x^2 - 5$

x	$y = g(x)$
-3	4
-2	-1
-1	-4
0	-5
1	-4
2	-1
3	4

44. $h(x) = x^3 + 3$

x	$y = h(x)$
-2	-5
-1	2
0	3
1	4

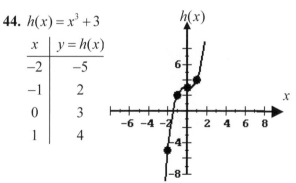

71

© 2006 Pearson Education, Inc., Upper Saddle River, NJ. All rights reserved. This material is protected under all copyright laws as they currently exist. No portion of this material may be reproduced, in any form or by any means, without permission in writing from the publisher.

45. From the graph $f(-2) = 0$.

x	-1	-3	-4	-5	-6	-7
$f(x)$	5	-3	-4	-3	0	5

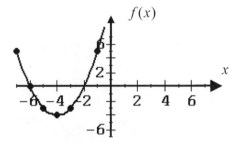

46. From the graph $f(-2) = 3$

x	$f(x)$
-3	4
-1	2
0	1
1	0
2	-1
3	0
4	1

47. $f(x) = -\dfrac{4}{5}x + 3$

x	$f(x) = -\dfrac{4}{5}x + 3$
-5	7
0	3
10	-5

48. $f(x) = 2x^2 - 3x + 4$

x	$f(x) = 2x^2 - 3x + 4$
-3	31
0	4
4	24

49. $f(x) = 3x^3 - 4$

x	$f(x) = 3x^3 - 4$
-1	-7
0	-4
2	20

50. $f(x) = \dfrac{7}{2x + 3}$

x	$f(x) = \dfrac{7}{2x + 3}$
-2	-7
0	$\dfrac{7}{3}$
2	1

51. $m = \dfrac{y_2 - y_1}{x_2 - x_1}$

$$m = \dfrac{-5 - (-6)}{3 - (-5)} = \dfrac{1}{8}$$

52. $m = \dfrac{y_2 - y_1}{x_2 - x_1} = \dfrac{2 - 10}{-4 - 1} = \dfrac{8}{5}$

$$m_n = -\dfrac{1}{m} = -\dfrac{1}{\dfrac{8}{5}} = -\dfrac{5}{8}$$

53. $m = \dfrac{y_2 - y_1}{x_2 - x_1} = \dfrac{8 - (-6)}{4.5 - 2.5} = 7$

$$m_p = m = 7$$

54.
$$y = mx + b$$
$$y = \dfrac{5}{6}x + (-5)$$
$$6y = 5x - 30$$
$$5x - 6y = 30$$

72

© 2006 Pearson Education, Inc., Upper Saddle River, NJ. All rights reserved. This material is protected under all copyright laws as they currently exist. No portion of this material may be reproduced, in any form or by any means, without permission in writing from the publisher.

55. $y = 5x - 2$, $m = 5$, $m_p = 5$

$$y - y_1 = m_p(x - x_1)$$
$$y - 10 = 5(x - 4)$$
$$y - 10 = 5x - 20$$
$$y = 5x - 10$$

56. $m = \dfrac{y_2 - y_1}{x_2 - x_1} = \dfrac{6 - 3}{5 - (-7)} = \dfrac{1}{4}$

$$y - y_1 = m(x - x_1)$$
$$y - 6 = \frac{1}{4}(x - 5)$$
$$y - 6 = \frac{1}{4}x - \frac{5}{4}$$
$$y = \frac{1}{4}x + \frac{19}{4}$$

57. $3x - 6y = 9$

$$6y = 3x - 9$$
$$y = \frac{1}{2}x - \frac{3}{2}, \quad m = \frac{1}{2}, \quad m_\perp = -2$$
$$y - y_1 = m(x - x_1)$$
$$y - (-1) = -2(x - (-2))$$
$$y + 1 = -2x - 4$$
$$2x + y = -5$$

58. $(5, 6) \rightarrow x = 5$

59. $f(x) = 35 + 0.15x$

60. $f(x) = 15,000 + 500x$

61. $f(x) = 18,000 - 65x$

How Am I Doing? Chapter 3 Test

1. $y = \dfrac{1}{3}x - 2$

x	y
-3	-3
0	-2
3	-1

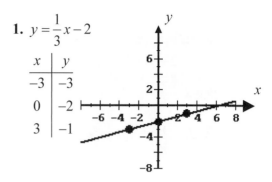

2. $2x - 3 = 1$

$$2x = 4$$
$$x = 2$$

x	y
2	-2
2	0
2	2

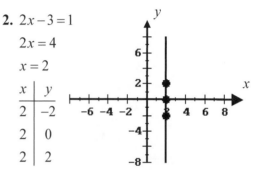

3. $5x + 3y = 9$

x	y
0	3
3	-2
6	-7

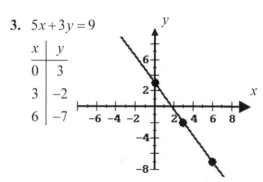

4. $2x + 3y = -10$

x	y
-2	-2
1	-4
4	-6

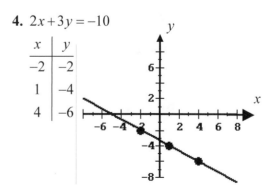

73

© 2006 Pearson Education, Inc., Upper Saddle River, NJ. All rights reserved. This material is protected under all copyright laws as they currently exist. No portion of this material may be reproduced, in any form or by any means, without permission in writing from the publisher.

5. $m = \dfrac{y_2 - y_1}{x_2 - x_1}$

  $m = \dfrac{-3 - (-6)}{2 - \dfrac{1}{2}}$

  $m = 2$

6. $m = \dfrac{y_2 - y_1}{x_2 - x_1}$

  $m = \dfrac{5 - 5}{-7 - 6}$

  $m = 0$

7. $9x + 7y = 13$

  $7y = -9x + 13$

  $y = -\dfrac{9}{7}x + \dfrac{13}{7}$

  $m = -\dfrac{9}{7}$

8. $6x - 7y - 1 = 0$

  $7y = 6x - 1$

  $y = \dfrac{6}{7}x - \dfrac{1}{7}$

  $m = \dfrac{6}{7}, \ m_\perp = -\dfrac{7}{6}$

  $y - y_1 = m_\perp (x - x_1)$

  $y - (-2) = -\dfrac{7}{6}(x - 0)$

  $y + 2 = -\dfrac{7}{6}x$

  $6y + 12 = -7x$

  $7x + 6y = -12$

9. $m = \dfrac{y_2 - y_1}{x_2 - x_1}$

  $m = \dfrac{-2 - (-1)}{5 - (-3)} = -\dfrac{1}{8}$

  $y - y_1 = m(x - x_1)$

  $y - (-2) = -\dfrac{1}{8}(x - 5)$

  $8y + 16 = -x + 5$

  $x + 8y = -11$

10. $y = 2$

11. $y = mx + b$

  $y = -5x + (-8)$

  $y = -5x - 8$

12. $y \geq -4x$

  Test point: $(0,2)$

  $2 \geq -4(2)$

  $2 \geq -8$ True

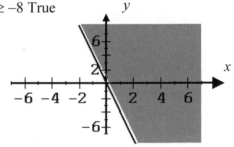

13. $4x - 2y < -6$

  Test point: $(0,0)$

  $4(0) - 2(0) < -6$

  $0 < -6$ False

74

© 2006 Pearson Education, Inc., Upper Saddle River, NJ. All rights reserved. This material is protected under all copyright laws as they currently exist.
No portion of this material may be reproduced, in any form or by any means, without permission in writing from the publisher.

14. Domain $= \{0, 1, 2\}$

Range $= \{-4, -1, 0, 1, 4\}$

15. $f(x) = 2x - 3$

$$f\left(\frac{3}{4}\right) = 2\left(\frac{3}{4}\right) - 3$$

$$f\left(\frac{3}{4}\right) = -\frac{3}{2}$$

16. $g(x) = \frac{1}{2}x^2 + 3$

$$g(-4) = \frac{1}{2}(-4)^2 + 3$$

$$g(-4) = 11$$

17. $h(x) = \left|-\frac{2}{3}x + 4\right|$

$$h(-9) = \left|-\frac{2}{3}(-9) + 4\right|$$

$$h(-9) = |10|$$

$$h(-9) = 10$$

18. $p(x) = -2x^3 + 3x^2 + x - 4$

$$p(-2) = -2(-2)^3 + 3(-2)^2 + (-2) - 4$$

$$p(-2) = 22$$

19. $g(x) = 5 - x^2$

x	$g(x)$
-2	1
-1	4
0	5
1	4
2	1

20. $h(x) = x^3 - 4$

x	y
0	-4
1	-3
2	4

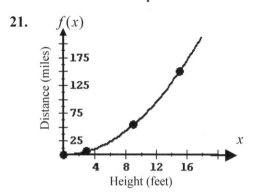

21.

From the graph $f(4) = 10$

Cumulative Test for Chapters 1-3

1. Inverse property of addition.

2. $3(4-6)^2 + \sqrt{16} + 12 \div (-3)$

$$= 3(-2)^2 + 4 + (-4)$$

$$= 3(4)$$

$$= 12$$

3. $\left(3x^2 y^{-3}\right)^{-4} = 3^{-4} x^{-8} y^{12} = \dfrac{y^{12}}{81x^8}$

4. $5x(2x - 3y) - 3(x^2 + 4)$

$$= 10x^2 - 15xy - 3x^2 - 12$$

$$= 7x^2 - 15xy - 12$$

5. $0.000437 = 4.37 \times 10^{-4}$

75

© 2006 Pearson Education, Inc., Upper Saddle River, NJ. All rights reserved. This material is protected under all copyright laws as they currently exist.
No portion of this material may be reproduced, in any form or by any means, without permission in writing from the publisher.

6. $3(x-2)>6$ or $5-3(x+1)>8$

$$3x-6>6 \qquad 5-3x-3>8$$
$$3x>12 \qquad\quad -3x>6$$
$$x>4 \qquad\qquad x<-2$$

7. $2a-x=\dfrac{1}{3}(6x-y)$

$$6a-3x=6x-y$$
$$-9x=-6a-y$$
$$9x=6a+y$$
$$x=\dfrac{6a+y}{9}$$

8. Let $w=$ the width.
$$P=2l+2w$$
$$92=2(2w+1)+2w$$
$$46=(2w+1)+w=2w+1+w$$
$$46=3w+1 \Rightarrow 3w+1=46$$
$$3w=45$$
$$w=15 \text{ cm for width}$$
$$2w+1=31 \text{ cm for length}$$

9. Let $x=$ the amount invested at 5%.
$$0.05x+0.08(3000-x)=189$$
$$0.05x+240-0.08x=189$$
$$-0.03x=-51$$
$$x=1700$$
$$3000-1700=1300$$

Sharim invested $1700 at 5% and $1300 at 8%.

10. $A=\dfrac{1}{2}\pi r^2$

$$A=\dfrac{1}{2}(3.14)(3)^2$$
$$A=14.13 \text{ in.}^2$$

11. $4x-6y=10$

x	y
-2	-3
1	-1
4	1

12. $m=\dfrac{y_2-y_1}{x_2-x_1}=\dfrac{5-1}{6-(-2)}=\dfrac{1}{2}$

13. $m=\dfrac{y_2-y_1}{x_2-x_1}=\dfrac{1-3}{5-4}=-2$

$$y-y_1=m(x-x_1)$$
$$y-1=-2(x-5)$$
$$y-1=-2x+10$$
$$2x+y=11$$

14. $\qquad y=\dfrac{2}{3}x-4$

$$m=\dfrac{2}{3},\ m_\perp=-\dfrac{3}{2}$$
$$y-y_1=m_\perp(x-x_1)$$
$$y-(-3)=-\dfrac{3}{2}(x-(-2))$$
$$2y+6=-3x-6$$
$$3x+2y=-12$$

© 2006 Pearson Education, Inc., Upper Saddle River, NJ. All rights reserved. This material is protected under all copyright laws as they currently exist. No portion of this material may be reproduced, in any form or by any means, without permission in writing from the publisher.

15. $D = \left\{ \frac{1}{2}, 2, 3, 5 \right\}$

$R = \{-1, 2, 7, 8\}$

Yes, the relation is a function.

16. $f(x) = -2x^2 - 4x + 1$

$f(-3) = -2(-3)^2 - 4(-3) + 1$

$f(-3) = -5$

17. $p(x) = -\frac{1}{3}x + 2$

x	$p(x) = -\frac{1}{3}x + 2$
-3	3
0	2
3	1

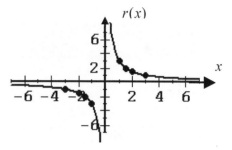

18. $h(x) = |x - 2|$

x	$h(x) = |x - 2|$
0	2
1	1
2	0
3	1
4	2

19. $r(x) = \frac{3}{x}$

x	$r(x) = \frac{3}{x}$		x	$r(x) = \frac{3}{x}$
-3	-1		1	3
-2	$-\frac{3}{2}$		$\frac{3}{2}$	2
$-\frac{3}{2}$	-2		2	$\frac{3}{2}$
-1	-3		3	1

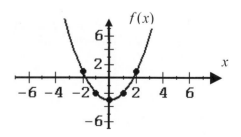

20. $f(x) = x^2 - 3$

x	$f(x) = x^2 - 3$
-2	1
-1	-2
0	-3
1	-2
2	1

77

© 2006 Pearson Education, Inc., Upper Saddle River, NJ. All rights reserved. This material is protected under all copyright laws as they currently exist. No portion of this material may be reproduced, in any form or by any means, without permission in writing from the publisher.

21. $y \le -\dfrac{3}{2}x + 3$

Test point: $(0,0)$

$0 \le -\dfrac{3}{2}(0) + 3$

$0 \le 3$ True

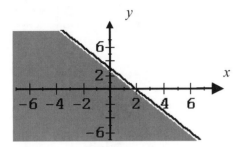

22. $f(x) = -2x^3 + 4$

x	$f(x) = -2x^3 + 4$
-2	20
0	4
3	-50

23. $f(x) = 32,500 - 1400x$

24. $2005 - 1990 = 15$

$\qquad f(15) = 32,500 - 1400(15)$

$\qquad f(15) = 11,500$

11,500 cars will travel each weekday on Route 1 in the year 2005.

© 2006 Pearson Education, Inc., Upper Saddle River, NJ. All rights reserved. This material is protected under all copyright laws as they currently exist. No portion of this material may be reproduced, in any form or by any means, without permission in writing from the publisher.

Chapter 4

4.1 Exercises

1. There is no solution. There is no point (x, y) that satisfies both equations.

   The graph of such a system yields two parallel lines.

3. A system of two linear equations in two unknowns can have an infinite number of solutions, one solution, or no solutions.

5. $4x + 1 = 6 - y$

   $4\left(\dfrac{3}{2}\right) + 1 \overset{?}{=} 6 - (-1), \ 7 = 7$

   $2x - 5y = 8$

   $2\left(\dfrac{3}{2}\right) - 5(-1) \overset{?}{=} 8, \ 8 = 8$

   $\left(\dfrac{3}{2}, -1\right)$ is a solution.

7. $3x + y = 2$
   $2x - y = 3$

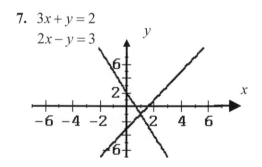

   $(1, -1)$ is the solution.

9. $2x + 3y = 6$
   $2x + y = -2$

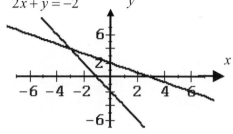

   $(-3, 4)$ is the solution.

11. $\quad y = -x + 3$

   $x + y = -\dfrac{2}{3}$

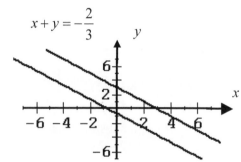

   The system has no solution.

13. $\quad y = -2x + 5$

   $3y + 6x = 15$

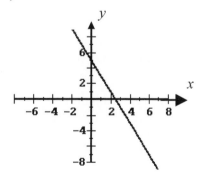

   There are an infinite number of solutions.

79

© 2006 Pearson Education, Inc., Upper Saddle River, NJ. All rights reserved. This material is protected under all copyright laws as they currently exist. No portion of this material may be reproduced, in any form or by any means, without permission in writing from the publisher.

15. $3x + 2y = -17$ **(1)**

$\quad\ 2x + y = 3$ **(2)**

Solve **(2)** for y and substitute into **(1)**

$$y = 3 - 2x$$

$$3x + 2(3 - 2x) = -17$$

$$3x + 6 - 4x = -17$$

$$x = 23$$

Substitute $x = 23$ into **(2)** and solve for y

$$2(23) + y = 3$$

$$46 + y = 3$$

$$y = -43$$

$(23, -43)$ is the solution.

Check:

(1) $3(23) + 2(-43) \overset{?}{=} -17, \ -17 = -17$

(2) $2(23) + (-43) \overset{?}{=} 3, \ 3 = 3$

17. $-x + 3y = -8$ **(1)**

$\quad\ 2x - y = 6$ **(2)**

Solve **(2)** for y and substitute into **(1)**

$$y = 2x - 6$$

$$-x + 3(2x - 6) = -8$$

$$-x + 6x - 18 = -8$$

$$5x = 10$$

$$x = 2$$

Substitute $x = 2$ into **(1)**

$$-2 + 3y = -8$$

$$3y = -6$$

$$y = -2$$

$(2, -2)$ is the solution.

Check:

(1) $-2 + 3(-2) \overset{?}{=} -8, \ -8 = -8$

(2) $2(2) - (-2) \overset{?}{=} 6, \ 6 = 6$

19. $2x - \dfrac{1}{2}y = -3$ **(1)**

$\quad\ \dfrac{x}{5} + 2y = \dfrac{19}{5}$ **(2)**

Solve **(2)** for y and substitute into **(1)**

$$\frac{x}{5} + 2y = \frac{19}{5}$$

$$x + 10y = 19$$

$$y = \frac{19 - x}{10}$$

$$2x - \frac{1}{2}\left(\frac{19 - x}{10}\right) = -3$$

$$40x - 19 + x = -60$$

$$41x = -41$$

$$x = -1$$

Substitute $x = -1$ into **(1)** and solve for y

$$2(-1) - \frac{1}{2}y = -3$$

$$-4 - y = -6$$

$$-y = -2$$

$$y = 2$$

$(-1, 2)$ is the solution.

Check:

(1) $2(-1) - \dfrac{1}{2}(2) \overset{?}{=} -3, \ -3 = -3$

(2) $\dfrac{-1}{5} + 2(2) \overset{?}{=} \dfrac{19}{5}, \ \dfrac{19}{5} = \dfrac{19}{5}$

21. $\dfrac{3}{2}x - \dfrac{1}{10}y = 6$ **(1)**

$\quad\ \dfrac{1}{2}x + \dfrac{3}{10}y = 2$ **(2)**

Solve **(2)** for y and substitute into **(1)**

$$\frac{1}{2}x + \frac{3}{10}y = 2$$

$$5x + 3y = 20$$

$$y = \frac{20 - 5x}{3}$$

© 2006 Pearson Education, Inc., Upper Saddle River, NJ. All rights reserved. This material is protected under all copyright laws as they currently exist. No portion of this material may be reproduced, in any form or by any means, without permission in writing from the publisher.

21. $\dfrac{3}{2}x - \dfrac{1}{10} \cdot \dfrac{20-5x}{3} = 6$

$$45x - 20 + 5x = 180$$
$$50x = 200$$
$$x = 4$$

Substitute $x = 4$ into **(1)** and solve for y

$$\dfrac{3}{2}(4) - \dfrac{1}{10}y = 6$$

$$6 - \dfrac{1}{10}y = 6$$

$$y = 0$$

$(4, 0)$ is the solution.

Check:

(1) $\dfrac{7}{2}(1) + \dfrac{5}{2}(-3) \overset{?}{=} -4, \ -4 = -4$

(2) $3(1) + \dfrac{2}{3}(-3) \overset{?}{=} 1, \ 1 = 1$

23. $9x + 2y = 2$ **(1)**
  $3x + 5y = 5$ **(2)**

Multiply **(2)** by -3 and add to **(1)**

$$9x + 2y = 2$$
$$\underline{-9x - 15y = -15}$$
$$-13y = -13$$
$$y = 1$$

Substitute $y = 1$ into **(1)**

$$9x + 2(1) = 2$$
$$9x + 2 = 2$$
$$9x = 0$$
$$x = 0$$

$(0, \ 1)$ is the solution.

Check:

(1) $9(0) + 2(1) \overset{?}{=} 2, \ 2 = 2$

(2) $3(0) + 5(1) \overset{?}{=} 5, \ 5 = 5$

25. $6s - 3t = 1$ **(1)**
  $5s + 6t = 15$ **(2)**

Multiply **(1)** by 2 and add to **(2)**

$$12s - 6t = 2$$
$$\underline{5s + 6t = 15}$$
$$17s = 17$$
$$s = 1$$

Substitute $s = 1$ into **(2)**

$$5(1) + 6t = 15$$
$$6t = 10$$
$$t = \dfrac{5}{3}$$

$\left(1, \dfrac{5}{3}\right)$ is the solution.

Check:

(1) $6(1) - 3 \cdot \dfrac{5}{3} \overset{?}{=} 1, \ 1 = 1$

(2) $5(1) + 6 \cdot \dfrac{5}{3} \overset{?}{=} 15, \ 15 = 15$

27. $\dfrac{7}{2}x + \dfrac{5}{2}y = -4$ **(1)**

  $3x + \dfrac{2}{3}y = 1$ **(2)**

Clear fractions

  $7x + 5y = -8$ **(1)**
  $9x + 2y = 3$ **(2)**

Multiply **(1)** by 2 and **(2)** by -5 and add

$$14x + 10y = -16$$
$$\underline{-45x - 10y = -15}$$
$$-31x = -31$$
$$x = 1$$

Substitute $x = 1$ into **(2)**

$$9(1) + 2y = 3$$
$$2y = -6$$
$$y = -3$$

© 2006 Pearson Education, Inc., Upper Saddle River, NJ. All rights reserved. This material is protected under all copyright laws as they currently exist. No portion of this material may be reproduced, in any form or by any means, without permission in writing from the publisher.

$(1, -3)$ is the solution.

Check:

(1) $\dfrac{7}{2}(1) + \dfrac{5}{2}(-3) \overset{?}{=} -4, \ -4 = -4$

(2) $3(1) + \dfrac{2}{3}(-3) \overset{?}{=} 1, \ 1 = 1$

29. $1.6x + 1.5y = 1.8 \rightarrow 16x + 15y = 18$ **(1)**

$\quad\ 0.4x + 0.3y = 0.6 \rightarrow \ \ 4x + 3y = 6$ **(2)**

Multiply **(2)** by -5 and add to **(1)**

$$16x + 15y = 18$$
$$\underline{-20x - 15y = -30}$$
$$-4x = -12$$
$$x = 3$$

Substitute $x = 3$ into **(1)**

$$16(3) + 15y = 1.8$$
$$48 + 15y = 1.8$$
$$15y = -30$$
$$y = -2$$

$(3, -2)$ is the solution.

Check:

(1) $1.6(3) + 1.5(-2) \overset{?}{=} 1.8, \ 1.8 = 1.8$

(2) $0.4(3) + 0.3(-2) \overset{?}{=} 0.6, \ 0.6 = 0.6$

31. $\quad 7x - y = 6 \qquad$ **(1)**

$\qquad 3x + 2y = 22 \qquad$ **(2)**

Solve **(1)** for y and substitute into **(2)**

$$7x - y = 6$$
$$y = 7x - 6$$
$$3x + 2(7x - 6) = 22$$
$$3x + 14x - 12 = 22$$
$$17x = 34$$
$$x = 2$$

Substitute $x = 2$ into **(1)**

$$7(2) - y = 6$$
$$y = 8$$

$(2, 8)$ is the solution.

Check:

(1) $7(2) - 8 \overset{?}{=} 6, \ 6 = 6$

(2) $3(2) + 2(8) \overset{?}{=} 22, \ 22 = 22$

33. $\quad 3x + 4y = 8 \qquad$ **(1)**

$\qquad 5x + 6y = 10 \qquad$ **(2)**

Multiply **(1)** 5 and **(2)** by -3 and add

$$15x + 20y = 40$$
$$\underline{-15x - 18y = -30}$$
$$2y = 10$$
$$y = 5$$

Substitute $y = 5$ into **(1)**

$$3x + 4(5) = 8$$
$$3x + 20 = 8$$
$$3x = -12$$
$$x = -4$$

$(-4, 5)$ is the solution.

Check:

(1) $3(-4) + 4(5) \overset{?}{=} 8, \ 8 = 8$

(2) $5(-4) + 6(5) \overset{?}{=} 10, \ 10 = 10$

35. $\quad 2x + y = 4 \qquad\qquad$ **(1)**

$\qquad \dfrac{2}{3}x + \dfrac{1}{4}y = 2 \overset{\times 12}{\rightarrow} 8x + 3y = 24$ **(2)**

Solve **(1)** for y and substitute into **(2)**

$$y = 4 - 2x$$
$$8x + 3(4 - 2x) = 2$$
$$8x + 12 - 6x = 24$$
$$2x = 12$$
$$x = 6$$

Substitute $x = 6$ into **(1)**

© 2006 Pearson Education, Inc., Upper Saddle River, NJ. All rights reserved. This material is protected under all copyright laws as they currently exist. No portion of this material may be reproduced, in any form or by any means, without permission in writing from the publisher.

$$2(6) + y = 4$$
$$12 + y = 4$$
$$y = -8$$

$(6, -8)$ is the solution.

Check:

(1) $7(2) - 8 \overset{?}{=} 6, \ 6 = 6$

(2) $3(2) + 2(8) \overset{?}{=} 22, \ 22 = 22$

37. $0.2x = 0.1y - 1.2$ **(1)**
   $2x - y = 6$ **(2)**

Solve **(2)** for y and substitute into **(1)**
$$y = 2x - 6$$
$$0.2x = 0.1(2x - 6) - 1.2$$
$$0.2x = 0.2x - 0.6 - 1.2$$
$$0 = -1.8$$

This is an inconsistent system of equations and has no solution.

39. $5x - 7y = 12$ **(1)**
  $-10x + 14y = -24$ **(2)**

Multiply **(1)** by 2 and add to **(2)**
$$10x - 14y = 24$$
$$\underline{-10x + 14y = -24}$$
$$0 = 0$$

This is a dependent system of equations and has an infinite number of solutions.

41. Multiply both equations by 10 to clear decimals
  $8x + 9y = 13$ **(1)**
  $6x - 5y = 45$ **(2)**

Multiply **(1)** 5 and **(2)** by 9 and add
$$40x + 45y = 65$$
$$\underline{54x - 45y = 405}$$
$$94x = 4760$$
$$x = 5$$

Substitute $x = 5$ into **(1)**
$$8(5) + 9y = 13$$
$$40 + 9y = 13$$
$$9y = -27$$
$$y = -3$$

$(5, -3)$ is the solution.

Check:

(1) $0.8(5) + 0.9(-3) \overset{?}{=} 1.3, \ 1.3 = 1.3$

(2) $0.6(5) - 0.5(-3) \overset{?}{=} 4.5, \ 4.5 = 4.5$

43. $\dfrac{4}{5}b = \dfrac{1}{5} + a \Rightarrow 4b = 1 + 5a$

  $15a - 12b = 4 \Rightarrow 15a - 3(4b) = 4$
  $15a - 3(1 + 5a) = 4$
  $15a - 3 - 15a = 4$
  $-3 = 4$

This is an inconsistent system of equations and has no solution.

45. $\dfrac{3}{8}x + y = 14 \Rightarrow 3x + 8y = 112 \overset{\times 7}{\rightarrow}$

  $2x - \dfrac{7}{4}y = 18 \Rightarrow 8x - 7y = 72 \overset{\times 8}{\rightarrow}$

  $21x + 56y = 784$
  $\underline{64x - 56y = 576}$
  $85x \qquad\;\; = 1360$
  $x = 16$

Substitute $x = 16$ into the first equation
$$\frac{3}{8}(16) + y = 14$$
$$6 + y = 14$$
$$y = 8$$

$(16, 8)$ is the solution.

Check:

(1) $\dfrac{3}{8}(16) + 8 \overset{?}{=} 14, \ 14 = 14$

© 2006 Pearson Education, Inc., Upper Saddle River, NJ. All rights reserved. This material is protected under all copyright laws as they currently exist. No portion of this material may be reproduced, in any form or by any means, without permission in writing from the publisher.

(2) $2(16) - \dfrac{7}{4}(8) \overset{?}{=} 18, \ 18 = 18$

(b)

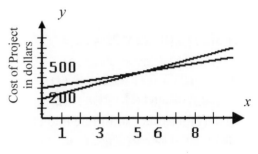

x	$y = 300 + 30x$	x	$y = 200 + 50x$
0	300	0	200
4	420	4	400
8	540	8	600

47. $3.2x - 1.5y = -3 \Rightarrow 32x - 15y = -30$ **(1)**

$0.7x + y = 2 \Rightarrow 7x + 10y = 20$ **(2)**

Multiply **(1)** by 2 and **(2)** 3 and add

$64x - 30y = -60$

$\underline{21x + 30y = 60}$

$85x = 0$

$x = 0$

Substitute $x = 0$ into **(2)**

$7(0) + 10y = 20$

$10y = 20$

$y = 2$

$(0, 2)$ is the solution.

Check:

(1) $3.2(0) - 1.5(2) \overset{?}{=} -3, \ -3 = -3$

(2) $0.7(0) + 2 \overset{?}{=} 2, \ 2 = 2$

49. $3 - (2x + 1) = y + 6$ **(1)**

$x + y + 5 = 1 - x$ **(2)**

Solve **(1)** for y and substitute in **(1)**

$3 - (2x + 1) = y + 6$

$y = 3 - 2x - 1 - 6$

$y = -2x - 4$

$x - 2x - 4 + 5 = 1 - x$

$1 = 1$

This is a dependent system and has and infinite number of solutions.

51. (a) $y = 200 + 50x$ for Old World Tile

$y = 300 + 30x$ for Modern Bath

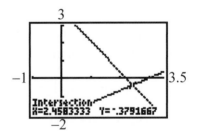

Cost of Project in dollars — Number of Hours of Labor

(c) From the graph the cost will be the same for 5 hours of installing new tile.
(d) From the graph Modern Bathroom Headquarters will cost less to remove old tile and install new tile if the time needed to install the new tile is 6 hrs.

53. $y_1 = -1.7x + 3.8$

$y_2 = 0.7x - 2.1$

Intersection
X=2.4583333   Y=-.3791667

To the nearest hundredth, the point of intersection is $(2.46, -0.38)$.

84

© 2006 Pearson Education, Inc., Upper Saddle River, NJ. All rights reserved. This material is protected under all copyright laws as they currently exist. No portion of this material may be reproduced, in any form or by any means, without permission in writing from the publisher.

55. $0.5x + 1.1y = 5.5 \Rightarrow y_1 = \dfrac{(5.5 - 0.5x)}{1.1}$

$-3.1x + 0.9y = 13.1 \Rightarrow y_2 = \dfrac{13.1 + 3.1x}{0.9}$

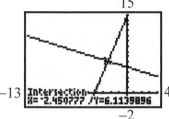

The point of intersection is $(2.45, 6.11)$.

Cumulative Review Problems

57. $\dfrac{\$200,000,000}{9,000,000 \text{ tons}} \left(\dfrac{\text{ton}}{2000 \text{ pounds}} \right)$

$\approx \$0.01$ per pound

4.2 Exercises

1. $2x - 3y + 2z = -7$ **(1)**
    $x + 4y - z = 10$ **(2)**
    $3x + 2y + z = 4$ **(3)**

Check:

(1) $2(2) - 3(1) + 2(-4) \overset{?}{=} -7, \ -7 = -7$

(2) $2 + 4(1) - (-4) \overset{?}{=} 10, \ 10 = 10$

(3) $3(2) + 2(1) + (-4) \overset{?}{=} 4, \ 4 = 4$

$(2, 1, -4)$ is a solution.

3. $3x + 2y - z = 6$ **(1)**
    $x - y - z = -8$ **(2)**
    $4x + y + 2z = 5$ **(3)**

Check:

(1) $3(-1) + 2(5) - 1 \overset{?}{=} 6, \ 6 = 6$

(2) $-1 - 5 - 2(1) \overset{?}{=} -8, \ -8 = -8$

(3) $4(-1) + 5 + 2(1) \overset{?}{=} 5, \ 3 \neq 5$

$(-1, 5, 1)$ is not a solution to the system.

5. $x + y + 2z = 0$ **(1)**
    $2x - y - z = 1$ **(2)**
    $x + 2y + 3z = 1$ **(3)**

Add **(1)** and **(2)**
    $3x + z = 1$ **(4)**

Add $2 \cdot$ **(2)** and **(3)**
    $5x + z = 3$ **(5)**

Subtract **(5)** from **(4)**
    $-2x = -2$

    $x = 1$

Substitute $x = 1$ into **(5)**
    $5(1) + z = 3$

    $z = -2$

Substitute $x = 1, \ z = -2$ into **(1)**
    $1 + y + 2(-2) = 0$

    $1 + y - 4 = 0$

    $y = 3$

$(1, 3, -2)$ is the solution.

7. $x + 2y - 3z = -11$ **(1)**
    $-2x + y - z = -11$ **(2)**
    $x + y + z = 6$ **(3)**

Add **(2)** and **(3)**
    $-x + 2y = -5$ **(4)**

Add $3 \cdot$ **(3)** and **(1)**
    $4x + 5y = 7$ **(5)**

Add $4 \cdot$ **(4)** and **(5)**
    $13y = -13$

    $y = -1$

Substitute $y = -1$ into **(5)**
    $4x + 5(-1) = 7$

    $4x - 5 = 7$

    $4x = 12$

    $x = 3$

85

© 2006 Pearson Education, Inc., Upper Saddle River, NJ. All rights reserved. This material is protected under all copyright laws as they currently exist. No portion of this material may be reproduced, in any form or by any means, without permission in writing from the publisher.

Substitute $x = 3$, $y = -1$ into (3)

$$3 + (-1) + z = 6$$
$$2 + z = 6$$
$$z = 4$$

$(3, -1, 4)$ is the solution.

9. $8x - 5y + z = 15$ **(1)**

$\quad\ 3x + y - z = -7$ **(2)**

$\quad\ x + 4y + z = -3$ **(3)**

Add **(1)** and **(2)**

$$8x - 5y + z = 15$$
$$\underline{3x + y - z = -7}$$
$$11x - 4y = 8 \qquad \textbf{(4)}$$

Add **(2)** and **(3)**

$$3x + y - z = -7$$
$$\underline{x + 4y + z = -3}$$
$$4x + 5y \ \ = -10 \ \ \textbf{(5)}$$

Add 5 times **(4)** and 4 times **(5)**

$$55x - 20y = 40$$
$$\underline{16x + 20y = -40}$$
$$76x \qquad = 0$$
$$x = 0$$

Substitute $x = 0$ into **(5)**

$$4(0) + 5y = -10$$
$$5y = -10$$
$$y = -2$$

Substitute $x = 0$, $y = 2$ into **(1)**

$$8(0) - 5(-2) + z = 15$$
$$10 + z = 15$$
$$z = 5$$

$(0, -2, 5)$ is the solution.

11. $\quad x + 4y - z = -5$ **(1)**

$\quad\ -2x - 3y + 2z = 5$ **(2)**

$\quad\ x - \dfrac{2}{3}y + z = \dfrac{11}{3}$ **(3)**

Add **(1)** and **(3)**

$$2x + \frac{10}{3}y = -\frac{4}{3} \ \ \textbf{(4)}$$

Add $2 \cdot$ **(1)** and **(2)**

$$5y = -5$$
$$y = -1$$

Substitute $y = -1$ into **(4)**

$$2x + \frac{10}{3}(-1) = -\frac{4}{3}$$
$$6x - 10 = -4$$
$$6x = 6$$
$$x = 1$$

Substitute $x = 1$ and $y = -1$ into **(3)**

$$1 - \frac{2}{3}(-1) + z = \frac{11}{3}$$
$$3 + 2 + 3z = 11$$
$$3z = 6$$
$$z = 2$$

$(1, -1, 2)$ is the solution.

13.

$$2x + 2z = -7 + 3y \Rightarrow 2x - 3y + 2z = -7 \quad \textbf{(1)}$$
$$2 \cdot \left(\frac{3}{2}x + y + \frac{1}{2}z \right) = 2 \cdot 2 \Rightarrow 3x + 2y + z = 4 \ \textbf{(2)}$$
$$x + 4y = 10 + z \Rightarrow \qquad x + 4y - z = 10 \qquad \textbf{(3)}$$

Add **(1)** and 2 times**(3)**

$$4x + 5y = 13 \quad \textbf{(4)}$$

Add **(3)** and 2 times**(2)**

$$4x + 6y = 14 \quad \textbf{(5)}$$

Subtract **(5)** from **(4)**

$$-y = -1$$
$$y = 1$$

Substitute $y = 1$ into **(5)**

$$4x + 6(1) = 14$$
$$4x = 8$$
$$x = 2$$

Substitute $x = 2$, $y = 1$ into **(3)**

© 2006 Pearson Education, Inc., Upper Saddle River, NJ. All rights reserved. This material is protected under all copyright laws as they currently exist. No portion of this material may be reproduced, in any form or by any means, without permission in writing from the publisher.

$$2 + 4(1) - z = 10$$
$$6 - z = 10$$
$$-z = 4$$
$$z = -4$$
$(2, 1, -4)$ is the solution.

15. $a = 8 + 3b - 2c \Rightarrow a - 3b + 2c = 8$ **(1)**
$$4a + 2b - 3c = 10 \text{ (2)}$$
$$c = 10 + b - 2a \Rightarrow 2a - b + c = 10 \text{ (3)}$$
Add $3 \cdot$ **(1)** and $2 \cdot$ **(2)**
$$3a - 9b + 6c = 24$$
$$\underline{8a + 4b - 6c = 20}$$
$$11a - 5b = 44 \quad \textbf{(4)}$$
Add **(2)** and $3 \cdot$ **(3)**
$$4a + 2b - 3c = 10$$
$$\underline{6a - 3b + 3c = 30}$$
$$10a - b = 40 \quad \textbf{(5)}$$
Add **(4)** and -5 times **(5)**
$$11a - 5b = 44$$
$$\underline{-50a + 5b = -200}$$
$$-39a = -156$$
$$a = 4$$
Substitute $a = 4$ into **(5)**
$$10(4) - b = 40$$
$$40 - b = 40$$
$$-b = 0$$
$$b = 0$$
Substitute $a = 4$, $b = 0$ into **(3)**
$$c = 10 + 0 - 2(4) = 2$$
$(4, \ 0, \ 2)$ is the solution.

17. Multiply all three equations by 10 to clear decimals.
$$2a + b + 2c = 1 \qquad \textbf{(1)}$$
$$3a + 2b + 4c = -1 \qquad \textbf{(2)}$$
$$6a + 11b + 2c = 3 \qquad \textbf{(3)}$$
Subtract **(3)** from **(1)**

$$-4a - 10b = -2$$
$$2a + 5b = 1 \qquad \textbf{(4)}$$
Add $-2 \cdot$ **(1)** and **(2)**
$$-a = -3$$
$$a = 3$$
Substitute $a = 3$ into **(4)**
$$2(3) + 5b = 1$$
$$6 + 5b = 1$$
$$5b = -5$$
$$b = -1$$
Substitute $a = 3$, $b = -2$ into **(1)**
$$2(3) + (-1) + 2c = 1$$
$$6 - 1 + 2c = 1$$
$$2c = -4$$
$$c = -2$$
$(3, -1, -2)$ is the solution.

19. When a calculator is used it is convenient to keep all three equations together as the operations are performed.

$$x - 4y + 4z = -3.72186$$
$$-x + 3y - z = 5.98115$$
$$2x - y + 5z = 7.93645$$

Now perform two operations on the system; first, add the first equation to the second and add -2 times the first to the third. Note that this *does not* change the first equation but the second and third.

$$x - 4y + 4z = -3.72186$$
$$-y + 3z = 2.25929$$
$$7y - 3z = 15.38017$$
Add the second equation to the third
$$x - 4y + 4z = -3.72186$$
$$-y + 3z = 2.25929$$
$$6y = 17.63946$$

87

© 2006 Pearson Education, Inc., Upper Saddle River, NJ. All rights reserved. This material is protected under all copyright laws as they currently exist. No portion of this material may be reproduced, in any form or by any means, without permission in writing from the publisher.

From the third equation $y = 2.93991$ which may be substituted into the second equation to give $z = 1.73307$. Substituting these values for x and y into the first equation gives $x = 1.10551$.
$(1.10551, 2.93991, 1.73307)$ is the solution.

21.
$$x + y = 1 \quad \textbf{(1)}$$
$$y - z = -3 \quad \textbf{(2)}$$
$$2x + 3y + z = 1 \quad \textbf{(3)}$$
Add **(2)** and **(3)**
$$2x + 4y = -2 \Rightarrow x + 2y = -1$$
$$-1 \cdot \textbf{(1)} \Rightarrow \quad \underline{-x - y = -1}$$
$$y = -2$$
Substitute $y = -2$ into **(1)**
$$x + y = 1$$
$$x - 2 = 1$$
$$x = 3$$
Substitute $y = -2$ into **(2)**
$$-2 - z = -3$$
$$-z = -1$$
$$z = 1$$
$(3, -2, 1)$ is the solution.

23.
$$-y + 2z = 1 \quad \textbf{(1)}$$
$$x + y + z = 2 \quad \textbf{(2)}$$
$$-x + 3z = 2 \quad \textbf{(3)}$$
Add **(2)** and **(3)**
$$y + 4z = 4 \quad \textbf{(4)}$$
Add **(1)** and **(4)**
$$6z = 5$$
Substitute $z = \dfrac{5}{6}$ into **(4)**

$$y + 4\left(\frac{5}{6}\right) = 4$$
$$6y + 20 = 24$$
$$6y = 4$$
$$y = \frac{2}{3}$$
Substitute $z = \dfrac{5}{6}$, $y = \dfrac{2}{3}$ into **(2)**
$$x + \frac{2}{3} + \frac{5}{6} = 2$$
$$x = \frac{1}{2}$$
$\left(\dfrac{1}{2}, \dfrac{2}{3}, \dfrac{5}{6}\right)$ is the solution.

25.
$$x - 2y + z = 0 \quad \textbf{(1)}$$
$$-3x - y = -6 \quad \textbf{(2)}$$
$$y - 2z = -7 \quad \textbf{(3)}$$
Multiply **(1)** by 2 and add to **(3)**
$$2x - 3y = -7 \quad \textbf{(4)}$$
Multiply **(2)** by -3 and add to **(4)**
$$11x = 11$$
$$x = 1$$
Substitute $x = 1$ into **(2)**
$$-3 - y = -6$$
$$y = 3$$
Substitute $x = 1$, $y = 3$ into **(1)**
$$1 - 6 + z = 0$$
$$z = 5$$
$(1, 3, 5)$ is the solution.

88

© 2006 Pearson Education, Inc., Upper Saddle River, NJ. All rights reserved. This material is protected under all copyright laws as they currently exist. No portion of this material may be reproduced, in any form or by any means, without permission in writing from the publisher.

27.

$$\frac{a}{2} - b + c = 8 \qquad \textbf{(1)}$$

$$\frac{3}{2}a + b + 2c = 0 \qquad \textbf{(2)}$$

$$a + c = 2 \qquad \textbf{(3)}$$

Add **(1)** and **(2)**

$$2a + 3c = 8 \qquad \textbf{(4)}$$

Subtract $3 \cdot$ **(3)** from **(4)**

$$-a = 2$$

$$a = -2$$

Substitute $a = -2$ into **(3)**

$$-2 + c = 2$$

$$c = 4$$

Substitute $a = -2,\ c = 4$ into **(1)**

$$\frac{-2}{2} - b + 4 = 8$$

$$-b = 5$$

$$b = -5$$

$(-2, -5, 4)$ is the solution.

29.

$$2x + y = -3 \qquad \textbf{(1)}$$

$$2y + 16z = -18 \qquad \textbf{(2)}$$

$$-7x - 3y + 4z = 6 \qquad \textbf{(3)}$$

Add **(2)** and $-4 \cdot$ **(3)**

$$2y + 16z = -18$$

$$\underline{28x + 12y - 16z = -24}$$

$28x + 14y \quad\quad = -42$ and dividing by 14

$2x + y = -3$ which is **(1)**

The system of equations is a dependent system and has an infinite number of solutions.

31.

$$3x + 3y - 3z = -1 \qquad \textbf{(1)}$$

$$4x + y - 2z = 1 \qquad \textbf{(2)}$$

$$-2x + 4y - 2z = -8 \qquad \textbf{(3)}$$

Subtract **(3)** from **(2)**

$$6x - 3y = 9 \qquad \textbf{(4)}$$

Multiply **(1)** by -2 and add to 3 times **(2)**

$$6x - 3y = 5 \qquad \textbf{(5)}$$

Comparing **(4)** and **(5)** gives $5 = 9$ which is false. This is an inconsistent system of equations and has no solution.

Cumulative Review Problems

33. $|3 - 2x| = 5$

$$3 - 2x = 5 \quad \text{or} \quad 3 - 2x = -5$$

$$-2x = 2 \qquad\qquad -2x = -8$$

$$x = -1 \qquad\qquad x = 4$$

35. $m = \dfrac{y_2 - y_1}{x_2 - x_1} = \dfrac{4 - 3}{1 - (-2)} = \dfrac{1}{3}$

$$y - y_1 = m(x - x_1)$$

$$y - 4 = \frac{1}{3}(x - 1)$$

$$3y - 12 = x - 1$$

$$x - 3y = -11$$

37. Let $c =$ the number of cattle purchased, $h =$ the number of horses purchased, and $s =$ the number of sheep purchased, then

$$c + 601 = 1.8(h + 346)$$

$$s + 545 = 1.74(h + 346)$$

where h can be any number. Let $h = 0$, which gives

$$c + 601 = 1.8(346) = 622.8$$

$$c = 21.8$$

$$s + 545 = 1.74(346) = 602.04$$

$$s = 57.04$$

The rancher should buy no horses, 22 cattle, and 57 sheep. After the purchase he will have 346 horses, 623 cattle and 602 sheep.

89

© 2006 Pearson Education, Inc., Upper Saddle River, NJ. All rights reserved. This material is protected under all copyright laws as they currently exist. No portion of this material may be reproduced, in any form or by any means, without permission in writing from the publisher.

How Am I Doing? Sections 4.1-4.2

1. $4x - y = -1$ **(1)**

$3x + 2y = 13$ **(2)**

Solve **(1)** for y and substitute into **(2)**

$$4x - y = -1$$
$$-y = -1 - 4x$$
$$y = 1 + 4x$$
$$3x + 2(1 + 4x) = 13$$
$$3x + 2 + 8x = 13$$
$$11x = 11$$
$$x = 1$$

Substitute $x = 1$ into **(2)**

$$3(1) + 2y = 13$$
$$2y = 10$$
$$y = 5$$

$(1, 5)$ is the solution.

2. $3x + 2y = 9$ **(1)**

$5x + 4y = 13$ **(2)**

Add -2 times **(1)** to **(2)**

$$-6x - 4y = -18$$
$$\underline{5x + 4y = 13}$$
$$-x \qquad = -5$$
$$x = 5$$

Substitute $x = 5$ into **(1)**

$$3(5) + 2y = 9$$
$$15 + 2y = 9$$
$$2y = -6$$
$$y = -3$$

$(5, -3)$ is the solution.

3. $5x - 2y = 27$ **(1)**

$3x - 5y = -18$ **(2)**

Multiply **(1)** by 5, and **(2)** by -2 and add

$$25x - 10y = 135$$
$$\underline{-6x + 10y = 36}$$
$$19x = 171$$
$$x = 9$$

Substitute $x = 9$ into **(1)**

$$5(9) - 2y = 27$$
$$45 - 2y = 27$$
$$2y = 18$$
$$y = 9$$

The solution is $(9, 9)$.

4. $7x + 3y = 15$ **(1)**

$\dfrac{1}{3}x - \dfrac{1}{2}y = 2$ **(2)**

Multiply **(2)** by 6 to clear fractions

$$2x - 3y = 12 \qquad \textbf{(3)}$$

Add **(1)** and **(3)**

$$7x + 3y = 15$$
$$\underline{2x - 3y = 12}$$
$$9x = 27$$
$$x = 3$$

Substitute $x = 3$ into **(1)**

$$7(3) + 3y = 15$$
$$3y = -6$$
$$y = -2$$

The solution is $(3, -2)$.

5. $2x = 3 + y$ **(1)**

$3y = 6x - 9$ **(2)**

Solve **(1)** for y

$$y = 2x - 3 \text{ and substitute into } \textbf{(2)}$$
$$3(2x - 3) = 6x - 9$$
$$6x - 9 = 6x - 9$$
$$0 = 0$$

© 2006 Pearson Education, Inc., Upper Saddle River, NJ. All rights reserved. This material is protected under all copyright laws as they currently exist. No portion of this material may be reproduced, in any form or by any means, without permission in writing from the publisher.

The equations are dependent and the system has an infinite number of solutions.

6. Multiply both equations by 10 to clear decimals

$$2x + 7y = -10 \qquad \textbf{(1)}$$
$$5x + 6y = -2 \qquad \textbf{(2)}$$

Multiply **(1)** by 5 and **(2)** by -2 and add

$$10x + 35y = -50$$
$$\underline{-10x - 12y = 4}$$
$$23y = -46$$
$$y = -2$$

Substitute $y = -2$ into **(1)**

$$2x + 7(-2) = -10$$
$$2x - 14 = -10$$
$$2x = 4$$
$$x = 2$$

The solution is $(2, -2)$.

7. $\quad 6x - 9y = 15 \quad \textbf{(1)}$
$\quad\;\; -4x + 6y = 8 \quad \textbf{(2)}$

Add 2 times **(1)** to 3 times **(2)**

$$12x - 18y = 30$$
$$\underline{-12x + 18y = 54}$$
$$0 = 84$$

This is an inconsistent system with no solution. The lines are parallel.

8. $3x + 2y - 5z = -22$

$$3(-1) + 2(-2) - 5(3) \overset{?}{=} -22, \; -22 = -22$$
$$2x + 3y - 2z = 13$$

$$2(-1) + 3(-2) - 2(3) \overset{?}{=} 13, \;\; 13 = 13$$
$$x + y + 2z = 6$$

$$-1 + (-2) + 2(3) \overset{?}{=} 6, \;\; 3 \neq 6$$
$$(-1, -2, 3) \text{ is not a solution.}$$

9. $5x - 2y + z = -1 \qquad \textbf{(1)}$
$\quad\;\; 3x + y - 2z = 6 \qquad \textbf{(2)}$
$\quad\;\; -2x + 3y - 5z = 7 \qquad \textbf{(3)}$

Multiply **(1)** by 2 and add to **(2)**

$$10x - 4y + 2z = -2$$
$$\underline{3x + y - 2z = 6}$$
$$13x - 3y = 4 \qquad \textbf{(4)}$$

Multiply **(1)** by 5 and add to **(3)**

$$25x - 10y + 5z = -5$$
$$\underline{-2x + 3y - 5z = 7}$$
$$23x - 7y = 2 \qquad \textbf{(5)}$$

Multiply **(4)** by 7 and **(5)** by -3 and add

$$91x - 21y = 28$$
$$\underline{-69x + 21y = -6}$$
$$22x = 22$$
$$x = 1$$

Substitute $x = 1$ into **(5)**

$$23(1) - 7y = 2$$
$$7y = 21$$
$$y = 3$$

Substitute $x = 1$, $y = 3$ into **(1)**

$$5(1) - 2(3) + z = -1$$
$$5 - 6 + z = -1$$
$$z = 0$$

The solution is $(1, 3, 0)$.

10. $\quad 2x - y + 3z = -1 \qquad \textbf{(1)}$
$\quad\;\;\;\; 5x + y + 6z = 0 \qquad \textbf{(2)}$
$\quad\;\;\;\; 2x - 2y + 3z = -2 \qquad \textbf{(3)}$

Add **(1)** and **(2)**

$$2x - y + 3z = -1$$
$$\underline{5x + y + 6z = 0}$$
$$7x \quad\;\; + 9z = -1 \quad \textbf{(4)}$$

© 2006 Pearson Education, Inc., Upper Saddle River, NJ. All rights reserved. This material is protected under all copyright laws as they currently exist. No portion of this material may be reproduced, in any form or by any means, without permission in writing from the publisher.

Add 2 times **(2)** to **(3)**

$$10x + 2y + 12z = 0$$
$$\underline{2x - 2y + 3z = -2}$$
$$12x + 15y = -2 \quad \textbf{(5)}$$

Add 5 times **(4)** to -3 times **(5)**

$$35x + 45z = -5$$
$$\underline{-36x - 45z = 6}$$
$$-x = 1$$
$$x = -1$$

Substitute $x = -1$ into **(4)**

$$7(-1) + 9z = -1$$
$$9z = 6$$
$$z = \frac{2}{3}$$

Substitute $x = -1$, $z = \frac{2}{3}$ into **(2)**

$$5(-1) + y + 6\left(\frac{2}{3}\right) = 0$$
$$-5 + y + 4 = 0$$
$$y - 1 = 0$$
$$y = 1$$

$\left(-1, 1, \frac{2}{3}\right)$ is the solution.

11. $\quad x + y + 2z = 9 \qquad\qquad$ **(1)**
$\qquad 3x + 2y + 4z = 16 \qquad$ **(2)**
$\qquad\qquad 2y + z = 10 \qquad\qquad$ **(3)**

Solve **(3)** for z and substitute into **(1)** and **(2)**

$$z = 10 - y$$
$$x + y + 2(10 - 2y) = 9$$
$$x + y + 20 - 4y = 9$$
$$x - 3y = -11 \qquad \textbf{(4)}$$
$$3x + 2y + 4(10 - 2y) = 16$$
$$3x + 2y + 40 - 8y = 16$$
$$3x - 6y = -24 \qquad \textbf{(5)}$$

Multiply (4) by -2 and (5) and add to **(5)**

$$-2x + 6y = 22$$
$$\underline{3x + 6y = -24}$$
$$x = -2$$

Substitute $x = -2$ into **(5)**

$$3(-2) - 6y = -24$$
$$-6y = -18$$
$$y = 3$$

Substitute $x = -2$, $y = 3$ into **(1)**

$$-2 + 3 + 2z = 9$$
$$2z = 8$$
$$z = 4$$

The solution is $(-2, 3, 4)$.

12. $\quad x - 2z = -5 \qquad\qquad$ **(1)**
$\qquad\qquad y - 3z = -3 \qquad\qquad$ **(2)**
$\qquad 2x - z = -4 \qquad\qquad$ **(3)**

Solve **(3)** for z and substitute into **(1)**

$$z = 2x + 4$$
$$x - 2(2x + 4) = -5$$
$$x - 4x - 8 = -5$$
$$-3x = 3$$
$$x = -1$$

Substitute $x = -1$ into **(3)**

$$2(-1) - z = -4$$
$$-z = -2$$
$$z = 2$$

Substitute $z = 2$ into **(2)**

$$y - 3(2) = -3$$
$$y - 6 = -3$$
$$y = 3$$

The solution is $(-1, 3, 2)$.

© 2006 Pearson Education, Inc., Upper Saddle River, NJ. All rights reserved. This material is protected under all copyright laws as they currently exist. No portion of this material may be reproduced, in any form or by any means, without permission in writing from the publisher.

4.3 Exercises

1. Let $x =$ the smaller number
   and $y =$ the larger number
   $x + y = 87 \Rightarrow y = 87 - x$
   $y - 2x = 12 \Rightarrow 87 - x - 2x = 12$
   $87 - 3x = 12$
   $-3x = -75$
   $x = 25$, the smaller number
   $y = 87 - 25 = 62$, the larger number

3. Let $x =$ number of heavy equipment
   operators and $y =$ number of laborers.
   $x + y = 35 \Rightarrow y = 35 - x$
   $140x + 90y = 3950$
   $140x + 90(35 - x) = 3950$
   $140x + 3150 - 90x = 3950$
   $50x = 800$
   $x = 16$
   $y = 35 - x = 35 - 16 = 19$
   16 heavy equipment operators and 19
   laborers were employed.

5. $x =$ number of tickets for regular coach
   seats
   $y =$ number of tickets for sleeper car
   seats
   $x + y = 98$ **(1)**
   $120x + 290y = 19,750$ **(2)**
   Solve **(1)** for y and substitute into **(2)**.
   $y = 98 - x$
   $120x + 290(98 - x) = 19,750$
   $120x + 28,420 - 290x = 19,750$
   $-170x = -8670$
   $x = 51$
   Substitute 51 for x in **(1)**

$51 + y = 98$
$y = 47$
Number of coach tickets = 51
Number of sleeper tickets = 47

7. $x =$ number of experienced managers
   $y =$ number of newly hired managers
   $2x + 5y = 140 \xrightarrow{\times 3} 6x + 15y = 420$
   $3x + 8y = 215 \xrightarrow{\times -2} \underline{-6x - 16y = -430}$
   $ -y = -10$
   $ y = 10$
   $2x + 5(10) = 140$
   $2x + 50 = 140$
   $2x = 90$
   $x = 45$
   The company should train 45 experienced
   managers and 10 newly hired managers.

9. $x =$ number of packages of old fertilizer
   $y =$ number of packages of new fertilizer
   $50x + 65y = 3125 \xrightarrow{\times 6} 300x + 390y = 18,750$
   $60x + 45y = 2925 \xrightarrow{\times -5} -300x - 225y = -14,625$
   $ 165y = 4125$
   $y = 25$ new packages
   $50x + 65(25) = 3125$
   $50x + 1625 = 3125$
   $50x = 1500$
   $x = 30$ old packages

11. $x =$ cost of one doughnut
    $y =$ cost of one large coffee
    $3x + 4y = 4.91$ **(1)**
    $5x + 6y = 7.59$ **(2)**
    Multiply **(1)** by 5 and add to -3 times **(2)**

93

© 2006 Pearson Education, Inc., Upper Saddle River, NJ. All rights reserved. This material is protected under all copyright laws as they currently exist.
No portion of this material may be reproduced, in any form or by any means, without permission in writing from the publisher.

$$15x + 20y = 24.55$$
$$-15x - 18y = -22.77$$
$$\overline{\ 2y = 1.78}$$
$$y = 0.89$$

Substitute 0.89 for y in **(1)** and solve for x
$$3x + 4(0.89) = 4.91$$
$$3x = 1.35$$
$$x = 0.45$$

The cost of one doughnut is $0.45.
The cost of one large coffee is $0.89.

13. $x =$ speed of plane in still air
      $y =$ speed of wind

$$(x - y)\left(\frac{7}{6}\right) \cdot \frac{6}{7} = 210 \cdot \frac{6}{7}$$

$$(x + y)\left(\frac{5}{6}\right) \cdot \frac{6}{5} = 210 \cdot \frac{6}{5}$$

$$x - y = 180$$
$$\underline{x + y = 252}$$
$$2x \qquad = 432$$
$$x = 216$$

$$y = 252 - x = 36$$

plane: 216 mph; wind:36 mph

15. $x =$ speed in still water
      $y =$ speed of current

$$(x - y) \cdot \frac{2}{3} = 8 \Rightarrow x = y + 12$$

$$(x + y) \cdot \frac{1}{2} = 8 \Rightarrow (y + 12 + y) \cdot \frac{1}{2} = 8$$

$$2y + 12 = 16 \Rightarrow 2y = 4$$

$$y = 2 \text{ mph, speed of current}$$

$$x = y + 12 = 14 \text{ mph, speed of boat}$$

17. $x =$ number of free throws
      $y =$ number of regular shots
$$x + y = 21 \rightarrow \qquad x + y = 21$$
$$x + 2y = 32 \xrightarrow{\times(-1)} \underline{-x - 2y = -32}$$
$$-y = -11$$
$$y = 11 \text{ regular shots}$$

$$x + 11 = 21$$
$$x = 21 - 11$$
$$x = 10 \text{ free throws}$$

19. $x =$ weekend minutes
      $y =$ weekday minutes
$$x + y = 625 \Rightarrow y = 625 - x$$
$$0.05x + 0.08y = 43.40$$
$$0.05x + 0.08(625 - x) = 43.4$$
$$-0.03x = -6.6 \Rightarrow x = 220$$
$$y = 625 - x = 405$$

Nick talked 405 minutes on the weekdays
and 220 minutes on weekends.

21. $x =$ cost of truck, $y =$ cost of car
$$256x + 183y = 5,791,948$$
$$64x + 107y = 2,507,612 \xrightarrow{\times(-4)}$$
$$-256x - 428y = -10,030,448$$
$$\underline{256x + 183y = 5,791,948}$$
$$-245y = -4,238,500$$
$$y = \$17,300 \text{ for cars}$$
$$64x + 107(17,300) = 2,507,612$$
$$64x + 1,851,100 = 2,507,612$$
$$64x = 656,512$$
$$x = \$10,258 \text{ for trucks}$$

© 2006 Pearson Education, Inc., Upper Saddle River, NJ. All rights reserved. This material is protected under all copyright laws as they currently exist. No portion of this material may be reproduced, in any form or by any means, without permission in writing from the publisher.

23. $x =$ number of pens

$y =$ number of notebooks

$z =$ number of highlighters

$$x + y + z = 12 \qquad \textbf{(1)}$$
$$1.2x + 3y + 0.9z = 20.70 \qquad \textbf{(2)}$$
$$x = z + 2 \qquad \textbf{(3)}$$

$\textbf{(1)} \ y = 12 - z - x = 12 - z - (z + 2)$

$y = 10 - 2z$

$\textbf{(2)} \ 1.2(z + 2) + 3(10 - 2z) + 0.9z = 20.70$

$-3.9z = -11.7 \Rightarrow z = 3$ highlighters

$x = z + 2 = 5$ pens

$y = 10 - 2z = 4$ notebooks

25. $x =$ number of adults

$y =$ number of high school students

$z =$ number of children

$$5x + 3y + 2z = 1010 \qquad \textbf{(1)}$$
$$7x + 4y + 3z = 1390 \qquad \textbf{(2)}$$
$$x + y + z = 300 \qquad \textbf{(3)}$$

Multiply -7 times **(3)** and add to **(2)**

$-3y - 4z = -710, \ 3y + 4z = 710 \ \textbf{(4)}$

Multiply -5 times **(3)** and add to **(1)**

$-2y - 3z = -490, \ 2y + 3z = 490 \ \textbf{(5)}$

Add $2 \cdot \textbf{(4)}$ and $-3 \cdot \textbf{(5)}$

$-z = -50$

$z = 50$

Substitute $z = 50$ into **(5)**

$2y + 3(50) = 490$

$2y = 340$

$y = 170$

Substitute $y = 170, z = 50$ into $\qquad \textbf{(3)}$

$x + 170 + 50 = 300$

$x = 80$

The number of adults attending was 80, the number of high school students was 170, and the number of children was 50.

27. $x =$ number of children under 12

$y =$ number of adults

$z =$ number of senior citizens

$$x + y + z = 12,000 \qquad \textbf{(1)}$$
$$0.25x + y + 0.5z = 10,700 \qquad \textbf{(2)}$$
$$0.35x + 1.5y + 0.5z = 15,820 \qquad \textbf{(3)}$$

Add -0.25 times **(1)** to **(2)**

$-0.25x - 0.25y - 0.25z = -3000$

$\underline{0.25x + y + 0.5z = 10,700}$

$0.75y + 0.25z = 7700 \qquad \textbf{(4)}$

Add -0.35 times **(1)** to **(3)**

$-0.35x - 0.35y - 0.35z = -4200$

$\underline{0.35x + 1.5y + 0.5z = 15,820}$

$0.75y + 0.25z = 7700 \qquad \textbf{(5)}$

Add -1.15 times **(4)** to 0.75 times **(5)**

$-.08626y - 0.2875z = -8855$

$\underline{0.8625y + 0.1125z = 8715}$

$-0.175z = -140$

$z = 800$

Substitute 800 for z in **(1)**

$x + y = 11,200 \qquad \textbf{(6)}$

Add -1 times **(3)** to **(2)**

$0.25x + y + 0.5z = 10,700$

$\underline{-0.35x - 1.5y - 0.5z = -15,820}$

$-0.1x - 0.5y = -5120 \qquad \textbf{(7)}$

Add 0.5 times **(6)** to **(7)**

$0.5x + 0.5y = 5600$

$\underline{-0.1x - 0.5y = -5120}$

$0.4x = 480$

$x = 1200$

Substitute 1200 for x in **(6)**

$1200 + y = 11,200$

$y = 10,000$

12,000 children, 10,000 adults, and 800 senior citizens normally ride.

© 2006 Pearson Education, Inc., Upper Saddle River, NJ. All rights reserved. This material is protected under all copyright laws as they currently exist. No portion of this material may be reproduced, in any form or by any means, without permission in writing from the publisher.

29. $x =$ number of small pizzas

$y =$ number of medium pizzas

$z =$ number of large pizzas

$$x + y + z = 20$$
$$3x + 4y + 5z = 82$$
$$5x + 9y + 12z = 181$$

Add -3 times first equation and -5 times first equation to third equation

$$x + y + z = 20$$
$$y + 2z = 22$$
$$4y + 7z = 81$$

Add -4 times second equation to third equation

$$x + y + z = 20$$
$$y + 2z = 22$$
$$-z = -7$$

$z = 7$ large pizzas

$y + 2z = 22,\ y + 2(7) = 22$

$y = 8$ medium pizzas

$x + 8 + 7 = 20$

$x = 5$ small pizzas

31. $x =$ number of Box A

$y =$ number of Box B

$z =$ number of Box C

$$10x + 5y + 4z = 51 \qquad \textbf{(1)}$$
$$3x + 2y + z = 16 \qquad \textbf{(2)}$$
$$3x + 3y + 2z = 23 \qquad \textbf{(3)}$$

Add **(1)** and $-4 \cdot$ **(2)**

$$10x + 5y + 4z = 51$$
$$\underline{-12x - 8y - 4z = -64}$$
$$-2x - 3y \quad\ = -13 \Rightarrow 2x + 3y = 13 \ \ \textbf{(4)}$$

Add (1) and $-2 \cdot$ **(3)**

$$10x + 5y + 4z = 51$$
$$\underline{-6x - 6y - 4z = -46}$$
$$4x - y \quad\ = 5 \qquad \textbf{(5)}$$

Add (4) and $3 \cdot$ **(5)**

$$2x + 3y = 13$$
$$\underline{12x - 3y = 15}$$
$$14x \quad\ = 28$$

$x = 2$ of the A boxes

Substitute $x = 2$ in **(5)**

$$4(2) - y = 5$$
$$8 - y = 5 \Rightarrow -y = 5 - 8 = -3$$

$y = 3$ of the B boxes

Substitute $x = 2,\ y = 3$ in **(2)**

$$3(2) + 2(3) + z = 16$$
$$6 + 6 + z = 16 \Rightarrow 12 + z = 16$$
$$z = 16 - 12$$
$$z = 4$ of the C boxes$$

33. $x =$ measure of first angle

$y =$ measure of second angle

$z =$ measure of second angle

$$x + y + z = 180$$
$$x + y = \frac{1}{2}z$$
$$8x = y + z$$

Clear fractions and write variables on LHS

$$x + y + z = 180 \qquad \textbf{(1)}$$
$$2x + 2y - z = 0 \qquad \textbf{(2)}$$
$$8x - y - z = 0 \qquad \textbf{(3)}$$

Add **(1)** and **(2)**

$3x + 3y = 180$ and dividing by 3

$$x + y = 60 \qquad \textbf{(4)}$$

Add **(1)** and **(3)**

$$9x = 180 \Rightarrow x = 20$$

Substitute $x = 20$ into **(4)**

$$20 + y = 60 \Rightarrow y = 40$$

Substitute $x = 20,\ y = 40$ into **(1)**

$$20 + 40 + z = 180,\ z = 120$$

The angles are $20°,\ 40°,\ 120°$.

© 2006 Pearson Education, Inc., Upper Saddle River, NJ. All rights reserved. This material is protected under all copyright laws as they currently exist. No portion of this material may be reproduced, in any form or by any means, without permission in writing from the publisher.

35. x, y, z, q = number of A, B, C, and D packages respectively

$$
\begin{array}{rrrrr}
42x & +20y & +0z & +10q & =134 \\
20x & +10y & +20z & +0q & =150 \\
34x & +0y & +10z & +20q & =178 \\
50x & +35y & +30z & +40q & =405
\end{array}
$$

Add $-\dfrac{20}{42}\times$ first eqn. to second eqn.

Add $-\dfrac{30}{42}\times$ first eqn. to third eqn.

Add $-\dfrac{50}{42}\times$ first eqn. to fourth eqn.

$$
\begin{array}{rrrrr}
42x & +20y & +0z & +10q & =134 \\
0x & +\dfrac{10}{21}y & +20z & -\dfrac{100}{21}q & =\dfrac{1810}{21} \\
0x & -\dfrac{340}{21}y & +10z & +\dfrac{250}{21}q & =\dfrac{1460}{21} \\
0x & +\dfrac{235}{21}y & +30z & +\dfrac{590}{21}q & =\dfrac{5155}{21}
\end{array}
$$

Add $34\times$ second eqn. to third eqn.
Add $-23.5\times$ second eqn. to fourth eqn.

$$
\begin{array}{rrrrr}
42x & +20y & +0z & +10q & =134 \\
0x & +\dfrac{10}{21}y & +20z & -\dfrac{100}{21}q & =\dfrac{1810}{21} \\
0x & +0y & +690z & -150q & =3000 \\
0x & +0y & -440z & +140q & =-1780
\end{array}
$$

Add $\dfrac{44}{69}\times$ third eqn. to fourth eqn.

$$
\begin{array}{rrrrr}
42x & +20y & +0z & +10q & =134 \\
0x & +\dfrac{10}{21}y & +20z & -\dfrac{100}{21}q & =\dfrac{1810}{21} \\
0x & +0y & +690z & -150q & =3000 \\
0x & +0y & +0z & +\dfrac{1023}{23}q & =\dfrac{3060}{23}
\end{array}
$$

$$\dfrac{1020}{23}q = \dfrac{3060}{23},\ q = 3$$

Substitute $q = 3$ into third equation
$$690z - 150(3) = 3000,\ z = 5$$
Substitute $z = 5$, $q = 3$ into second eqn
$$\dfrac{10}{21}y + 20(5) - \dfrac{10}{21}(3) = \dfrac{1810}{21},\ y = 1$$
Substitute $y = 1$, $z = 5$, $q = 3$ into the first equation
$$42x + 20(5) + 0(5) + 10(3) = 134$$
$$x = 2$$
The scientist should use 2 A packages, 1 B package, 5 C packages, and 3 D packages.

Cumulative Review

37. $0.06x + 0.15(0.5 - x) = 0.04$
$0.06x + 0.075 - 0.15x = 0.04$

$-0.09x = -0.035 \Rightarrow x = \dfrac{-0.035}{-0.09} = \dfrac{35}{90}$

$x = \dfrac{7(5)}{18(5)} = \dfrac{7}{18}$

39. $6a(2x - 3y) = 7ax - 3$
$12ax - 18ay = 7ax - 3$

$5ax = 18ay - 3 \Rightarrow x = \dfrac{18ay - 3}{5a}$

4.4 Exercises

1. In the graph of the system $y > 3x + 1$, $y < -2x + 5$ the boundary lines should be dashed because they are not included in the solution.

3. Test the point in both regions.
$y < -2x + 3$, $-4 < -2(3) + 3 = -3$, True
$y > 5x - 3$, $-4 > 5(3) - 3 = 12$, False
The point $(3, -4)$ does not lie in the solution region.

© 2006 Pearson Education, Inc., Upper Saddle River, NJ. All rights reserved. This material is protected under all copyright laws as they currently exist. No portion of this material may be reproduced, in any form or by any means, without permission in writing from the publisher.

5. $y \geq 2x - 1$

Test point: $(0,0)$

$0 \geq 2(0) - 1$

$0 \geq -1$ True

$x + y \leq 6$

Test point: $(0,0)$

$0 + 0 \leq 6$

$0 \leq 6$ True

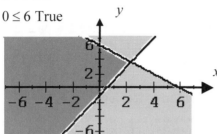

7. $y \geq -4x$

Test Point: $(0,2)$

$2 \geq -4(0)$

$2 \geq 0$ True

$y \geq 3x - 2$

Test point: $(0,0)$

$0 \geq 3(0) - 2$

$0 \geq -2$ True

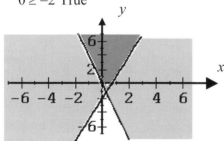

9. $y \geq 2x - 3$, Test point: $(0,0)$

$0 \geq 2(0) - 3 \Rightarrow 0 \geq -3$ True

$y \leq \dfrac{2}{3}x$, Test point: $(0,2)$

$2 \leq \dfrac{2}{3}(0) \Rightarrow 2 \leq 0$ False

9.

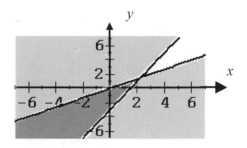

11. $x - y \geq -1$

Test point: $(0,0) \Rightarrow 0 - 0 \geq -1$

$0 \geq -1$ True

$-3x - y \leq 4$, Test point: $(0,0)$

$-3(0) - 0 \leq 4 \Rightarrow 0 \leq 4$ True

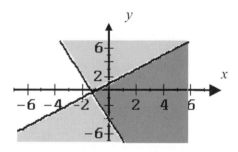

13. $x + 2y < 6$

Test point: $(0,0)$

$0 + 2(0) < 6$

$0 < 6$ True

$y < 3$

Test point: $(0,0)$

$0 < 3$ True

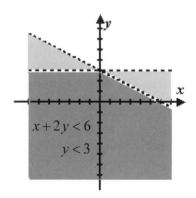

98

© 2006 Pearson Education, Inc., Upper Saddle River, NJ. All rights reserved. This material is protected under all copyright laws as they currently exist. No portion of this material may be reproduced, in any form or by any means, without permission in writing from the publisher.

15. $y < 4,\ x > -2$

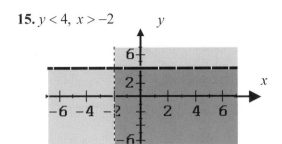

17. $x - 4y \geq -4$

Test point: $(0,0)$

$0 - 4(0) \geq -4$

$0 \geq -4$ True

$3x + y \leq 3$

Test point: $(0,0)$

$3(0) + 0 \leq 3$

$0 \leq 3$ True

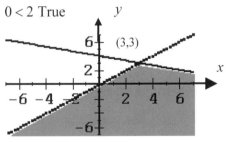

19. $3x + 2y < 6$

Test point: $(0,0)$

$3(0) + 2(0) < 6$

$0 < 6$ True

$3x + 2y > -6$

Test point: $(0,0)$

$3(0) + 2(0) > -6$

$0 > -6$ True

21. $x + y \leq 5$

Test point: $(0,0)$

$0 + 0 \leq 5$

$0 \leq 5$ True

$2x - y \geq 1$

Test point: $(0,0)$

$2(0) - 0 \geq 1$

$0 \geq 1$ False

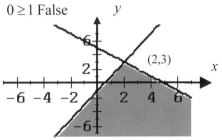

23. $x + 3y \leq 12$

Test point: $(0,0)$

$0 + 3(0) \leq 12$

$0 \leq 12$ True

$y < x$

Test point: $(2,0)$

$0 < 2$ True

25. $x + y \geq 1$

Test point: $(0,0)$

$0 + 0 \geq 1$

$0 \geq 1$ False

$x - y \geq 1$

99

© 2006 Pearson Education, Inc., Upper Saddle River, NJ. All rights reserved. This material is protected under all copyright laws as they currently exist.
No portion of this material may be reproduced, in any form or by any means, without permission in writing from the publisher.

25. Test point: (0,0)

$0 - 0 \geq 1$

$0 \geq 1$ False

$x \geq 3$

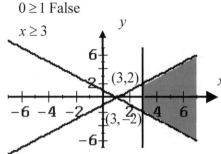

27. $y \leq 3x + 6$

Test point: $(0,0) \Rightarrow 0 \leq 3(0) + 6$

$0 \leq 6$ True

$4x + 3y \leq 3$

Test point: $(0,0) \Rightarrow 4(0) + 3(0) \leq 3$

$0 \leq 3$ True

$x \geq -2, \ y \geq -3$

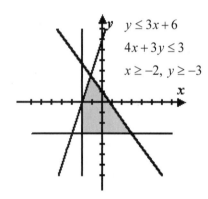

$y \leq 3x + 6$

$4x + 3y \leq 3$

$x \geq -2, \ y \geq -3$

29. (a)

$N \leq 2D$, Test point: (2,2)

$2 \leq 2(2) \Rightarrow 2 \leq 4$ True

$4N + 3D \leq 20$, Test point: (2,2)

$4(2) + 3(2) \leq 20 \Rightarrow 8 + 6 \leq 20$

$14 \leq 20$, True

$N \geq 0, \ D \geq 0$

29.

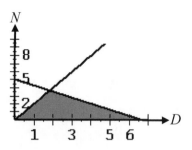

(b) Yes, (3,2) is in the shaded region.

(c) No, (1,4) is not in the shaded region.

Cumulative Review

31. $m = \dfrac{y_2 - y_1}{x_2 - x_1} = \dfrac{-4 - (-2)}{3 - (-1)} = -\dfrac{1}{2}$

33. $-3x^2 y - x^2 + 5y^2$

$= -3(2)^2(-1) - (2)^2 + 5(-1)^2$

$= 13$

35. $x = $ money taken in or rainy day

$y = $ money taken in on sunny day

$2x + 5y = 23,400 \Rightarrow y = \dfrac{23,400 - 2x}{5}$

$4x + 3y = 25,800$

$4x + 3\left(\dfrac{23,400 - 2x}{5}\right) = 25,800$

$20x + 70,200 - 6x = 129,000$

$14x = 58,800$

$x = 4200$

$y = \dfrac{23,400 - 2x}{5} = \dfrac{23,400 - 2(4200)}{5}$

$y = 3000$

The Cape Cod Cinema takes in $4200 on a rainy day and $3000 on a sunny day.

100

© 2006 Pearson Education, Inc., Upper Saddle River, NJ. All rights reserved. This material is protected under all copyright laws as they currently exist. No portion of this material may be reproduced, in any form or by any means, without permission in writing from the publisher.

37. $x = $ sales, $y = $ number of weeks

Hector: $0.05x + 200y = 7400$

$$y = \frac{7400 - 0.05x}{200}$$

Fernando: $0.08x + 100y = 9200$

$$0.08x + 100\frac{7400 - 0.05x}{200} = 9200$$

$$16x + 740,000 - 5x = 1,840,000$$

$$11x = 1,100,000$$

$$x = 100,000$$

$$y = \frac{7400 - 0.05x}{200}$$

$$y = \frac{7400 - 0.05(100,000)}{200} = 12$$

They had each worked 12 weeks and had $100,000 in sales.

Putting Your Skills to Work

1. Plan A: $C = 20 + 0.52x$
    Plan B: $C = 30 + 0.40x$

2.

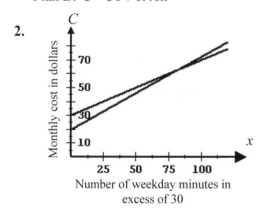

Number of weekday minutes in excess of 30

The equations appear to intersect at an x value of 83 which represents 113 minutes of weekday cell phone use per month.

3. $C = 20 + 0.52x$

$$C = 30 + 0.40x$$

$$20 + 0.52x = 30 + 0.40x$$

$$0.12x = 10$$

$$x = 83.\overline{3}$$

The answers are approximately equal.

4. For Gina with no excess minutes Plan A would be $20 and Plan B would be $30 so Plan A is more economical for Gina. For Aaron with 2 weekday hours each month or 120 weekday minutes per month Plan A would be $20 + 0.52(120 - 30) = \$66.8$ and Plan B would be $30 + 0.40(120 - 30) = \$66$ so Plan B is more economical for Aaron.

5. Using 10 weekday hours per month or 600 weekday minutes per month Aaron's bill with Plan B would be
$$C = 30 + 0.40(600 - 30)$$
$$C = \$258$$

6. Since Aaron's estimated phone usage of 120 weekday minutes per month is less than the number of free minutes in each plan, Plan C would be $40 and Plan D would be $45 with Plan C being the cheaper.

7. If Aaron uses 8 weekday hours per month or 480 weekday minutes per month his monthly bill would be
Plan A: $20 + 0.52(480 - 30) = \$254$
Plan B: $30 + 0.40(480 - 30) = \$180.30$
Plan C: $40 + 0.30(480 - 30) = \$175$
Plan D: $45 since 480 weekday minutes per month is less than the free 600 weekday minutes per month. Plan D is now cheaper.

101

© 2006 Pearson Education, Inc., Upper Saddle River, NJ. All rights reserved. This material is protected under all copyright laws as they currently exist. No portion of this material may be reproduced, in any form or by any means, without permission in writing from the publisher.

Chapter 4 Review Problems

1. $x + 2y = 8$
   $x - y = 2$

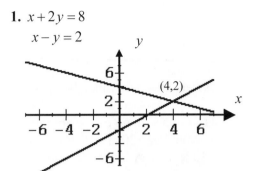

The solution is $(4,2)$

2. $x + y = 2$
   $3x - y = 6$

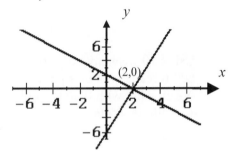

The solution is $(2,0)$.

3. $2x + y = 6$
   $3x + 4y = 4$

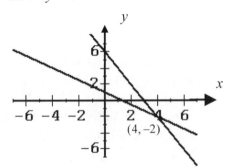

The solution is $(4,-2)$.

4. $3x - 2y = -9,\ y = \dfrac{9+3x}{2}$

$$2x + y = 1$$

$$2x + \frac{9+3x}{2} = 1$$

$$4x + 9 + 3x = 2$$

$$7x = -7$$

$$x = -1$$

$$y = \frac{9+3x}{2}$$

$$y = \frac{9+3(-1)}{2}$$

$$y = 3$$

The solution is $(-1,3)$.

5. $-6x - y = 1,\ y = -6x - 1$

$$3x - 4y = 31$$

$$3x - 4(-6x - 1) = 31$$

$$3x + 24x + 4 = 31$$

$$27x = 27$$

$$x = 1$$

$$y = -6x - 1$$

$$y = -6(1) - 1$$

$$y = -7$$

The solution is $(1,-7)$.

6. $4x - 3y = 15,\ y = \dfrac{4x-15}{3}$

$$7x - y = 5$$

$$7x - \frac{4x-15}{3} = 5$$

$$21x - 4x + 15 = 15$$

$$17x = 0,\ x = 0$$

$$y = \frac{4x-15}{3} = \frac{4(0)-15}{3} = -5$$

The solution is $(0,-5)$.

102

© 2006 Pearson Education, Inc., Upper Saddle River, NJ. All rights reserved. This material is protected under all copyright laws as they currently exist. No portion of this material may be reproduced, in any form or by any means, without permission in writing from the publisher.

7. $-7x + y = -4, \; y = 7x - 4$

$5x + 2y = 11$

$5x + 2(7x - 4) = 11$

$5x + 14x - 8 = 11$

$19x = 19$

$x = 1$

$y = 7x - 4 = 7(1) - 4 = 3$

The solution is $(1, 3)$.

8. $-2x + 5y = -12, \; -6x + 15y = -36$

$3x + y = 1, \qquad \underline{6x + 2y = 2}$

$\qquad\qquad\qquad\qquad 17y = -34$

$\qquad\qquad\qquad\qquad\quad y = -2$

$3x + y = 1$

$3x - 2 = 1$

$3x = 3$

$x = 1$

The solution is $(1, -2)$.

9. $-3x + 4y = 9, \; -15x + 20y = 45$

$5x + 3y = -15, \; \underline{15x + 9y = -45}$

$\qquad\qquad\qquad\qquad 29y = 0$

$\qquad\qquad\qquad\qquad\; y = 0$

$-3x + 4y = 9$

$-3x + 4(0) = 9$

$-3x = 9$

$x = -3$

The solution is $(-3, 0)$.

10. $7x - 4y = 2, \qquad -35x + 20y = -10$

$6x - 5y = -3, \qquad \underline{24x - 20y = -12}$

$\qquad\qquad\qquad\qquad -11x = -22$

$\qquad\qquad\qquad\qquad\quad x = 2$

$6x - 5y = -3$

$6(2) - 5y = -3$

$-5y = -15$

$y = 3$

The solution is $(2, 3)$.

11. $5x + 2y = 3, \qquad 35x + 14y = 21$

$7x + 5y = -20, \quad \underline{-35x - 25y = 100}$

$\qquad\qquad\qquad\qquad\qquad -11y = 121$

$\qquad\qquad\qquad\qquad\qquad\quad y = -11$

$5x + 2y = 3$

$5x + 2(-11) = 3$

$5x = 25$

$x = 5$

The solution is $(5, -11)$.

12. $x = 3 - 2y \Rightarrow 3x = 9 - 6y \Rightarrow 3x + 6y = 2$

$\qquad\qquad\qquad\qquad\qquad\qquad\qquad 3x + 6y = 8$

Inconsistent system. No solution.

13. $x + 5y = 10, \; x = 10 - 5y$

$y = 2 - \dfrac{1}{5}x = 2 - \dfrac{1}{5}(10 - 5y)$

$5y = 10 - 10 + 5y$

$0 = 0$

Dependent system. Infinite number of solutions.

14. $7x + 6y = -10$

$2x + y = 0, \; y = -2x$

$7x + 6(-2x) = -10$

$7x - 12x = -10$

$-5x = -10$

$x = 2$

$y = -2x = -2(2) = -4$

The solution is $(2, -4)$.

© 2006 Pearson Education, Inc., Upper Saddle River, NJ. All rights reserved. This material is protected under all copyright laws as they currently exist. No portion of this material may be reproduced, in any form or by any means, without permission in writing from the publisher.

15. $3x + 4y = 1$, $y = \dfrac{1 - 3x}{4}$

$$9x - 2y = -4 \Rightarrow 9x - 2 \cdot \dfrac{1 - 3x}{4} = -4$$

$$18x - 1 + 3x = -8$$

$$21x = -7$$

$$x = -\dfrac{1}{3}$$

$$y = \dfrac{1 - 3 \cdot \left(-\dfrac{1}{3}\right)}{4}$$

$$y = \dfrac{1}{2}$$

The solution is $\left(-\dfrac{1}{3}, \dfrac{1}{2}\right)$.

16. $x + \dfrac{1}{3}y = 1$, $x = 1 - \dfrac{1}{3}y$

$$\dfrac{1}{4}x - \dfrac{3}{4}y = -\dfrac{9}{4}$$

$$\dfrac{1}{4}\left(1 - \dfrac{1}{3}y\right) - \dfrac{3}{4}y = -\dfrac{9}{4}$$

$$1 - \dfrac{1}{3}y - 3y = -9$$

$$-\dfrac{10}{3}y = -10$$

$$y = 3$$

$$x = 1 - \dfrac{1}{3}y = 1 - \dfrac{1}{3}(3) = 1 - 1$$

$$x = 0$$

The solution is $(0,3)$.

17. $\dfrac{2}{3}x + y = 1$

$$\underline{-\dfrac{2}{3}x - 2y = -\dfrac{5}{3}}$$

$$-y = -\dfrac{2}{3}$$

$$y = \dfrac{2}{3}$$

$$\dfrac{2}{3}x + \dfrac{2}{3} = 1$$

$$\dfrac{2}{3}x = \dfrac{1}{3}$$

$$x = \dfrac{1}{2}$$

The solution is $\left(\dfrac{1}{2}, \dfrac{2}{3}\right)$.

18. $3a + 8b = 0$, $3a + 8b = 0$

$9a + 2b = 11$, $\underline{-36a - 8b = -44}$

$$-33a \qquad = -44$$

$$a = \dfrac{4}{3}$$

$$3 \cdot \dfrac{4}{3} + 8b = 0$$

$$8b = -4$$

$$b = -\dfrac{1}{2}$$

The solution is $\left(\dfrac{4}{3}, -\dfrac{1}{2}\right)$.

19. $3a + 5b = -2$, $6a + 10b = -4$

$10b = -6a - 4$, $\underline{-6a - 10b = 4}$

$$0 = 0$$

Dependent system. Infinite number of solutions.

104

© 2006 Pearson Education, Inc., Upper Saddle River, NJ. All rights reserved. This material is protected under all copyright laws as they currently exist. No portion of this material may be reproduced, in any form or by any means, without permission in writing from the publisher.

20. $x+3=3y+1, \ x=3y-2$

$1-2(x-2)=6y+1$

$1-2(3y-2-2)=6y+1$

$1-6y+8=6y+1$

$-12y=-8$

$y=\dfrac{2}{3}$

$x=3y-2=3\left(\dfrac{2}{3}\right)-2=2-2$

$x=0$

The solution is $\left(0,\dfrac{2}{3}\right)$.

21. $10(x+1)-13=-8y, \ y=\dfrac{10x-3}{-8}$

$4(2-y)=5(x+1)$

$8-4y=5x+4$

$8-4\left(\dfrac{10x-3}{-8}\right)=5x+4$

$16+10x-3=10x+8$

$13=8$

Inconsistent system. No solution.

22. $0.3x-0.2y=0.7, \quad 0.6x-0.4y=1.4$

$\underline{-0.6x+0.4y=0.3, \quad -0.6x+0.4y=0.3}$

$\hspace{5.5cm}0=1.7$

Inconsistent system. No solution.

23. $0.2x-0.1y=0.8, \quad 0.6x-0.3y=2.4$

$\underline{0.1x+0.3y=1.1, \quad 0.1x+0.3y=1.1}$

$\hspace{4.7cm}0.7x=3.5$

$\hspace{5.5cm}x=5$

$0.2x-0.1y=0.8$

$0.2(5)-0.1y=0.8$

$-0.1y=-0.2$

$y=2$

23. The solution is $(5,2)$.

24. $3x-2y-z=3$ $\quad$ **(1)**

$\quad 2x+\ y+z=1$ $\quad$ **(2)**

$\quad\ -x-\ y+z=-4$ $\quad$ **(3)**

Add (1) and (2)

$\quad 5x-y=4$ $\hspace{2cm}$ **(4)**

Add (1) and (3)

$\quad 2x-3y=-1$ $\hspace{1.5cm}$ **(5)**

Add -3 times **(4)** to **(5)**

$\quad -15x+3y=-12$

$\quad \underline{\ \ 2x-3y=-1\ \ }$

$\quad -13x\hspace{1.3cm}=-13$

$\hspace{2cm}x=1$

Substitute $x=1$ into **(4)**

$\quad 5(1)-y=4$

$\hspace{1cm}-y=-1$

$\hspace{1.3cm}y=1$

Substitute $x=1, \ y=1$ into **(2)**

$\quad 2(1)+1+z=1$

$\hspace{1.8cm}z=-2$

The solution is $(1,1,-2)$.

25. $-2x+\ y-\ z=-7$ $\quad$ **(1)**

$\quad\ x-2y-\ z=2$ $\hspace{1cm}$ **(2)**

$\quad 6x+4y+2z=4$ $\hspace{1cm}$ **(3)**

Add 2 times **(2)** to **(3)**

$\quad 2x-4y-2z=4$

$\quad \underline{6x+4y+2z=4}$

$\quad 8x\hspace{2cm}=8$

$\hspace{2cm}x=1$

Substitute $x=1$ into **(1)** and **(2)**

$\quad -2+y-z=-7 \Rightarrow \ y-z=-5$ $\quad$ **(4)**

$\quad 1-2y-z=2 \Rightarrow -2y-z=1$ $\hspace{0.8cm}$ **(5)**

Add -1 times **(5)** to **(4)**

105

© 2006 Pearson Education, Inc., Upper Saddle River, NJ. All rights reserved. This material is protected under all copyright laws as they currently exist. No portion of this material may be reproduced, in any form or by any means, without permission in writing from the publisher.

$$y - z = -5$$
$$\underline{2y + z = -1}$$
$$3y \quad = -6$$
$$y = -2$$

Substitute $x = 1$, $y = -2$ into (3)
$$6(1) + 4(-2) + 2z = 4$$
$$2z = 6$$
$$z = 3$$

The solution is $(1, -2, 3)$.

26. $\quad 2x + 5y + z = 3 \qquad$ **(1)**
$\qquad x + y + 5z = 42 \qquad$ **(2)**
$\qquad 2x + y \quad = 7 \qquad$ **(3)**

Solve (1) for z and substitute into (2)
$$z = 3 - 2x - 5y$$
$$x + y + 5(3 - 2x - 5y) = 42$$
$$x + y + 15 - 10x - 25y = 42$$
$$-9x - 24y = 27 \qquad \textbf{(4)}$$

Solve (3) for y, and substitute into (4)
$$y = 7 - 2x$$
$$-9x - 24(7 - 2x) = 27$$
$$-9x - 168 + 48x = 27$$
$$39x = 195$$
$$x = 5$$

Substitute $x = 5$ into $y = 7 - 2x$
$$y = 7 - 2(5) = 7 - 10 = -3$$
$$y = -3$$

Substitute $x = 5$, $y = -3$ into
$$z = 3 - 2x - 5y$$
$$z = 3 - 2(5) - 5(-3) = 8$$
$$z = 8$$

The solution is $(5, -3, 8)$.

27. $\quad x + 2y + z = 5 \qquad$ **(1)**
$\qquad 3x - 8y \quad = 17 \qquad$ **(2)**
$\qquad 2y + z = -2 \qquad$ **(3)**

Solve (1) for x, and substitute into (2)

$$x = 5 - 2y - z$$
$$3(5 - 2y - z) - 8y = 17$$
$$15 - 6y - 3z - 8y = 17$$
$$3z = -14y - 2$$
$$z = \frac{-14y - 2}{3}.$$

Substitute $z = \dfrac{-14y - 2}{3}$ into (3)
$$2y + \frac{-14y - 2}{3} = -2$$
$$6y - 14y - 2 = -6$$
$$-8y = -4$$
$$y = \frac{1}{2}$$

Substitute $y = \dfrac{1}{2}$ into (3)
$$2\left(\frac{1}{2}\right) + z = -2$$
$$1 + z = -2$$
$$z = -3$$

Substitute $y = \dfrac{1}{2}$ into (2)
$$3x - 8\left(\frac{1}{2}\right) = 17$$
$$3x - 4 = 17$$
$$3x = 21$$
$$x = 7$$

The solution is $\left(7, \dfrac{1}{2}, -3\right)$.

28. $\quad 2x - 4y + 3z = 0 \qquad$ **(1)**
$\qquad x - 2y - 5z = 13 \qquad$ **(2)**
$\qquad 5x + 3y - 2z = 19 \qquad$ **(3)**

Multiply (2) by -2 and add to (1)
$$13z = -26$$
$$z = -2$$

106

© 2006 Pearson Education, Inc., Upper Saddle River, NJ. All rights reserved. This material is protected under all copyright laws as they currently exist.
No portion of this material may be reproduced, in any form or by any means, without permission in writing from the publisher.

Multiply (2) by -5 and add to (3)
$$13y + 23z = -46$$
$$13y + 23(-2) = -46$$
$$13y = 0$$
$$y = 0$$
Substitute $y = 0$, $z = -2$ into (2)
$$x - 2(0) - 5(-2) = 13$$
$$x + 10 = 13$$
$$x = 3$$
The solution is $(3, 0, -2)$.

29. $\quad 5x + 2y + 3z = 10 \qquad$ **(1)**
$\qquad 6x - 3y + 4z = 24 \qquad$ **(2)**
$\qquad -2x + y + 2z = 2 \qquad$ **(3)**
Add 3 times **(3)** to **(2)**
$$10z = 30$$
$$z = 3$$
Add -2 times **(3)** to **(1)**
$$9x - z = 6$$
$$9x - (3) = 6$$
$$9x = 9$$
$$x = 1$$
Substitute $x = 1$, $z = 3$ into **(3)**
$$-2(1) + y + 2(3) = 2$$
$$-2 + y + 6 = 2$$
$$y = -2$$
The solution is $(1, -2, 3)$.

30. $3x + 2y = 7 \qquad$ **(1)**
$\quad 2x + 7z = -26 \qquad$ **(2)**
$\qquad 5y + z = 6 \qquad$ **(3)**
Solve **(3)** for z and substitute into **(2)**
$$2x + 7(6 - 5y) = -26$$
$$2x + 42 - 35y = -26$$
$$2x = 35y - 68$$
$$x = \frac{35y - 68}{2}$$

Substitute $x = \dfrac{35y - 68}{2}$ into **(1)**
$$3\left(\frac{35y - 68}{2} \right) + 2y = 7$$
$$105y - 204 + 4y = 14$$
$$109y = 218$$
$$y = 2$$
Substitute $y = 2$ into **(3)**
$$5(2) + z = 6$$
$$10 + z = 6$$
$$z = -4$$
Substitute $y = 2$ into **(1)**
$$3x + 2(2) = 7$$
$$3x + 4 = 7$$
$$3x = 3$$
$$x = 1$$
The solution is $(1, 2, -4)$.

31. $x - y = 2 \qquad$ **(1)**
$\quad 5x + 7y - 5z = 2 \qquad$ **(2)**
$\quad 3x - 5y + 2z = -2 \qquad$ **(3)**
Add 2 times **(2)** to 5 times **(3)**
$$25x - 11y = -6 \qquad \textbf{(4)}$$
Solve **(1)** for x and substitute into **(4)**
$$x = 2 + y$$
$$25(2 + y) - 11y = -6$$
$$50 + 25y - 11y = -6$$
$$14y = -56$$
$$y = -4$$
Substitute $y = -4$ into **(1)**
$$x - (-4) = 2$$
$$x + 4 = 2$$
$$x = -2$$
Substitute $x = -2$, $y = -4$ into **(3)**

© 2006 Pearson Education, Inc., Upper Saddle River, NJ. All rights reserved. This material is protected under all copyright laws as they currently exist. No portion of this material may be reproduced, in any form or by any means, without permission in writing from the publisher.

$$3(-2) - 5(-4) + 2z = -2$$
$$-6 + 20 + 2z = -2$$
$$2z = -16$$
$$z = -8$$
The solution is $(-2, -4, -8)$.

32. $v = $ speed of plane in still air
$w = $ speed of wind
$$720 = (v - w) \cdot 3 \qquad v - w = 240$$
$$720 = (v + w)(2.5) \qquad \underline{v + w = 288}$$
$$2v = 528$$
$$v = 264$$

$w = 288 - v = 288 - 264 = 24$
The speed of the plane in still air is 264 mph and the wind speed is 24 mph.

33. $T = $ number of touchdowns
$F = $ number of field goals
$$T + F = 11 \qquad \textbf{(1)}$$
$$7T + 3F = 65 \qquad \textbf{(2)}$$
Solve **(1)** for F and substitute into **(2)**
$$F = 11 - T$$
$$7T + 3(11 - T) = 65$$
$$7T + 33 - 3T = 65$$
$$4T = 32$$
$$T = 8 \text{ touchdowns}$$
Substitute $T = 8$ into **(1)**
$$8 + F = 11$$
$$F = 3 \text{ field goals}$$

34. $x = $ number of laborers
$y = $ number of mechanics
$$70x + 90y = 1950 \qquad \textbf{(1)}$$
$$80x + 100y = 2200 \qquad \textbf{(2)}$$
Divide both equations by 10
$$7x + 9y = 195 \qquad \textbf{(1)}$$
$$8x + 10y = 220 \qquad \textbf{(2)}$$
Add -8 times **(1)** to 7 times **(2)**

$$-2y = -20$$
$$y = 10$$
Substitute $y = 10$ into **(2)**
$$8x + 10(10) = 220$$
$$8x = 120$$
$$x = 15$$
The circus hired 15 laborers and 10 mechanics.

35. $x = $ number of children's tickets
$y = $ number of adult tickets
$$x + y = 590 \qquad \textbf{(1)}$$
$$6x + 11y = 4790 \qquad \textbf{(2)}$$
Solve **(1)** for y substitute into **(2)**
$$6x + 11(590 - x) = 4790$$
$$6x + 6490 - 11x = 4790$$
$$-5x = -1700$$
$$x = 340$$
$$y = 590 - x$$
$$y = 590 - 340 = 250$$
There were 340 children's tickets sold and 250 adult tickets.

36. $x = $ cost of hat
$y = $ cost of shirt
$z = $ cost of pants
$$2x + 5y + 4z = 129 \qquad \textbf{(1)}$$
$$x + y + 2z = 42 \qquad \textbf{(2)}$$
$$2x + 3y + z = 63 \qquad \textbf{(3)}$$
Add -2 times **(2)** and **(1)**
$$3y = 45$$
$$y = 15$$
Substitute $y = 15$ into **(2)** and solve for x
$$x + 15 + 2z = 42$$
$$x = 27 - 2z$$
Substitute $x = 27 - 2z$ and $y = 15$ into **(3)**

© 2006 Pearson Education, Inc., Upper Saddle River, NJ. All rights reserved. This material is protected under all copyright laws as they currently exist. No portion of this material may be reproduced, in any form or by any means, without permission in writing from the publisher.

$$2(27-2z)+3(15)+z=63$$
$$54-4z+45+z=63$$
$$-3z=-36$$
$$z=12$$

Substitute $y=15$, $z=12$ into **(2)**
$$x+15+2(12)=42$$
$$x+15+24=42$$
$$x=3$$

The hats cost \$3, shirts \$15, and pants \$12.

37. $J=$ Jess' score

$N=$ Nick's score

$C=$ Chris' score
$$J+C+N=249 \quad \textbf{(1)}$$
$$J=C+20 \quad\quad \textbf{(2)}$$
$$2N=J+C+6 \quad \textbf{(3)}$$

Substitute J from **(2)** into **(1)** and **(3)**
$$C+20+C+N=249 \Rightarrow 2C=229-N$$
$$2N=C+20+C+6 \Rightarrow 2C=2N-26$$

from which $229-N=2N-26$
$$3N=255$$
$$N=85, \text{ Nick's score}$$

and $2C=229-85=144$
$$C=72, \text{ Chris' score}$$

and $J=C+20=72+20$
$$J=92, \text{ Jess' score}$$

38. $x=$ cost of jelly

$y=$ cost of peanut butter

$z=$ cost of honey
$$4x+3y+5z=9.8 \quad \textbf{(1)}$$
$$2x+2y+z=4.20 \quad \textbf{(2)}$$
$$3x+4y+2z=7.70 \quad \textbf{(3)}$$

Add **(1)** and -5 times **(2)**
$$-6x-7y=-11.2 \quad \textbf{(4)}$$

Add -2 times **(2)** to **(3)**

$$-x=-0.7$$
$$x=0.7$$

Substitute $x=0.7$ into   **(4)**
$$-6(0.7)-7y=-11.2$$
$$-7y=-7$$
$$y=1$$

Substitute $x=0.7$, $y=1$ into **(2)**
$$2(0.7)+2(1)+z=4.2$$
$$z=0.8$$

The cost of a jar of jelly is \$0.70, the cost of a jar of peanut butter is \$1, and the cost of a jar of honey is \$0.80.

39. $x=$ number of buses

$y=$ number of station wagons

$z=$ number of sedans
$$x+y+z=9 \quad\quad\quad \textbf{(1)}$$
$$40x+8y+5z=127 \quad \textbf{(2)}$$
$$8(3y)+5(2z)=126$$
$$24y+10z=126 \quad\quad \textbf{(3)}$$

Add -40 times **(1)** to **(2)**
$$-32y-35z=-233 \quad \textbf{(4)}$$

Add 32 times **(3)** to 24 times **(4)**
$$-520z=-1560$$
$$z=3$$

Substitute $z=3$ into **(3)**
$$24y+10(3)=126$$
$$24y=96$$
$$y=3$$

Substitute $y=4$, $z=3$ into **(1)**
$$x+4+3=9$$
$$x=2$$

They should use 2 buses, 4 station wagons, and 3 sedans.

40. $-x-5z=-5 \quad\quad \textbf{(1)}$
$\quad\quad 13x+2z=2 \quad\quad \textbf{(2)}$

Solve **(1)** for x and substitute into **(2)**

© 2006 Pearson Education, Inc., Upper Saddle River, NJ. All rights reserved. This material is protected under all copyright laws as they currently exist.
No portion of this material may be reproduced, in any form or by any means, without permission in writing from the publisher.

$$x = 5 - 5z$$
$$13(5 - 5z) + 2z = 2$$
$$65 - 65z + 2z = 2$$
$$-63z = -63$$
$$z = 1$$

Substitute $z = 1$ into **(1)**
$$-x - 5(1) = -5$$
$$-x = 0$$
$$x = 0$$

The solution is $(0, 1)$.

41. $x - y = 1$

$5x + y = 7$

Adding gives
$$6x = 8$$
$$x = \frac{4}{3} \text{ and}$$
$$5 \cdot \frac{4}{3} + y = 7$$
$$y = \frac{1}{3}$$

The solution is $\left(\frac{4}{3}, \frac{1}{3} \right)$.

42. $2x + 5y = 4$ **(1)**

$5x - 7y = -29$ **(2)**

Solve **(1)** for y and substitute into **(2)**
$$y = \frac{4 - 2x}{5}$$
$$5x - 7\frac{4 - 2x}{5} = -29$$
$$25x - 28 + 14x = -145$$
$$39x = -117$$
$$x = -3$$

Substitute $x = -3$ into **(1)**

$$2(-3) + 5y = 4$$
$$-6 + 5y = 4$$
$$5y = 10$$
$$y = 2$$

The solution is $(-3, 2)$.

43. $\frac{x}{2} - 3y = -6$ **(1)**

$\frac{4}{3}x + 2y = 4$ **(2)**

Solve **(1)** for x and substitute into **(2)**
$$x = 6y - 12$$
$$\frac{4}{3}(6y - 12) + 2y = 4$$
$$24y - 48 + 6y = 12$$
$$30y = 60$$
$$y = 2$$
$$x = 6y - 12 = 6(2) - 12 = 0$$

The solution is $(0, 2)$.

44. $\frac{3}{5}x - y = 6$ **(1)**

$x + \frac{y}{3} = 10$ **(2)**

Solve **(1)** for y and substitute into **(2)**
$$y = \frac{3}{5}x - 6$$
$$x + \frac{\frac{3}{5}x - 6}{5} = 10$$
$$5x + \frac{3}{5}x - 6 = 50$$
$$25x + 3x - 30 = 250$$
$$28x = 280$$
$$x = 10$$

Substitute $x = 10$ into **(2)**

110

© 2006 Pearson Education, Inc., Upper Saddle River, NJ. All rights reserved. This material is protected under all copyright laws as they currently exist. No portion of this material may be reproduced, in any form or by any means, without permission in writing from the publisher.

$$10 + \frac{y}{3} = 10$$
$$y = 0$$

The solution is $(10, 0)$.

45. $\dfrac{x+1}{5} = y + 2$ **(1)**

$\dfrac{2y+7}{3} = x - y$ **(2)**

Solve **(1)** for y and substitute into **(2)**

$$y = \frac{x+1}{5} - 2$$

$$\frac{2\left(\dfrac{x+1}{5} - 2\right) + 7}{3} = x - \frac{x+1}{5} + 2$$

$$2\left(\frac{x+1}{5} - 2\right) + 7 = 3x - \frac{3x+3}{5} + 6$$

$$2(x + 1 - 10) + 35 = 15x - 3x - 3 + 30$$

$$2x - 18 + 35 = 12x + 27$$

$$10x = -10$$

$$x = -1$$

$$y = \frac{x+1}{5} - 2 = \frac{-1+1}{5} - 2 = -2$$

The solution is $(-1, -2)$.

46. $3(2 + x) = y + 1$
$$6 + 3x = y + 1$$
$$y = 3x + 5 \qquad \textbf{(1)}$$
$$5(x - y) = -7 - 3y$$
$$5x - 5y = -7 - 3y$$
$$5x - 2y = -7 \qquad \textbf{(2)}$$

Substitute y from **(1)** into **(2)**
$$5x - 2(3x + 5) = -7$$
$$5x - 6x - 10 = -7$$
$$-x = 3$$
$$x = -3$$

Substitute $x = -3$ into **(1)**
$$y = 3x + 5 = 3(-3) + 5$$
$$y = -9 + 5 = -4$$

The solution is $(-3, -4)$.

47. $7(x + 3) = 2y + 25$
$$7x + 21 = 2y + 25$$
$$7x - 2y = 4 \qquad \textbf{(1)}$$
$$3(x - 6) = -2(y + 1)$$
$$3x - 18 = -2y - 2$$
$$3x + 2y = 16 \qquad \textbf{(2)}$$

Add **(1)** and **(2)**
$$10x = 20$$
$$x = 2$$

Substitute $x = 2$ into **(2)**
$$3(2) + 2y = 16$$
$$2y = 10$$
$$y = 5$$

The solution is $(2, 5)$.

48. Multiply both equations by 10 to clear decimals.
$$3x - 4y = 9 \qquad \textbf{(1)}$$
$$2x - 3y = 4 \qquad \textbf{(2)}$$

Solve **(1)** for y and substitute into **(2)**
$$y = \frac{3x - 9}{4}$$

$$2x - 3\frac{3x - 9}{4} = 4$$

$$8x - 9x + 27 = 16$$

$$-x = -11$$

$$x = 11$$

$$y = \frac{3x - 9}{4} = \frac{3(11) - 9}{4} = 6$$

The solution is $(11, 6)$.

49. Solve the first equation for y and substitute into the second equation

© 2006 Pearson Education, Inc., Upper Saddle River, NJ. All rights reserved. This material is protected under all copyright laws as they currently exist. No portion of this material may be reproduced, in any form or by any means, without permission in writing from the publisher.

$$y = 1.2x - 1.6$$
$$x + 1.5(1.2x - 1.6) = 6$$
$$x + 1.8x - 2.4 = 6$$
$$2.8x = 8.4$$
$$x = 3$$
$$y = 1.2(3) - 1.6$$
$$y = 2$$

The solution is $(3,2)$.

50. $x - \dfrac{y}{2} + \dfrac{1}{2}z = -1$ **(1)**

$2x + \dfrac{5}{2}z = -1$ **(2)**

$\dfrac{3}{2}y + 2z = 1$ **(3)**

Solve **(2)** for x and **(3)** for y and substitute into **(1)**

$$x = \dfrac{-\dfrac{5}{2}z - 1}{2}$$

$$y = \dfrac{2(1 - 2z)}{3} = \dfrac{2 - 4z}{3}$$

$$\dfrac{-\dfrac{5}{2}z - 1}{2} - \dfrac{\dfrac{2 - 4z}{3}}{2} + \dfrac{1}{2}z = -1$$

$$-\dfrac{5}{2}z - 1 - \dfrac{2 - 4z}{3} + z = -2$$

$$-15z - 6 - 4 + 8z + 6z = -12$$

$$-z = -2$$

$$z = 2$$

$$x = \dfrac{-\dfrac{5}{2}z - 1}{2} = \dfrac{-\dfrac{5}{2}(2) - 1}{2} = -3$$

$$y = \dfrac{2 - 4z}{3} = \dfrac{2 - 4(2)}{3} = -2$$

The solution is $(-3, -2, 2)$.

51. $2x - 3y + 2z = 0$ **(1)**

$x + 2y - z = 2$ **(2)**

$2x + y + 3z = -1$ **(3)**

Add **(1)** and 2 times **(2)**

$4x + y = 4$ **(4)**

Add 3 times **(2)** and **(3)**

$5x + 5y = 5 \Rightarrow x + y = 1$ **(5)**

Solve **(4)** for y and substitute into **(5)**

$$y = 4 - 4x$$
$$x + (4 - 4x) = 1$$
$$x + 4 - 4x = 1$$
$$-3x = -3$$
$$x = 1$$
$$y = 4 - 4x$$
$$y = 4 - 4(1) = 0$$

Substitute $x = 1$, $y = 0$ into **(1)**

$$2(1) - 3(0) + 2z = 0$$
$$2 + 2z = 0$$
$$2z = -2$$
$$z = -1$$

The solution is $(1, 0, -1)$.

52. $x - 4y + 4z = -1$ **(1)**

$2x - y + 5z = -3$ **(2)**

$x - 3y + z = 4$ **(3)**

Add **(1)** and -4 times **(3)**

$-3x + 8y = -17$ **(4)**

Add **(2)** and -5 times **(3)**

$-3x + 14y = -23$ **(5)**

Subtract **(5)** from **(4)**

$$-6y = 6$$
$$y = -1$$

Substitute $y = -1$ into **(4)**

$$-3x + 8(-1) = -17$$
$$-3x = -9$$
$$x = 3$$

Substitute $x = 3$, $y = -1$ into **(3)**

© 2006 Pearson Education, Inc., Upper Saddle River, NJ. All rights reserved. This material is protected under all copyright laws as they currently exist. No portion of this material may be reproduced, in any form or by any means, without permission in writing from the publisher.

$$3 - 3(-1) + z = 4$$
$$z = -2$$
The solution is $(3, -1, -2)$.

53. $x - 2y + z = -5$ **(1)**
$$2x + z = -10 \quad\quad \textbf{(2)}$$
$$y - z = 15 \quad\quad \textbf{(3)}$$
Solve **(3)** for y
$$y = z + 15 \quad\quad \textbf{(4)}$$
Solve **(2)** for x
$$x = \frac{-z - 10}{2} \quad\quad \textbf{(5)}$$
Substitute **(4)** and **(5)** into **(1)**
$$\frac{-z - 10}{2} - 2(z + 15) + z = -5$$
$$-z - 10 - 4z - 60 + 2z = -10$$
$$3z = 60$$
$$z = -20$$
Substitute $z = -20$ into **(4)** and **(5)**
$$x = \frac{-(-20) - 10}{2} = 5$$
$$y = -20 + 15 = -5$$
The solution is $(5, -5, -20)$.

54. $x - y \le 3$
Test point: $(0,0)$
$$0 - 0 \le 3$$
$$0 \le 3 \text{ True}$$
$$y \le -\frac{1}{4}x + 2$$
$$0 \le -\frac{1}{4}(0) + 2$$
$$0 \le 2 \text{ True}$$

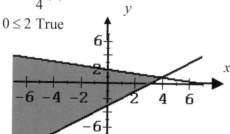

55. $-2x + 3y < 6$
Test point: $(0,0)$
$$-2(0) + 3(0) < 6$$
$$0 < 6 \text{ True}$$
$$y > -2$$

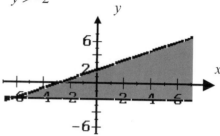

56. $x + y > 1$
Test point: $(0,0)$
$$0 + 0 > 1$$
$$0 > 1 \text{ False}$$
$$2x - y < 5$$
Test point: $(0,0)$
$$2(0) - 0 < 5$$
$$0 < 5 \text{ True}$$

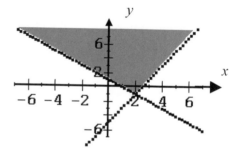

57. $x + y \ge 4$
Test point: $(0,0)$
$$0 + 0 \ge 4$$
$$0 \ge 4 \text{ False}$$
$$y \le x$$
Test point: $(2,0)$
$$0 \le 2 \text{ True}$$
$$x \le 6$$

© 2006 Pearson Education, Inc., Upper Saddle River, NJ. All rights reserved. This material is protected under all copyright laws as they currently exist.
No portion of this material may be reproduced, in any form or by any means, without permission in writing from the publisher.

57.

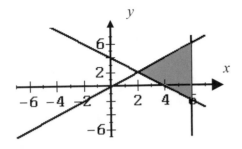

How Am I Doing? Chapter 4 Test

1. Solve the first equation for y and substitute into the second equation

$$y = x - 3$$
$$2x - 3(x - 3) = -1$$
$$2x - 3x + 9 = -1$$
$$-x = -10$$
$$x = 10$$
$$y = 10 - 3$$
$$y = 7$$

The solution is $(10, 7)$.

2. Multiply the first equation by 3 and the second equation by -2 and add

$$9x + 6y = 3$$
$$\underline{-10x - 6y = -6}$$
$$-x\qquad\ \ = -3$$
$$x = 3$$

Substitute $x = 3$ into the first equation

$$3(3) + 2y = 1$$
$$2y = -8$$
$$y = -4$$

The solution is $(3, -4)$.

3. $5x - 3y = 3$ **(1)**
　　$7x + y = 25$ **(2)**
Add 3 times **(2)** to **(1)**

$$26x = 78$$
$$x = 3$$
$$7x + y = 25$$
$$7(3) + y = 25$$
$$y = 4$$

The solution is $(3, 4)$.

4.　　$\dfrac{1}{4}a - \dfrac{3}{4}b = -1$ 　　　**(1)**

　　　$\dfrac{1}{3}a + b = \dfrac{5}{3}$ 　　　　**(2)**

Solve **(2)** for b and substitute into **(1)**

$$b = \frac{5}{3} - \frac{1}{3}a$$

$$\frac{1}{4}a - \frac{3}{4}\left(\frac{5}{3} - \frac{1}{3}a\right) = -1$$

$$a - 5 + a = -4$$

$$2a = 1$$

$$a = \frac{1}{2}$$

$$b = \frac{5}{3} - \frac{1}{3}a$$

$$b = \frac{5}{3} - \frac{1}{3} \cdot \frac{1}{2} = \frac{3}{2}$$

The solution is $\left(\dfrac{1}{2}, \dfrac{3}{2}\right)$.

5.　　$\dfrac{1}{3}x + \dfrac{5}{6}y = 2$ 　　**(1)**

　　　$\dfrac{3}{5}x - y = -\dfrac{7}{5}$ 　　**(2)**

Solve **(2)** for y and substitute into **(1)**

$$y = \frac{3}{5}x + \frac{7}{5}$$

$$\frac{1}{3}x + \frac{5}{6}\left(\frac{3}{5}x + \frac{7}{5}\right) = 2$$

114

© 2006 Pearson Education, Inc., Upper Saddle River, NJ. All rights reserved. This material is protected under all copyright laws as they currently exist. No portion of this material may be reproduced, in any form or by any means, without permission in writing from the publisher.

$$2x + 3x + 7 = 12$$
$$5x = 5$$
$$x = 1$$
$$y = \frac{3}{5}x + \frac{7}{5}$$
$$y = \frac{3}{5}(1) + \frac{7}{5}$$
$$y = 2$$

The solution is $(1, 2)$.

6. Multiply the first equation by 2 and add
$$16x - 6y = 10$$
$$\underline{-16x + 6y = 8}$$
$$0 = 18$$

Inconsistent system. No solution.

$$
\begin{array}{rcrcrcr}
3x & + & 5y & - & 2z & = & -5 \\
\textbf{7. } 2x & + & 3y & - & z & = & -2 \\
2x & + & 4y & + & 6z & = & 18
\end{array}
$$

Multiply first equation by $-\frac{2}{3}$ and add to the second and third equation
$$
\begin{array}{rcrcrcr}
3x & + & 5y & - & 2z & = & -5 \\
 & & -\frac{1}{3}y & + & \frac{1}{3}z & = & \frac{4}{3} \\
 & & \frac{2}{3}y & + & \frac{22}{3}z & = & \frac{64}{3}
\end{array}
$$

Multiply second equation by 2 and add to the third equation
$$
\begin{array}{rcrcrcr}
3x & + & 5y & - & 2z & = & -5 \\
 & & -\frac{1}{3}y & + & \frac{1}{3}z & = & \frac{4}{3} \\
 & & & & 8z & = & 24 \\
 & & & & z & = & 3
\end{array}
$$

From the second equation
$$-\frac{1}{3}y + \frac{1}{3}(3) = \frac{4}{3} \Rightarrow y = -1$$

From the first equation
$$3x + 5(-1) - 2(3) = -5, \; x = 2$$
The solution is $(2, -1, 3)$.

$$
\begin{array}{rcrcrcr}
 & 3x & + & 2y & & & = & 0 \\
\textbf{8.} & 2x & - & y & + & 3z & = & 8 \\
 & 5x & + & 3y & + & z & = & 4
\end{array}
$$

Multiply the first equation by $-\frac{2}{3}$ and add to the second equation and then multiply the first equation by $-\frac{5}{3}$ and add to the third equation
$$
\begin{array}{rcrcrcr}
3x & + & 2y & & & = & 0 \\
 & & -\frac{7}{3}y & + & 3z & = & 8 \\
 & & -\frac{1}{3}y & + & z & = & 4
\end{array}
$$

Multiply the second equation by $-\frac{1}{7}$ and add to the third equation
$$
\begin{array}{rcrcrcr}
3x & + & 2y & & & = & 0 \\
 & & -\frac{7}{3}y & + & 3z & = & 8 \\
 & & & & \frac{4}{7}z & = & \frac{20}{7}
\end{array}
$$
$$\frac{4}{7}z = \frac{20}{7}$$
$$z = 5$$

From second equation
$$-\frac{7}{3}y + 3(5) = 8 \Rightarrow y = 3$$
From the first equation
$$3x + 2(3) = 0, \; x = -2$$
The solution is $(-2, 3, 5)$.

115

© 2006 Pearson Education, Inc., Upper Saddle River, NJ. All rights reserved. This material is protected under all copyright laws as they currently exist. No portion of this material may be reproduced, in any form or by any means, without permission in writing from the publisher.

$$\begin{array}{rcrcrcr} x & + & 5y & + & 4z & = & -3 \\ x & - & y & - & 2z & = & -3 \\ x & + & 2y & + & 3z & = & -5 \end{array}$$

9.

Multiply the first equation by -1 and add to the second and third equation

$$\begin{array}{rcrcrcr} x & + & 5y & + & 4z & = & -3 \\ & & -6y & - & 6z & = & 0 \\ & & -3y & - & z & = & -2 \end{array}$$

Multiply the second equation by $-\dfrac{1}{2}$ and add to the third equation

$$\begin{array}{rcrcrcr} x & + & 5y & + & 4z & = & -3 \\ & & -6y & - & 6z & = & 0 \\ & & & & 2z & = & -2 \end{array}$$

$2z = -2$, $z = -1$

From the second equation

$-6y - 6(-1) = 0$, $y = 1$

From the first equation

$x + 5(1) + 4(-1) = -3$, $x = -4$

The solution is $(-4, 1, -1)$.

10. $v =$ speed of plane in still air

$w =$ speed of wind

$1000 = (v + w)(2) \Rightarrow v + w = 500$

$\underline{1000 = (v - w)(2.5) \Rightarrow v - w = 400}$

$2v = 900$

$v = 450$

$450 + w = 500$

$w = 50$

The speed of the plane in still air is 450 mph. The speed of the wind is 50 mph.

11. $p =$ price of a pen

$m =$ price of a mug

$s =$ price of a shirt

$4p + m + s = 20$　**(1)**

$2p + 2m = 11$　**(2)**

$6p + m + 2s = 33$　**(3)**

Add -1 times **(1)** to **(3)**

$2p + s = 13$　　　　**(4)**

Add -2 times **(3)** to **(2)**

$-10p - 4s = -55$　　**(5)**

Add 5 times **(4)** to **(5)**

$s = \$10$ for a shirt

Substitute $s = 10$ into **(4)**

$2p + 10 = 13$

$2p = 3$

$p = \$1.50$ for a pen

Substitute $s = 10$, $p = 1.5$ into **(1)**

$4(1.5) + m + 10 = 20$

$m = \$4$ for a mug

12. $x =$ daily charge

$y =$ mileage charge

$5x + 150y = 180$　**(1)**

$7x + 320y = 274$　**(2)**

Multiply **(1)** by $-\dfrac{7}{5}$ and add to **(2)**

$110y = 22$

$y = 0.2$

From first equation

$5x + 150(0.2) = 180$

$5x = 150$

$x = 30$

They charge \$30 per day and \$0.20 per mile.

13. $x + 2y \le 6$

Test point: $(0,0)$

$0 + 2(0) \le 6$

$0 \le 6$ True

$-2x + y \ge -2$

Test point: $(0,0)$

$-2(0) + 0 \ge -2$

$0 \ge -2$ True

116

© 2006 Pearson Education, Inc., Upper Saddle River, NJ. All rights reserved. This material is protected under all copyright laws as they currently exist. No portion of this material may be reproduced, in any form or by any means, without permission in writing from the publisher.

13.

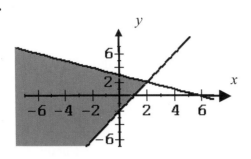

14. $3x + y > 8$

Test point: (0,0)

$3(0) + 0 > 8$

$0 > 8$ False

$x - 2y > 5$

Test point: (0,0)

$0 - 2(0) > 5$

$0 > 5$ False

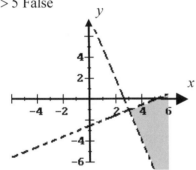

Cumulative Test for Chapters 1-4

1. Identity property of addition.

2. $\sqrt{25} + (2-3)^3 + 20 \div (-10)$

$= 5 + (-1)^3 + (-2)$

$= 5 + (-1) + (-2)$

$= 4 + (-2)$

$= 2$

3. $(5x^{-2})(3x^{-4}y^2)$

$= 15x^{-6}y^2$

$= \dfrac{15y^2}{x^6}$

4. $2x - 4[x - 3(2x+1)]$

$= 2x - 4[x - 6x - 3]$

$= 2x - 4[-5x - 3]$

$= 2x + 20x + 12$

$= 22x + 12$

5. $A = P(3 + 4rt)$

$P = \dfrac{A}{3 + 4rt}$

6. $\dfrac{1}{4}x + 5 = \dfrac{1}{3}(x - 2)$

$3x + 60 = 4x - 8$

$x = 68$

7. $4x - 8y = 10$

x	y
-2	$-\dfrac{9}{4}$
0	$-\dfrac{5}{4}$
4	$\dfrac{3}{4}$

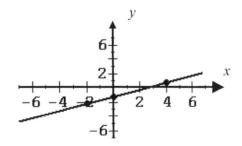

117

© 2006 Pearson Education, Inc., Upper Saddle River, NJ. All rights reserved. This material is protected under all copyright laws as they currently exist. No portion of this material may be reproduced, in any form or by any means, without permission in writing from the publisher.

8. $m = \dfrac{y_2 - y_1}{x_2 - x_1} = \dfrac{-1-(-2)}{6-(-4)} = \dfrac{1}{10}$

9. $4x + 3 - 13x - 7 < 2(3 - 4x)$

$-9x - 4 < 6 - 8x$

$-x < 10$

$x > -10$

-10

10. $\dfrac{2x-1}{3} \le 7$ and $2(x+1) \ge 12$

$2x - 1 \le 21 \qquad 2x + 2 \ge 12$

$2x \le 22 \qquad\quad 2x \ge 10$

$x \le 11 \qquad\quad x \ge 5$

$5 \le x \le 11$

5   11

11. $5x + 6y = -2$

$6y = -5x - 2$

$y = -\dfrac{5}{6}x - \dfrac{1}{3}, \ m = -\dfrac{5}{6}, \ m_\perp = \dfrac{6}{5}$

$y - y_1 = m(x - x_1)$

$y - (-3) = \dfrac{6}{5}(x - 2)$

$5y + 15 = 6x - 12$

$6x - 5y = 27$

$x = $ length of first side
$x + 7 = $ length of second side
$x - 6 = $ length of third side

$x + 7 + 2x - 6 = 69$

$1 = 69$

68

m, first side

4 m, second side

8 m, third side

13. $x = $ amount invested at 7%

$6000 - x = $ amount invested at 9%

$0.07x + 0.09(6000 - x) = 510$

$0.07x + 540 - 0.09x = 510$

$-0.02x = -30$

$x = 1500$

$6000 - x = 4500$

Victor invested $1500 at 7% and $4500 at 9%.

14. $\quad 5x + 2y = 2 \qquad$ **(1)**

$\quad 4x + 3y = -4 \qquad$ **(2)**

Solve **(1)** for y and substitute into **(2)**

$2y = 2 - 5x$

$y = \dfrac{2 - 5x}{2}$

$4x + 3\dfrac{2 - 5x}{2} = -4$

$8x + 6 - 15x = -8$

$-7x = -14$

$x = 2$

$y = \dfrac{2 - 5x}{2} = \dfrac{2 - 5(2)}{2} = -4$

The solution is $(2, -4)$.

15. Solve the second equation for y and substitute into the first equation

$y = -\dfrac{1}{4}x$

$\dfrac{1}{2}x - 3\left(-\dfrac{1}{4}x\right) = 5$

$2x + 3x = 20$

$5x = 20$

$x = 4$

$y = -\dfrac{1}{4} \cdot 4 = -1$

The solution is $(4, -1)$.

118

...nc., Upper Saddle River, NJ. All rights reserved. This material is protected under all copyright laws as they currently exist.
...r of this material may be reproduced, in any form or by any means, without permission in writing from the publisher.

16. $x = $ cost of shirt

$y = $ cost of slacks

$5x + 8y = 345$ **(1)**

$7x + 3y = 237$ **(2)**

Solve **(1)** for y and substitute into **(2)**

$8y = 345 - 5x$

$$y = \frac{345 - 5x}{8}$$

$$7x + 3\frac{345 - 5x}{8} = 237$$

$56x + 1035 - 15x = 1896$

$41x = 861$

$x = 21$

$$y = \frac{345 - 5x}{8} = \frac{345 - 5(21)}{8} = 30$$

The shirts cost \$21 and the slacks cost \$30.

17. $7x - 6y = 17$ **(1)**

$3x + y = 18$ **(2)**

Solve **(2)** for y and substitute into **(1)**

$y = 18 - 3x$

$7x - 6(18 - 3x) = 17$

$7x - 108 + 18x = 17$

$25x = 125$

$x = 5$

$y = 18 - 3x = 18 - 3(5) = 3$

The solution is $(5, 3)$.

18.

$$
\begin{array}{rrrrrrr}
x & + & 3y & + & z & = & 5 \\
2x & - & 3y & - & 2z & = & 0 \\
x & - & 2y & + & 3z & = & -9
\end{array}
$$

Multiply first equation by -2 and add to the second equation, then multiply the first equation by -1 and add to the third equation.

$$
\begin{array}{rrrrrrr}
x & + & 3y & + & z & = & 5 \\
 & - & 9y & - & 4z & = & -10 \\
 & - & 5y & + & 2z & = & -14
\end{array}
$$

Multiply the second equation by $-\dfrac{5}{9}$ and add

to third equation.

$$
\begin{array}{rrrrrrr}
x & + & 3y & + & z & = & 5 \\
 & - & 9y & - & 4z & = & -10 \\
 & & & + & \dfrac{38}{9}z & = & -\dfrac{76}{9}
\end{array}
$$

From the third equation

$$\frac{38}{9}z = -\frac{76}{9}, \ z = -2$$

From the second equation

$-9y - 4(-2) = -10, \ y = 2$

From the first equation

$x + 3(2) + (-2) = 5, \ x = 1$

The solution is $(1, 2, -2)$.

19. $-5x + 6y = 2$ **(1)**

$10x - 12y = -4$ **(2)**

Multiplying **(1)** by 2 and adding to **(2)** gives $0 = 0$. Dependent system. Infinite number of solutions.

20. $x - y \geq -4$ $x + 2y \geq 2$

    Test point: $(0, 0)$ Test point: $(0, 0)$

    $0 - 0 \geq -4$ $0 + 2(0) \geq 2$

    $0 \geq -4$ True $0 \geq 2$ False

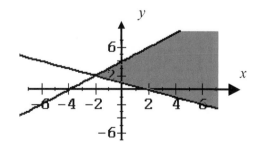

© 2006 Pearson Education, Inc., Upper Saddle River, NJ. All rights reserved. This material is protected under all copyright laws as they currently exist. No portion of this material may be reproduced, in any form or by any means, without permission in writing from the publisher.

Chapter 5

5.1 Exercises

1. $2x^2 - 5x + 3$ Trinomial, 2nd degree

3. $-3.2a^4bc^3$ Monomial, 8th degree

5. $\dfrac{3}{5}m^3n - \dfrac{2}{5}mn$ Binomial, 4th degree

7. $p(x) = 5x^2 - 9x - 12$
$p(3) = 5(3^2) - 9(3) - 12$
$p(3) = 6$

9. $g(x) = -3x^3 - x^2 + 4x + 2$
$g(2) = -3(2^3) - 2^2 + 4(2) + 2$
$g(2) = -18$

11. $h(x) = 2x^4 - x^3 + 2x^2 - 4x - 3$
$h(-1) = 2(-1)^4 - (-1)^3 + 2(-1)^2$
$\qquad\qquad\qquad - 4(-1) - 3$
$h(-1) = 6$

13. $(x^2 + 3x - 2) + (-2x^2 - 5x + 1)$
$\quad + (x^2 - x - 5)$
$= x^2 + 3x - 2 - 2x^2 - 5x + 1 + x^2 - x - 5$
$= -3x - 6$

15. $(7m^3 + 4m^2 - m + 2.5)$
$\qquad\qquad\qquad - (-3m^3 + 5m + 3.8)$
$= 7m^3 + 4m^2 - m + 2.5 + 3m^3 - 5m - 3.8$
$= 10m^3 + 4m^2 - 6m - 1.3$

17. $(5a^3 - 2a^2 - 6a + 8) + (5a + 6)$
$\qquad\qquad\qquad - (-a^2 - a + 2)$
$= 5a^3 - 2a^2 - 6a + 8 + 5a + 6$
$\qquad\qquad\qquad + a^2 + a - 2$
$= 5a^3 - a^2 + 12$

19. $\left(\dfrac{1}{2}x^2 - 7x\right) + \left(\dfrac{1}{3}x^2 + \dfrac{1}{4}x\right)$
$= \dfrac{1}{2}x^2 - 7x + \dfrac{1}{3}x^2 + \dfrac{1}{4}x$
$= \dfrac{5}{6}x^2 - \dfrac{27}{4}x$
$= \dfrac{5}{6}x^2 - 6\dfrac{3}{4}x$

21. $(2.3x^3 - 5.6x^2 - 2) - (5.5x^3 - 7.4x^2 + 2)$
$= 2.3x^3 - 5.6x^2 - 2 - 5.5x^3 + 7.4x^2 - 2$
$= -3.2x^3 + 1.8x^2 - 4$

23. $(5x + 8)(2x + 9) = 10x^2 + 45x + 16x + 72$
$\qquad\qquad\qquad\qquad = 10x^2 + 61x + 72$

25. $(5w + 2d)(3a - 4b)$
$\quad = 15aw - 20bw + 6ad - 8bd$

27. $(3x - 2y)(-4x + y)$
$\quad = -12x^2 + 3xy + 8xy - 2y^2$
$\quad = -12x^2 + 11xy - 2y^2$

29. $(7r - s^2)(-4a - 11s^2)$
$\quad = -28ar - 77rs^2 + 4as^2 + 11s^4$

31. $(5x - 8y)(5x + 8y) = 25x^2 - 64y^2$

120

© 2006 Pearson Education, Inc., Upper Saddle River, NJ. All rights reserved. This material is protected under all copyright laws as they currently exist. No portion of this material may be reproduced, in any form or by any means, without permission in writing from the publisher.

33. $(5a-2b)^2 = 25a^2 - 20ab + 4b^2$

35. $(7m-1)^2 = 49m^2 - 14m + 1$

37. $(4+3x^2)(4-3x^2) = 16 - 9x^4$

39. $(3m^3+1)^2 = 9m^6 + 6m^3 + 1$

41. $2x(3x^2 - 5x + 1) = 6x^3 - 10x^2 + 2x$

43. $-\dfrac{1}{3}xy(2x - 6y + 15)$

$\quad = -\dfrac{2}{3}x^2 y + 2xy^2 - 5xy$

45. $(2x-3)(x^2 - x + 1)$

$\quad = 2x^3 - 2x^2 + 2x - 3x^2 + 3x - 3$

$\quad = 2x^3 - 5x^2 + 5x - 3$

47. $(3x^2 - 2xy - 6y^2)(2x - y)$

$\quad = 6x^3 - 3x^2 y - 4x^2 y + 2xy^2 - 12xy^2 + 6y^3$

$\quad = 6x^3 - 7x^2 y - 10xy^2 + 6y^3$

49. $\left(\dfrac{3}{2}x^2 - x + 1\right)(x^2 + 2x - 6)$

$\quad = \dfrac{3}{2}x^4 + 3x^3 - 9x^2$

$\qquad\qquad - x^3 - 2x^2 + 6x$

$\qquad\qquad\qquad + x^2 + 2x - 6$

$\quad = \dfrac{3}{2}x^4 + 2x^3 - 10x^2 + 8x - 6$

51. $(5a^3 - 3a^2 + 2a - 4)(a - 3)$

$\quad = 5a^4 - 15a^3 - 3a^3 + 9a^2 + 2a^2 - 6a$

$\qquad\qquad\qquad\qquad\qquad - 4a + 12$

$\quad = 5a^4 - 18a^3 + 11a^2 - 10a + 12$

53. $(x+2)(x-3)(2x-5)$

$\quad = (x^2 - x - 6)(2x - 5)$

$\quad = 2x^3 - 5x^2 - 2x^2 + 5x - 12x + 30$

$\quad = 2x^3 - 7x^2 - 7x + 30$

55. $\quad (a+3)(2-a)(4-3a)$

$\quad = (2a - a^2 + 6 - 3a)(4 - 3a)$

$\quad = (-a^2 - a + 6)(4 - 3a)$

$\quad = -4a^2 + 3a^3 - 4a + 3a^2 + 24 - 18a$

$\quad = 3a^3 - a^2 - 22a + 24$

57. $V = (2x^2 + 5x + 8)(3x + 5)$

$\quad V = 6x^3 + 10x^2 + 15x^2 + 25x + 24x + 40$

$\quad V = 6x^3 + 25x^2 + 49x + 40 \text{ cm}^3$

59. $p(t) = -0.03t^2 + 78$

$\quad p(3) = -0.03(3)^2 + 78$

$\quad p(3) = 77.73 \text{ parts per million}$

61. $p(t) = -0.03t^2 + 78$

$\quad p(50) = -0.03(50)^2 + 78$

$\quad p(50) = 3 \text{ parts per million}$

Cumulative Review

63. $\dfrac{1}{2}x + 4 \le \dfrac{2}{3}(x-3) + 1$

$\quad 3x + 24 \le 4x - 12 + 6$

$\qquad -x \le -30$

$\qquad\quad x \ge 30$

69. $2500\dfrac{\text{ft}}{\text{min}} \cdot t = (31{,}000 - 8000) \text{ ft}$

$\quad t = \dfrac{23{,}000 \text{ ft}}{2500\dfrac{\text{ft}}{\text{min}}} = 9.2 \text{ min to reach 8000 ft.}$

121

© 2006 Pearson Education, Inc., Upper Saddle River, NJ. All rights reserved. This material is protected under all copyright laws as they currently exist. No portion of this material may be reproduced, in any form or by any means, without permission in writing from the publisher.

5.2 Exercises

1. $(24x^2 - 8x - 44) \div 4$

$$\frac{24x^2}{4} - \frac{8x}{4} - \frac{44}{4} = 6x^2 - 2x - 11$$

3. $(27x^4 - 9x^3 + 63x^2) \div 9x$

$$\frac{27x^4}{9x} - \frac{9x^3}{9x} + \frac{63x^2}{9x} = 3x^3 - x^2 + 7x$$

5. $\dfrac{8b^4 - 6b^3 - b^2}{2b^2} = \dfrac{8b^4}{2b^2} - \dfrac{6b^3}{2b^2} - \dfrac{b^2}{2b^2}$

$$= 4b^2 - 3b - \frac{1}{2}$$

7. $\dfrac{18a^3b^2 + 12a^2b^2 - 4ab^2}{2ab^2}$

$$= \frac{18a^3b^2}{2ab^2} + \frac{12a^2b^2}{2ab^2} - \frac{4ab^2}{2ab^2}$$

$$= 9a^2 + 6a - 2$$

9. $(5x^2 - 17x + 6) \div (x - 3)$

$$\begin{array}{r} 5x - 2 \\ x-3 \overline{)5x^2 - 17x + 6} \\ \underline{5x^2 - 15x} \\ -2x + 6 \\ \underline{-2x + 6} \end{array}$$

$(5x^2 - 17x + 6) \div (x - 3) = 5x - 2$

11. $(15x^2 + 23x + 4) \div (5x + 1)$

$$\begin{array}{r} 3x + 4 \\ 5x+1 \overline{)15x^2 + 23x + 4} \\ \underline{15x^2 + 3x} \\ 20x + 4 \\ \underline{20x + 4} \end{array}$$

$(15x^2 + 23x + 4) \div (5x + 1) = 3x + 4$

11. $(15x^2 + 23x + 4) \div (5x + 1) = 3x + 4$

Check: $(5x + 1)(3x + 4) = 15x^2 + 23x + 4$

13. $(28x^2 - 29x + 6) \div (4x - 3)$

$$\begin{array}{r} 7x - 2 \\ 4x-3 \overline{)28x^2 - 29x + 6} \\ \underline{28x^2 - 21x} \\ -8x + 6 \\ \underline{-8x + 6} \end{array}$$

$(28x^2 - 29x + 6) \div (4x - 3) = 7x - 2$

Check: $(4x - 3)(7x - 2) = 28x^2 - 29x + 6$

15. $(x^3 - x^2 + 11x - 1) \div (x + 1)$

$$\begin{array}{r} x^2 - 2x + 13 \\ x+1 \overline{)x^3 - x^2 + 11x - 1} \\ \underline{x^3 + x^2} \\ -2x^2 + 11x \\ \underline{-2x^2 - 2x} \\ 13x - 1 \\ \underline{13x + 13} \\ -14 \end{array}$$

$(x^3 - x^2 + 11x - 1) \div (x + 1)$

$$= x^2 - 2x + 13 - \frac{14}{x + 1}$$

Check: $(x + 1)\left(x^2 - 2x + 13 - \dfrac{14}{x + 1} \right)$

$$= (x + 1)(x^2 - 2x + 13) - (x + 1)\left(\frac{14}{x + 1} \right)$$

$$= x^3 - 2x^2 + 13x + x^2 - 2x + 13 - 14$$

$$= x^3 - x^2 + 11x - 1$$

© 2006 Pearson Education, Inc., Upper Saddle River, NJ. All rights reserved. This material is protected under all copyright laws as they currently exist. No portion of this material may be reproduced, in any form or by any means, without permission in writing from the publisher.

17. $(2x^3 - x^2 - 7) \div (x - 2)$

$$
\begin{array}{r}
2x^2 + 3x + 6 \\
x-2 \overline{\smash{)}\, 2x^3 - x^2 + 0x - 7} \\
\underline{2x^3 - 4x^2} \\
3x^2 + 0x \\
\underline{3x^2 - 6x} \\
6x - 7 \\
\underline{6x - 12} \\
5
\end{array}
$$

$(2x^3 - x^2 - 7) \div (x - 2)$

$= 2x^2 + 3x + 6 + \dfrac{5}{x - 2}$

19. $\dfrac{4x^3 - 6x^2 - 3}{2x + 1}$

$$
\begin{array}{r}
2x^2 - 4x + 2 \\
2x+1 \overline{\smash{)}\, 4x^3 - 6x^2 + 0x - 3} \\
\underline{4x^3 + 2x^2} \\
-8x^2 + 0x \\
\underline{-8x^2 - 4x} \\
4x - 3 \\
\underline{4x + 2} \\
-5
\end{array}
$$

21. $\dfrac{2x^4 - x^3 + 16x^2 - 4}{2x - 1}$

$$
\begin{array}{r}
x^3 + 8x + 4 \\
2x-1 \overline{\smash{)}\, 2x^4 - x^3 + 16x^2 + 0x - 4} \\
\underline{2x^4 - x^3} \\
16x^2 + 0x \\
\underline{16x^2 - 8x} \\
8x - 4 \\
\underline{8x - 4}
\end{array}
$$

21. $\dfrac{2x^4 - x^3 + 16x^2 - 4}{2x - 1} = x^3 + 8x + 4$

23. $\dfrac{6t^4 - 5t^3 - 8t^2 + 16t - 8}{3t^2 + 2t - 4}$

$$
\begin{array}{r}
2t^2 - 3t + 2 \\
3t^2+2t-4 \overline{\smash{)}\, 6t^4 - 5t^3 - 8t^2 + 16t - 8} \\
\underline{6t^4 + 4t^3 - 8t^2} \\
-9t^3 \qquad + 16t \\
\underline{-9t^3 - 6t^2 + 12t} \\
6t^2 + 4t - 8 \\
\underline{6t^2 + 4t - 8}
\end{array}
$$

$\dfrac{6t^4 - 5t^3 - 8t^2 + 16t - 8}{3t^2 + 2t - 4} = 2t^2 - 3t + 2$

25. $A = LW$

$18x^3 - 21x^2 + 11x - 2 = (6x^2 - 5x + 2)W$

$W = \dfrac{18x^3 - 21x^2 + 11x - 2}{6x^2 - 5x + 2}$

$$
\begin{array}{r}
3x - 1 \\
6x^2-5x+2 \overline{\smash{)}\, 18x^3 - 21x^2 + 11x - 2} \\
\underline{18x^3 - 15x^2 + 6x} \\
-6x^2 + 5x - 2 \\
\underline{-6x^2 + 5x - 2}
\end{array}
$$

The width of the solar panel is $3x - 1$ meters.

27. The graphs of $y_1 = \dfrac{2x^2 - x - 10}{2x - 5}$ and

$y_2 = x + 2$ coincide.

Cumulative Review

27. $m = \dfrac{y_2 - y_1}{x_2 - x_1} = \dfrac{0 - (-1)}{-\dfrac{1}{3} - \dfrac{1}{2}} = -\dfrac{6}{5}$

123

© 2006 Pearson Education, Inc., Upper Saddle River, NJ. All rights reserved. This material is protected under all copyright laws as they currently exist. No portion of this material may be reproduced, in any form or by any means, without permission in writing from the publisher.

29. $2(x+5)-3y=5x-(2-y)$

$2x+10-3y=5x-2+y$

$3x=12-4y$

$x=\dfrac{12-4y}{3}$

31. From the table, if one person likes Grape, then it is Curt

	Coke	RB	Grape	7-Up	Orange	Ale
Sylvia	yes	no	no			
Curt		yes		yes	no	
Fritz	yes		no	no		yes

5.3 Exercises

1. $(2x^2-11x-8)\div(x-6)$

$$\underline{6}\begin{array}{rrr} 2 & -11 & -8 \\ & 12 & 6 \\ \hline 2 & 1 & \underline{-2} \end{array}$$

$(2x-11x-8)\div(x-6)=$

$2x+1+\dfrac{-2}{x-6}$

3. $(3x^3+x^2-x+4)\div(x+1)$

$$\underline{-1}\begin{array}{rrrr} 3 & 1 & -1 & 4 \\ & -3 & 2 & -1 \\ \hline 3 & -2 & 1 & \underline{3} \end{array}$$

$(3x^3+x^2-x+4)\div(x+1)$

$=3x^2-2x+1+\dfrac{3}{x+1}$

5. $(x^3+7x^2+17x+15)\div(x+3)$

$$\underline{-3}\begin{array}{rrrr} 1 & 7 & 17 & 15 \\ & -3 & -12 & -15 \\ \hline 1 & 4 & 5 & \underline{0} \end{array}$$

$(x^3+7x^2+17x+15)\div(x+3)$

$=x^2+4x+5$

7. $(7x^3+6x^2-40x-15)\div(x-2)$

$$\underline{2}\begin{array}{rrrr} 7 & 6 & -40 & -15 \\ & 14 & 40 & 0 \\ \hline 7 & 20 & 0 & \underline{-15} \end{array}$$

$(7x^3+6x^2-40x-15)\div(x-2)$

$=7x^2+20x+\dfrac{-15}{x-2}$

9. $(x^3-2x^2+8)\div(x+2)$

$$\underline{-2}\begin{array}{rrrr} 1 & -2 & 0 & 8 \\ & -2 & 8 & -16 \\ \hline 1 & -4 & 8 & \underline{-8} \end{array}$$

$(x^3-2x^2+8)\div(x+2)$

$=x^2-4x+8+\dfrac{-8}{x+2}$

11. $(6x^4+13x^3+35x-24)\div(x+3)$

$$\underline{-3}\begin{array}{rrrrr} 6 & 13 & 0 & 35 & -24 \\ & -18 & 15 & -45 & 30 \\ \hline 6 & -5 & 15 & -10 & \underline{6} \end{array}$$

$(x^3-2x^2+8)\div(x+2)$

$=6x^3-5x^2+15x-10+\dfrac{6}{x+3}$

13. $(2x^4+3x^3+x^2+2x+5)\div(x+1)$

$$\underline{-1}\begin{array}{rrrrr} 2 & 3 & 1 & 2 & 5 \\ & -2 & -1 & 0 & -2 \\ \hline 2 & 1 & 0 & 2 & \underline{3} \end{array}$$

$(2x^4+3x^3+x^2+2x+5)\div(x+1)$

$=2x^3+x^2+2+\dfrac{3}{x+1}$

124

© 2006 Pearson Education, Inc., Upper Saddle River, NJ. All rights reserved. This material is protected under all copyright laws as they currently exist. No portion of this material may be reproduced, in any form or by any means, without permission in writing from the publisher.

15. $(3x^5 + x - 1) \div (x + 1)$

$$\underline{-1}\; \begin{array}{rrrrrr} 3 & 0 & 0 & 0 & 1 & -1 \\ & -3 & 3 & -3 & 3 & -4 \\ \hline 3 & -3 & 3 & -3 & 4 & \underline{|-5} \end{array}$$

$(3x^5 + x - 1) \div (x + 1)$

$= 3x^4 - 3x^3 + 3x^2 - 3x + 4 + \dfrac{-5}{x+1}$

17. $(7x^5 - x^3 + 3x^2 + 2) \div (x + 1)$

$$\underline{-1}\; \begin{array}{rrrrrr} 7 & 0 & -1 & 3 & 0 & 2 \\ & -7 & 7 & -6 & 3 & -3 \\ \hline 7 & -7 & 6 & -3 & 3 & \underline{|-1} \end{array}$$

$(7x^5 - x^3 + 3x^2 + 2) \div (x + 1)$

$= 7x^4 - 7x^3 + 6x^2 - 3x + 3 + \dfrac{-1}{x+1}$

19. $(x^6 - 5x^3 + x^2 + 12) \div (x + 1)$

$$\underline{-1}\; \begin{array}{rrrrrrr} 1 & 0 & 0 & -5 & 1 & 0 & 12 \\ & -1 & 1 & -1 & 6 & -7 & 7 \\ \hline 1 & -1 & 1 & -6 & 7 & -7 & \underline{|19} \end{array}$$

$(x^6 - 5x^3 + x^2 + 12) \div (x + 1)$

$= x^5 - x^4 + x^3 - 6x^2 + 7x - 7 + \dfrac{19}{x+1}$

21. $(x^3 + 2.5x^2 - 3.6x + 5.4) \div (x - 1.2)$

$$\underline{1.2}\; \begin{array}{rrrr} 1 & 2.5 & -3.6 & 5.4 \\ & 1.2 & 4.44 & 1.008 \\ \hline 1 & 3.7 & 0.84 & \underline{|6.408} \end{array}$$

$(x^3 + 2.5x^2 - 3.6x + 5.4) \div (x - 1.2)$

$= x^2 + 3.7x + 0.84 + \dfrac{6.408}{x - 1.2}$

23. $(2x^4 + 12x^3 + ax^2 - 5x + 75) \div (x + 5)$

$$\underline{-5}\; \begin{array}{rrrrr} 2 & 12 & a & -5 & 75 \\ & -10 & -10 & -5a+50 & 25a-225 \\ \hline 2 & 2 & a-10 & -5a+45 & \underline{|25a-150} \end{array}$$

Remainder $= 0 \Rightarrow 25a - 150 = 0,\; a = 6$

25. $(4x^3 - 6x^2 + 6) \div (2x + 3)$

$$\underline{-\dfrac{3}{2}}\; \begin{array}{rrrr} 4 & -6 & 0 & 6 \\ & & -6 & 18 & -27 \\ \hline 4 & -12 & 18 & \underline{|-21} \end{array}$$

$(4x^3 - 6x^2 + 6) \div (2x + 3)$

$= \dfrac{4x^2 - 12x + 18}{2} + \dfrac{-21}{2x+3}$

$= 2x^2 - 6x + 9 + \dfrac{-21}{2x+3}$

27. We are using the basic property of fractions that for any nonzero polynomial a, b, and c, $\dfrac{ac}{bc} = \dfrac{a}{b}$.

Cumulative Review

29. $2,000,000 \text{ gallon} \cdot \dfrac{0.134 \text{ cubic feet}}{\text{gallon}}$

$= 268,000 \text{ cubic feet}$

31. $p(x) = 2x^4 - 3x^2 + 6x - 1$

$p(-3) = 2(-3)^4 - 3(-3)^2 + 6(-3) - 1$

$p(-3) = 116$

5.4 Exercises

1. $80 - 10y = 10(8 - y)$

3. $5a^2 - 25a = 5a(a - 5)$

125

© 2006 Pearson Education, Inc., Upper Saddle River, NJ. All rights reserved. This material is protected under all copyright laws as they currently exist. No portion of this material may be reproduced, in any form or by any means, without permission in writing from the publisher.

5. $3c^2x^3 - 9cx - 6c = 3c(cx^3 - 3x - 2)$

7. $30y^4 + 24y^3 + 18y^2 = 6y^2(5y^2 + 4y + 3)$

9. $15ab^2 + 5ab - 10a^3b = 5ab(3b + 1 - 2a^2)$

11. $12xy^3 - 24x^3y^2 + 36x^2y^4 - 60x^4y^3$
$= 12xy^2(y - 2x^2 + 3xy^2 - 5x^3y)$

13. $3x(x + y) - 2(x + y) = (x + y)(3x - 2)$

15. $5b(a - 3b) + 8(-3b + a)$
$= 5b(a - 3b) + 8(a - 3b)$
$= (a - 3b)(5b + 8)$

17. $3x(a + 5b) + (a + 5b) = (a + 5b)(3x + 1)$

19. $2a^2(3x - y) - 5b^3(3x - y)$
$= (3x - y)(2a^2 - 5b^3)$

21. $3x(5x + y) - 8y(5x + y) - (5x + y)$
$= (5x + y)(3x - 8y - 1)$

23. $2a(a - 6b) - 3b(a - 6b) - 2(a - 6b)$
$= (a - 6b)(2a - 3b - 2)$

25. $x^3 + 5x^2 + 3x + 15$
$= x^2(x + 5) + 3(x + 5)$
$= (x + 5)(x^2 + 3)$

27. $2x + 6 - 3ax - 9a = 2(x + 3) - 3a(x + 3)$
$= (x + 3)(2 - 3a)$

29. $ab - 4a + 12 - 3b = a(b - 4) - 3(-4 + b)$
$= a(b - 4) - 3(b - 4)$
$= (b - 4)(a - 3)$

31. $5x - 30 - 2xy + 12y = 5(x - 6) - 2y(x - 6)$
$= (x - 6)(5 - 2y)$

33. $9y + 2x - 6 - 3xy = 2x - 6 - 3xy + 9y$
$= 2(x - 3) - 3y(x - 3)$
$= (x - 3)(2 - 3y)$

35. $yz^2 - 15 - 3z^2 + 5y = yz^2 - 3z^2 + 5y - 15$
$= z^2(y - 3) + 5(y - 3)$
$= (y - 3)(z^2 + 5)$

37. $s^3r - t - s^2 + srt = s^3r - s^2 + srt - t$
$= s^2(sr - 1) + t(sr - 1)$
$= (sr - 1)(s^2 + t)$

39. $\frac{1}{3}x^3 + \frac{1}{2}x^2 + \frac{1}{6}x = x\left(\frac{1}{3}x^2 + \frac{1}{2}x + \frac{1}{6}\right)$

Cumulative Review

41. $6x - 2y = -12$

x	y
-2	0
-1	3
0	6

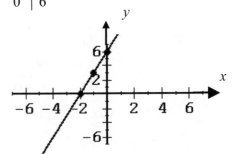

43. $m = \dfrac{y_2 - y_1}{x_2 - x_1} = \dfrac{-1 - 3}{6 - 2} = -1$

© 2006 Pearson Education, Inc., Upper Saddle River, NJ. All rights reserved. This material is protected under all copyright laws as they currently exist. No portion of this material may be reproduced, in any form or by any means, without permission in writing from the publisher.

45. $x =$ number of multiple choice
  questions answered correctly
$$4x + 5(22 - 4 - x) = 82$$
$$4x + 110 - 20 - 5x = 82$$
$$-x = -8$$
$$x = 8$$
The student answered 8 multiple-choice
questions correctly.

5.5 Exercises

1. $x^2 + 8x + 7 = (x + 1)(x + 7)$

3. $x^2 - 9x + 14 = (x - 7)(x - 2)$

5. $x^2 - 10x + 24 = (x - 6)(x - 4)$

7. $a^2 + 4a - 45 = (a + 9)(a - 5)$

9. $x^2 - xy - 42y^2 = (x - 7y)(x + 6y)$

11. $x^2 - 15xy + 14y^2 = (x - 14y)(x - y)$

13. $x^4 - 3x^2 - 40 = (x^2 - 8)(x^2 + 5)$

15. $x^4 + 16x^2y^2 + 63y^4$
$$= (x^2 + 7y^2)(x^2 + 9y^2)$$

17. $2x^2 + 26x + 44 = 2(x^2 + 13x + 22)$
$$= 2(x + 11)(x + 2)$$

19. $x^3 + x^2 - 20x = x(x^2 + x - 20)$
$$= x(x + 5)(x - 4)$$

21. $2x^2 - x - 1 = (2x + 1)(x - 1)$

23. $6x^2 - 7x - 5 = (3x - 5)(2x + 1)$

25. $3a^2 - 8a + 5 = (3a - 5)(a - 1)$

27. $8a^2 + 14a - 9 = (4a + 9)(2a - 1)$

29. $2x^2 + 13x + 15 = (2x + 3)(x + 5)$

31. $3x^4 - 8x^2 - 3 = (3x^2 + 1)(x^2 - 3)$

33. $6x^2 + 35xy + 11y^2 = (3x + y)(2x + 11y)$

35. $7x^2 + 11xy - 6y^2 = (7x - 3y)(x + 2y)$

37. $4x^3 + 4x^2 - 15x = x(4x^2 + 4x - 15)$
$$= x(2x + 5)(2x - 3)$$

39. $10x^4 + 15x^3 + 5x^2 = 5x^2(2x^2 + 3x + 1)$
$$= 5x^2(2x + 1)(x + 1)$$

41. $x^2 - 2x - 63 = (x - 9)(x + 7)$

43. $6x^2 + x - 2 = (3x + 2)(2x - 1)$

45. $x^2 - 20x + 51 = (x - 17)(x - 3)$

47. $15x^2 + x - 2 = (5x + 2)(3x - 1)$

49. $2x^2 + 4x - 96 = 2(x^2 + 2x - 48)$
$$= 2(x + 8)(x - 6)$$

51. $18x^2 + 21x + 6 = 3(6x^2 + 7x + 2)$
$$= 3(3x + 2)(2x + 1)$$

53. $27ax^2 + 99ax - 36a = 9a(3x^2 + 11x - 4)$
$$= 9a(3x - 1)(x + 4)$$

55. $6x^3 + 26x^2 - 20x = 2x(3x^2 + 13x - 10)$
$$= 2x(3x - 2)(x + 5)$$

© 2006 Pearson Education, Inc., Upper Saddle River, NJ. All rights reserved. This material is protected under all copyright laws as they currently exist.
No portion of this material may be reproduced, in any form or by any means, without permission in writing from the publisher.

57. $3x^4 - 2x^2 - 5 = (3x^2 - 5)(x^2 + 1)$

59. $9a^2 - 18ab - 7b^2 = (3a + b)(3a - 7b)$

61. $x^6 - 10x^3 - 39 = (x^3 - 13)(x^3 + 3)$

63. $4x^3 y + 2x^2 y - 2xy = 2xy(2x^2 + x - 1)$
$$= 2xy(2x - 1)(x + 1)$$

65. $30x^2 + 19x - 5 = (6x + 5)(5x - 1)$
One possibility would be $6x + 5$ rows with $5x - 1$ trees in each row. Another possibility would be $5x - 1$ rows with $6x + 5$ trees in each row.

Cumulative Review

67. $A = \pi r^2 \approx 3.14(3)^2 = 28.26$ in.^{2}

69. (a) $m = \dfrac{48}{156} = \dfrac{4}{13} \approx 30.8\%$

(b) Yes, the hill violates the city ordinance because the hill has a slope of 30.8% which is greater than 30%.

71. $x =$ number of racks
$y =$ number of helmets
$$x + y = 120$$
$$60x + 70y = 7950$$
$$-60x - 60y = -7200$$
$$\underline{60x + 70y = 7950}$$
$$10y = 750$$
$$y = 75$$
$$x + 75 = 120$$
$$x = 45$$
They should stock 45 bike racks and 75 helmets.

How Am I Doing? Sections 5.1-5.5

1. $(5x^2 - 3x + 2) + (-3x^2 - 5x - 8)$
$$-(x^2 + 3x - 10)$$
$$= 5x^2 - 3x + 2 - 3x^2 - 5x - 8$$
$$- x^2 - 3x + 10$$
$$= x^2 - 11x + 4$$

2. $(x^2 - 3x - 4)(2x - 3)$
$$= 2x^3 - 3x^2 - 6x^2 + 9x - 8x + 12$$
$$= 2x^3 - 9x^2 + x + 12$$

3. $(5a - 8)(a - 7)$
$$= 5a^2 - 35a - 8a + 56$$
$$= 5a^2 - 43a + 56$$

4. $(2y - 3)(2y + 3)$
$$= 4y^2 - 3^3$$
$$= 4y^2 - 9$$

5. $(3x^2 + 4)^2$
$$= (3x^2)^2 + 2(3x^2)(4) + 4^2$$
$$= 9x^4 + 24x^2 + 16$$

6. $p(x) = 2x^3 - 5x^2 - 6x + 1$
$$p(-3) = 2(-3)^3 - 5(-3)^2 - 6(-3) + 1$$
$$p(-3) = -80$$

7. $\dfrac{25x^3 y^2 - 30x^2 y^3 - 50x^2 y^2}{5x^2 y^2}$
$$= \dfrac{25x^3 y^2}{5x^2 y^2} - \dfrac{30x^2 y^3}{5x^2 y^2} - \dfrac{50x^2 y^2}{5x^2 y^2}$$
$$= 5x - 6y - 10$$

© 2006 Pearson Education, Inc., Upper Saddle River, NJ. All rights reserved. This material is protected under all copyright laws as they currently exist. No portion of this material may be reproduced, in any form or by any means, without permission in writing from the publisher.

8. $(3y^3 - 5y^2 + 2y - 1) \div (y - 2)$

$$
\require{enclose}
\begin{array}{r}
3y^2 + y + 4 \\[2pt]
y-2 \enclose{longdiv}{3y^3 - 5y^2 + 2y - 1} \\
\end{array}
$$

$$\underline{3y^3 - 6y^2}$$
$$y^2 + 2y$$
$$\underline{y^2 - 2y}$$
$$4y - 1$$
$$\underline{4y - 8}$$
$$7$$

$(3y^3 - 5y^2 + 2y - 1) \div (y - 2)$

$= 3y^2 + y + 4 + \dfrac{7}{y - 2}$

9. $(2x^4 + 9x^3 + 8x^2 - 9x - 10) \div (2x + 5)$

$$
\begin{array}{r}
x^3 + 2x^2 - x - 2 \\
2x+5 \enclose{longdiv}{2x^4 + 9x^3 + 8x^2 - 9x - 10}
\end{array}
$$

$$\underline{2x^4 + 5x^3}$$
$$4x^3 + 8x^2$$
$$\underline{4x^2 + 10x^2}$$
$$-2x^2 - 9x$$
$$\underline{-2x^2 - 5x}$$
$$-4x - 10$$
$$\underline{-4x - 10}$$
$$0$$

$(2x^4 + 9x^3 + 8x^2 - 9x - 10) \div (2x + 5)$

$= x^3 + 2x^2 - x - 2$

10. $(2x^4 + 10x^3 + 11x^2 - 6x - 9) \div (x + 3)$

$$
\begin{array}{r|rrrrr}
-3 & 2 & 10 & 11 & -6 & -9 \\
   &   & -6 & -12 & 3 & 9 \\
\hline
   & 2 & 4 & -1 & -3 & \underline{|0} \\
\end{array}
$$

$(2x^4 + 10x^3 + 11x^2 - 6x - 9) \div (x + 3)$

$= 2x^3 + 4x^2 - x - 3$

11. $24a^3b^2 + 36a^4b^2 - 60a^3b^3$

$\quad = 12a^3b^2(2 + 3a - 5b)$

12. $3x(4x - 3y) - 2(4x - 3y)$

$\quad = (4x - 3y)(3x - 2)$

13. $10wx + 6zx - 15yz - 25wy$

$\quad = 2x(5w + 3z) - 5y(3z + 5w)$

$\quad = (5w + 3z)(2x - 5y)$

14. $10a^2 - 8ab - 5ab + 4b^2$

$\quad = 2a(5a - 4b) - b(5a - 4b)$

$\quad = (5a - 4b)((2a - b)$

15. $x^2 - 7x + 10 = (x - 5)(x - 2)$

16. $4y^2 - 4y - 15 = (2y - 5)(2y + 3)$

17. $28x^2 - 19xy + 3y^2 = (7x - 3y)(4x - y)$

18. $2x^2 + 17x + 35 = (x + 5)(2x + 7)$

19. $3x^2 - 6x - 72 = 3(x^2 - 2x - 24)$

$\qquad\qquad\qquad = 3(x + 4)(x - 6)$

20. $8x^2 - 18x + 9 = (4x - 3)(2x - 3)$

129

© 2006 Pearson Education, Inc., Upper Saddle River, NJ. All rights reserved. This material is protected under all copyright laws as they currently exist.
No portion of this material may be reproduced, in any form or by any means, without permission in writing from the publisher.

5.6 Exercises

1. There will be two terms, both of which are perfect squares, which have the form $a^2 - b^2$.

3. There will be two terms, both of which are perfect cubes, which have the form $a^3 + b^3$.

5. $a^2 - 64 = (a+8)(a-8)$

7. $16x^2 - 81 = (4x+9)(4x-9)$

9. $64x^2 - 1 = (8x+1)(8x-1)$

11. $49m^2 - 9n^2 = (7m+3n)(7m-3n)$

13. $100y^2 - 81 = (10y+9)(10y-9)$

15. $1 - 81x^2y^2 = (1+9xy)(1-9xy)$

17. $32x^2 - 18 = 2(16x^2 - 9)$
$= 2(4x+3)(4x-3)$

19. $5x - 20x^3 = 5x(1-4x^2)$
$= 5x(1+2x)(1-2x)$

21. $9x^2 - 6x + 1 = (3x-1)^2$

23. $49x^2 - 14x + 1 = (7x-1)^2$

25. $81w^2 + 36wt + 4t^2 = (9w+2t)^2$

27. $36x^2 + 60xy + 25y^2 = (6x+5y)^2$

29. $8x^2 + 24x + 18 = 2(4x^2 + 12x + 9)$
$= 2(2x+3)^2$

31. $3x^3 - 24x^2 + 48x = 3x(x^2 - 8x + 16)$
$= 3x(x-4)^2$

33. $x^3 - 27 = (x-3)(x^2 + 3x + 9)$

35. $x^3 + 125 = (x+5)(x^2 - 5x + 25)$

37. $64x^3 - 1 = (4x-1)(16x^2 + 4x + 1)$

39. $125x^3 - 8 = (5x-2)(25x^2 + 10x + 4)$

41. $1 - 27x^3 = (1-3x)(1+3x+9x^2)$

43. $64x^3 + 125 = (4x+5)(16x^2 - 20x + 25)$

45. $64s^6 + t^6 = (4s^2 + t^2)(16s^4 - 4s^2t^2 + t^4)$

47. $6y^3 - 6 = 6(y^3 - 1)$
$= 6(y-1)(y^2 + y + 1)$

49. $3x^3 - 24 = 3(x^3 - 8)$
$= 3(x-2)(x^2 + 2x + 4)$

51. $x^5 - 8x^2y^3 = x^2(x^3 - 8y^3)$
$= x^2(x-2y)(x^2 + 2xy + 4y^2)$

53. $25w^4 - 1 = (5w^2 + 1)(5w^2 - 1)$

55. $b^4 + 6b^2 + 9 = (b^2 + 3)^2$

57. $49m^6 - 81 = (7m^3 + 9)(7m^3 - 9)$

59. $36y^6 - 60y^3 + 25$
$= (6y^3)^2 - 2(6y^3)(5) + 5^2$
$= (6y^3 - 5)^2$

130

© 2006 Pearson Education, Inc., Upper Saddle River, NJ. All rights reserved. This material is protected under all copyright laws as they currently exist. No portion of this material may be reproduced, in any form or by any means, without permission in writing from the publisher.

61. $2a^8 - 50 = 2((a^4)^2 - 5^2)$
$$= 2(a^4 + 5)(a^4 - 5)$$

63. $125m^3 + 8n^3$
$$= (5m + 2n)(25m^2 - 10mn + 4n^2)$$

65. $24a^3 - 3b^3 = 3(8a^3 - b^3)$
$$= 3(2a - b)(4a^2 + 2ab + b^2)$$

67. $4w^2 - 20wz + 25z^2 = (2w - 5z)^2$

69. $36a^2 - 81b^2 = 9(4a^2 - 9b^2)$
$$= 9(2a + 3b)(2a - 3b)$$

71. $16x^4 - 81y^4$
$$= (4x^2 + 9y^2)(4x - 9y^2)$$
$$= (4x^2 + 9y^2)(2x + 3y)(2x - 3y)$$

73. $125m^6 + 8 = (5m^2)^3 + 2^3$
$$= (5m^2 + 2)(25m^4 - 10m^2 + 4)$$

75. $25x^2 + 25x + 4 = (5x)^2 + 25x + 2^2$
$$25 \neq 2(5)(2) = 20$$
$$25x^2 + 25x + 4 = (5x + 4)(5x + 1)$$

77. $4x^2 - 15x + 9 = (2x)^2 - 15x + (3)^2$
$$2(2x)(3) = 12x \neq 15x$$
$$4x^2 - 15x + 9 = (4x - 3)(x - 3)$$

79. $A = (4x)(4x) - y^2$
$$A = 16x^2 - y^2$$
$$A = (4x - y)(4x + y) \text{ ft}^2$$

Cumulative Review

81.
$$3200x + 29{,}000 = 1200x + 27{,}000 + 20{,}000$$
$$3200x + 29{,}000 = 1200x + 47{,}000$$
$$2000x = 18{,}000$$
$$x = 9$$
In 9 years, the year 2005, the bachelor's degree in math will be offered $20,000 per year more than a bachelor's degree in marketing.

83. $x = $ length of second side
$$\frac{2}{3}x + x + x - 14 = 66$$
$$\frac{8}{3}x = 80$$
$$x = 30$$
$$\frac{2}{3}x = 20$$
$$x - 14 = 16$$
The first side is 20 cm, the second side is 30 cm, and the third side is 16 cm.

5.7 Exercises

1. In any factoring problem the first step is to factor out <u>a common factor if possible</u>.

3. $49x^2 + 9y^2 = (7x)^2 + (9y)^2$ has the form $a^2 + b^2$, the sum of two squares, which cannot be factored; it is prime.

5. $3xy - 6yz = 3y(x - 2z)$

7. $y^2 + 7y - 18 = (y + 9)(y - 2)$

9. $3x^2 - 8x + 5 = (3x - 5)(x - 1)$

© 2006 Pearson Education, Inc., Upper Saddle River, NJ. All rights reserved. This material is protected under all copyright laws as they currently exist. No portion of this material may be reproduced, in any form or by any means, without permission in writing from the publisher.

11. $ax - 2xy + 3aw - 6wy$
$$= x(a - 2y) + 3w(a - 2y)$$
$$= (a - 2y)(x + 3w)$$

13. $8x^3 - 125y^3$
$$= (2x - 5y)(4x^2 + 10xy + 25y^2)$$

15. $x^2 + 2xy - xz = x(x + 2y - z)$

17. $x^2 + 16$ Prime

19. $64y^2 - 25z^2 = (8y - 5z)(8y + 5z)$

21. $6x^2 - 23x - 4 = (6x + 1)(x - 4)$

23. $3x^2 - x - 1$ is prime.

25. $x^3 - 11x^2 + 30x = x(x^2 - 11x + 30)$
$$= x(x - 6)(x - 5)$$

27. $25x^2 - 40x + 16 = (5x - 4)^2$

29. $6a^2 - 6a - 36 = 6(a^2 - a - 6)$
$$= 6(a - 3)(a + 2)$$

31. $3x^2 - 3x - xy + y = 3x(x - 1) - y(x - 1)$
$$= (x - 1)(3x - y)$$

33. $81a^4 - 1 = (9a^2 + 1)(9a^2 - 1)$
$$= (9a^2 + 1)(3a + 1)(3a - 1)$$

35. $2x^5 - 16x^3 - 18x$
$$= 2x(x^4 - 8x^2 - 9)$$
$$= 2x(x^2 + 1)(x^2 - 9)$$
$$= 2x(x^2 + 1)(x + 3)(x - 3)$$

37. $8a^3b - 50ab^3 = 2ab(4a^2 - 25b^2)$
$$= 2ab(2a + 5b)(2a - 5b)$$

39. $4x^2 - 8x - 6 = 2(2x^2 - 4x - 3)$

41. $S = 10x(x - 10) + 16y(x - 10)$
$$S = 10x^2 - 100x + 16xy - 160y \text{ ft}^2$$

Cumulative Review

43. $3x - 2 \leq -5 + 2(x - 3)$
$$3x - 2 \leq -5 + 2x - 6$$
$$x \leq -9$$

45. $\left| \dfrac{1}{3}(5 - 4x) \right| > 4$

$\dfrac{1}{3}(5 - 4x) < -4$ or $\dfrac{1}{3}(5 - 4x) > 4$

$5 - 4x < -12$ $\qquad$ $5 - 4x > 12$

$-4x < -17$ $\qquad\qquad$ $-4x > 7$

$x > \dfrac{17}{4}$ $\qquad\qquad$ $x < -\dfrac{7}{4}$

47. $\dfrac{255 + 206 + 254 + 285 + 475}{5} = 295$

The average value of the net receipts for a 2-year period for the Republican Party was \$295 million.

49. $292 + (0.491)(292) = 435.372$

The expected net receipts for the Democratic Party in the 2005-2006 period would be approximately \$435.4 million.

© 2006 Pearson Education, Inc., Upper Saddle River, NJ. All rights reserved. This material is protected under all copyright laws as they currently exist. No portion of this material may be reproduced, in any form or by any means, without permission in writing from the publisher.

1. $x^2 - x - 6 = 0$

$(x-3)(x+2) = 0$

$x - 3 = 0$ or $x + 2 = 0$

$x = 3$ $x = -2$

Check: $3^2 - 3 - 6 \overset{?}{=} 0,\ 0 = 0$

$(-2)^2 - (-2) - 6 \overset{?}{=} 0,\ 0 = 0$

3. $5x^2 - 6x = 0$

$x(5x - 6) = 0$

$x = 0$ or $5x - 6 = 0$

$x = \dfrac{6}{5}$

Check: $5(0)^2 - 6(0) \overset{?}{=} 0,\ 0 = 0$

$5\left(\dfrac{6}{5}\right)^2 - 6\left(\dfrac{6}{5}\right) \overset{?}{=} 0,\ 0 = 0$

5. $25x^2 - 36 = 0$

$(5x + 6)(5x - 6) = 0$

$5x + 6 = 0$ or $5x - 6 = 0$

$x = -\dfrac{6}{5}$ $x = \dfrac{6}{5}$

Check: $25\left(-\dfrac{6}{5}\right)^2 - 36 \overset{?}{=} 0,\ 0 = 0$

$25\left(\dfrac{6}{5}\right)^2 - 36 \overset{?}{=} 0,\ 0 = 0$

7. $3x^2 - 2x - 8 = 0$

$(3x + 4)(x - 2) = 0$

$3x + 4 = 0$ or $x - 2 = 0$

$x = -\dfrac{4}{3}$ $x = 2$

7. Check: $3\left(-\dfrac{4}{3}\right)^2 - 2\left(-\dfrac{4}{3}\right) - 8 \overset{?}{=} 0,\ 0 = 0$

$3(2)^2 - 2(2) - 8 \overset{?}{=} 0,\ 0 = 0$

9. $8x^2 - 3 = 2x$

$8x^2 - 2x - 3 = 0$

$(4x - 3)(2x + 1) = 0$

$4x - 3 = 0$ or $2x + 1 = 0$

$x = \dfrac{3}{4}$ $x = -\dfrac{1}{2}$

Check: $8\left(\dfrac{3}{4}\right)^2 - 3 \overset{?}{=} 2\left(\dfrac{3}{4}\right),\ \dfrac{3}{2} = \dfrac{3}{2}$

$8\left(-\dfrac{1}{2}\right)^2 - 3 \overset{?}{=} 2\left(-\dfrac{1}{2}\right),\ -1 = -1$

11. $8x^2 = 11x - 3$

$8x^2 - 11x + 3 = 0$

$(8x - 3)(x - 1) = 0$

$8x - 3 = 0$ or $x - 1 = 0$

$x = \dfrac{3}{8}$ $x = 1$

Check: $8\left(\dfrac{3}{8}\right)^2 \overset{?}{=} 11\left(\dfrac{3}{8}\right) - 3,\ \dfrac{9}{8} = \dfrac{9}{8}$

$8(1)^2 \overset{?}{=} 11(1) - 3,\ 8 = 8$

13. $x^2 + \dfrac{5}{3}x = \dfrac{2}{3}x$

$x^2 + x = 0$

$x(x + 1) = 0$

$x = 0$ or $x + 1 = 0$

$x = -1$

133

© 2006 Pearson Education, Inc., Upper Saddle River, NJ. All rights reserved. This material is protected under all copyright laws as they currently exist.
No portion of this material may be reproduced, in any form or by any means, without permission in writing from the publisher.

13. Check: $0^2 + \frac{5}{3}(0) \overset{?}{=} \frac{2}{3}(0)$, $0 = 0$

$$1^2 + \frac{5}{3}(-1) \overset{?}{=} \frac{2}{3}(-1), \; -\frac{2}{3} = -\frac{2}{3}$$

15. $25x^2 + 10x + 1 = 0$

$$(5x + 1)^2 = 0$$

$$5x + 1 = 0$$

$$x = -\frac{1}{5} \text{ double root}$$

Check: $25\left(-\frac{1}{5}\right)^2 + 10\left(-\frac{1}{5}\right) + 1 \overset{?}{=} 0$

$$0 = 0$$

17. $x^3 + 5x^2 + 6x = 0$

$$x(x^2 + 5x + 6) = 0$$

$$x(x + 3)(x + 2) = 0$$

$$x = 0 \text{ or } x + 3 = 0 \text{ or } x + 2 = 0$$

$$x = -3 \qquad x = -2$$

Check: $0^3 + 5(0)^2 + 6(0) \overset{?}{=} 0$, $0 = 0$

$$(-3)^3 + 5(-3)^2 + 6(-3) \overset{?}{=} 0, \; 0 = 0$$

$$(-2)^3 + 5(-2)^2 + 6(-2) \overset{?}{=} 0, \; 0 = 0$$

19. $\frac{x^3}{6} - 8x = \frac{x^2}{3}$

$$x^3 - 2x^2 - 48x = 0$$

$$x(x^2 - 2x - 48) = 0$$

$$x(x - 8)(x + 6) = 0$$

$$x = 0 \text{ or } x - 8 = 0 \text{ or } x + 6 = 0$$

$$x = 8 \qquad x = -6$$

19. Check: $\frac{0^3}{6} - 8(0) \overset{?}{=} \frac{0^2}{3}$, $0 = 0$

$$\frac{(8)^3}{6} - 8(8) \overset{?}{=} \frac{(8)^2}{3}, \; \frac{64}{3} = \frac{64}{3}$$

$$\frac{(-6)^3}{6} - 8(-6) \overset{?}{=} \frac{(-6)^2}{3}, \; 12 = 12$$

21. $3x^3 - 10x = 17x$

$$3x^3 - 27x = 0$$

$$3x(x^2 - 9) = 0$$

$$3x(x + 3)(x - 3) = 0$$

$$3x = 0 \text{ or } x + 3 = 0 \text{ or } x - 3 = 0$$

$$x = 0 \qquad x = -3 \qquad x = 3$$

Check: $3(0)^3 - 10(0) \overset{?}{=} 17(0)$, $0 = 0$

$$3(-3)^3 - 10(-3) \overset{?}{=} 17(-3), \; -51 = -51$$

$$3(3)^3 - 10(3) \overset{?}{=} 17(3), \; 51 = 51$$

23. $3x^3 + 15x^2 = 42x$

$$3x^3 + 15x^2 - 42x = 0$$

$$3x(x^2 + 5x - 14) = 0$$

$$3x(x + 7)(x - 2) = 0$$

$$3x = 0 \text{ or } x + 7 = 0 \text{ or } x - 2 = 0$$

$$x = 0 \qquad x = -7 \qquad x = 2$$

Check: $3(0)^3 + 15(0)^2 \overset{?}{=} 42(0)$, $0 = 0$

$$3(-7)^3 + 15(-7)^2 \overset{?}{=} 42(-7), \; -294 = -294$$

$$3(2)^3 + 15(2)^2 \overset{?}{=} 42(2), \; 84 = 84$$

© 2006 Pearson Education, Inc., Upper Saddle River, NJ. All rights reserved. This material is protected under all copyright laws as they currently exist. No portion of this material may be reproduced, in any form or by any means, without permission in writing from the publisher.

25.
$$\frac{7x^2 - 3}{2} = 2x$$
$$7x^2 - 3 = 4x$$
$$7x^2 - 4x - 3 = 0$$
$$(7x + 3)(x - 1) = 0$$
$$7x + 3 = 0 \text{ or } x - 1 = 0$$
$$x = -\frac{3}{7} \qquad x = 1$$

Check: $\dfrac{7\left(-\dfrac{3}{7}\right)^2 - 3}{2} \overset{?}{=} 2\left(-\dfrac{3}{7}\right), \ -\dfrac{6}{7} = -\dfrac{6}{7}$

$$\frac{7(1)^2 - 3}{2} \overset{?}{=} 2(1), \ 2 = 2$$

27.
$$2(x + 3) = -3x + 2(x^2 - 3)$$
$$2x + 6 = -3x + 2x^2 - 6$$
$$2x^2 - 5x - 12 = 0$$
$$(2x + 3)(x - 4) = 0$$
$$2x + 3 = 0 \text{ or } x - 4 = 0$$
$$x = -\frac{3}{2} \qquad x = 4$$

Check:
$$2\left(-\frac{3}{2} + 3\right) \overset{?}{=} -3\left(-\frac{3}{2}\right) + 2\left(\left(-\frac{3}{2}\right)^2 - 3\right)$$
$$3 = 3$$
$$2(4 + 3) \overset{?}{=} -3(4) + 2(4^2 - 3)$$
$$14 = 14$$

29.
$$7x^2 + 6 = 2x^2 + 2(4x + 3)$$
$$5x^2 + 6 = 8x + 6$$
$$5x^2 - 8x = 0$$
$$x(5x - 8) = 0$$
$$x = 0 \text{ or } 5x - 8 = 0$$
$$x = \frac{8}{5}$$

Check: $7(0)^2 + 6 \overset{?}{=} 2(0)^2 + 2(4(0) + 3)$
$$6 = 6$$
$$7\left(\frac{8}{5}\right)^2 + 6 \overset{?}{=} 2\left(\frac{8}{5}\right)^2 + 2\left(4\left(\frac{8}{5}\right) + 3\right)$$
$$\frac{598}{25} = \frac{598}{25}$$

31. $2x^2 - 3x + c = 0$
$$2\left(-\frac{1}{2}\right)^2 - 3\left(-\frac{1}{2}\right) + c = 0 \Rightarrow 2 + c = 0$$
$$c = -2$$
$$2x^2 - 3x - 2 = 0 \Rightarrow (2x + 1)(x - 2) = 0$$
$$(2x + 1) = 0 \text{ or } (x - 2) = 0$$
$$2x + 1 = 0 \qquad x - 2 = 0$$
$$x = -\frac{1}{2} \qquad x = 2$$
$x = 2$ is the other solution.

33. $A = \dfrac{1}{2}bh = \dfrac{1}{2}(h + 2)h = 180$
$$h^2 + 2h - 360 = 0$$
$$(h - 18)(h + 20) = 0$$
$$h - 18 = 0 \quad \text{or} \quad h + 20 = 0$$
$$h = 18 \qquad\qquad h = -20, \text{ reject}$$
$h = 18$ in. for the altitude
$b = h + 2 = 20$ in. for the base

© 2006 Pearson Education, Inc., Upper Saddle River, NJ. All rights reserved. This material is protected under all copyright laws as they currently exist. No portion of this material may be reproduced, in any form or by any means, without permission in writing from the publisher.

35. $A = \dfrac{1}{2}bh = 104$

$\dfrac{1}{2}(3h+2)h = 104$

$3h^2 + 2h = 208$

$3h^2 + 2h - 208 = 0$

$(h-8)(3h+26) = 0$

$h - 8 = 0 \quad \text{or} \quad 3h + 26 = 0$

$h = 8 \qquad\qquad h = -\dfrac{26}{3}$

$\qquad\qquad\qquad\qquad \text{reject, } h > 0$

$b = 3h + 2 = 3(8) + 2 = 26$

(a) The altitude is 8 feet and the base is 26 feet.

(b) $8 \text{ feet}\left(\dfrac{\text{yard}}{3 \text{ feet}}\right) = 2\dfrac{2}{3} \text{ yards}$

$26 \text{ feet}\left(\dfrac{\text{yard}}{3 \text{ feet}}\right) = 8\dfrac{2}{3} \text{ yards}$

The altitude is $2\dfrac{2}{3}$ yards and the

base is $8\dfrac{2}{3}$ yards .

37. $A = LW = 896$
$W(W+4) = 896$

$W^2 + 4W - 896 = 0$

$(W-28)(W+32) = 0$

$W - 28 = 0 \quad \text{or} \quad W + 32 = 0$

$W = 28 \qquad\qquad W = -32$

$\qquad\qquad\qquad\qquad \text{reject, } W > 0$

$L = W + 4 = 32$

(a) The width is 28 cm and the length is 32 cm.

(b) The width is 280 mm and the length is 320 mm.

39. $s^2 = 4s + 96$

$s^2 - 4s - 96 = 0$

$(s-12)(s+8) = 0$

$s - 12 = 0 \quad \text{or} \quad s + 8 = 0$

$s = 12 \qquad\qquad s = -8$

$\qquad\qquad\qquad \text{reject, } s > 0$

Each side of the rug is 12 feet.

41. $V = LWH = 198$
$L \cdot 2(L+2) = 198$

$L^2 + 2L - 99 = 0$

$(L+11)(L-9) = 0$

$L + 11 = 0 \quad \text{or} \quad L - 9 = 0$

$L = -11 \qquad\qquad L = 9$

reject, $L > 0$

$H = L + 2 = 11$

The length is 9 inches and the height is 11 inches.

43. $A = LW = 54$
$(2W-3)W = 54$

$2W^2 - 3W - 54 = 0$

$(W-6)(2W+9) = 0$

$W - 6 = 0 \quad \text{or} \quad W + 9 = 0$

$W = 6 \qquad\qquad W = -9 \text{ reject, } W > 0$

$L = 2W - 3 = 9$

The length of the landing area is 9 miles and the width is 6 miles.

© 2006 Pearson Education, Inc., Upper Saddle River, NJ. All rights reserved. This material is protected under all copyright laws as they currently exist. No portion of this material may be reproduced, in any form or by any means, without permission in writing from the publisher.

45. $x = $ length of old side
$2x + 1 = $ length on new side
$$x^2 + 176 = (2x + 1)^2$$
$$3x^2 + 4x - 175 = 0$$
$$(3x + 25)(x - 7) = 0$$
$$x - 7 = 0 \quad \text{or} \quad 3x + 25 = 0$$

$\qquad x = 7 \qquad\qquad x = -\dfrac{25}{7} \text{ reject, } x > 0$

$2x + 1 = 15$
The old target is a square 7 cm on a side and the new target is a square 15 cm on a side.

47. $P = 2n^2 - 19n - 10$
$$410 = 2n^2 - 19n - 10$$
$$2n^2 - 19n - 420 = 0$$
$$(2n + 21)(n - 20) = 0$$
$$2n + 21 = 0 \quad \text{or} \quad n - 20 = 0$$

$\qquad n = -\dfrac{21}{2} \qquad\qquad n = 20$

reject, $n > 0$
20 units are produced when the profit is \$410.

49. $P = 2n^2 - 19n - 10$
$$-52 = 2n^2 - 19n + 42$$
$$2n^2 - 19n + 42 = 0$$
$$(2n - 7) \quad \text{or} \quad (n - 6) = 0$$

$\qquad n = \dfrac{7}{2} \qquad\qquad n = 6$

reject, n is a positive integer.
Producing 6 units will result in a loss of \$52.

51. $N = 28x^2 + 80x + 560$
$$N = 28(20)^2 + 80(20) + 560$$
$$N = 13,360$$

51. There were 13,360 mutual funds in the year 2000.

53. $N = 28x^2 + 80x + 560$
$$668 = 28x^2 + 80x + 560$$
$$7x^2 + 20x - 27 = 0$$
$$(7x + 27)(x - 1) = 0$$
$$7x + 27 = 0 \quad \text{or} \quad x - 1 = 0$$

$\qquad x = -\dfrac{27}{7} \qquad\qquad x = 1$

reject, $x > 0$
There were 668 mutual funds in 1981.

Cumulative Review

55. $(2x^3 y^2)^3 (5xy^2)^2$
$$= 2^3 (x^3)^3 (y^2)^3 5^2 x^2 (y^2)^2$$
$$= 8x^{3(3)} y^{2(3)} 25x^2 y^{2(2)}$$
$$= 200x^{9+2} y^{6+4}$$
$$= 200x^{11} y^{10}$$

57. Solve the second equation for y and substitute into the first equation
$$y = -x - 1$$
$$x - 2(-x - 1) = 8$$
$$x + 2x + 2 = 8$$
$$3x = 6$$
$$x = 2$$
$$y = -x - 1$$
$$y = -2 - 1$$
$$y = -3$$
The solution is $(2, -3)$.

137

© 2006 Pearson Education, Inc., Upper Saddle River, NJ. All rights reserved. This material is protected under all copyright laws as they currently exist. No portion of this material may be reproduced, in any form or by any means, without permission in writing from the publisher.

Putting Your Skills to Work

1. $f(x) = -7x^2 - 1250x + 200,000$

$\quad f(0) = 200,000$ blacksmiths in 1900

$\quad f(30) = -7(30)^2 - 1250(30) + 200,000$

$\quad f(30) = 156,200$ blacksmiths in 1930

2. $f(x) = -7x^2 - 1250x + 200,000$

$\quad f(40) = -7(40)^2 - 1250(40) + 200,000$

$\quad f(40) = 138,800$ blacksmiths in 1940

$\quad f(30) = -7(60)^2 - 1250(60) + 200,000$

$\quad f(30) = 99,800$ blacksmiths in 1960

3. $f(x) = -7x^2 - 1250x + 200,000$

$\quad f(90) = -7(90)^2 - 1250(90) + 200,000$

$\quad f(90) = 30,800$ blacksmiths in 1990

$\quad \dfrac{30,800 - 200,000}{30,800} = -0.846$

There was an 84.6% decrease from 1900 to 1990.

4. $f(x) = -7x^2 - 1250x + 200,000$

$\quad f(100) = -7(100)^2 - 1250(100) + 200,000$

$\quad f(100) = 5000$ blacksmiths in 2000

$\quad \dfrac{5000 - 138,800}{138,800} = -0.964$

There was a 96.4% decrease from 1940 to 2000.

5. $f(x) = 0.11x^3 - 1.9x^2 + 9.4x + 26$

$\quad f(2) = 0.11(2)^3 - 1.9(2)^2 + 9.4(2) + 26$

$\quad f(2) = 38.08 \rightarrow 38,000$ jobs in 2000

$\quad f(4) = 0.11(4)^3 - 1.9(4)^2 + 9.4(4) + 26$

$\quad f(4) = 40.24 \rightarrow 40,000$ jobs in 2002

5. $f(6) = 0.11(6)^3 - 1.9(6)^2 + 9.4(6) + 26$

$\quad f(6) = 37.76 \rightarrow 38,000$ jobs in 2004

$\quad f(8) = 0.11(8)^3 - 1.9(8)^2 + 9.4(8) + 26$

$\quad f(8) = 35.92 \rightarrow 36,000$ jobs in 2006

$\quad f(10) = 0.11(10)^3 - 1.9(10)^2 + 9.4(10) + 26$

$\quad f(10) = 40 \rightarrow 40,000$ jobs in 2008

$\quad f(12) = 0.11(12)^3 - 1.9(12)^2 + 9.4(12) + 26$

$\quad f(12) = 55.28 \rightarrow 55,000$ jobs in 2010

6.

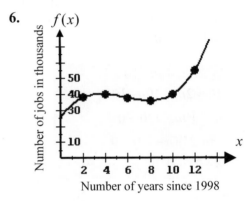

Number of years since 1998

7. $f(14) = 0.11(14)^3 - 1.9(14)^2 + 9.4(14) + 26$

$\quad f(14) = 87.04 \rightarrow 87,000$ jobs in 2012

8. Answers may vary but certainly changes in technology would be a factor.

Chapter 5 Review Problems

1. $(x^2 - 3x + 5) + (-2x^2 - 7x + 8)$

$\quad = x^2 - 3x + 5 - 2x^2 - 7x + 8$

$\quad = -x^2 - 10x + 13$

2. $(-4x^2y - 7xy + y) + (5x^2y + 2xy - 9y)$

$\quad = -4x^2y - 7xy + y + 5x^2y + 2xy - 9y$

$\quad = x^2y - 5xy - 8y$

© 2006 Pearson Education, Inc., Upper Saddle River, NJ. All rights reserved. This material is protected under all copyright laws as they currently exist. No portion of this material may be reproduced, in any form or by any means, without permission in writing from the publisher.

3. $(-6x^2 + 7xy - 3y^2) - (5x^2 - 3xy - 9y^2)$
$= -6x^2 + 7xy - 3y^2 - 5x^2 + 3xy + 9y^2$
$= -11x^2 + 10xy + 6y^2$

4. $(-13x^2 + 9x - 14) - (-2x^2 - 6x + 1)$
$= -13x^2 + 9x - 14 + 2x^2 + 6x - 1)$
$-11x^2 + 15x - 15$

5. $(3x - 1) - (2 - 8x) + (x + 7)$
$= 3x - 1 - 2 + 8x + x + 7$
$= 12x + 4$

6. $(x^2 + 4) + (3x - 5) - (2x^2 - x)$
$= x^2 + 4 + 3x - 5 - 2x^2 + x$
$= -x^2 + 4x - 1$

7. $p(x) = 3x^3 - 2x^2 - 6x + 1$
$p(-4) = 3(-4)^3 - 2(-4)^2 - 6(-4) + 1$
$p(-4) = -199$

8. $p(x) = 3x^3 - 2x^2 - 6x + 1$
$p(-1) = 3(-1)^3 - 2(-1)^2 - 6(-1) + 1$
$p(-1) = 2$

9. $p(x) = 3x^3 - 2x^2 - 6x + 1$
$p(3) = 3(3)^3 - 2(3)^2 - 6(3) + 1$
$p(3) = 46$

10. $g(x) = -2x^4 + x^3 - 5x - 2$
$g(2) = -2(2)^4 + (2)^3 - 5(2) - 2 = -36$

11. $g(x) = -2x^4 + x^3 - 5x - 2$
$g(-3) = -2(-3)^4 + (-3)^3 - 5(-3) - 2$
$g(-3) = -176$

12. $g(x) = -2x^4 + x^3 - 5x - 2$
$g(0) = -2(0)^4 + (0)^3 - 5(0) - 2$
$g(0) = -2$

13. $h(x) = -x^3 - 6x^2 + 12x - 4$
$h(3) = -(3)^3 - 6(3)^2 + 12(3) - 4$
$h(3) = -49$

14. $h(x) = -x^3 - 6x^2 + 12x - 4$
$h(-2) = -(-2)^3 - 6(-2)^2 + 12(-2) - 4$
$h(-2) = -44$

15. $h(x) = -x^3 - 6x^2 + 12x - 4$
$h(0) = -(0)^3 - 6(0)^2 + 12(0) - 4$
$h(0) = -4$

16. $3xy(x^2 - xy + y^2)$
$= 3x^3y - 3x^2y^2 + 3xy^3$

17. $(3x^2 + 1)(2x - 1) = 6x^3 - 3x^2 + 2x - 1$

18. $(5x^2 + 3)^2 = 25x^4 + 30x^2 + 9$

19. $(x - 3)(2x - 5)(x + 2)$
$= (2x^2 - 11x + 15)(x + 2)$
$= 2x^3 + 4x^2 - 11x^2 - 22x + 15x + 30$
$= 2x^3 - 7x^2 - 7x + 30$

20. $(x^2 - 3x + 1)(-2x^2 + x - 2)$
$= -2x^4 + x^3 - 2x^2$
$\quad + 6x^3 - 3x^2 + 6x$
$\quad\quad - 2x^2 + x - 2$
$= -2x^4 + 7x^3 - 7x^2 + 7x - 2$

139

© 2006 Pearson Education, Inc., Upper Saddle River, NJ. All rights reserved. This material is protected under all copyright laws as they currently exist.
No portion of this material may be reproduced, in any form or by any means, without permission in writing from the publisher.

21. $(3x-5)(3x^2+2x-4)$

$= 9x^3 + 6x^2 - 12x - 15x^2 - 10x + 20$

$= 9x^3 - 9x^2 - 22x + 20$

22. $(6xy-7)(6xy+7)$

$= 36x^2y^2 + 42xy - 42xy - 49$

$= 36x^2y^2 - 49$

23. $(5a-2b^2)(3a-4b^2)$

$= 15a^2 - 20ab^2 - 6b^2a + 8b^4$

$= 15a^2 - 20ab^2 - 6ab^2 + 8b^4$

$= 15a^2 - 26ab^2 + 8b^4$

24. $(25x^3y - 15x^2y - 100xy) \div (-5xy)$

$$\frac{25x^3y - 15x^2y - 100xy}{-5xy}$$

$$= \frac{25x^3y}{-5xy} - \frac{15x^2y}{-5xy} - \frac{100xy}{-5xy}$$

$$= -5x^2 + 3x + 20$$

25. $(12x^2 - 16x - 4) \div (3x + 2)$

$$\begin{array}{r} 4x - 8 \\ 3x+2{\overline{\smash{\big)}\,12x^2 - 16x - 4}} \\ \underline{12x^2 + 8x} \\ -24x - 4 \\ \underline{-24x - 16} \\ 12 \end{array}$$

$(12x^2 - 16x - 4) \div (3x + 2)$

$$= 4x - 8 + \frac{12}{3x+2}$$

26. $(2x^3 + x^2 - x + 1) \div (2x + 3)$

$$\begin{array}{r} x^2 - x + 1 \\ 2x+3{\overline{\smash{\big)}\,2x^3 + x^2 - x + 1}} \\ \underline{2x^3 + 3x^2} \\ -2x^2 - x \\ \underline{-2x^2 - 3x} \\ 2x + 1 \\ \underline{2x + 3} \\ -2 \end{array}$$

$(2x^3 + x^2 - x + 1) \div (2x + 3)$

$$= x^2 - x + 1 + \frac{-2}{2x+3}$$

27. $(3y^3 - 2y + 5) \div (y - 3)$

$$\begin{array}{r} 3y^2 + 9y + 25 \\ y-3{\overline{\smash{\big)}\,3y^3 + 0y^2 - 2y + 5}} \\ \underline{3y^3 - 9y^2} \\ 9y^2 - 2y \\ \underline{9y^2 - 27y} \\ 25y + 5 \\ \underline{25y - 75} \\ 80 \end{array}$$

$(3y^3 - 2y + 5) \div (y - 3)$

$$= 3y^2 + 9y + 25 + \frac{80}{y-3}$$

© 2006 Pearson Education, Inc., Upper Saddle River, NJ. All rights reserved. This material is protected under all copyright laws as they currently exist.
No portion of this material may be reproduced, in any form or by any means, without permission in writing from the publisher.

28. $(15a^4 - 3a^3 + 4a^2 + 4) \div (3a^2 - 1)$

$$
\begin{array}{r}
5a^2 - a + 3 \\
3a^2 - 1 \overline{)15a^4 - 3a^3 + 4a^2 + 0a + 4} \\
\underline{15a^4 \qquad\quad -5a^2} \\
-3a^3 + 9a^2 \\
\underline{-3a^3 \qquad\quad +a} \\
9a^2 \quad -a \\
\underline{9a^2 \qquad -3} \\
-a + 7
\end{array}
$$

$(15a^4 - 3a^3 + 4a^2 + 0a + 4) \div (3a^2 - 1)$

$= 5a^2 - a + 3 + \dfrac{-a + 7}{3a^2 - 1}$

29. $(2x^4 - x^2 + 6x + 3) \div (x - 1)$

$$
\begin{array}{r}
2x^3 + 2x^2 + x + 7 \\
x - 1 \overline{)2x^4 + 0x^3 - x^2 + 6x + 3} \\
\underline{2x^4 - 2x^3} \\
2x^3 - x^2 \\
\underline{2x^3 - 2x^2} \\
x^2 + 6x \\
\underline{x^2 - x} \\
7x + 3 \\
\underline{7x - 7} \\
10
\end{array}
$$

$(2x^4 - x^2 + 6x + 3) \div (x - 1)$

$= 2x^3 + 2x^2 + x + 7 + \dfrac{10}{x - 1}$

30. $(2x^4 - 13x^3 + 16x^2 - 9x + 20) \div (x - 5)$

$$
\begin{array}{r}
2x^3 - 3x^2 + x - 4 \\
x - 5 \overline{)2x^4 - 13x^3 + 16x^2 - 9x + 2} \\
\underline{2x^4 - 10x^3} \\
-3x^3 + 16x^2 \\
\underline{-3x^3 + 15x^2} \\
x^2 - 9x \\
\underline{x^2 - 5x} \\
-4x + 20 \\
\underline{-4x + 20}
\end{array}
$$

$(2x^4 - 13x^3 + 16x^2 - 9x + 2) \div (x - 5)$

$= 2x^3 - 3x^2 + x - 4$

31. $(3x^4 + 5x^3 - x^2 + x - 2) \div (x + 2)$

$$
\begin{array}{r}
3x^3 - x^2 + x - 1 \\
x + 2 \overline{)3x^4 + 5x^3 - x^2 + x - 2} \\
\underline{3x^4 + 6x^3} \\
-x^3 - x^2 \\
\underline{-x^3 - 2x^2} \\
x^2 + x \\
\underline{x^2 + 2x} \\
-x - 2 \\
\underline{-x - 2}
\end{array}
$$

$(3x^4 + 5x^3 - x^2 + x - 2) \div (x + 2)$

$= 3x^3 - x^2 + x - 1$

32. $6a^2b - 3ab^2 - 3ab = 3ab(2a - b - 1)$

33. $x^5 - 3x^4 + 2x^2 = x^2(x^3 - 3x^2 + 2)$

34. $12mn - 8m = 4m(3n - 2)$

35. $2x + 6 - xy - 3y = 2(x + 3) - y(x + 3)$
$\qquad\qquad\qquad\quad = (x + 3)(2 - y)$

141

© 2006 Pearson Education, Inc., Upper Saddle River, NJ. All rights reserved. This material is protected under all copyright laws as they currently exist.
No portion of this material may be reproduced, in any form or by any means, without permission in writing from the publisher.

36. $8x^2y + x^2b + 8y + b$

$= x^2(8y + b) + (8y + b)$

$= (8y + b)(x^2 + 1)$

37. $3ab - 15a - 2b + 10 = 3a(b - 5) - 2(b - 5)$

$= (b - 5)(3a - 2)$

38. $x^2 - 9x - 22 = (x - 11)(x + 2)$

39. $4x^2 - 5x - 6 = (4x + 3)(x - 2)$

40. $6x^2 + 5x - 21 = (3x + 7)(2x - 3)$

41. $100x^2 - 49 = (10x + 7)(10x - 7)$

42. $4x^2 - 28x + 49 = (2x - 7)^2$

43. $8a^3 - 27 = (2a - 3)(4a^2 + 6a + 9)$

44. $9x^2 - 121 = (3x + 11)(3x - 11)$

45. $5x^2 - 11x + 2 = (5x - 1)(x - 2)$

46. $x^3 + 8x^2 + 12x = x(x^2 + 8x + 12)$

$= x(x + 6)(x + 2)$

47. $x^2 - 8wy + 4wx - 2xy$

$= x^2 + 4wx - 8wy - 2xy$

$= x(x + 4w) - 2y(4w + x)$

$= x(x + 4w) - 2y(x + 4w)$

$= (x + 4w)(x - 2y)$

48. $36x^2 + 25$ is prime.

49. $2x^2 - 7x - 3$ is prime.

50. $x^2 + 6xy - 27y^2 = (x + 9y)(x - 3y)$

51. $27x^4 - x = x(27x^3 - 1)$

$= x(3x - 1)(9x^2 + 3x + 1)$

52. $21a^2 + 20ab + 4b^2 = (7a + 2b)(3a + 2b)$

53. $-3a^3b^3 + 2a^2b^4 - a^2b^3$

$= -a^2b^3(3a - 2b + 1)$

54. $a^4b^4 + a^3b^4 - 6a^2b^4 = a^2b^4(a^2 + a - 6)$

$= a^2b^4(a + 3)(a - 2)$

55. $3x^4 - 5x^2 - 2 = (3x^2 + 1)(x^2 - 2)$

56. $9a^2b + 15ab - 14b = b(9a^2 + 15a - 14)$

$= b(3a + 7)(3a - 2)$

57. $2x^2 + 7x - 6$ is prime.

58. $3x^2 + 5x + 4$ is prime.

59. $4y^4 - 13y^3 + 9y^2 = y^2(4y^2 - 13y + 9)$

$= y^2(4y - 9)(y - 1)$

60. $y^4 + 2y^3 - 35y^2 = y^2(y^2 + 2y - 35)$

$= y^2(y + 7)(y - 5)$

61. $4x^2y^2 - 12x^2y - 8x^2 = 4x^2(y^2 - 3y - 2)$

62. $3x^4 - 7x^2 - 6 = (3x^2 + 2)(x^2 - 3)$

63. $a^2 + 5ab^3 + 4b^6 = (a + b^3)(a + 4b^3)$

64. $3x^2 - 12 - 8x + 2x^3$

$= 3(x^2 - 4) + 2x(x^2 - 4)$

$= (3 + 2x)(x^2 + 4)$

$= (2 + 3x)(x + 2)(x - 2)$

© 2006 Pearson Education, Inc., Upper Saddle River, NJ. All rights reserved. This material is protected under all copyright laws as they currently exist.
No portion of this material may be reproduced, in any form or by any means, without permission in writing from the publisher.

65. $2x^4 - 12x^2 - 54 = 2(x^4 - 6x^2 - 27)$
$$= 2(x^2 - 9)(x^2 + 3)$$
$$= 2(x + 3)(x - 3)(x^2 + 3)$$

66. $8a + 8b - 4bx - 4ax$
$$= 4(2a + 2b - ax - bx)$$
$$= 4(2(a + b) - x(a + b))$$
$$= 4(a + b)(2 - x)$$

67. $8x^4 + 34x^2 y^2 + 21y^4$
$$= (4x^2 + 3y^2)(2x^2 + 7y^2)$$

68. $4x^3 + 10x^2 - 6x = 2x(2x^2 + 5x - 3)$
$$= 2x(2x - 1)(x + 3)$$

69. $2a^2 x - 15ax + 7x = x(2a^2 - 15a + 7)$
$$= x(2a - 1)(a - 7)$$

70. $16x^4 y^2 - 56x^2 y + 49 = (4x^2 y - 7)^2$

71. $128x^3 y - 2xy = 2xy(64x^2 - 1)$
$$= 2xy(8x - 1)(8x + 1)$$

72. $5xb - 28y + 4by - 35x$
$$= 5xb - 35x + 4by - 28y$$
$$= 5x(b - 7) + 4y(b - 7)$$
$$= (b - 7)(5x + 4y)$$

73. $27abc^2 - 12ab = 3ab(9c^2 - 4)$
$$= 3ab(3c + 2)(3c - 2)$$

74. $5x^2 - 9x - 2 = 0$
$$(5x + 1)(x - 2) = 0$$
$$5x + 1 = 0 \text{ or } x - 2 = 0$$
$$x = -\frac{1}{5} \qquad x = 2$$

75. $2x^2 - 11x + 12 = 0$
$$(2x - 3)(x - 4) = 0$$
$$2x - 3 = 0 \text{ or } x - 4 = 0$$
$$x = \frac{3}{2} \qquad x = 4$$

76. $(2x - 1)(3x - 5) = 20$
$$6x^2 - 13x + 5 = 20$$
$$6x^2 - 13x - 15 = 0$$
$$(6x + 5)(x - 3) = 0$$
$$6x + 5 = 0 \text{ or } x - 3 = 0$$
$$x = -\frac{5}{6} \qquad x = 3$$

77. $\qquad 7x^2 = 21x$
$$7x^2 - 21x = 0$$
$$7x(x - 3) = 0$$
$$7x = 0 \text{ or } x - 3 = 0$$
$$x = 0 \qquad x = 3$$

78. $3x^2 + 14x + 3 = -1 + 4(x + 1)$
$$3x^2 + 14x + 3 = -1 + 4x + 4$$
$$3x^2 + 10x = 0$$
$$x(3x + 10) = 0$$
$$x = 0 \text{ or } 3x + 10 = 0$$
$$x = 0 \qquad x = -\frac{10}{3}$$

79. $\qquad x^3 + 7x^2 = -12x$
$$x^3 + 7x^2 + 12x = 0$$
$$x(x^2 + 7x + 12) = 0$$
$$x(x + 4)(x + 3) = 0$$
$$x = 0 \text{ or } x + 4 = 0 \text{ or } x + 3 = 0$$
$$x = 0 \qquad x = -4 \qquad x = -3$$

143

© 2006 Pearson Education, Inc., Upper Saddle River, NJ. All rights reserved. This material is protected under all copyright laws as they currently exist.
No portion of this material may be reproduced, in any form or by any means, without permission in writing from the publisher.

80.
$$A = \frac{1}{2}bh = 77$$
$$b(b+3) = 154$$
$$b^2 + 3b - 154 = 0$$
$$(b+14)(b-11) = 0$$
$$b+14 = 0 \;\text{ or }\; b-11 = 0$$
$$b = -14 \qquad b = 11$$

reject, $b > 0$ $h = b+3 = 14$

The base of the triangle is 11 meters and the altitude is 14 meters.

81.
$$A = LW = 40$$
$$(3W - 2)W = 40$$
$$3W^2 - 2W - 40 = 0$$
$$(3W + 10)(W - 4) = 0$$
$$3W + 10 = 0 \;\text{ or }\; W - 4 = 0$$
$$W = -\frac{10}{3} \qquad W = 4$$

reject, $W > 0$ $L = 3W - 2 = 10$

The length is 10 miles and the width is 4 miles.

82. $P = 3x^2 - 7x - 10 = 30$
$$3x^2 - 7x - 40 = 0$$
$$(3x + 8)(x - 5) = 0$$
$$3x + 8 = 0 \;\text{ or }\; x - 5 = 0$$
$$x = -\frac{8}{3} \qquad x = 5$$

reject, $x > 0$

Five calculators should be made.

83. $x = $ length of old side
$2x + 3 = $ length of new side
$$x^2 + 24 = (2x + 3)^2$$
$$x^2 + 24 = 4x^2 + 12x + 9$$
$$3x^2 + 12x - 15 = 0$$
$$x^2 + 4x - 5 = 0$$
$$(x + 5)(x - 1) = 0$$
$$x + 5 = 0 \;\text{ or }\; x - 1 = 0$$
$$x = -5 \qquad x = 1$$

reject, $x > 0, \; 2x + 3 = 5$

The old side is 1 yard and the new side is 5 yards.

How Am I Doing? Chapter 5 Test

1. $(3x^2 y - 2xy^2 - 6) + (5 + 2xy^2 - 7x^2 y)$
$$= 3x^2 y - 2xy^2 - 6 + 5 + 2xy^2 - 7x^2 y$$
$$= -4x^2 y - 1$$

2. $(5a^2 - 3) - (2 + 5a) - (4a - 3)$
$$= 5a^2 - 3 - 2 - 5a - 4a + 3$$
$$= 5a^2 - 9a - 2$$

3. $-2x(x + 3y - 4) = -2x^2 - 6xy + 8x$

4. $(2x - 3y^2)^2 = 4x^2 - 12xy^2 + 9y^4$

5. $(x - 2)(2x^2 + x - 1)$
$$= 2x^3 + x^2 - x - 4x^2 - 2x + 2$$
$$= 2x^3 - 3x^2 - 3x + 2$$

6. $(-15x^3 - 12x^2 + 21x) \div (-3x)$
$$= \frac{-15x^3}{-3x} - \frac{12x^2}{-3x} + \frac{21x}{-3x}$$
$$= 5x^2 + 4x - 7$$

© 2006 Pearson Education, Inc., Upper Saddle River, NJ. All rights reserved. This material is protected under all copyright laws as they currently exist. No portion of this material may be reproduced, in any form or by any means, without permission in writing from the publisher.

7. $(2x^4 - 7x^3 + 7x^2 - 9x + 10) \div (2x - 5)$

$$
\begin{array}{r}
x^3 - x^2 + x - 2 \\
2x-5\overline{\smash{\big)}\,2x^4 - 7x^3 + 7x^2 - 9x + 10} \\
\underline{2x^4 - 5x^3} \\
-2x^3 + 7x^2 \\
\underline{-2x^3 + 5x^2} \\
2x^2 - 9x \\
\underline{2x^2 - 5x} \\
-4x + 10 \\
\underline{-4x + 10}
\end{array}
$$

$(2x^4 - 7x^3 + 7x^2 - 9x + 10) \div (2x - 5)$

$= x^3 - x^2 + x - 2$

8. $(x^3 - x^2 - 5x + 2) \div (x + 2)$

$$
\begin{array}{r}
x^2 - 3x + 1 \\
x+2\overline{\smash{\big)}\,x^3 - x^2 - 5x + 2} \\
\underline{x^3 + 2x^2} \\
-3x^2 - 5x \\
\underline{-3x^2 - 6x} \\
x + 2 \\
\underline{x + 2}
\end{array}
$$

$(x^3 - x^2 - 5x + 2) \div (x + 2)$

$= x^2 - 3x + 1$

9. $(x^4 + x^3 - x - 3) \div (x + 1)$

$$
\begin{array}{r|rrrrr}
-1 & 1 & 1 & 0 & -1 & -3 \\
 & & -1 & 0 & 0 & 1 \\
\hline
 & 1 & 0 & 0 & -1 & \underline{|-2}
\end{array}
$$

$(x^4 + x^3 - x - 3) \div (x + 1)$

$= x^3 - 1 + \dfrac{-2}{x+1}$

10. $121x^2 - 25y^2 = (11x + 5y)(11x - 5y)$

11. $9x^2 + 30xy + 25y^2 = (3x + 5y)^2$

12. $x^3 - 26x^2 + 48x = x(x^2 - 26x + 48)$
$$= x(x - 2)(x - 24)$$

13. $4x^3y + 8x^2y^2 + 4x^2y = 4x^2y(x + 2y + 1)$

14. $x^2 - 6wy + 3xy - 2wx$
$$= x^2 + 3xy - 2wx - 6wy$$
$$= x(x + 3y) - 2w(x + 3y)$$
$$= (x + 3y)(x - 2w)$$

15. $2x^2 - 3x + 2$ is prime.

16. $18x^2 + 3x - 15 = 3(6x^2 + x - 5)$
$$= 3(6x - 5)(x + 1)$$

17. $54a^4 - 16a = 2a(27a^3 - 8)$
$$= 2a(3a - 2)(9a^2 + 6a + 4)$$

18. $9x^5 - 6x^3y + xy^2 = x(9x^4 - 6x^2y + y^2)$
$$= x(3x^2 - y)^2$$

19. $3x^4 + 17x^2 + 10 = (3x^2 + 2)(x^2 + 5)$

20. $3x - 10ay + 6y - 5ax$
$$= 3x - 5ax + 6y - 10ay$$
$$= x(3 - 5a) + 2y(3 - 5a)$$
$$= (3 - 5a)(x + 2y)$$

21. $p(x) = -2x^3 - x^2 + 6x - 10$
$$p(2) = -2(2)^3 - (2)^2 + 6(2) - 10$$
$$p(2) = -18$$

© 2006 Pearson Education, Inc., Upper Saddle River, NJ. All rights reserved. This material is protected under all copyright laws as they currently exist. No portion of this material may be reproduced, in any form or by any means, without permission in writing from the publisher.

22. $p(x) = -2x^3 - x^2 + 6x - 10$

$p(-3) = -2(-3)^3 - (-3)^2 + 6(-3) - 10$

$p(-3) = 17$

23. $\qquad x^2 = 5x + 14$

$x^2 - 5x - 14 = 0$

$(x - 7)(x + 2) = 0$

$x - 7 = 0 \ \text{ or } \ x + 2 = 0$

$\qquad x = 7 \qquad\qquad x = -2$

24. $3x^2 - 11x - 4 = 0$

$(3x + 1)(x - 4) = 0$

$3x + 1 = 0 \ \text{ or } \ x - 4 = 0$

$\qquad x = -\dfrac{1}{3} \qquad x = 4$

25. $7x^2 + 6x = 8x$

$7x^2 - 2x = 0$

$x(7x - 2) = 0$

$x = 0 \ \text{ or } \ 7x - 2 = 0$

$x = 0 \qquad\qquad x = \dfrac{2}{7}$

26. $\qquad A = \dfrac{1}{2}bh = \dfrac{1}{2}b(b - 4) = 70$

$b^2 - 4b = 140$

$b^2 - 4b - 140 = 0$

$(b + 10)(b - 14) = 0$

$b + 10 = 0 \ \text{ or } \ b - 14 = 0$

$\qquad b = -10 \qquad b = 14$

reject, $b > 0 \qquad h = b - 4 = 10$

The base of the triangle is 14 inches and the altitude of the triangle is 10 inches.

Cumulative Test for Chapters 1-5

1. $3(5 \cdot 2) = (3 \cdot 5)2$ illustrates the associative property of multiplication.

2. $\dfrac{2 + 6(-2)}{(2 - 4)^3 + 3} = \dfrac{2 - 12}{(-2)^3 + 3}$

$\qquad = \dfrac{-10}{-8 + 3}$

$\qquad = \dfrac{-10}{-5}$

$\qquad = 2$

3. $7x - 3\{1 + 2(x - y)\} = 7x - 3\{1 + 2x - 2y\}$

$\qquad = 7x - 3 - 6x + 6y$

$\qquad = x - 3 + 6y$

4. $5x + 7y = 2$

$5x = 2 - 7y$

$x = \dfrac{2 - 7y}{5}$

5. $\dfrac{1}{2}(x - 3) + \dfrac{x}{5} = x - 1$

$5x - 15 + 2x = 10x - 10$

$-3x = 5$

$x = -\dfrac{5}{3}$

6. $m = \dfrac{y_2 - y_1}{x_2 - x_1}$

$m = \dfrac{-3 - 5}{-2 - 1}$

$m = \dfrac{8}{3}$

146

© 2006 Pearson Education, Inc., Upper Saddle River, NJ. All rights reserved. This material is protected under all copyright laws as they currently exist. No portion of this material may be reproduced, in any form or by any means, without permission in writing from the publisher.

7. $y = -\dfrac{2}{3}x + 4$

x	y
-3	6
0	4
3	2

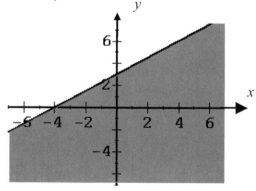

8. $3x - 4y \geq -12$

Test point: $(0,0)$

$3(0) + 4(0) \geq -12$

$0 \geq -12,$ true

9. $-3(x+2) < 5x - 2(4+x)$

$-3x - 6 < 5x - 8 - 2x$

$-6x < -2$

$x > \dfrac{1}{3}$

10. $P = 2L + 2W = 46$

$2(2W + 5) + 2W = 46$

$4W + 10 + 2W = 46$

$6W = 36$

$W = 6$

$L = 2W + 5 = 17$

The length of the rectangle is 17 meters and the width of the rectangle is 6 meters.

11. $3x^3 - 2xy - x^2 + 5$

$= 3(1)^3 - 2(1)(0) - (1)^2 + 5$

$= 7$

12. $a\{ab - 2b(a+4)\} = a\{ab - 2ba - 8b\}$

$= a\{-ab - 8b\}$

$= -a^2b - 8ab$

13. $(5x - 2)(2x^2 - 3x - 4)$

$= 10x^3 - 15x^2 - 20x - 4x^2 + 6x + 8$

$= 10x^3 - 19x^2 - 14x + 8$

14. $(-21x^3 + 14x^2 - 28x) \div (7x)$

$\dfrac{-21x^3}{7x} + \dfrac{14x^2}{7x} - \dfrac{28x}{7x} = -3x^2 + 2x - 4$

15. $(2x^3 - 3x^2 + 3x - 4) \div (x - 2)$

$$
\begin{array}{r}
2x^2 + x + 5 \\
x - 2 \overline{\smash{)}2x^3 - 3x^2 + 3x - 4} \\
\underline{2x^3 - 4x^2} \\
x^2 + 3x \\
\underline{x^2 - 2x} \\
5x - 4 \\
\underline{5x - 10} \\
6
\end{array}
$$

147

© 2006 Pearson Education, Inc., Upper Saddle River, NJ. All rights reserved. This material is protected under all copyright laws as they currently exist. No portion of this material may be reproduced, in any form or by any means, without permission in writing from the publisher.

15. $(2x^3 - 3x^2 + 3x - 4) \div (x - 2)$

$\quad = 2x^2 + x + 5 + \dfrac{6}{x-2}$

16. $2x^3 - 10x^2 = 2x^2(x-5)$

17. $64x^2 - 49 = (8x + 7)(8x - 7)$

18. $3x^2 - 2x - 8 = (3x + 4)(x - 2)$

19. $25x^2 + 60x + 36 = (5x + 6)^2$

20. $3x^2 - 15x - 42 = 3(x^2 - 5x - 14)$

$\quad\quad\quad\quad\quad\quad\quad = 3(x - 7)(x + 2)$

21. $2x^2 + 24x + 40$

$\quad = 2(x^2 + 12x + 20)$

$\quad = 2(x + 10)(x + 2)$

22. $16x^2 + 9$ is prime.

23. $6x^3 + 11x^2 + 3x = x(6x^2 + 11x + 3)$

$\quad\quad\quad\quad\quad\quad\quad = x(3x + 1)(2x + 3)$

24. $27x^4 + 64x = x(27x^3 + 64)$

$\quad\quad\quad\quad\quad\quad = x(3x + 4)(9x^2 - 12x + 16)$

25. $2x - 6 - 5xy + 15y = 2(x - 3) - 5y(x - 3)$

$\quad\quad\quad\quad\quad\quad\quad\quad = (x - 3)(2 - 5y)$

26. $\quad 3x^2 - 4x - 4 = 0$

$\quad (3x + 2)(x - 2) = 0$

$\quad 3x + 2 = 0 \ \text{ or } \ x - 2 = 0$

$\quad\quad x = -\dfrac{2}{3} \quad\quad x = 2$

27. $\quad\quad x^2 - 8x = 33$

$\quad\quad x^2 - 8x - 33 = 0$

$\quad\quad (x - 11)(x + 3) = 0$

$\quad\quad x - 11 = 0 \ \text{ or } \ x + 3 = 0$

$\quad\quad\quad x = 11 \quad\quad\quad x = -3$

28. $A = \dfrac{1}{2}bh = \dfrac{1}{2}b(2b + 1) = 68$

$\quad 2b^2 + b - 136 = 0$

$\quad (2b + 17)(b - 8) = 0$

$\quad 2b + 17 = 0 \ \text{ or } \ b - 8 = 0$

$\quad b = -\dfrac{17}{2} \quad\quad\quad b = 8$

reject, $b > 0$ $h = 2b + 1 = 17$

The base of the triangle is 8 meters and the altitude of the triangle is 17 meters.

© 2006 Pearson Education, Inc., Upper Saddle River, NJ. All rights reserved. This material is protected under all copyright laws as they currently exist. No portion of this material may be reproduced, in any form or by any means, without permission in writing from the publisher.

Chapter 6

6.1 Exercises

1. $2x - 6 \neq 0$

$\quad 2x \neq 6$

$\quad\quad x \neq 3$

All real numbers except 3

3. $x^2 - 5x - 36 \neq 0$

$\quad (x-9)(x+4) \neq 0$

$\quad\quad x \neq -4, 9$

All real numbers except -4 and 9

5. $\dfrac{-18x^4 y}{12x^2 y^6} = -\dfrac{6x^2 y \cdot 3x^2}{6x^2 y \cdot 2y^5}$

$\quad\quad = -\dfrac{3x^2}{2y^5}$

7. $\dfrac{3x^3 - 24x^2}{6x - 48} = \dfrac{3x^2(x-8)}{6(x-8)}$

$\quad\quad = \dfrac{x^2}{2}$

9. $\dfrac{9x^2}{12x^2 - 15x} = \dfrac{3x \cdot 3x}{3x(4x-5)}$

$\quad\quad = \dfrac{3x}{4x-5}$

11. $\dfrac{5x^2 y^2 - 15xy^2}{10x^3 y - 20x^3 y^2} = \dfrac{5xy^2(x-3)}{10x^3 y(1-2y)}$

$\quad\quad = \dfrac{y(x-3)}{2x^2(1-2y)}$

13. $\dfrac{2x + 10}{2x^2 - 50} = \dfrac{2(x+5)}{2(x+5)(x-5)}$

$\quad\quad = \dfrac{1}{x-5}$

15. $\dfrac{2y^2 - 8}{2y + 4} = \dfrac{2(y+2)(y-2)}{2(y+2)} = y - 2$

17. $\dfrac{2x^2 - x^3 - x^4}{x^4 - x^3} = \dfrac{-x^2(x^2 + x - 2)}{x^3(x-1)}$

$\quad\quad = -\dfrac{(x+2)(x-1)}{x(x-1)}$

$\quad\quad = -\dfrac{x+2}{x}$

19. $\dfrac{2y^2 + y - 10}{4 - y^2} = \dfrac{(2y+5)(y-2)}{-(y+2)(y-2)}$

$\quad\quad = -\dfrac{2y+5}{y+2}$

21. $\dfrac{-8mn^5}{3m^4 n^3} \cdot \dfrac{9m^3 n^3}{6mn} = \dfrac{-2 \cdot 4 \cdot 3 \cdot 3 m^4 n^4 n^4}{2 \cdot 3 \cdot 3 m^4 n^4 m}$

$\quad\quad = \dfrac{-4n^4}{m}$

23. $\dfrac{3a^2}{a^2 + 4a + 4} \cdot \dfrac{a^2 - 4}{3a} = \dfrac{3a \cdot a(a+2)(a-2)}{3a \cdot (a+2)(a+2)}$

$\quad\quad = \dfrac{a(a-2)}{a+2}$

25. $\dfrac{x^2 + 5x + 7}{x^2 - 5x + 6} \cdot \dfrac{3x - 6}{x^2 + 5x + 7}$

$\quad\quad = \dfrac{3(x-2)}{(x-2)(x-3)} = \dfrac{3}{x-3}$

27. $\dfrac{x^2 - 5xy - 24y^2}{x - y} \cdot \dfrac{x^2 + 6xy - 7y^2}{x + 3y}$

$\quad\quad = \dfrac{(x-8y)(x+3y)}{(x-y)} \cdot \dfrac{(x+7y)(x-y)}{(x+3y)}$

$\quad\quad = (x-8y)(x+7y)$

© 2006 Pearson Education, Inc., Upper Saddle River, NJ. All rights reserved. This material is protected under all copyright laws as they currently exist. No portion of this material may be reproduced, in any form or by any means, without permission in writing from the publisher.

29. $\dfrac{y^2-3y-10}{2y^2-y-1}\cdot\dfrac{2y^2+11y+5}{2y^2-50}$

$=\dfrac{(y-5)(y+2)}{(2y+1)(y-1)}\cdot\dfrac{(2y+1)(y+5)}{2(y-5)(y+5)}$

$=\dfrac{y+2}{2(y-1)}$

31. $\dfrac{x^3-125}{x^5y}\cdot\dfrac{x^3y^2}{x^2+5x+25}$

$=\dfrac{(x-5)(x^2+5x+25)}{x^3y\cdot x^2}\cdot\dfrac{x^3y\cdot y}{(x^2+5x+25)}$

$=\dfrac{y(x-5)}{x^2}$

33. $\dfrac{2mn-m}{15m^3}\div\dfrac{2n-1}{3m^2}$

$=\dfrac{m(2n-1)}{5m\cdot3m^2}\cdot\dfrac{3m^2}{(2n-1)}$

$=\dfrac{1}{5}$

35. $\dfrac{b^2-6b+9}{5b^2-16b+3}\div\dfrac{6b-3}{15b-3}$

$=\dfrac{(b-3)^2}{(b-3)(5b-1)}\cdot\dfrac{3(5b-1)}{3(2b-1)}$

$=\dfrac{b-3}{2b-1}$

37. $\dfrac{x^2-xy-6y^2}{x^2+2}\div(x^2+2xy)$

$=\dfrac{(x+2y)(x-3y)}{(x^2+2)}\cdot\dfrac{1}{x(x+2y)}$

$=\dfrac{x-3y}{x(x^2+2)}$

39. $\dfrac{7x}{y^2}\div21x^3=\dfrac{7x}{y^2}\cdot\dfrac{1}{7x\cdot3x^2}=\dfrac{1}{3x^2y^2}$

41. $\dfrac{3x^2-2x}{6x-4}=\dfrac{x(3x-2)}{2(3x-2)}=\dfrac{x}{2}$

43. $\dfrac{x^2y-49y}{x^2y^3}\cdot\dfrac{3x^2y-21xy}{x^2-14x+49}$

$=\dfrac{y(x+7)(x-7)}{x^2y^3}\cdot\dfrac{3xy(x-7)}{(x-7)(x-7)}$

$=\dfrac{3(x+7)}{xy}$

45. $\dfrac{x^2-9x+18}{x^2y^3}\div\dfrac{x^2-8x+12}{x^4y^2}$

$=\dfrac{(x-3)(x-6)}{x^2y^3}\cdot\dfrac{x^4y^2}{(x-6)(x-2)}$

$=\dfrac{x^2(x-3)}{y(x-2)}$

47. $\dfrac{a^2-a-12}{2a^2+5a-12}=\dfrac{(a-4)(a+3)}{(2a-3)(a+4)}$

49. Graphing $y_1=3.6x^2+1.8x-4.3$ and using the *zero* feature to find the intercepts shows the domain of $f(x)=\dfrac{2x+5}{3.6x^2+1.8x-4.3}$ is all real number except $x\approx-1.4$ and $x\approx0.9$.

51. $P(x)=\dfrac{90(1+1.5x)}{1+0.5x}$

$P(1)=\dfrac{90(1+1.5(1))}{1+0.5(1)}$

$P(1)=150$

© 2006 Pearson Education, Inc., Upper Saddle River, NJ. All rights reserved. This material is protected under all copyright laws as they currently exist. No portion of this material may be reproduced, in any form or by any means, without permission in writing from the publisher.

53. $P(x) = \dfrac{90(1+1.5x)}{1+0.5x}$

$P(6) = \dfrac{90(1+1.5(6))}{1+0.5(6)}$

$P(6) = 225$

55. $P(x)$

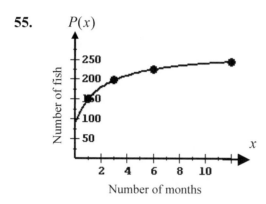

Number of months

Cumulative Review

57. $y = -\dfrac{3}{2}x + 4$

$y = -\dfrac{3}{2}(0) + 4 = 4 \Rightarrow (0,4)$

$y = -\dfrac{3}{2}(2) + 4 = 1 \Rightarrow (2,1)$

$y = -\dfrac{3}{2}(4) + 4 = -2 \Rightarrow (4,-2)$

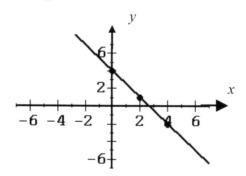

59. Solve the first equation for y and substitute into the second equation.

59.
$$y = 2x - 8$$
$$x + 3(2x - 8) = 4$$
$$x + 6x - 24 = 4$$
$$7x = 28$$
$$x = 4$$
$$y = 2x - 8$$
$$y = 2(4) - 4 = 0$$

The solution is $(4,0)$.

61. $\dfrac{2 \text{ inquiries}}{\text{minute}} \cdot \dfrac{60 \text{ minutes}}{\text{hour}} \cdot \dfrac{33 \text{ hours}}{\text{week}}$

$= 3960 \dfrac{\text{inquiries}}{\text{week}}$

63. $69,399(0.37) = $ deaths in spring 2000

$\dfrac{69,399}{1.07}(0.37) = $ deaths in spring 1999

$\dfrac{69,399}{1.07^2}(0.37) = $ deaths in spring 1998

72,103 people have died

6.2 Exercises

1. The factors are 5, x, and y. The factor y is repeated in one fraction three times. Since the highest power of y is 3, the LCD is $5xy^3$.

3. $x - 1 = x - 1$

$x^2 - 2x + 1 = (x-1)^2$

$LCD = (x-1)^2$

5. $LCD = 2m^3n^2$

7. $LCD = (x+2)(3x+4)^3$

151

© 2006 Pearson Education, Inc., Upper Saddle River, NJ. All rights reserved. This material is protected under all copyright laws as they currently exist. No portion of this material may be reproduced, in any form or by any means, without permission in writing from the publisher.

9. $3x^2 + 2x = x(3x+2)$

$18x^2 + 9x - 2 = (6x-1)(3x+2)$

$LCD = x(6x-1)(3x+2)$

11. $\dfrac{3}{x+4} + \dfrac{2}{x^2-16}$

$= \dfrac{3(x-4)}{(x+4)(x-4)} + \dfrac{2}{(x+4)(x-4)}$

$= \dfrac{3x-12+2}{(x+4)(x-4)}$

$= \dfrac{3x-10}{(x+4)(x-4)}$

13. $\dfrac{12}{5x^2} \cdot \dfrac{y}{y} + \dfrac{2}{5xy} \cdot \dfrac{x}{x} = \dfrac{12y+2x}{5x^2 y}$

15. $\dfrac{3}{x^2-7x+12} + \dfrac{5}{x^2-4x}$

$= \dfrac{3x}{(x-4)(x-3)x} + \dfrac{5(x-3)}{x(x-4)(x-3)}$

$= \dfrac{3x+5x-15}{x(x-4)(x-3)}$

$= \dfrac{8x-15}{x(x-4)(x-3)}$

17. $\dfrac{6x}{2x-5} + 4 = \dfrac{6x+4(2x-5)}{2x-5}$

$= \dfrac{6x+8x-20}{2x-5}$

$= \dfrac{14x-20}{2x-5}$

19. $\dfrac{-5y}{y^2-1} + \dfrac{6}{y^2-2y+1}$

$= \dfrac{-5y(y-1)}{(y-1)^2(y+1)} + \dfrac{6(y+1)}{(y-1)^2(y+1)}$

$= \dfrac{-5y^2+5y+6y+6}{(y-1)^2(y+1)}$

$= \dfrac{-5y^2+11y+6}{(y-1)^2(y+1)}$

21. $\dfrac{a+5}{a^2-4} + \dfrac{a-3}{2a-4}$

$= \dfrac{2(a+5)}{2(a+2)(a-2)} + \dfrac{(a-3)(a+2)}{2(a-2)(a+2)}$

$= \dfrac{2a+10+a^2-a-6}{2(a+2)(a-2)}$

$= \dfrac{a^2+a+4}{2(a+2)(a-2)}$

23. $\dfrac{5}{x-4} - \dfrac{3}{x+1} = \dfrac{5(x+1)-3(x-4)}{(x-4)(x+1)}$

$= \dfrac{5x+5-3x+12}{(x-4)(x+1)}$

$= \dfrac{2x+17}{(x-4)(x+1)}$

25. $\dfrac{1}{x^2-x-2} - \dfrac{3}{x^2+2x+1}$

$= \dfrac{1(x+1)}{(x-2)(x+1)(x+1)} - \dfrac{3(x-2)}{(x+1)(x+1)(x-2)}$

$= \dfrac{x+1-3x+6}{(x-2)(x+1)^2}$

$= \dfrac{-2x+7}{(x-2)(x+1)^2}$

152

© 2006 Pearson Education, Inc., Upper Saddle River, NJ. All rights reserved. This material is protected under all copyright laws as they currently exist. No portion of this material may be reproduced, in any form or by any means, without permission in writing from the publisher.

27. $\dfrac{4y}{y^2+3y+2}-\dfrac{y-3}{y+2}$

$=\dfrac{4y}{(y+2)(y+1)}-\dfrac{(y-3)(y+1)}{(y+2)(y+1)}$

$=\dfrac{4y-y^2+2y+3}{(y+2)(y+1)}$

$=\dfrac{-y^2+6y+3}{(y+2)(y+1)}$

29. $a+3+\dfrac{2}{3a-5}$

$=\dfrac{(a+3)(3a-5)+2}{3a-5}$

$=\dfrac{3a^2+4a-15+2}{3a-5}$

$=\dfrac{3a^2+4a-13}{3a-5}$

31. $P(x)=R(x)-C(x)$

$P(x)=\dfrac{80-24x}{2-x}-\dfrac{60-12x}{3-x}$

$=\dfrac{8(10-3x)(3-x)-12(5-x)(2-x)}{(2-x)(3-x)}$

$=\dfrac{8(30-19x+3x^2)-12(10-7x+x^2)}{x^2-5x+6}$

$=\dfrac{240-152x+24x^2-120+84x-12x^2}{x^2-5x+6}$

$=\dfrac{12x^2-68x+120}{x^2-5x+6}$

33. $P(x)=R(x)-C(x)$

$P(x)=\dfrac{12x^2-68x+120}{x^2-5x+6}$

$P(10)=\dfrac{12(10)^2-68(10)+120}{(10)^2-5(10)+6}$

$P(10)=11.4285714286\ldots$

33. If ten machines per day are manufactured, the daily profit will be $11,429.

35. $3x-2+\dfrac{5x}{3x-2}+\dfrac{2x^2}{(3x-2)^2}$

$=\dfrac{(3x-2)^3+5x(3x-2)+2x^2}{(3x-2)^2}$

$=\dfrac{27x^3-54x^2+36x-8+15x^2-10x+2x^2}{(3x-2)^2}$

$=\dfrac{27x^3-37x^2+26x-8}{(3x-2)^2}$

Cumulative Review

37. $\dfrac{|2-7|-3\cdot4}{2\sqrt{16}-1^2\cdot4+5\cdot2}=\dfrac{|-5|-12}{2\cdot4-1\cdot4+10}$

$=\dfrac{5-12}{8-4+10}$

$=\dfrac{-7}{14}$

$=-\dfrac{1}{2}$

39. Assume people reading the letters worked 24 hours per day.

$\dfrac{10\text{ letters}}{\text{person}\cdot\text{hour}}\cdot5\text{ people}=\dfrac{50\text{ letters}}{\text{hour}}$

$\dfrac{50\text{ letters}}{\text{hour}}\cdot x=73,000\text{ letters}$

$x=1460\text{ hours}\cdot\dfrac{\text{day}}{24\text{ hours}}$

$x=60.8\overline{3}\text{ days}$

It would take 1460 hours or about 60.83 days to read all the letters.

153

© 2006 Pearson Education, Inc., Upper Saddle River, NJ. All rights reserved. This material is protected under all copyright laws as they currently exist. No portion of this material may be reproduced, in any form or by any means, without permission in writing from the publisher.

41. $x =$ cost of Tony's car

$x + 1500 =$ cost of Alreda's car

$2x + 1000 =$ cost of Melissa's car

$x + x + 1500 + 2x + 1000 = 26,500$

$4x = 24,000$

$x = 6000$

$x + 1500 = 7500$

$2x + 1000 = 13,000$

Tony's car cost \$6000, Melissa's car cost \$13,000, and Alreda's car cost \$7500.

43. $x =$ speed of boat in still water

$y =$ speed of current

$75 = (x - y)5 \Rightarrow x - y = 15$

$\underline{75 = (x + y)3 \Rightarrow x + y = 25}$

$2x = 40$

$x = 20$

$20 + y = 25$

$y = 5$

The speed of the boat in still water is 20 km/hr and the speed of the current is 5 km/hr.

6.3 Exercises

1. $\dfrac{\dfrac{7}{x}}{\dfrac{3}{xy}} = \dfrac{7}{x} \cdot \dfrac{xy}{3} = \dfrac{7y}{3}$

3. $\dfrac{\dfrac{2x}{x+5}}{\dfrac{x^2}{x-1}} = \dfrac{2x}{x+5} \cdot \dfrac{x-1}{x^2}$

$= \dfrac{2(x-1)}{x(x+5)}$

5. $\dfrac{1 - \dfrac{6}{5y}}{\dfrac{3}{y} + 1} \cdot \dfrac{5y}{5y} = \dfrac{5y - 6}{15 + 5y} = \dfrac{5y - 6}{5(y + 3)}$

7. $\dfrac{\dfrac{y}{6} - \dfrac{1}{2y}}{\dfrac{3}{2y} - \dfrac{1}{y}} \cdot \dfrac{6y}{6y} = \dfrac{y^2 - 3}{9 - 6} = \dfrac{y^2 - 3}{3}$

9. $\dfrac{\dfrac{2}{y^2 - 9}}{\dfrac{3}{y+3} + 1} \cdot \dfrac{(y+3)(y-3)}{(y+3)(y-3)}$

$= \dfrac{2}{3(y-3) + y^2 - 9} = \dfrac{2}{3y - 9 + y^2 - 9}$

$= \dfrac{2}{y^2 + 3y - 18} = \dfrac{2}{(y+6)(y-3)}$

11. $\dfrac{\dfrac{3}{2x+4} + \dfrac{1}{2}}{\dfrac{2}{x^2-4} + \dfrac{x}{x+2}}$

$= \dfrac{\dfrac{6 + 2x + 4}{2(2x+4)}}{\dfrac{2(x+2) + x(x+2)(x-2)}{(x+2)(x-2)(x+2)}}$

$= \dfrac{6 + 2x + 4}{2(2x+4)} \cdot \dfrac{(x+2)(x-2)(x+2)}{2(x+2) + x(x+2)(x-2)}$

$= \dfrac{2x + 10}{4(x+2)} \cdot \dfrac{(x-2)(x+2)}{2 + x(x-2)}$

$= \dfrac{2(x+5)}{4} \cdot \dfrac{(x-2)}{2 + x^2 - 2x}$

$= \dfrac{(x+5)(x-2)}{2(x^2 - 2x + 2)}$

154

© 2006 Pearson Education, Inc., Upper Saddle River, NJ. All rights reserved. This material is protected under all copyright laws as they currently exist. No portion of this material may be reproduced, in any form or by any means, without permission in writing from the publisher.

13. $\dfrac{-8}{\dfrac{6x}{x-1}-4}\cdot\dfrac{(x-1)}{(x-1)}=\dfrac{-8(x-1)}{6x-4(x-1)}$

$$=\dfrac{-8(x-1)}{6x-4x+4}$$

$$=\dfrac{-8(x-1)}{2x+4}$$

$$=\dfrac{-8(x-1)}{2(x+2)}$$

$$=-\dfrac{4(x-1)}{x+2}$$

15. $\dfrac{\dfrac{1}{2x+3}+\dfrac{2}{4x^2+12x+9}}{\dfrac{5}{2x^2+3x}}$

$$=\dfrac{\dfrac{1}{2x+3}+\dfrac{2}{(2x+3)(2x+3)}}{\dfrac{5}{x(2x+3)}}\cdot\dfrac{x(2x+3)^2}{x(2x+3)^2}$$

$$=\dfrac{x(2x+3)+2x}{5(2x+3)}$$

$$=\dfrac{2x^2+3x+2x}{5(2x+3)}$$

$$=\dfrac{2x^2+5x}{5(2x+3)}$$

$$=\dfrac{x(2x+5)}{5(2x+3)}$$

17. $\dfrac{\dfrac{3}{x-y}+\dfrac{1}{2}}{1-\dfrac{x}{x-y}}\cdot\dfrac{2(x-y)}{2(x-y)}=\dfrac{6+x-y}{2(x-y)-2x}$

$$=\dfrac{6+x-y}{2x-2y-2x}$$

$$=-\dfrac{6+x-y}{2y}$$

19. $\dfrac{\dfrac{1}{x-a}-\dfrac{1}{x}}{a}\cdot\dfrac{x(x-a)}{x(x-a)}=\dfrac{x-(x-a)}{ax(x-a)}$

$$=\dfrac{x-x+a}{ax(x-a)}$$

$$=\dfrac{a}{ax(x-a)}$$

$$=\dfrac{1}{x(x-a)}$$

21. $1-\dfrac{1}{1-\dfrac{1}{y-2}}\cdot\dfrac{y-2}{y-2}=1-\dfrac{y-2}{y-2-1}$

$$=1-\dfrac{y-2}{y-3}$$

$$=\dfrac{y-3-y+2}{y-3}$$

$$=-\dfrac{1}{y-3}$$

23. $\dfrac{\dfrac{x^2-1}{6x^2+3x}}{\dfrac{x-1}{2x^2}}=\dfrac{(x+1)(x-1)}{3x(2x+1)}\cdot\dfrac{2x^2}{(x-1)}$

$$=\dfrac{2x(x+1)}{3(2x+1)}$$

Cumulative Review

25. $|2-3x|=4$

$\qquad 2-3x=4$ or $2-3x=-4$

$\qquad 3x=-2 \qquad\qquad -3x=-6$

$\qquad x=-\dfrac{2}{3} \qquad\qquad x=2$

155

© 2006 Pearson Education, Inc., Upper Saddle River, NJ. All rights reserved. This material is protected under all copyright laws as they currently exist. No portion of this material may be reproduced, in any form or by any means, without permission in writing from the publisher.

27. $|7x - 3 - 2x| < 6$

$|5x - 3| < 6$

$-6 < 5x - 3 < 6$

$-3 < 5x < 9$

$-\dfrac{3}{5} < x < \dfrac{9}{5}$

29. (a) $\dfrac{\$4000}{\text{inch}} \cdot \dfrac{12 \text{ inches}}{\text{foot}} \cdot \dfrac{5280 \text{ feet}}{\text{mile}}$

$= \dfrac{\$253,440,000}{\text{mile}}$

$\$253,440,000$ was spent per mile in the 1970's.

(b) $\$4,860,000,000 - \$570,000,000$

$= \$4,290,000,000$

$\dfrac{\$660,000,000}{\text{mile}} \cdot x = \$4,290,000,000$

$x = 6.5$ miles

A total of 6.5 miles can be built with the budget limit.

How Am I Doing? Sections 6.1-6.3

1. $\dfrac{49x^2 - 9}{7x^2 + 4x - 3} = \dfrac{(7x - 3)(7x + 3)}{(x + 1)(7x - 3)}$

$= \dfrac{7x + 3}{x + 1}$

2. $\dfrac{x^2 - 4x - 21}{x^2 + x - 56} = \dfrac{(x - 7)(x + 3)}{(x - 7)(x + 8)} = \dfrac{x + 3}{x + 8}$

3. $\dfrac{2x^3 - 5x^2 - 3x}{x^3 - 8x^2 + 15x} = \dfrac{x(2x^2 - 5x - 3)}{x(x^2 - 8 + 15)}$

$= \dfrac{(2x + 1)(x - 3)}{(x - 5)(x - 3)}$

$= \dfrac{2x + 1}{x - 5}$

4. $\dfrac{6a - 30}{3a + 3} \cdot \dfrac{9a^2 + a - 8}{2a^2 - 15a + 25}$

$= \dfrac{6(a - 5)}{3(a + 1)} \cdot \dfrac{(9a - 8)(a + 1)}{(2a - 5)(a - 5)}$

$= \dfrac{2(9a - 8)}{2a - 5}$

5. $\dfrac{5x^3 y^2}{x^2 y + 10xy^2 + 25y^3} \div \dfrac{2x^4 y^5}{3x^3 - 75xy^2}$

$= \dfrac{5x^3 y^2}{y(x^2 + 10xy + 5y^2)} \cdot \dfrac{3x(x^2 - 25y^2)}{2x^4 y^5}$

$= \dfrac{15}{2y^4} \cdot \dfrac{(x - 5y)(x + 5y)}{(x + 5y)(x + 5y)}$

$= \dfrac{15(x - 5y)}{2y^4(x + 5y)}$

6. $\dfrac{8x^3 + 1}{4x^2 + 4x + 1} \cdot \dfrac{6x + 3}{4x^2 - 2x + 1}$

$= \dfrac{(2x + 1)(4x^2 - 2x + 1)}{4x^2 + 4x + 1} \cdot \dfrac{3(2x + 1)}{4x^2 - 2x + 1}$

$= \dfrac{3(2x + 1)^2}{4x^2 + 4x + 1} = \dfrac{3(4x^2 + 4x + 1)}{(4x^2 + 4x + 1)} = 3$

7. $\dfrac{x}{3x - 6} - \dfrac{4}{3x} = \dfrac{x^2}{3x(x - 2)} - \dfrac{4(x - 2)}{3x(x - 2)}$

$= \dfrac{x^2 - 4x + 8}{3x(x - 2)}$

8. $\dfrac{2}{x + 5} + \dfrac{3}{x - 5} + \dfrac{7x}{x^2 - 25}$

$= \dfrac{2(x - 5)}{(x + 5)(x - 5)} + \dfrac{3(x + 5)}{(x - 5)(x + 5)}$

$+ \dfrac{7x}{(x - 5)(x + 5)}$

$= \dfrac{2x - 10 + 3x + 15 + 7x}{(x - 5)(x + 5)} = \dfrac{12x + 5}{(x - 5)(x + 5)}$

© 2006 Pearson Education, Inc., Upper Saddle River, NJ. All rights reserved. This material is protected under all copyright laws as they currently exist. No portion of this material may be reproduced, in any form or by any means, without permission in writing from the publisher.

9. $\dfrac{y+1}{y^2+y-12}-\dfrac{y-3}{y^2+7y+12}$

$=\dfrac{(y+1)(y+3)}{(y+4)(y-3)(y+3)}$

$\qquad\qquad -\dfrac{(y-3)(y-3)}{(y+4)(y+3)(y-3)}$

$=\dfrac{y^2+4y+3-y^2+6y-9}{(y+4)(y+3)(y-3)}$

$=\dfrac{10y-6}{(y+4)(y+3)(y-3)}$

10. $\dfrac{x+1}{x+4}+\dfrac{4-x^2}{x^2-16}=\dfrac{x+1}{x+4}-\dfrac{x^2-4}{(x+4)(x-4)}$

$=\dfrac{(x+1)(x-4)-(x^2-4)}{(x+4)(x-4)}$

$=\dfrac{x^2-3x-4-x^2+4}{(x+4)(x-4)}$

$=\dfrac{-3x}{(x+4)(x-4)}$

11. $\dfrac{\dfrac{1}{12x}+\dfrac{5}{3x}}{\dfrac{2}{3x^2}}\cdot\dfrac{12x^2}{12x^2}=\dfrac{x+20x}{8}$

$=\dfrac{21x}{8}$

12. $\dfrac{\dfrac{x}{4x^2-1}}{3-\dfrac{2}{2x+1}}=\dfrac{\dfrac{x}{(2x+1)(2x-1)}}{\dfrac{3(2x+1)-2}{2x+1}}$

$=\dfrac{x}{(2x+1)(2x-1)}\cdot\dfrac{2x+1}{6x+3-2}$

$=\dfrac{x}{(2x-1)(6x+1)}$

13. $\dfrac{\dfrac{5}{x}+3}{\dfrac{6}{x}-2}\cdot\dfrac{x}{x}=\dfrac{5+3x}{6-2x}$

14. $\dfrac{\dfrac{x}{x+2}+\dfrac{5}{x}}{\dfrac{x+2}{x}+\dfrac{3}{x+2}}\cdot\dfrac{x(x+2)}{x(x+2)}=\dfrac{x^2+5(x+2)}{(x+2)^2+3x}$

$=\dfrac{x^2+5x+10}{x^2+4x+4+3x}$

$=\dfrac{x^2+5x+10}{x^2+7x+4}$

6.4 Exercises

1. $\dfrac{2}{x}+\dfrac{3}{2x}=\dfrac{7}{6}$

$\qquad 12+9=7x$

$\qquad 7x=21$

$\qquad x=3$

$\qquad \text{check:}\dfrac{2}{3}+\dfrac{3}{2(3)}\overset{?}{=}\dfrac{7}{6},\ \dfrac{7}{6}=\dfrac{7}{6}$

3. $3-\dfrac{2}{x}=\dfrac{1}{4x}$

$\qquad 12x-8=1$

$\qquad 12x=9$

$\qquad x=\dfrac{3}{4}$

$\qquad \text{check:}3-\dfrac{2}{\dfrac{3}{4}}\overset{?}{=}\dfrac{1}{4\cdot\dfrac{3}{4}},\ \dfrac{1}{3}=\dfrac{1}{3}$

© 2006 Pearson Education, Inc., Upper Saddle River, NJ. All rights reserved. This material is protected under all copyright laws as they currently exist. No portion of this material may be reproduced, in any form or by any means, without permission in writing from the publisher.

5. $\dfrac{5}{2x+3}+\dfrac{1}{x}=\dfrac{3}{x}$

$5x+2x+3=3(2x+3)$

$7x+3=6x+9$

$x=6$

check: $\dfrac{5}{2(6)+3}+\dfrac{1}{6}\overset{?}{=}\dfrac{3}{6},\ \dfrac{1}{2}=\dfrac{1}{2}$

7. $\dfrac{2}{y}=\dfrac{5}{y-3}$

$2y-6=5y$

$3y=-6$

$y=-2$

check: $\dfrac{2}{-2}\overset{?}{=}\dfrac{5}{-2-3},\ -1=-1$

9. $\dfrac{y+6}{y+3}-2=\dfrac{3}{y+3}$

$y+6-2y-6=3$

$-y=3$

$y=-3$

No solution.

11. $\dfrac{1}{3x}-\dfrac{2}{x}=\dfrac{-5}{x+4}$

$x+4-2(3(x+4))=-5(3x)$

$x+4-6x-24=-15x$

$10x=20$

$x=2$

check: $\dfrac{1}{3(2)}-\dfrac{2}{2}\overset{?}{=}\dfrac{-5}{2+4},\ -\dfrac{5}{6}=-\dfrac{5}{6}$

13. $\dfrac{2x+3}{x+3}=\dfrac{2x}{x+1}$

$(2x+3)(x+1)=2x(x+3)$

$2x^2+5x+3=2x^2+6x$

$x=3$

13. check: $\dfrac{2\cdot3+3}{3+3}\overset{?}{=}\dfrac{2\cdot3}{3+1},\ \dfrac{3}{2}=\dfrac{3}{2}$

15. $\dfrac{3}{y^2-1}=\dfrac{6}{y^2-y}$

$\dfrac{3}{(y-1)(y+1)}=\dfrac{6}{y(y-1)}$

$3y=6y+6$

$3y=-6$

$y=-2$

check: $\dfrac{3}{(-2)^2-1}\overset{?}{=}\dfrac{6}{(-2)^2-(-2)},\ 1=1$

17. $\dfrac{3}{2x-1}+\dfrac{3}{2x+1}=\dfrac{8x}{4x^2-1}$

$\dfrac{3}{2x-1}+\dfrac{3}{2x+1}=\dfrac{8x}{(2x+1)(2x-1)}$

$3(2x+1)+3(2x-1)=8x$

$6x+3+6x-3=8x$

$4x=0$

$x=0$

check:

$\dfrac{3}{2(0)-1}+\dfrac{3}{2(0)+1}\overset{?}{=}\dfrac{8(0)}{4(0)^2-1},\ 0=0$

19. $\dfrac{5}{y-3}+2=\dfrac{3}{3y-9}=\dfrac{3}{3(y-3)}$

$15+6(y-3)=3$

$12+6y-18=0$

$6y=6$

$y=1$

check: $\dfrac{5}{1-3}+2\overset{?}{=}\dfrac{3}{3(1)-9},\ -\dfrac{1}{2}=-\dfrac{1}{2}$

158

© 2006 Pearson Education, Inc., Upper Saddle River, NJ. All rights reserved. This material is protected under all copyright laws as they currently exist. No portion of this material may be reproduced, in any form or by any means, without permission in writing from the publisher.

21.

$$1 - \frac{10}{z-3} = \frac{-5}{3z-9} = \frac{-5}{3(z-3)}$$

$$3(z-3) - 30 = -5$$

$$3z - 9 = 25$$

$$3z = 34$$

$$z = \frac{34}{3}$$

check: $1 - \dfrac{10}{\dfrac{34}{3} - 3} \overset{?}{=} \dfrac{-5}{3 \cdot \dfrac{34}{3} - 9},\ \dfrac{1}{5} = -\dfrac{1}{5}$

23.

$$\frac{8}{3x+2} - \frac{7x+4}{3x^2+5x+2} = \frac{2}{x+1}$$

$$\frac{8}{3x+2} - \frac{7x+4}{(3x+2)(x+1)} = \frac{2}{x+1}$$

$$8(x+1) - (7x+4) = 2(3x+2)$$

$$8x + 8 - 7x - 4 = 6x + 4$$

$$5x = 0$$

$$x = 0$$

check: $\dfrac{8}{3(0)+2} - \dfrac{7(0)+4}{3(0)^2+5(0)+2} \overset{?}{=} \dfrac{2}{(0)+1}$

$$2 = 2$$

25.

$$\frac{4}{z^2-9} = \frac{2}{z^2-3z}$$

$$\frac{4}{(z-3)(z+3)} = \frac{2}{z(z-3)}$$

$$4z = 2(z+3)$$

$$4z = 2z + 6$$

$$2z = 6$$

$z = 3$ which gives a division
by zero, no solution.

27.

$$\frac{2x+3}{2} + \frac{1}{x+1} = x$$

$$(2x+3)(x+1) + 2 = 2x(x+1)$$

$$2x^2 + 5x + 3 + 2 = 2x^2 + 2x$$

$$3x = -5$$

$$x = -\frac{5}{3}$$

check: $\dfrac{2\left(-\dfrac{5}{3}\right)+3}{2} + \dfrac{1}{-\dfrac{5}{3}+1} \overset{?}{=} -\dfrac{5}{3}$

$$-\frac{5}{3} = -\frac{5}{3}$$

29. When the solved-for value of the
variable causes the denominator of any
fraction to equal to 0, or when the
variable drops out and leaves a false
statement.

31.

$$\frac{153.8}{x^2+4.9x-39.56} = \frac{75.3}{x+9.2} + \frac{84.2}{x-4.3}$$

$$\frac{153.8}{(x+9.2)(x-4.3)} = \frac{75.3}{x+9.2} + \frac{84.2}{x-4.3}$$

$$153.8 = 75.3(x-4.3) + 84.2(x+9.2)$$

$$153.8 = 75.3x - 323.79 + 84.2x + 774.64$$

$$159.5x = -297.05$$

$$x \approx -1.9$$

Cumulative Review

33. $7x^2 - 63 = 7(x^2-9) = 7(x+3)(x-3)$

35. $64x^3 - 27y^3 = (4x)^3 - (3y)^3$
$$= (4x-3y)(16x^2+12xy+9y^2)$$

© 2006 Pearson Education, Inc., Upper Saddle River, NJ. All rights reserved. This material is protected under all copyright laws as they currently exist.
No portion of this material may be reproduced, in any form or by any means, without permission in writing from the publisher.

37. 25% of the 160,000 couples,
   $= (0.25)(160,000)$, or 80,000 couples
   will attend counseling for more than
   one year but less than two years. 25%
   of these 80,000 or $(0.25)(80,000) =$
   20,000 will remain married.

6.5 Exercises

1. $x = \dfrac{y-b}{m}$

   $mx = y - b$

   $m = \dfrac{y-b}{x}$

3. $\dfrac{1}{f} = \dfrac{1}{a} + \dfrac{1}{b}$

   $ab = bf + af$

   $ab - bf = af$

   $b(a - f) = af$

   $b = \dfrac{af}{a-f}$

5. $\dfrac{V}{lh} = w$

   $lh = \dfrac{V}{w}$

   $h = \dfrac{V}{lw}$

7. $F = \dfrac{xy + xz}{2}$

   $xy + xz = 2F$

   $x(y + z) = 2F$

   $x = \dfrac{2F}{y+z}$

9. $\dfrac{r^3}{V} = \dfrac{3}{4\pi}$

   $3V = 4\pi r^3$

   $V = \dfrac{4}{3}\pi r^3$

11. $\dfrac{E}{e} = \dfrac{R+r}{r}$

   $e(R + r) = Er$

   $e = \dfrac{Er}{R+r}$

13. $\dfrac{P_1 V_1}{T_1} = \dfrac{P_2 V_2}{T_2}$

   $P_2 V_2 T_1 = P_1 V_1 T_2$

   $T_1 = \dfrac{P_1 V_1 T_2}{P_2 V_2}$

15. $\dfrac{S - 2lw}{2w + 2l} = h$

   $S - 2lw = 2wh + 2lh$

   $2wh + 2lw = S - 2lh$

   $w(2h + 2l) = S - 2lh$

   $w = \dfrac{S - 2lh}{2h + 2l}$

17. $E = T_1 - \dfrac{T_1}{T_2}$

   $ET_2 = T_1 T_2 - T_1$

   $T_1(T_2 - 1) = ET_2$

   $T_1 = \dfrac{ET_2}{T_2 - 1}$

160

© 2006 Pearson Education, Inc., Upper Saddle River, NJ. All rights reserved. This material is protected under all copyright laws as they currently exist. No portion of this material may be reproduced, in any form or by any means, without permission in writing from the publisher.

19.
$$m = \frac{y_2 - y_1}{x_2 - x_1}$$
$$mx_2 - mx_1 = y_2 - y_1$$
$$mx_1 = mx_2 + y_1 - y_2$$
$$x_1 = \frac{mx_2 + y_1 - y_2}{m}$$

21.
$$\frac{2D - at^2}{2t} = V$$
$$2D - at^2 = 2Vt$$
$$2D = 2Vt + at^2$$
$$D = \frac{2Vt + at^2}{2}$$

23.
$$Q = \frac{kA(t_1 - t_2)}{L}$$
$$QL = kAt_1 - kAt_2$$
$$kAt_2 = kAt_1 - QL$$
$$t_2 = \frac{kAt_1 - QL}{kA}$$

25.
$$\frac{T_2 W}{T_2 - T_1} = q$$
$$T_2 W = qT_2 - qT_1$$
$$qT_2 - T_2 W = qT_1$$
$$T_2(q - W) = qT_1$$
$$T_2 = \frac{qT_1}{q - W}$$

27.
$$\frac{s - s_o}{v_o + gt} = t$$
$$s - s_o = v_o t + gt^2$$
$$v_o t = s - s_o - gt^2$$
$$v_o = \frac{s - s_o - gt^2}{t}$$

29.
$$\frac{1.98V}{1.96V_o} = 0.983 + 5.936(T - T_o)$$
$$\frac{1.98V}{1.96V_o} = 0.983 + 5.936T - 5.936T_o$$
$$5.936T = 5.936T_o + \frac{1.98V}{1.96V_o} - 0.983$$
$$T \approx T_o + 0.1702\left(\frac{V}{V_o}\right) - 0.1656$$

31.
$$\frac{3}{55} = \frac{6.5}{x}$$
$$3x = 357.5$$
$$x = 119.1\overline{6}$$
The two cities are approximately 119.2 kilometers apart.

33.
$$\frac{60}{88} = \frac{x}{80}$$
$$88x = 4800$$
$$x = 54.\overline{54}$$
The speed limit is approximately 54.55 mph.

35.
$$\frac{35}{x} = \frac{22}{50}$$
$$22x = 1750$$
$$x = 79.\overline{54}$$
The number of grizzly bears, to the nearest whole number, is 80.

37. $x =$ number of officers
$$\frac{2}{7} = \frac{x}{117 - x}$$
$$234 - 2x = 7x$$
$$9x = 234$$
$$x = 26 \text{ officers}$$
$$117 - 26 = 91 \text{ seamen}$$

161

© 2006 Pearson Education, Inc., Upper Saddle River, NJ. All rights reserved. This material is protected under all copyright laws as they currently exist. No portion of this material may be reproduced, in any form or by any means, without permission in writing from the publisher.

39. $x =$ number of people in marketing

$$\frac{4}{13} = \frac{x}{187 - x}$$

$$748 - 4x = 13x$$

$$17x = 748$$

$$x = 44$$

$$187 - 44 = 143$$

There are 44 people in marketing and 143 people in sales.

41. $\dfrac{L}{W} = \dfrac{10}{8} \Rightarrow L = \dfrac{10}{8}W$

$$2L + 2W = 54$$

$$\frac{10}{8}W + W = 27$$

$$W = 12 \text{ in. for the width}$$

$$L = \frac{10}{8}(12) = 15 \text{ in. for the length}$$

43. $x =$ number preferring new software

$$\frac{3}{11} = \frac{x}{280 - x}$$

$$840 - 3x = 11x$$

$$14x = 840$$

$$x = 60$$

Sixty people prefer the new software.

45. $\dfrac{4}{9} = \dfrac{x}{78 - x} \Rightarrow 312 - 4x = 9x$

$$13x = 312$$

$$x = 24 \text{ powerboats}$$

$$78 - x = 54 \text{ sailboats}$$

47. $\dfrac{x}{8} = \dfrac{12}{15}$

$$15x = 96$$

$$x = 6.4$$

The wall is 6.4 feet high.

49. $\dfrac{F}{M} = \dfrac{7}{4} = \dfrac{F}{112}$

$$4F = 112(7) = 784$$

$$F = 196$$

She should eat fish 196 times.

51. $\dfrac{t}{6} + \dfrac{t}{9} = 1$

$$\frac{5}{18}t = 1$$

$$t = \frac{18}{5} = 3.6$$

It will take them 3.6 hours to do the work together.

53. $\dfrac{1}{t} \cdot 2 + \dfrac{1}{3} \cdot 2 = 1$

$$6 + 2t = 3t$$

$$t = 6$$

Using just the hot water pipe the pool will fill in 6 hours.

55. $\dfrac{b}{a} = \dfrac{x + 8}{c}$

$$\frac{5}{2} = \frac{x + 8}{116}$$

$$2x + 16 = 580$$

$$2x = 564$$

$$x = 282$$

The width of the river is 282 feet.

Cumulative Review

57. $7x - 3y = 8$

$$3y = 7x - 8$$

$$y = \frac{7}{3}x - \frac{8}{3} \Rightarrow m = \frac{7}{3}, \ b = -\frac{8}{3}$$

© 2006 Pearson Education, Inc., Upper Saddle River, NJ. All rights reserved. This material is protected under all copyright laws as they currently exist. No portion of this material may be reproduced, in any form or by any means, without permission in writing from the publisher.

59. $\quad y = 3x - 7 \Rightarrow m = 3 \Rightarrow m_\perp = -\dfrac{1}{3}$

$$y - y_1 = m(x - x_1)$$

$$y - 1 = -\frac{1}{3}(x - 6)$$

$$y = -\frac{1}{3}x + 2 + 1$$

$$y = -\frac{1}{3}x + 3$$

61. $F =$ value of full scholarship

$$3750F + 3750\left(\frac{F}{2}\right) = 50,000,000$$

$$5625F = 50,000,000$$

$$F = 8888.\overline{8}$$

$$\frac{F}{2} = 4444.\overline{4}$$

Full scholarships were \$8888.89 per student and partial scholarships were \$4444.44 per student.

Putting Your Skills to Work

1. $M = \dfrac{P\left(\dfrac{r}{12}\right)}{1 - \left(1 + \dfrac{r}{12}\right)^{-m}}$

$$M = \dfrac{8388\left(\dfrac{0.039}{12}\right)}{1 - \left(1 + \dfrac{0.039}{12}\right)^{-36}}$$

$$M = \$247.27$$

2. $M = \dfrac{P\left(\dfrac{r}{12}\right)}{1 - \left(1 + \dfrac{r}{12}\right)^{-m}} = \dfrac{8388\left(\dfrac{0.069}{12}\right)}{1 - \left(1 + \dfrac{0.069}{12}\right)^{-72}}$

$$M = \$142.60$$

3. $247.27(36) = \$8901.72$ for 36 months

$142.60(72) = \$10,267.20$ for 72 months

4. $8901.72 - 8388$

$= \$513.72$ for 36 months

$10,267.20 - 8388$

$= \$1879.20$ for 72 months

5. $P = 0.9(17,500 - 2000) = 13,950$

$$M = \dfrac{P\left(\dfrac{r}{12}\right)}{1 - \left(1 + \dfrac{r}{12}\right)^{-m}}$$

$$M = \dfrac{13,950\left(\dfrac{0.059}{12}\right)}{1 - \left(1 + \dfrac{0.059}{12}\right)^{-72}}$$

$M = \$230.53$/month at 5.9%

$0.9(17,500) \div 48 = \$328.13$/month at 0%

6. $0.1(17,500 - 2000) + 230.53(72)$

$= \$18,148.16$ at 5.9%

$0.1(17,500) + 328.13(48)$

$= \$17,500.24$ at 0%

7. The 5.9% plan has a lower down payment and lower monthly payments; the 0% plan has a lower overall cost.

© 2006 Pearson Education, Inc., Upper Saddle River, NJ. All rights reserved. This material is protected under all copyright laws as they currently exist. No portion of this material may be reproduced, in any form or by any means, without permission in writing from the publisher.

8. advantages: lower monthly payment and no down payment
disadvantages: you don't own the car at the end of the lease

Chapter 6 Review Problems

1. $\dfrac{6x^3 - 9x^2}{12x^2 - 18x} = \dfrac{3x^2(2x-3)}{6x(2x-3)} = \dfrac{x}{2}$

2. $\dfrac{15x^4}{5x^2 - 20x} = \dfrac{15x^4}{5x(x-4)} = \dfrac{3x^3}{x-4}$

3. $\dfrac{26x^3y^2}{39xy^4} = \dfrac{13 \cdot 2x \cdot x^2 y^2}{13 \cdot 3xy^2 y^2} = \dfrac{2x^2}{3y^2}$

4. $\dfrac{42a^4bc^3}{24a^7b} = \dfrac{7c^3}{4a^{7-4}} = \dfrac{7c^3}{4a^3}$

5. $\dfrac{2x^2 - 5x + 3}{3x^2 + 2x - 5} = \dfrac{(2x-3)(x-1)}{(3x+5)(x-1)} = \dfrac{2x-3}{3x+5}$

6. $\dfrac{ax + 2a - bx - 2b}{3x^2 - 12} = \dfrac{a(x+2) - b(x+2)}{3(x^2 - 4)}$

$= \dfrac{(a-b)\cancel{(x+2)}}{3(x-2)\cancel{(x+2)}}$

$= \dfrac{a-b}{3(x-2)}$

7. $\dfrac{4x^2 - 1}{x^2 - 4} \cdot \dfrac{2x^2 + 4x}{4x+2}$

$= \dfrac{(2x-1)(2x+1)}{(x+2)(x-2)} \cdot \dfrac{2x(x+2)}{2(2x+1)}$

$= \dfrac{x(2x-1)}{x-2}$

8. $\dfrac{3y}{4xy - 6y^2} \cdot \dfrac{2x - 3y}{12xy}$

$= \dfrac{3y}{2y(2x-3y)} \cdot \dfrac{(2x-3y)}{12xy} = \dfrac{1}{8xy}$

9. $\dfrac{y^2 + 8y - 20}{y^2 + 6y - 16} \cdot \dfrac{y^2 + 3y - 40}{y^2 + 6y - 40}$

$= \dfrac{(y+10)(y-2)}{(y+8)(y-2)} \cdot \dfrac{(y+8)(y-5)}{(y+10)(y-4)}$

$= \dfrac{y-5}{y-4}$

10. $\dfrac{3x^3 y}{x^2 + 7x + 12} \cdot \dfrac{x^2 + 8x + 15}{6xy^2}$

$= \dfrac{3xx^2 y}{(x+4)(x+3)} \cdot \dfrac{(x+5)(x+3)}{3 \cdot 2xyy}$

$= \dfrac{x^2(x+5)}{2y(x+4)}$

11. $\dfrac{2x + 12}{3x - 15} \div \dfrac{2x^2 - 6x - 20}{x^2 - 10x + 25}$

$= \dfrac{2(x+6)}{3(x-5)} \cdot \dfrac{(x-5)(x-5)}{2(x-5)(x+2)}$

$= \dfrac{x+6}{3(x+2)}$

12. $\dfrac{2a^4 b^5}{6x^2 + x - 1} \div \dfrac{10a^5 b^2}{3x^2 + 5x - 2}$

$= \dfrac{2a^4 b^5}{(3x-1)(2x+1)} \cdot \dfrac{(3x-1)(x+2)}{10a^5 b^2}$

$= \dfrac{b^3(x+2)}{5a(2x+1)}$

164

© 2006 Pearson Education, Inc., Upper Saddle River, NJ. All rights reserved. This material is protected under all copyright laws as they currently exist. No portion of this material may be reproduced, in any form or by any means, without permission in writing from the publisher.

13.
$$\frac{9y^2 - 3y - 2}{6y^2 - 13y - 5} \div \frac{3y^2 + 10y - 8}{2y^2 + 13y + 20}$$
$$= \frac{(3y+1)(3y-2)}{(3y+1)(2y-5)} \cdot \frac{(y+4)(2y+5)}{(y+4)(3y-2)}$$
$$= \frac{2y+5}{2y-5}$$

14.
$$\frac{4a^2 + 12a + 5}{2a^2 - 7a - 13} \div (4a^2 + 2a)$$
$$= \frac{(2a+1)(2a+5)}{2a^2 - 7a - 13} \cdot \frac{1}{2a(2a+1)}$$
$$= \frac{2a+5}{2a(2a^2 - 7a - 13)}$$

15.
$$\frac{x-5}{2x+1} - \frac{x+1}{x-2}$$
$$= \frac{(x-5)(x-2) - (2x+1)(x+1)}{(2x+1)(x-2)}$$
$$= \frac{x^2 - 7x + 10 - 2x^2 - 3x - 1}{(2x+1)(x-2)}$$
$$= \frac{-x^2 - 10x + 9}{(2x+1)(x-2)} = -\frac{x^2 + 10x - 9}{(2x+1)(x-2)}$$

16.
$$\frac{5}{4x} + \frac{-3}{x+4} = \frac{5(x+4) - 3(4x)}{4x(x+4)}$$
$$= \frac{5x + 20 - 12x}{4x(x+4)}$$
$$= \frac{-7x + 20}{4x(x+4)}$$

17.
$$\frac{(2y-1)(3)}{12y(3)} - \frac{(3y+2)(4)}{9y(4)}$$
$$= \frac{6y - 3 - 12y - 8}{36y}$$
$$= \frac{-6y - 11}{36y}$$

18.
$$\frac{4}{y+5} + \frac{3y+2}{y^2 - 25}$$
$$= \frac{4(y-5)}{(y+5)(y-5)} + \frac{3y+2}{(y+5)(y-5)}$$
$$= \frac{4y - 20 + 3y + 2}{(y+5)(y-5)}$$
$$= \frac{7y - 18}{(y+5)(y-5)}$$

19.
$$\frac{4y}{y^2 + 2y + 1} + \frac{3}{y^2 - 1}$$
$$= \frac{4y(y-1)}{(y+1)^2(y-1)} + \frac{3(y+1)}{(y+1)^2(y-1)}$$
$$= \frac{4y^2 - 4y + 3y + 3}{(y+1)^2(y-1)}$$
$$= \frac{4y^2 - y + 3}{(y+1)^2(y-1)}$$

20.
$$\frac{y^2 - 4y - 19}{y^2 + 8y + 15} - \frac{2y - 3}{y+5}$$
$$= \frac{y^2 - 4y - 19}{(y+5)(y+3)} - \frac{(2y-3)(y+3)}{(y+5)(y+3)}$$
$$= \frac{y^2 - 4y - 19 - 2y^2 - 3y + 9}{(y+5)(y+3)}$$
$$= \frac{-y^2 - 7y - 10}{(y+5)(y+3)} = -\frac{(y+5)(y+2)}{(y+5)(y+3)}$$
$$= -\frac{y+2}{y+3}$$

© 2006 Pearson Education, Inc., Upper Saddle River, NJ. All rights reserved. This material is protected under all copyright laws as they currently exist. No portion of this material may be reproduced, in any form or by any means, without permission in writing from the publisher.

21. $\dfrac{a}{5-a} - \dfrac{2}{a+3} + \dfrac{2a^2 - 2a}{a^2 - 2a - 15}$

$= \dfrac{-a(a+3)}{(a-5)(a+3)} - \dfrac{2(a-5)}{(a+3)(a-5)} + \dfrac{2a(a-1)}{(a-5)(a+3)}$

$= \dfrac{-a^2 - 3a - 2a + 10 + 2a^2 - 2a}{(a+3)(a-5)}$

$= \dfrac{a^2 - 7a + 10}{(a+3)(a-5)} = \dfrac{(a-2)(a-5)}{(a+3)(a-5)}$

$= \dfrac{a-2}{a+3}$

22. $\dfrac{2}{x^2 + 8x + 16} - \dfrac{x}{2x^2 + 9x + 4}$

$= \dfrac{2}{(x+4)^2} - \dfrac{x}{(2x+1)(x+4)}$

$= \dfrac{2(2x+1) - x(x+4)}{(x+4)^2(2x+1)}$

$= \dfrac{4x + 2 - x^2 - 4x}{(x+4)^2(2x+1)}$

$= \dfrac{-x^2 + 2}{(x+4)^2(2x+1)}$

23. $5b - 1 - \dfrac{b+2}{b+3}$

$= \dfrac{5b(b+3) - (b+3) - (b+2)}{b+3}$

$= \dfrac{5b^2 + 15b - b - 3 - b - 2}{b+3}$

$= \dfrac{5b^2 + 13b - 5}{b+3}$

24. $\dfrac{1}{x} + \dfrac{3}{2x} + 3 + 2x = \dfrac{2}{2x} + \dfrac{3}{2x} + \dfrac{6x}{2x} + \dfrac{4x^2}{2x}$

$= \dfrac{2 + 3 + 6x + 4x^2}{2x} = \dfrac{4x^2 + 6x + 5}{2x}$

25. $\dfrac{\dfrac{5}{x} + 1}{1 - \dfrac{25}{x^2}} \cdot \dfrac{x^2}{x^2} = \dfrac{5x + x^2}{x^2 - 25}$

$= \dfrac{x(x+5)}{(x-5)(x+5)}$

$= \dfrac{x}{x-5}$

26. $\dfrac{\dfrac{4}{x+3}}{\dfrac{2}{x-2} - \dfrac{1}{x^2 + x - 6}}$

$= \dfrac{\dfrac{4}{x+3}}{\dfrac{2}{(x-2)} - \dfrac{1}{(x+3)(x-2)}} \cdot \dfrac{(x+3)(x-2)}{(x+3)(x-2)}$

$= \dfrac{4(x-2)}{2(x+3) - 1}$

$= \dfrac{4(x-2)}{2x + 6 - 1}$

$= \dfrac{4(x-2)}{2x + 5}$

27. $\dfrac{\dfrac{y}{y+1} + \dfrac{1}{y}}{\dfrac{y}{y+1} - \dfrac{1}{y}} \cdot \dfrac{y(y+1)}{y(y+1)} = \dfrac{y^2 + y + 1}{y^2 - y - 1}$

28. $\dfrac{\dfrac{10}{a+2} - 5}{\dfrac{4}{a+2} - 2} \cdot \dfrac{a+2}{a+2} = \dfrac{10 - 5a - 10}{4 - 2a - 4}$

$= \dfrac{5}{2}$

© 2006 Pearson Education, Inc., Upper Saddle River, NJ. All rights reserved. This material is protected under all copyright laws as they currently exist. No portion of this material may be reproduced, in any form or by any means, without permission in writing from the publisher.

29.

$$\dfrac{\dfrac{2}{x+4}-\dfrac{1}{x^2+4x}}{\dfrac{3}{2x+8}}$$

$$=\dfrac{\dfrac{2}{x+4}-\dfrac{1}{x(x+4)}}{\dfrac{3}{2(x+4)}}\cdot\dfrac{2x(x+4)}{2x(x+4)}$$

$$=\dfrac{4x-2}{3x}=\dfrac{2(2x-1)}{3x}$$

30.

$$\dfrac{\dfrac{y^2}{y^2-x^2}-1}{x+\dfrac{xy}{x-y}}$$

$$=\dfrac{\dfrac{-y^2}{(x-y)(x+y)}-1}{x+\dfrac{xy}{x-y}}\cdot\dfrac{(x-y)(x+y)}{(x-y)(x+y)}$$

$$=\dfrac{-y^2-x^2+y^2}{x(x-y)(x+y)+xy(x+y)}$$

$$=\dfrac{-x^2}{x(x+y)(x-y+y)}$$

$$=\dfrac{-x}{(x+y)x}=\dfrac{-1}{x+y}$$

31.

$$\dfrac{\dfrac{2x+1}{x-1}}{1+\dfrac{x}{x+1}}\cdot\dfrac{(x+1)(x-1)}{(x+1)(x-1)}$$

$$=\dfrac{(2x+1)(x+1)}{(x+1)(x-1)+x(x-1)}$$

$$=\dfrac{2x^2+3x+1}{x^2-1+x^2-x}=\dfrac{(2x+1)(x+1)}{2x^2-x-1}$$

$$=\dfrac{(2x+1)(x+1)}{(2x+1)(x-1)}=\dfrac{x+1}{x-1}$$

32.

$$\dfrac{\dfrac{3}{x}-\dfrac{2}{x+1}}{\dfrac{5}{x^2+5x+4}-\dfrac{1}{x+4}}$$

$$=\dfrac{\dfrac{3}{x}-\dfrac{2}{x+1}}{\dfrac{5}{(x+4)(x+1)}-\dfrac{1}{x+4}}\cdot\dfrac{x(x+1)(x+4)}{x(x+1)(x+4)}$$

$$=\dfrac{3(x+1)(x+4)-2x(x+4)}{5x-x(x+1)}$$

$$=\dfrac{3x^2+15x+12-2x^2-8x}{5x-x^2-x}$$

$$=\dfrac{x^2+7x+12}{-x^2+4x}$$

$$=\dfrac{(x+4)(x+3)}{-x(x-4)}$$

$$=\dfrac{-(x+3)(x+4)}{x(x-4)}$$

33.

$$\dfrac{3}{2}=1-\dfrac{1}{x-1}$$

$$3(x-1)=2(x-1)-2$$

$$3x-3=2x-2-2$$

$$x=-1$$

check: $\dfrac{3}{2}\overset{?}{=}1-\dfrac{1}{-1-1},\ \dfrac{3}{2}=\dfrac{3}{2}$

34.

$$\dfrac{3}{7}+\dfrac{4}{x+1}=1$$

$$3(x+1)+28=7(x+1)$$

$$3x+3+28=7x+7$$

$$4x=24$$

$$x=6$$

check: $\dfrac{3}{7}+\dfrac{4}{6+1}\overset{?}{=}1,\ 1=1$

167

© 2006 Pearson Education, Inc., Upper Saddle River, NJ. All rights reserved. This material is protected under all copyright laws as they currently exist. No portion of this material may be reproduced, in any form or by any means, without permission in writing from the publisher.

35. $\dfrac{7}{2x-3}+\dfrac{3}{x+2}=\dfrac{6}{2x-3}$

$$7(x+2)+3(2x-3)=6(x+2)$$

$$7x+14+6x-9=6x+12$$

$$7x=7$$

$$x=1$$

check: $\dfrac{7}{2(1)-3}+\dfrac{3}{1+2}\overset{?}{=}\dfrac{6}{2(1)-3}, \; -6=-6$

36. $\dfrac{9}{5x-2}-\dfrac{2}{x}=\dfrac{1}{x}$

$$9x-2(5x-2)=5x-2$$

$$9x-10x+4=5x-2$$

$$-6x=-6$$

$$x=1$$

check: $\dfrac{9}{5(1)-2}-\dfrac{2}{1}\overset{?}{=}\dfrac{1}{1}, \; 1=1$

37. $\dfrac{5}{2a}=\dfrac{2}{a}-\dfrac{1}{12}$

$$30=24-a$$

$$a=-6$$

check: $\dfrac{5}{2(-6)}\overset{?}{=}\dfrac{2}{-6}-\dfrac{1}{12}, \; -\dfrac{5}{12}=-\dfrac{5}{12}$

38. $\dfrac{1}{2a}=\dfrac{2}{a}-\dfrac{3}{10}$

$$5=20-3a$$

$$3a=15$$

$$a=5$$

check: $\dfrac{1}{2(5)}\overset{?}{=}\dfrac{2}{5}-\dfrac{3}{10}, \; \dfrac{1}{10}=\dfrac{1}{10}$

39. $\dfrac{1}{y}+\dfrac{1}{2y}=2$

$$2+1=4y$$

$$y=\dfrac{3}{4}$$

check: $\dfrac{1}{\dfrac{3}{4}}+\dfrac{1}{2\cdot\dfrac{3}{4}}\overset{?}{=}2, \; 2=2$

40. $\dfrac{5}{y^2}+\dfrac{7}{y}=\dfrac{6}{y^2}$

$$5+7y=6$$

$$7y=1$$

$$y=\dfrac{1}{7}$$

check: $\dfrac{5}{\left(\dfrac{1}{7}\right)^2}+\dfrac{7}{\dfrac{1}{7}}\overset{?}{=}\dfrac{6}{\left(\dfrac{1}{7}\right)^2}, \; 294=294$

41. $\dfrac{a+2}{2a+6}=\dfrac{3}{2}-\dfrac{3}{a+3}$

$$a+2=3(a+3)-3(2)$$

$$a+2=3a+9-6$$

$$2a=-1$$

$$a=-\dfrac{1}{2}$$

check: $\dfrac{-\dfrac{1}{2}+2}{2\left(-\dfrac{1}{2}\right)+6}\overset{?}{=}\dfrac{3}{2}-\dfrac{3}{-\dfrac{1}{2}+3}, \; \dfrac{3}{10}=\dfrac{3}{10}$

© 2006 Pearson Education, Inc., Upper Saddle River, NJ. All rights reserved. This material is protected under all copyright laws as they currently exist.
No portion of this material may be reproduced, in any form or by any means, without permission in writing from the publisher.

42. $\dfrac{5}{a+5}+\dfrac{a+4}{2a+10}=\dfrac{3}{2}$

$$\dfrac{5}{a+5}+\dfrac{a+4}{2(a+5)}=\dfrac{3}{2}$$

$$10+a+4=3(a+5)$$

$$14+a=3a+15$$

$$2a=-1$$

$$a=-\dfrac{1}{2}$$

check: $\dfrac{5}{-\dfrac{1}{2}+5}+\dfrac{-\dfrac{1}{2}+4}{2\left(-\dfrac{1}{2}+10\right)}\overset{?}{=}\dfrac{3}{2}, \ \dfrac{3}{2}=\dfrac{3}{2}$

43. $\dfrac{3x-23}{2x^2-5x-3}+\dfrac{2}{x-3}=\dfrac{5}{2x+1}$

$$\dfrac{3x-23}{(2x+1)(x-3)}+\dfrac{2}{x-3}=\dfrac{5}{2x+1}$$

$$3x-23+2(2x+1)=5(x-3)$$

$$3x-23+4x+2=5x-15$$

$$2x=6$$

$$x=3$$

No solution.

44. $\dfrac{2x-10}{2x^2-5x-3}+\dfrac{1}{x-3}=\dfrac{3}{2x+1}$

$$\dfrac{2x-10}{(2x+1)(x-3)}+\dfrac{1}{x-3}=\dfrac{3}{2x+1}$$

$$2x-10+2x+1=3(x-3)$$

$$4x-9=3x-9$$

$$x=0$$

check: $\dfrac{2(0)-10}{2(0)^2-5(0)-3}+\dfrac{1}{0-3}\overset{?}{=}\dfrac{3}{2(0)+1}$

$$3=3$$

45. $\dfrac{N}{V}=\dfrac{m}{M+N}$

$$MN+N^2=mV$$

$$MN=mV-N^2$$

$$M=\dfrac{mV-N^2}{N}$$

$$M=\dfrac{mV}{N}-N$$

46. $m=\dfrac{y-y_o}{x-x_o}$

$$mx-mx_o=y-y_o$$

$$mx=y-y_o+mx_o$$

$$x=\dfrac{y-y_o+mx_o}{m}$$

47. $\dfrac{1}{f}=\dfrac{1}{a}+\dfrac{1}{b}$

$$ab=fb+fa$$

$$ab-fa=fb$$

$$a(b-f)=fb$$

$$a=\dfrac{fb}{b-f}$$

48. $S=\dfrac{V_1t+V_2t}{2}$

$$t(V_1+V_2)=2S$$

$$t=\dfrac{2S}{V_1+V_2}$$

49. $d=\dfrac{LR_2}{R_2+R_1}$

$$dR_2+dR_1=LR_2$$

$$R_2(L-d)=dR_1$$

$$R_2=\dfrac{dR_1}{L-d}$$

© 2006 Pearson Education, Inc., Upper Saddle River, NJ. All rights reserved. This material is protected under all copyright laws as they currently exist. No portion of this material may be reproduced, in any form or by any means, without permission in writing from the publisher.

50.　$\dfrac{S-P}{Pr} = t$

$$Prt = S - P$$

$$r = \dfrac{S-P}{Pt}$$

51. $\dfrac{x^2 - x - 42}{x^2 - 2x - 35} = \dfrac{(x-7)(x+6)}{(x-7)(x+5)} = \dfrac{x+6}{x+5}$

52. $\dfrac{2x^2 - 5x - 3}{x^2 - 9} \cdot \dfrac{2x^2 + 5x - 3}{2x^2 + 5x + 2}$

$= \dfrac{(2x+1)(x-3)(2x-1)(x+3)}{(x+3)(x-3)(2x+1)(x+2)} = \dfrac{2x-1}{x+2}$

53. $\dfrac{-2x-1}{x+4} + 4x + 3$

$= \dfrac{-2x - 1 + (4x+3)(x+4)}{x+4}$

$= \dfrac{-2x - 1 + 4x^2 + 19x + 12}{x+4}$

$= \dfrac{4x^2 + 17x + 11}{x+4}$

54. $\dfrac{\dfrac{1}{x^2 - 3x + 2}}{\dfrac{3}{x-2} - \dfrac{2}{x-1}} = \dfrac{\dfrac{1}{(x-2)(x-1)}}{\dfrac{3}{x-2} - \dfrac{2}{x-1}}$

$= \dfrac{\dfrac{1}{(x-2)(x-1)}}{\dfrac{3}{x-2} - \dfrac{2}{x-1}} \cdot \dfrac{(x-2)(x-1)}{(x-2)(x-1)}$

$= \dfrac{1}{3(x-1) - 2(x-2)}$

$= \dfrac{1}{3x - 3 - 2x + 4}$

$= \dfrac{1}{x+1}$

55.　$\dfrac{5}{2} - \dfrac{3}{x+1} = \dfrac{2-x}{x+1}$

$$5(x+1) - 6 = 2(2 - x)$$

$$5x + 5 - 6 = 4 - 2x$$

$$7x = 5$$

$$x = \dfrac{5}{7}$$

56.　$\dfrac{7}{4} = \dfrac{S}{G} = \dfrac{S}{253 - S}$

$$1771 - 7S = 4S$$

$$11S = 1771$$

$$S = 161$$

$$G = 253 - 161 = 92$$

They ordered 161 scientific calculators and 92 graphing calculators.

57. $x =$ number of one-story homes

$$\dfrac{3}{13} = \dfrac{x}{112 - x}$$

$$336 - 3x = 13x$$

$$16x = 336$$

$$x = 21$$

$$112 - x = 91$$

Walter Johnson built 21 one-story homes and 91 two-story homes.

58.　$\dfrac{5}{7} = \dfrac{w}{l} = \dfrac{w}{\dfrac{168 - 2w}{2}} = \dfrac{2w}{168 - 2w}$

$$840 - 10w = 14w$$

$$24w = 840$$

$$w = 35$$

$$l = \dfrac{168 - 2w}{2} = 49$$

The enlarged photograph will be 35 inches wide and 49 inches long.

© 2006 Pearson Education, Inc., Upper Saddle River, NJ. All rights reserved. This material is protected under all copyright laws as they currently exist. No portion of this material may be reproduced, in any form or by any means, without permission in writing from the publisher.

59. $\dfrac{4}{3500} = \dfrac{x}{4900}$

$3500x = 19,600$

$x = 5.6$

The pump can empty the 4900-gallon pool in 5.6 hours.

60. $\dfrac{100}{P} = \dfrac{8}{40}$

$8P = 4000$

$P = 500$ rabbits

61. $x =$ number of officers

$\dfrac{2}{9} = \dfrac{x}{154-x}$

$308 - 2x = 9x$

$11x = 308$

$x = 28$ officers

62. $x =$ number of nautical miles

$\dfrac{7}{2} = \dfrac{x}{3.5}$

$2x = 24.5$

$x = 12.25$ nautical miles

63. $x =$ height of building

$\dfrac{7}{6} = \dfrac{x}{156}$

$6x = 1092$

$x = 182$ ft

64. $t =$ time for both to paint barn

$\dfrac{t}{12} + \dfrac{t}{18} = 1$

$\dfrac{5}{36}t = 1$

$t = 7.2$

It would take 7.2 hours to paint the barn if they worked together.

65. $t =$ time if both faucets are open

$\dfrac{t}{15} + \dfrac{t}{10} = 1$

$\dfrac{t}{6} = 1$

$t = 6$

It would take 6 minutes to fill if both faucets are left open.

66. $x =$ number of messages in Feb 2003

$\dfrac{918-863}{1} = \dfrac{x-918}{1}$

$x = 973$ million messages

67. $x =$ number of messages in Feb 2004

$\dfrac{918-651}{24} = \dfrac{x-918}{24}$

$918 - 615 = x - 918$

$x = 1185$ million messages

68. $x =$ number of messages in Dec. 2000

$\dfrac{651-430}{10} = \dfrac{1}{2} \cdot \dfrac{x-651}{10}$

$x = 2(221) + 651$

$x = 1093$ million messages

69. $x =$ number of messages in April 2001

$\dfrac{430-94}{24} = 2 \cdot \dfrac{x-430}{24}$

$\dfrac{336}{2} = x - 430$

$x = 168 + 430$

$x = 598$ million messages

© 2006 Pearson Education, Inc., Upper Saddle River, NJ. All rights reserved. This material is protected under all copyright laws as they currently exist.
No portion of this material may be reproduced, in any form or by any means, without permission in writing from the publisher.

How A I Doing? Chapter 6 Test

1. $\dfrac{x^3+3x^2+2x}{x^3-2x^2-3x}=\dfrac{x(x^2+3x+2)}{x(x-2x-3)}$

$=\dfrac{(x+2)(x+1)}{(x-3)(x+1)}$

$=\dfrac{x+2}{x-3}$

2. $\dfrac{-25p^4qr^3}{45pqr^6}=-\dfrac{5p^{4-1}}{9r^{6-3}}$

$=-\dfrac{5p^3}{9r^3}$

3. $\dfrac{2y^2+7y-4}{y^2+2y-8}\cdot\dfrac{2y^2-8}{3y^2+11y+10}$

$=\dfrac{(2y-1)(y+4)}{(y+4)(y-2)}\cdot\dfrac{2(y+2)(y-2)}{(3y+5)(y+2)}$

$=\dfrac{2(2y-1)}{3y+5}$

4. $\dfrac{4-2x}{3x^2-2x-8}\div\dfrac{2x^2+x-1}{9x+12}$

$=\dfrac{-2(x-2)}{(3x+4)(x-2)}\cdot\dfrac{3(3x+4)}{(2x-1)(x+1)}$

$=-\dfrac{6}{(2x-1)(x+1)}$

5. $\dfrac{3}{x}-\dfrac{2}{x+1}=\dfrac{3(x+1)-2x}{x(x+1)}$

$=\dfrac{3x+3-2x}{x(x+1)}$

$=\dfrac{x+3}{x(x+1)}$

6. $\dfrac{2}{x^2+5x+6}+\dfrac{3x}{x^2+6x+9}$

$=\dfrac{2(x+3)}{(x+3)(x+2)(x+3)}$

$+\dfrac{3x(x+2)}{(x+3)(x+3)(x+2)}$

$=\dfrac{2x+6+3x^2+6x}{(x+3)(x+2)(x+3)}$

$=\dfrac{3x^2+8x+6}{(x+3)^2(x+2)}$

7. $\dfrac{\dfrac{4}{y+2}-2}{5-\dfrac{10}{y+2}}\cdot\dfrac{y+2}{y+2}$

$=\dfrac{4-2(y+2)}{5(y+2)-10}$

$=\dfrac{4-2y-4}{5y+10-10}=\dfrac{-2y}{5y}$

$=-\dfrac{2}{5}$

8. $\dfrac{\dfrac{1}{x}-\dfrac{3}{x+2}}{\dfrac{2}{x^2+2x}}=\dfrac{\dfrac{1}{x}-\dfrac{3}{x+2}}{\dfrac{2}{x(x+2)}}\cdot\dfrac{x(x+2)}{x(x+2)}$

$=\dfrac{x+2-3x}{2}$

$=\dfrac{-2x+2}{2}$

$=\dfrac{2(-x+1)}{2}$

$=-x+1$

172

© 2006 Pearson Education, Inc., Upper Saddle River, NJ. All rights reserved. This material is protected under all copyright laws as they currently exist. No portion of this material may be reproduced, in any form or by any means, without permission in writing from the publisher.

9. $\dfrac{7}{4} = \dfrac{x+4}{x}$

$7x = 4x + 16$

$3x = 16$

$x = \dfrac{16}{3}$

check: $\dfrac{7}{4} \overset{?}{=} \dfrac{\frac{16}{3}+4}{\frac{16}{3}}, \ \dfrac{7}{4} = \dfrac{7}{4}$

10. $2 + \dfrac{x}{x+4} = \dfrac{3x}{x-4}$

$2(x+4)(x-4) + x(x-4) = 3x(x+4)$

$2x^2 - 32 + x^2 - 4x = 3x^2 + 12x$

$16x = -32$

$x = -2$

check: $2 + \dfrac{-2}{-2+4} \overset{?}{=} \dfrac{3(-2)}{-2-4}, \ 1 = 1$

11. $\dfrac{1}{2y+4} - \dfrac{1}{6} = \dfrac{-2}{3y+6}$

$\dfrac{1}{2(y+2)} - \dfrac{1}{6} = \dfrac{-2}{3(y+2)}$

$3 - (y+2) = -4$

$3 - y - 2 = -4$

$y = 5$

check: $\dfrac{1}{2(5)+4} - \dfrac{1}{6} \overset{?}{=} \dfrac{-2}{3(5)+6}, \ -\dfrac{2}{21} = -\dfrac{2}{21}$

12. $2 + \dfrac{3}{x} = \dfrac{2x}{x-1}$

$2x(x-1) + 3(x-1) = 2x^2$

$2x^2 - 2x + 3x - 3 = 2x^2$

$x = 3$

check: $2 + \dfrac{3}{3} \overset{?}{=} \dfrac{2(3)}{3-1}, \ 3 = 3$

13. $h = \dfrac{S - 2WL}{2W + 2L}$

$2hW + 2hL = S - 2WL$

$(2h + 2L)W = S - 2hL$

$W = \dfrac{S - 2hL}{2h + 2L}$

14. $\dfrac{3V}{\pi h} = r^2 \Rightarrow \pi r^2 h = 3V \Rightarrow h = \dfrac{3V}{\pi r^2}$

15. $\dfrac{3}{19} = \dfrac{x}{286 - x}$

$858 - 3x = 19x$

$22x = 858$

$x = 39$

$286 - 39 = 247$

39 got the bonus, 247 did not.

16. $\dfrac{500}{850} = \dfrac{W}{\dfrac{8100 - 2W}{2}}$

$\dfrac{500}{850} = \dfrac{2W}{8100 - 2W}$

$4,050,000 - 1000W = 1700W$

$2700W = 4,050,000$

$W = 1500$

$\dfrac{8100 - 2W}{2} = 2550$

The width is 1500 feet and the length is 2550 feet.

Cumulative Test for Chapters 1-6

1. $(3x^{-2}y)^2(x^4y^{-3}) = 9x^{-4}y^2x^4y^{-3}$

$= 9x^0y^{-1} = \dfrac{9}{y}$

© 2006 Pearson Education, Inc., Upper Saddle River, NJ. All rights reserved. This material is protected under all copyright laws as they currently exist. No portion of this material may be reproduced, in any form or by any means, without permission in writing from the publisher.

2. $\dfrac{2}{3}(3x-1)=\dfrac{2}{5}x+3$

$30x-10=6x+45$

$24x=55$

$x=\dfrac{55}{24}$

3. $-6x+2y=-12$

x	y
0	-6
1	-3
2	0

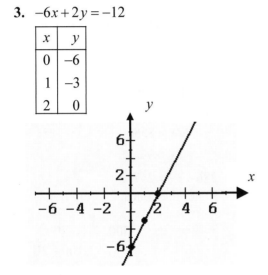

4. $5x-6y=8$

$6y=5x-8$

$y=\dfrac{5}{6}x-\dfrac{4}{3}\Rightarrow m=\dfrac{5}{6},\ m_{\text{p}}=\dfrac{5}{6}$

$y-y_1=m(x-x_1)$

$y-(-3)=\dfrac{5}{6}(x-(-1))$

$6y+18=5x+5$

$5x-6y=13$

5. $x=$ amount at 5%

$0.05x+0.08(7000-x)=539$

$0.05x+560-0.08x=539$

$-0.03x=-21$

$x=\$700$ at 5%

$7000-x=\$6300$ at 8%

6. $3(2-6x)>4(x+1)+24$

$6-18x>4x+4+24$

$-22x>22$

$x<-1$

7. $2x^2-3x-4y^2=2(-2)^2-3(-2)-4(3)^2$

$=2(4)+6-4(9)$

$=8+6-36$

$=14-36$

$=-22$

8. $|3x-4|\le 10$

$-10\le 3x-4\le 10$

$-6\le 3x\le 14$

$-2\le x\le \dfrac{14}{3}$

9. $8x^3-125y^3=(2x)^3-(5y)^3$

$=(2x-5y)(4x^2+10xy+25y^2)$

10. $81x^3-90x^2y+25xy^2$

$=x(81x^2-90xy+25y^2)$

$=x(9x-5y)^2$

11. $x^2+20x+36=0$

$(x+18)(x+2)=0$

$x+18=0\quad$ or $\ x+2=0$

$x=-18\qquad x=-2$

12. $3x^2-11x-4=0$

$(3x+1)(x-4)=0$

$3x+1=0\ $ or $\ x-4=0$

$3x+1=0\qquad x-4=0$

$x=-\dfrac{1}{3}\qquad x=4$

© 2006 Pearson Education, Inc., Upper Saddle River, NJ. All rights reserved. This material is protected under all copyright laws as they currently exist. No portion of this material may be reproduced, in any form or by any means, without permission in writing from the publisher.

13. $\dfrac{7x^2 - 28}{x^2 + 6x + 8} = \dfrac{7(x+2)(x-2)}{(x+4)(x+2)}$

$\qquad\qquad\qquad = \dfrac{7(x-2)}{x+4}$

14. $\dfrac{2x^2 + x - 1}{2x^2 - 9x + 4} \cdot \dfrac{3x^2 - 12x}{6x + 15}$

$\qquad = \dfrac{(2x-1)(x+1)}{(2x-1)(x-4)} \cdot \dfrac{3x(x-4)}{3(2x+5)}$

$\qquad = \dfrac{x(x+1)}{2x+5}$

15. $\dfrac{x^3 + 2x^2}{3x - 21} \div \dfrac{2x^3 + 5x^2 + 2x}{x - 7}$

$\qquad = \dfrac{x^2(x+2)}{3(x-7)} \cdot \dfrac{x-7}{x(2x^2 + 5x + 2)}$

$\qquad = \dfrac{x(x+2)}{3} \cdot \dfrac{1}{(2x+1)(x+2)}$

$\qquad = \dfrac{x}{3(2x+1)}$

16. $\dfrac{7}{3x - 3} - \dfrac{x+2}{x^2 - 1}$

$\qquad = \dfrac{7(x+1)}{3(x-1)(x+1)} - \dfrac{3(x+2)}{3(x-1)(x+1)}$

$\qquad = \dfrac{7x + 7 - 3x - 6}{3(x-1)(x+1)}$

$\qquad = \dfrac{4x + 1}{3(x-1)(x+1)}$

17. $\dfrac{\dfrac{1}{2x+1} + 1}{4 - \dfrac{3}{4x^2 - 1}}$

$\qquad = \dfrac{\dfrac{1}{2x+1} + 1}{4 - \dfrac{3}{(2x-1)(2x+1)}} \cdot \dfrac{(2x-1)(2x+1)}{(2x-1)(2x+1)}$

$\qquad = \dfrac{2x - 1 + (2x-1)(2x+1)}{4(2x-1)(2x+1) - 3}$

$\qquad = \dfrac{(2x-1)(1 + 2x + 1)}{16x^2 - 4 - 3}$

$\qquad = \dfrac{(2x-1)(2x+2)}{16x^2 - 7}$

$\qquad = \dfrac{2(x+1)(2x-1)}{16x^2 - 7}$

18. $\dfrac{3}{x-6} + \dfrac{4}{x+4} = \dfrac{3(x+4) + 4(x-6)}{(x-6)(x+4)}$

$\qquad\qquad\qquad = \dfrac{3x + 12 + 4x - 24}{(x-6)(x+4)}$

$\qquad\qquad\qquad = \dfrac{7x - 12}{(x-6)(x+4)}$

19. $\dfrac{1}{2x+3} - \dfrac{4}{4x^2 - 9} = \dfrac{3}{2x-3}$

$\qquad \dfrac{1}{2x+3} - \dfrac{4}{(2x+3)(2x-3)} = \dfrac{3}{2x-3}$

$\qquad\qquad\qquad 2x - 3 - 4 = 3(2x+3)$

$\qquad\qquad\qquad\qquad 2x - 7 = 6x + 9$

$\qquad\qquad\qquad\qquad\quad 4x = -16$

$\qquad\qquad\qquad\qquad\quad\ x = -4$

check: $\dfrac{1}{2(-4)+3} - \dfrac{4}{4(-4)^2 - 9} \overset{?}{=} \dfrac{3}{2(-4)-3}$

$\qquad\qquad\qquad\qquad -\dfrac{3}{11} = -\dfrac{3}{11}$

© 2006 Pearson Education, Inc., Upper Saddle River, NJ. All rights reserved. This material is protected under all copyright laws as they currently exist.
No portion of this material may be reproduced, in any form or by any means, without permission in writing from the publisher.

20. $\dfrac{1}{4x} - \dfrac{3}{2x} = \dfrac{5}{8}$

$$2 - 12 = 5x$$

$$5x = -10$$

$$x = -2$$

check: $\dfrac{1}{4(-2)} - \dfrac{3}{2(-2)} \overset{?}{=} \dfrac{5}{8}, \quad \dfrac{5}{8} = \dfrac{5}{8}$

21. $H = \dfrac{3b + 2x}{5 - 4b}$

$$5H - 4bH = 3b + 2x$$

$$3b + 4bH = 5H - 2x$$

$$b(3 + 4H) = 5H - 2x$$

$$b = \dfrac{5H - 2x}{3 + 4H}$$

22. $x =$ number patrolling on foot

$$\dfrac{3}{11} = \dfrac{x}{3234 - x}$$

$$9702 - 3x = 11x$$

$$14x = 9702$$

$$x = 693$$

$$3234 - x = 2541$$

693 are patrolling on foot and 2541 are patrolling in squad cars.

176

© 2006 Pearson Education, Inc., Upper Saddle River, NJ. All rights reserved. This material is protected under all copyright laws as they currently exist. No portion of this material may be reproduced, in any form or by any means, without permission in writing from the publisher.

Chapter 7

7.1 Exercises

1. $\left(\dfrac{3xy^{-1}}{z^2}\right)^4 = \dfrac{3^4 x^4 y^{-4}}{z^8} = \dfrac{81x^4}{y^4 z^8}$

3. $\left(\dfrac{2a^{-1}b^3}{-3b^2}\right)^3 = \dfrac{8a^{-3}b^9}{-27b^6} = -\dfrac{8b^3}{27a^3}$

5. $\left(\dfrac{2x^2}{y}\right)^{-3} = \dfrac{2^{-3}x^{-6}}{y^{-3}} = \dfrac{y^3}{8x^6}$

7. $\left(\dfrac{3xy^{-2}}{y^3}\right)^{-2} = \dfrac{3^{-2}x^{-2}y^4}{y^{-6}} = \dfrac{y^{10}}{9x^2}$

9. $(x^{\frac{3}{4}})^2 = x^{\frac{6}{4}} = x^{\frac{3}{2}}$

11. $(y^{12})^{\frac{2}{3}} = y^{12\cdot\frac{2}{3}} = y^8$

13. $\dfrac{x^{\frac{3}{5}}}{x^{\frac{1}{5}}} = x^{\frac{3}{5}-\frac{1}{5}} = x^{\frac{2}{5}}$

15. $\dfrac{x^{\frac{7}{12}}}{x^{\frac{1}{12}}} = x^{\frac{7}{12}-\frac{1}{12}} = x^{\frac{6}{12}} = x^{\frac{1}{2}}$

17. $\dfrac{x^3}{x^{\frac{1}{2}}} = x^{3-\frac{1}{2}} = x^{\frac{6}{2}-\frac{1}{2}} = x^{\frac{5}{2}}$

19. $x^{\frac{1}{7}} \cdot x^{\frac{3}{7}} = x^{\frac{1}{7}+\frac{3}{7}} = x^{\frac{4}{7}}$

21. $a^{\frac{3}{8}} \cdot a^{\frac{1}{2}} = a^{\frac{3}{8}+\frac{4}{8}} = a^{\frac{7}{8}}$

23. $y^{\frac{3}{5}} \cdot y^{-\frac{1}{10}} = y^{\frac{6}{10}-\frac{1}{10}} = y^{\frac{1}{2}}$

25. $x^{-\frac{3}{4}} = \dfrac{1}{x^{\frac{3}{4}}}$

27. $a^{-\frac{5}{6}}b^{\frac{1}{3}} = \dfrac{b^{\frac{1}{3}}}{a^{\frac{5}{6}}}$

29. $6^{-\frac{1}{2}} = \dfrac{1}{6^{\frac{1}{2}}}$

31. $2a^{-\frac{1}{4}} = \dfrac{2}{a^{\frac{1}{4}}}$

33. $(27)^{\frac{2}{3}} = \left(3^3\right)^{\frac{2}{3}} = 3^{3\cdot\frac{2}{3}} = 3^2 = 9$

35. $(4)^{\frac{3}{2}} = \left(2^2\right)^{\frac{3}{2}} = 2^{2\cdot\frac{3}{2}} = 2^3 = 8$

37. $(-8)^{\frac{5}{3}} = \left((-2)^3\right)^{\frac{5}{3}} = (-2)^{3\cdot\frac{5}{3}}$
$= (-2)^5 = -32$

39. $(-27)^{\frac{2}{3}} = \left((-3)^3\right)^{\frac{2}{3}} = (-3)^{3\cdot\frac{2}{3}} = (-3)^2 = 9$

41. $(x^{\frac{1}{2}}y^{\frac{1}{3}})(x^{\frac{1}{3}}y^{\frac{2}{3}}) = x^{\frac{1}{2}+\frac{1}{6}}y^{\frac{1}{3}+\frac{2}{3}} = x^{\frac{5}{6}}y$

43. $(7x^{\frac{1}{3}}y^{\frac{1}{4}})(-2x^{\frac{1}{4}}y^{-\frac{1}{6}}) = -14x^{\frac{7}{12}}y^{\frac{1}{12}}$

45. $6^2 \cdot 6^{-\frac{2}{3}} = 6^{\frac{6}{3}-\frac{2}{3}} = 6^{\frac{4}{3}}$

47. $\dfrac{2x^{\frac{1}{5}}}{x^{-\frac{1}{2}}} = 2x^{\frac{2}{10}+\frac{5}{10}} = 2x^{\frac{7}{10}}$

177

© 2006 Pearson Education, Inc., Upper Saddle River, NJ. All rights reserved. This material is protected under all copyright laws as they currently exist.
No portion of this material may be reproduced, in any form or by any means, without permission in writing from the publisher.

49. $\dfrac{-20x^2 y^{-\frac{1}{5}}}{5x^{-\frac{1}{2}}y} = -\dfrac{4x^{\frac{5}{2}}}{y^{\frac{6}{5}}}$

51. $\left(\dfrac{8a^2b^6}{a^{-1}b^3}\right)^{\frac{1}{3}} = \left(8a^3b^3\right)^{\frac{1}{3}} = 2ab$

53. $(-3x^{\frac{2}{5}}y^{\frac{3}{2}}z^{\frac{1}{3}})^2 = (-3)^2 x^{\frac{4}{5}}y^3 z^{\frac{2}{3}} = 9x^{\frac{4}{5}}y^3 z^{\frac{2}{3}}$

55. $x^{\frac{2}{3}}(x^{\frac{2}{3}} - x^{\frac{4}{5}}) = x^{\frac{6}{3}} - x^{\frac{2}{3}+\frac{4}{5}} = x^2 - x^{\frac{13}{15}}$

57. $m^{\frac{7}{8}}(m^{-\frac{1}{2}} + 2m) = m^{\frac{7}{8}-\frac{4}{8}} + 2m^{\frac{7}{8}+\frac{8}{8}}$

$$= m^{\frac{3}{8}} + 2m^{\frac{15}{8}}$$

59. $(8)^{-\frac{1}{3}} = \left(2^3\right)^{-\frac{1}{3}} = 2^{3\left(-\frac{1}{3}\right)} = 2^{-1} = \dfrac{1}{2}$

61. $(49)^{-\frac{3}{2}} = \left(7^2\right)^{-\frac{3}{2}} = 7^{2\left(-\frac{3}{2}\right)} = 7^{-3} = \dfrac{1}{7^3} = \dfrac{1}{343}$

63. $(81)^{\frac{3}{4}} + (25)^{\frac{1}{2}} = \left(3^4\right)^{\frac{3}{4}} + \left(5^2\right)^{\frac{1}{2}} = 3^{4\cdot\frac{3}{4}} + 5^{2\cdot\frac{1}{2}}$

$$= 3^3 + 5 = 27 + 5 = 32$$

65. $3y^{\frac{1}{2}} + y^{-\frac{1}{2}} = 3y^{\frac{1}{2}} \cdot \dfrac{y^{\frac{1}{2}}}{y^{\frac{1}{2}}} + \dfrac{1}{y^{\frac{1}{2}}} = \dfrac{3y+1}{y^{\frac{1}{2}}}$

67. $x^{-\frac{1}{3}} + 6^{\frac{4}{3}} = \dfrac{1}{x^{\frac{1}{3}}} + 6^{\frac{4}{3}} = \dfrac{1 + 6^{\frac{4}{3}}x^{\frac{1}{3}}}{x^{\frac{1}{3}}}$

69. $10a^{\frac{5}{4}} - 4a^{\frac{8}{5}} = 2a(5a^{\frac{1}{4}} - 2^{\frac{3}{5}})$

71. $6x^{\frac{7}{4}} - 15x^{\frac{3}{2}} = 3x\left(2x^{\frac{3}{4}} - 5x^{\frac{1}{2}}\right)$

73. $x^a \cdot x^{\frac{1}{4}} = x^{-\frac{1}{8}} \Rightarrow x^{a+\frac{1}{4}} = x^{-\frac{1}{8}}$

$$a + \dfrac{1}{4} = -\dfrac{1}{8}$$

$$a = -\dfrac{3}{8}$$

75. $r = 0.62(V)^{\frac{1}{3}}$

$$r = 0.62(27)^{\frac{1}{3}}$$

$$r = 0.62(3) = 1.86 \text{ m}$$

77. $r = \left(\dfrac{3V}{\pi h}\right)^{\frac{1}{2}}$

$$r = \left(\dfrac{3(314)}{3.14(12)}\right)^{\frac{1}{2}} = 5 \text{ feet}$$

Cumulative Review

79. $-4(x+1) = \dfrac{1}{3}(3 - 2x)$

$$-12(x+1) = 3 - 2x$$

$$-12x - 12 = 3 - 2x$$

$$-10x = 15$$

$$x = -\dfrac{3}{2}$$

81. $y = \dfrac{ax}{a+12}$

$$y = \dfrac{7 \cdot 400}{7+12} = \dfrac{2800}{19} \approx 147 \text{ mg}$$

The dose for a seven year old child corresponding to an adult dose of 400 milligrams should be about 147 milligrams.

178

© 2006 Pearson Education, Inc., Upper Saddle River, NJ. All rights reserved. This material is protected under all copyright laws as they currently exist. No portion of this material may be reproduced, in any form or by any means, without permission in writing from the publisher.

7.2 Exercises

1. A square root of a number is a value that when multiplied by itself is equal to the original number.

3. One answer is $\sqrt[3]{-8} = -2$ because $(-2)(-2)(-2) = -8$.

5. $\sqrt{100} = 10$

7. $\sqrt{16} + \sqrt{81} = 4 + 9 = 13$

9. $-\sqrt{\dfrac{1}{9}} = -\dfrac{1}{3}$

11. $\sqrt{-36}$ not a real number

13. $\sqrt{0.04} = 0.2$

15. $f(x) = \sqrt{3x + 21}$
$f(0) = \sqrt{3(0) + 21} = \sqrt{21} = 4.6$
$f(1) = \sqrt{3(1) + 21} = \sqrt{24} = 4.9$
$f(5) = \sqrt{3(5) + 21} = \sqrt{36} = 6$
$f(-4) = \sqrt{3(-4) + 21} = 3$
domain is $3x + 21 \geq 0$
$\qquad 3x \geq -21$
$\qquad\quad x \geq -7$

17. $f(x) = \sqrt{0.5x - 3}$
$f(6) = \sqrt{0.5(6) - 3} = \sqrt{3 - 3} = \sqrt{0} = 0$
$f(8) = \sqrt{0.5(8) - 3} = \sqrt{4 - 3} = \sqrt{1} = 1$
$f(14) = \sqrt{0.5(14) - 3} = \sqrt{7 - 3} = \sqrt{4} = 2$
$f(16) = \sqrt{0.5(16) - 3} = \sqrt{8 - 3} = \sqrt{5} = 2.2$
domain is $0.5x - 3 \geq 0$
$\qquad 0.5x \geq 3$
$\qquad\quad x \geq 6$

19. $f(x) = \sqrt{x - 1}$
$\qquad f(1) = \sqrt{1 - 1} = 0$
$\qquad f(2) = \sqrt{2 - 1} = 1$
$\qquad f(5) = \sqrt{5 - 1} = 2$
$\qquad f(10) = \sqrt{10 - 1} = 3$

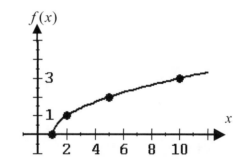

21. $f(x) = \sqrt{3x + 9}$
$\qquad f(-3) = \sqrt{3(-3) + 9} = 0$
$\qquad f\left(-\dfrac{8}{3}\right) = \sqrt{3\left(-\dfrac{8}{3}\right) + 9} = 1$
$\qquad f\left(-\dfrac{5}{3}\right) = \sqrt{3\left(-\dfrac{5}{3}\right) + 9} = 2$
$\qquad f(0) = \sqrt{3(0) + 9} = 3$

© 2006 Pearson Education, Inc., Upper Saddle River, NJ. All rights reserved. This material is protected under all copyright laws as they currently exist. No portion of this material may be reproduced, in any form or by any means, without permission in writing from the publisher.

21.

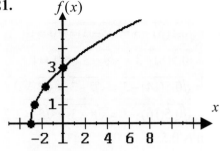

23. $\sqrt[3]{64} = 4$

25. $\sqrt[3]{-1000} = -10$

27. $\sqrt[4]{81} = 3$

29. $\sqrt[5]{243} = \sqrt[5]{3^5} = 3$

31. $\sqrt[5]{(8)^5} = 8$

33. $\sqrt[8]{(5)^8} = 5$

35. $\sqrt[3]{-\dfrac{1}{64}} = -\dfrac{1}{4}$

37. $\sqrt[3]{y} = y^{\frac{1}{3}}$

39. $\sqrt[5]{m^3} = m^{\frac{3}{5}}$

41. $\sqrt[5]{2x} = (2x)^{\frac{1}{5}}$

43. $\sqrt[7]{(a+b)^3} = (a+b)^{\frac{3}{7}}$

45. $\sqrt{\sqrt[3]{x}} = \left(x^{1/3}\right)^{1/2} = x^{1/6}$

47. $(\sqrt[6]{3x})^5 = \left((3x)^{1/6}\right)^5 = (3x)^{5/6}$

49. $\sqrt[6]{12^6} = 12$

51. $\sqrt[3]{x^3 y^6} = xy^2$

53. $\sqrt{36x^8 y^4} = 6x^4 y^2$

55. $\sqrt[4]{16a^8 b^4} = 2a^2 b$

57. $\sqrt[3]{-125x^{30}} = -5x^{10}$

59. $y^{4/7} = (\sqrt[7]{y})^4$

61. $7^{-\frac{2}{3}} = \dfrac{1}{7^{\frac{2}{3}}} = \dfrac{1}{\sqrt[3]{7^2}} = \dfrac{1}{\sqrt[3]{49}}$

63. $(2a+b)^{5/7} = (\sqrt[7]{2a+b})^5$

65. $(-x)^{3/5} = (\sqrt[5]{-x})^3$

67. $(2xy)^{3/5} = \sqrt[5]{(2xy)^3} = \sqrt[5]{8x^3 y^3}$

69. $4^{3/2} = \sqrt{4^3} = \sqrt{64} = 8$

71. $\left(\dfrac{4}{25}\right)^{\frac{1}{2}} = \sqrt{\dfrac{4}{25}} = \dfrac{2}{5}$

73. $\left(\dfrac{1}{8}\right)^{-\frac{1}{3}} = \left(8^{-1}\right)^{-\frac{1}{3}} = 8^{-1\left(-\frac{1}{3}\right)} = 8^{\frac{1}{3}} = \sqrt[3]{8} = 2$

75. $(25x^4)^{-\frac{1}{2}} = \dfrac{1}{\sqrt{25x^4}} = \dfrac{1}{5x^2}$

77. $\sqrt{121x^4} = 11x^2$

180

© 2006 Pearson Education, Inc., Upper Saddle River, NJ. All rights reserved. This material is protected under all copyright laws as they currently exist. No portion of this material may be reproduced, in any form or by any means, without permission in writing from the publisher.

79. $\sqrt{144a^6b^{24}} = 12a^3b^{12}$

81. $\sqrt{36x^6y^8z^{10}} = 6x^3y^4z^5$

83. $\sqrt[3]{216a^3b^9c^{12}} = 6ab^3c^4$

85. $\sqrt{25x^2} = 5|x|$

87. $\sqrt[3]{-8x^6} = -2x^2$

89. $\sqrt[4]{x^8y^{16}} = x^2y^4$

91. $\sqrt[4]{a^{12}b^4} = \sqrt[4]{(a^3b)^4} = \left|a^3b\right| = a^2\left|ab\right|$

93. $\sqrt{4x^8y^4} = 2x^4y^2$

95. $C = 120\sqrt[3]{n} + 375$

$C = 120\sqrt[3]{343} + 375 = 120(7) + 375$

$C = 1215$

Cost is \$1215 per day.

Cumulative Review

97. $0.14(4.567 \times 10^{17}) = 6.3938 \times 10^{16}$ Btu

7.3 Exercises

1. $\sqrt{8} = \sqrt{4 \cdot 2} = \sqrt{4}\sqrt{2} = 2\sqrt{2}$

3. $\sqrt{18} = \sqrt{9 \cdot 2} = \sqrt{9}\sqrt{2} = 3\sqrt{2}$

5. $\sqrt{28} = \sqrt{4 \cdot 7} = \sqrt{4}\sqrt{7} = 2\sqrt{7}$

7. $\sqrt{44} = \sqrt{4 \cdot 11} = \sqrt{4}\sqrt{11} = 2\sqrt{11}$

9. $\sqrt{9x^3} = \sqrt{9}\sqrt{x^2}\sqrt{x} = 3x\sqrt{x}$

11. $\sqrt{40a^6b^7} = \sqrt{4 \cdot 10a^6b^6b} = 2a^3b^3\sqrt{10b}$

13. $\sqrt{90x^3yz^4} = \sqrt{9 \cdot 10x^2xyz^4} = 3xz^2\sqrt{10xy}$

15. $\sqrt[3]{8} = 2$

17. $\sqrt[3]{40} = \sqrt[3]{8 \cdot 5} = 2\sqrt[3]{5}$

19. $\sqrt[3]{54a^2} = \sqrt[3]{27 \cdot 2a^2} = 3\sqrt[3]{2a^2}$

21. $\sqrt[3]{8a^3b^8} = \sqrt[3]{2^3a^3b^6b^2} = 2ab^2\sqrt[3]{b^2}$

23. $\sqrt[3]{24x^6y^{11}} = \sqrt[3]{8 \cdot 3x^6y^9y^2}$
$= 2x^2y^3\sqrt[3]{3y^2}$

25. $\sqrt[4]{81kp^{23}} = \sqrt[4]{3^4kp^{20}p^3}$
$= 3p^5\sqrt[4]{kp^3}$

27. $\sqrt[5]{-32x^5y^6} = \sqrt[5]{(-2)^5x^5y^5y}$
$= -2xy\sqrt[5]{y}$

29. $\sqrt[4]{1792} = a\sqrt[4]{7}$
$\sqrt[4]{256 \cdot 7} = a\sqrt[4]{7}$
$\sqrt[4]{4^4 \cdot 7} = a\sqrt[4]{7}$
$4\sqrt[4]{7} = a\sqrt[4]{7}$
$a = 4$

31. $4\sqrt{5} + 8\sqrt{5} = 12\sqrt{5}$

33. $4\sqrt{3} + \sqrt{7} - 5\sqrt{7} = 4\sqrt{3} - 4\sqrt{7}$

35. $3\sqrt{18} - \sqrt{2} = 3\sqrt{9 \cdot 2} - \sqrt{2}$
$= 9\sqrt{2} - \sqrt{2}$
$= 8\sqrt{2}$

© 2006 Pearson Education, Inc., Upper Saddle River, NJ. All rights reserved. This material is protected under all copyright laws as they currently exist. No portion of this material may be reproduced, in any form or by any means, without permission in writing from the publisher.

37. $4\sqrt{12} + \sqrt{27} = 4\sqrt{4\cdot 3} + \sqrt{9\cdot 3}$
$$= 8\sqrt{3} + 3\sqrt{3} = 11\sqrt{3}$$

39. $\sqrt{8} + \sqrt{50} - 2\sqrt{72}$
$$= \sqrt{4\cdot 2} + \sqrt{25\cdot 2} - 2\sqrt{36\cdot 2}$$
$$= 2\sqrt{2} + 5\sqrt{2} - 12\sqrt{2}$$
$$= -5\sqrt{2}$$

41. $-2\sqrt{50} + \sqrt{32} - 3\sqrt{8}$
$$= -2\sqrt{25\cdot 2} + \sqrt{16\cdot 2} - 3\sqrt{4\cdot 2}$$
$$= -10\sqrt{2} + 4\sqrt{2} - 6\sqrt{2}$$
$$= -12\sqrt{2}$$

43. $-5\sqrt{45} + 6\sqrt{20} + 3\sqrt{5}$
$$= -5\sqrt{9\cdot 5} + 6\sqrt{4\cdot 5} + 3\sqrt{5}$$
$$= -15\sqrt{5} + 12\sqrt{5} + 3\sqrt{5}$$
$$= 0$$

45. $3\sqrt{48x} - 2\sqrt{12x} = 3\sqrt{16\cdot 3x} - 2\sqrt{4\cdot 3x}$
$$= 12\sqrt{3x} - 4\sqrt{3x}$$
$$= 8\sqrt{3x}$$

47. $\sqrt{98x} + \sqrt{8x} + 5\sqrt{32x}$
$$= \sqrt{49\cdot 2x} + \sqrt{4\cdot 2x} + 5\sqrt{16\cdot 2x}$$
$$= 7\sqrt{2x} + 2\sqrt{2x} + 20\sqrt{2x}$$
$$= 29\sqrt{2x}$$

49. $\sqrt{44} - 3\sqrt{63x} + 4\sqrt{28x}$
$$= \sqrt{4\cdot 11} - 3\sqrt{9\cdot 7x} + 4\sqrt{4\cdot 7x}$$
$$= 2\sqrt{11} - 9\sqrt{7x} + 8\sqrt{7x}$$
$$= 2\sqrt{11} - \sqrt{7x}$$

51. $\sqrt{200x^3} - x\sqrt{32x}$
$$= \sqrt{100x^2\cdot 2x} - x\sqrt{16\cdot 2x}$$
$$= 10x\sqrt{2x} - 4x\sqrt{2x}$$
$$= 6x\sqrt{2x}$$

53. $\sqrt[3]{16} + 3\sqrt[3]{54} = \sqrt[3]{2^3\cdot 2} + 3\sqrt[3]{3^3\cdot 2}$
$$= 2\sqrt[3]{2} + 9\sqrt[3]{2}$$
$$= 11\sqrt[3]{2}$$

55. $-2\sqrt[3]{125x^3 y^4} + 3y^2\sqrt[3]{8x^3}$
$$= -2\sqrt[3]{5^3 x^3 y^3 y} + 3y^2\cdot 2x$$
$$= -10xy\sqrt[3]{y} + 6xy^2$$

57. $\sqrt{48} + \sqrt{27} + \sqrt{75}$
$$= 6.92820323$$
$$+ 5.196152423$$
$$+ 8.660254038 = 20.78460969$$
$12\sqrt{3} = 20.78460969$ which shows
$\sqrt{48} + \sqrt{27} + \sqrt{75} = 12\sqrt{3}$

59. $I = \sqrt{\dfrac{P}{R}} = \sqrt{\dfrac{500}{10}} = \sqrt{50} \approx 7.071$
The current is approximately 7.071 amps.

61. $T = 2\pi\sqrt{\dfrac{L}{32}} = 2(3.14)\sqrt{\dfrac{8}{32}} \approx 3.14$
The period of the pendulum is approximately 3.14 seconds.

Cumulative Review

63. $16x^3 - 56x^2 y + 49xy^2$
$$= x(16x^2 - 56xy + 49y^2)$$
$$= x(4x - 7y)^2$$

182

© 2006 Pearson Education, Inc., Upper Saddle River, NJ. All rights reserved. This material is protected under all copyright laws as they currently exist.
No portion of this material may be reproduced, in any form or by any means, without permission in writing from the publisher.

65. $S + M = 4.5 \Rightarrow S = 4.5 - M$
$0.2S + 0.25M = 2$
$0.2(4.5 - M) + 0.25M = 1$
$0.9 - 0.2M + 0.25M = 1$
$0.05M = 0.1, \; M = 2$
$S = 4.5 - M = 2.5$
2.5 small servings of scallops (fifteen scallops) and two small servings of skim milk (2 cups) would meet the requirement.

67. $\dfrac{250 - 307}{307} = \dfrac{-57}{307} = -0.1856677524\ldots$
A decrease of 18.6%.

69. $\dfrac{280 - 307}{307} = \dfrac{-27}{307} = -0.087947882736\ldots$
A decrease of 8.%.

7.4 Exercises

1. $\sqrt{5}\sqrt{7} = \sqrt{5 \cdot 7} = \sqrt{35}$

3. $\left(5\sqrt{2}\right)\left(-6\sqrt{5}\right) = -30\sqrt{2 \cdot 5} = -30\sqrt{10}$

5. $(2\sqrt{6})(-3\sqrt{2}) = -6\sqrt{12}$
$\qquad\qquad = -6\sqrt{4 \cdot 3} = -12\sqrt{3}$

7. $(-3\sqrt{y})(\sqrt{5x}) = -3\sqrt{5xy}$

9. $\left(3x\sqrt{2x}\right)\left(-2\sqrt{10xy}\right) = -6x\sqrt{20x^2 y}$
$\quad = -6x\sqrt{4x^2 \cdot 5y} = -12x^2\sqrt{5y}$

11. $5\sqrt{a}\left(3\sqrt{b} - 5\right) = 15\sqrt{ab} - 25\sqrt{a}$

13. $-2\sqrt{y}\left(\sqrt{2x} - 3\sqrt{5}\right) = -2\sqrt{2xy} + 6\sqrt{5y}$

15. $-\sqrt{a}\left(\sqrt{a} - 2\sqrt{b}\right) = -a + 2\sqrt{ab}$

17. $7\sqrt{x}(2\sqrt{3} - 5\sqrt{x}) = 14\sqrt{3x} - 35x$

19. $(3 - \sqrt{2})(8 + \sqrt{2}) = 24 - 5\sqrt{2} - 2$
$\qquad\qquad\qquad\qquad = 22 - 5\sqrt{2}$

21. $(2\sqrt{3} + \sqrt{2})(2\sqrt{3} - 4\sqrt{2}) = 12 - 6\sqrt{6} - 8$
$\qquad\qquad\qquad\qquad\qquad = 4 - 6\sqrt{6}$

23. $(\sqrt{7} + 4\sqrt{5x})(2\sqrt{7} + 3\sqrt{5x})$
$\quad = 2 \cdot 7 + 11\sqrt{35x} + 12(5x)$
$\quad = 14 + 11\sqrt{35x} + 60x$

25. $(\sqrt{3} + 2\sqrt{2})(\sqrt{5} + \sqrt{3})$
$\quad = \sqrt{15} + 3 + 2\sqrt{10} + 2\sqrt{6}$

27. $(\sqrt{5} - 2\sqrt{6})^2$
$\quad = (\sqrt{5})^2 - 4\sqrt{5}\sqrt{6} + (2\sqrt{6})^2$
$\quad = 5 - 4\sqrt{30} + 24$
$\quad = 29 - 4\sqrt{30}$

29. $(6 - 5\sqrt{a})^2 = 6^2 - 2(6)(5\sqrt{a}) + (5\sqrt{a})^2$
$\qquad\qquad\quad = 36 - 60\sqrt{a} + 25a$

31. $(\sqrt{3x + 4} + 3)^2$
$\quad = (\sqrt{3x + 4})^2 + 6\sqrt{3x + 4} + 9$
$\quad = 3x + 4 + 6\sqrt{3x + 4} + 9$
$\quad = 3x + 13 + 6\sqrt{3x + 4}$

33. $(\sqrt[3]{x^2})(3\sqrt[3]{4x} - 4\sqrt[3]{x^5}) = 3\sqrt[3]{4x^3} - 4\sqrt[3]{x^7}$
$\quad = 3x\sqrt[3]{4} - 4\sqrt[3]{x^6 \cdot x} = 3x\sqrt[3]{4} - 4x^2\sqrt[3]{x}$

183

© 2006 Pearson Education, Inc., Upper Saddle River, NJ. All rights reserved. This material is protected under all copyright laws as they currently exist. No portion of this material may be reproduced, in any form or by any means, without permission in writing from the publisher.

35. $\left(\sqrt[3]{3}+\sqrt[3]{2}\right)\left(\sqrt[3]{9}-\sqrt[3]{4}\right)$

$\quad = \sqrt[3]{27} - \sqrt[3]{12} + \sqrt[3]{18} - \sqrt[3]{8}$

$\quad = 3 - \sqrt[3]{12} + \sqrt[3]{18} - 2 = 1 + \sqrt[3]{18} - \sqrt[3]{12}$

37. $\sqrt{\dfrac{49}{25}} = \dfrac{\sqrt{49}}{\sqrt{25}} = \dfrac{7}{5}$

39. $\sqrt{\dfrac{12x}{49y^6}} = \dfrac{\sqrt{4\cdot 3x}}{\sqrt{49y^6}} = \dfrac{2\sqrt{3x}}{7y^3}$

41. $\sqrt[3]{\dfrac{8x^5 y^6}{27}} = \dfrac{\sqrt[3]{8x^3 y^6 \cdot x^2}}{\sqrt[3]{27}} = \dfrac{2xy^2 \sqrt[3]{x^2}}{3}$

43. $\dfrac{\sqrt[3]{5y^8}}{\sqrt[3]{27x^3}} = \dfrac{\sqrt[3]{5y^6 y^2}}{3x} = \dfrac{y^2 \sqrt[3]{5y^2}}{3x}$

45. $\dfrac{3}{\sqrt{2}} \cdot \dfrac{\sqrt{2}}{\sqrt{2}} = \dfrac{3\sqrt{2}}{2}$

47. $\sqrt{\dfrac{4}{3}} = \dfrac{\sqrt{4}}{\sqrt{3}} \cdot \dfrac{\sqrt{3}}{\sqrt{3}} = \dfrac{2\sqrt{3}}{3}$

49. $\dfrac{1}{\sqrt{5y}} \cdot \dfrac{\sqrt{5y}}{\sqrt{5y}} = \dfrac{\sqrt{5y}}{5y}$

51. $\dfrac{\sqrt{14a}}{\sqrt{2y}} \cdot \dfrac{\sqrt{2y}}{\sqrt{2y}} = \dfrac{\sqrt{28ay}}{2y} = \dfrac{\sqrt{4\cdot 7ay}}{2y}$

$\quad\quad = \dfrac{2\sqrt{7ay}}{2y} = \dfrac{\sqrt{7ay}}{y}$

53. $\dfrac{\sqrt{2}}{\sqrt{6x}} \cdot \dfrac{\sqrt{6x}}{\sqrt{6x}} = \dfrac{\sqrt{12x}}{6x} = \dfrac{\sqrt{4\cdot 3x}}{6x}$

$\quad\quad = \dfrac{2\sqrt{3x}}{6x} = \dfrac{\sqrt{3x}}{3x}$

55. $\dfrac{x}{\sqrt{5}-\sqrt{2}} \cdot \dfrac{\sqrt{5}+\sqrt{2}}{\sqrt{5}+\sqrt{2}} = \dfrac{x(\sqrt{5}+\sqrt{2})}{5-2}$

$\quad\quad\quad = \dfrac{x(\sqrt{5}+\sqrt{2})}{3}$

57. $\dfrac{2y}{\sqrt{6}+\sqrt{5}} \cdot \dfrac{\sqrt{6}-\sqrt{5}}{\sqrt{6}-\sqrt{5}} = \dfrac{2y\left(\sqrt{6}-\sqrt{5}\right)}{6-5}$

$\quad\quad\quad = 2y\left(\sqrt{6}-\sqrt{5}\right)$

59. $\dfrac{\sqrt{x}}{\sqrt{3x}+\sqrt{2}} \cdot \dfrac{\sqrt{3x}-\sqrt{2}}{\sqrt{3x}-\sqrt{2}} = \dfrac{x\sqrt{3}-\sqrt{2x}}{3x-2}$

61. $\dfrac{\sqrt{5}+\sqrt{3}}{\sqrt{5}-\sqrt{3}} \cdot \dfrac{\sqrt{5}+\sqrt{3}}{\sqrt{5}+\sqrt{3}} = \dfrac{5+2\sqrt{15}+3}{5-3}$

$\quad\quad = \dfrac{8+2\sqrt{15}}{2} = \dfrac{2(4+\sqrt{15})}{2} = 4+\sqrt{15}$

63. $\dfrac{\sqrt{3x}-2\sqrt{y}}{\sqrt{3x}+\sqrt{y}} \cdot \dfrac{\sqrt{3x}-\sqrt{y}}{\sqrt{3x}-\sqrt{y}}$

$\quad = \dfrac{3x-3\sqrt{3xy}+2y}{3x-y}$

65. $3\sqrt{8} - 5\sqrt{50} + \sqrt{98}$

$\quad = 3\sqrt{4\cdot 2} - 5\sqrt{25\cdot 2} + \sqrt{49\cdot 2}$

$\quad = 6\sqrt{2} - 25\sqrt{2} + 7\sqrt{2} = -12\sqrt{2}$

67. $\left(3\sqrt{2} - 5\sqrt{3}\right)\left(\sqrt{2} + 2\sqrt{3}\right)$

$\quad = 3\cdot 2 + 6\sqrt{6} - 5\sqrt{6} - 10\cdot 3$

$\quad = 6 + \sqrt{6} - 30 = -24 + \sqrt{6}$

184

© 2006 Pearson Education, Inc., Upper Saddle River, NJ. All rights reserved. This material is protected under all copyright laws as they currently exist. No portion of this material may be reproduced, in any form or by any means, without permission in writing from the publisher.

69. $\dfrac{9}{\sqrt{8x}} \cdot \dfrac{\sqrt{8x}}{\sqrt{8x}} = \dfrac{9\sqrt{4\cdot 2x}}{8x}$

$\qquad\qquad = \dfrac{18\sqrt{2x}}{8x} = \dfrac{9\sqrt{2x}}{4x}$

71. $\dfrac{\sqrt{5}+1}{\sqrt{5}+2} \cdot \dfrac{\sqrt{5}-2}{\sqrt{5}-2} = \dfrac{5-2\sqrt{5}+\sqrt{5}-2}{5-4}$

$\qquad\qquad = 5-2\sqrt{5}+\sqrt{5}-2$

$\qquad\qquad = 3-\sqrt{5}$

73. $\dfrac{\sqrt{6}}{2\sqrt{3}-\sqrt{2}} = 1.194938299...$

$\dfrac{\sqrt{3}+3\sqrt{2}}{5} = 1.194938299...$

The decimal approximations are the same. The student worked correctly.

75. $\dfrac{\sqrt{3}+2\sqrt{7}}{8} \cdot \dfrac{\sqrt{3}-2\sqrt{7}}{\sqrt{3}-2\sqrt{7}} = \dfrac{3-28}{8(\sqrt{3}+2\sqrt{7})}$

$\qquad\qquad\qquad = \dfrac{-25}{8(\sqrt{3}+2\sqrt{7})}$

77. $C = 0.18\dfrac{\sqrt{21}\sqrt{50}}{2} = 2.916333314...$

$2.92 is the cost to fertilize the lawn.

79. $A = LW = (\sqrt{x}+5)(\sqrt{x}+3)$

$A = x + 8\sqrt{x} + 15 \text{ mm}^2$

Cumulative Review

81. $2x+3y=13 \rightarrow \ 4x+6y=26$

$\quad 5x-2y=4 \ \rightarrow \underline{15x-6y=12}$

$\qquad\qquad\qquad\qquad 19x = 38$

$\qquad\qquad\qquad\qquad\quad x = 2$

$2(2)+3y=13 \Rightarrow 3y=9 \Rightarrow y=3$

$(2,3)$ is the solution.

83. From the table, she reaches her goal on January 11th.

day	consumption
2nd	$280 \div 2 = 140$
5th	$140 \div 2 = 70$
8th	$70 \div 2 = 35$
11th	$35 \div 2 = 17.5$

85. $15\% + 31\% + 26\% = 72\%$

How Am I Doing? Sections 7.1-7.4

1. $(-3x^{\frac{1}{4}}y^{\frac{1}{2}})(-2x^{-\frac{1}{2}}y^{3}) = 6x^{\frac{1}{4}-\frac{1}{2}}y^{\frac{1}{2}+\frac{1}{3}}$

$\qquad\qquad\qquad = 6x^{-\frac{1}{4}}y^{\frac{5}{6}} = \dfrac{6y^{\frac{5}{6}}}{x^{\frac{1}{4}}}$

2. $(-4x^{-\frac{1}{4}}y^{\frac{1}{3}})^{3} = (-4)^{3}x^{-\frac{3}{4}}y = -\dfrac{64y}{x^{\frac{3}{4}}}$

3. $\dfrac{-18x^{-2}y^{2}}{-3x^{-5}y^{\frac{1}{3}}} = 6x^{-2+5}y^{2-\frac{1}{3}} = 6x^{3}y^{\frac{5}{3}}$

4. $\left(\dfrac{27x^{2}y^{-5}}{x^{-4}y^{4}}\right)^{\frac{2}{3}} = \left(\dfrac{3^{3}x^{6}}{y^{9}}\right)^{\frac{2}{3}} = \left(\dfrac{3^{2}x^{4}}{y^{6}}\right) = \dfrac{9x^{4}}{y^{6}}$

5. $27^{-\frac{4}{3}} = \dfrac{1}{(3^{3})^{\frac{4}{3}}} = \dfrac{1}{3^{4}} = \dfrac{1}{81}$

6. $\sqrt[5]{-243} = \sqrt[5]{(-3)^{5}} = -3$

7. $\sqrt{169} + \sqrt[3]{-64} = 13 - 4 = 9$

8. $\sqrt{49x^{6}y^{20}} = \sqrt{(7x^{3}y^{10})^{2}} = 7x^{3}y^{10}$

© 2006 Pearson Education, Inc., Upper Saddle River, NJ. All rights reserved. This material is protected under all copyright laws as they currently exist. No portion of this material may be reproduced, in any form or by any means, without permission in writing from the publisher.

9. $\sqrt[3]{27a^{12}b^6c^{15}} = \sqrt[3]{27}\sqrt[3]{a^{12}}\sqrt[3]{b^6}\sqrt[3]{c^{15}}$

$\qquad\qquad = 3a^4b^2c^5$

10. $(\sqrt[6]{4x})^5 = \left((4x)^{\frac{1}{6}}\right)^5 = (4x)^{\frac{5}{6}}$

11. $\sqrt[4]{16x^{20}y^{28}} = \sqrt[4]{(2x^5y^7)^4} = 2x^5y^7$

12. $\sqrt[3]{32x^8y^{15}} = \sqrt[3]{8\cdot4x^2x^6y^{15}}$

$\qquad\qquad = \sqrt[3]{8}\sqrt[3]{x^6}\sqrt[3]{y^{15}}\sqrt[3]{4x^2}$

$\qquad\qquad = 2x^2y^5\sqrt[3]{4x^2}$

13. $\sqrt{44} - 2\sqrt{99} + 7\sqrt{11}$

$\quad = \sqrt{4\cdot11} - 2\sqrt{9\cdot11} + 7\sqrt{11}$

$\quad = 2\sqrt{11} - 2\cdot3\sqrt{11} + 7\sqrt{11}$

$\quad = 2\sqrt{11} - 6\sqrt{11} + 7\sqrt{11} = 3\sqrt{11}$

14. $3\sqrt{48y^3} - 2\sqrt[3]{16} + 3\sqrt[3]{54} - 5y\sqrt{12y}$

$= 3\sqrt{16y^2\cdot3y} - 2\sqrt[3]{8\cdot2} + 3\sqrt[3]{27\cdot2} - 5y\sqrt{4\cdot3y}$

$= 12y\sqrt{3y} - 4\sqrt[3]{2} + 9\sqrt[3]{2} - 10y\sqrt{3y}$

$= 2y\sqrt{3y} + 5\sqrt[3]{2}$

15. $(3\sqrt{3} - 5\sqrt{6})(\sqrt{12} - 3\sqrt{6})$

$\quad = 3\sqrt{36} - 9\sqrt{18} - 5\sqrt{72} + 15(6)$

$\quad = 3(6) - 9\sqrt{9\cdot2} - 5\sqrt{36\cdot2} + 90$

$\quad = 108 - 27\sqrt{2} - 30\sqrt{2}$

$\quad = 108 - 57\sqrt{2}$

16. $\dfrac{6}{\sqrt{20x}} \cdot \dfrac{\sqrt{20x}}{\sqrt{20x}} = \dfrac{6\sqrt{4\cdot5x}}{20x}$

$\qquad\qquad = \dfrac{12\sqrt{5x}}{20x} = \dfrac{3\sqrt{5x}}{5x}$

17. $\dfrac{\sqrt{2}+\sqrt{3}}{\sqrt{2}-\sqrt{3}} \cdot \dfrac{\sqrt{2}+\sqrt{3}}{\sqrt{2}+\sqrt{3}} = \dfrac{2+2\sqrt{6}+3}{2-3}$

$\qquad\qquad\qquad\qquad\qquad = -5 - 2\sqrt{6}$

7.5 Exercises

1. Isolate one of the radicals on one side of the equation.

3. $\sqrt{8x+1} = 5 \Rightarrow \left(\sqrt{8x+1}\right)^2 = 5^2$

$\qquad 8x+1 = 25$

$\qquad 8x = 24$

$\qquad x = 3$

check: $\sqrt{8(3)+1} \overset{?}{=} 5, \ \ 5 = 5$

$x = 3$ is the solution.

5. $\sqrt{7x-3} - 2 = 0$

$\qquad \sqrt{7x-3} = 2$

$\qquad 7x-3 = 4$

$\qquad 7x = 7$

$\qquad x = 1$

check: $\sqrt{7(1)-3} - 2 \overset{?}{=} 0, \ 0 = 0$

$x = 1$ is the solution.

7. $\qquad y+1 = \sqrt{5y-1}$

$\qquad y^2 + 2y + 1 = 5y - 1$

$\qquad y^2 - 3y + 2 = 0$

$\qquad (y-2)(y-1) = 0$

$\qquad\qquad y = 2, \ y = 1$

check: $2+1 \overset{?}{=} \sqrt{5(2)-1}, \ 3 = 3$

$\qquad 1+1 \overset{?}{=} \sqrt{5(1)-1}, \ 2 = 2$

$y = 2, \ y = 1$ is the solution.

© 2006 Pearson Education, Inc., Upper Saddle River, NJ. All rights reserved. This material is protected under all copyright laws as they currently exist.
No portion of this material may be reproduced, in any form or by any means, without permission in writing from the publisher.

9. $2x = \sqrt{x+3} \Rightarrow (2x)^2 = \left(\sqrt{x-3}\right)^2$

$4x^2 = x+3$

$4x^2 - x - 3 = 0$

$(4x+3)(x-1) = 0$

$x = -\dfrac{3}{4}, \ x = 1$

check: $2\left(-\dfrac{3}{4}\right) \overset{?}{=} \sqrt{-\dfrac{3}{4}+3}, \ -\dfrac{3}{2} \neq \dfrac{3}{2}$

$2(1) \overset{?}{=} \sqrt{1+3}, \ 2 = 2$

$x = 1$ is the solution.

11. $2 = 5 + \sqrt{2x+1} \Rightarrow \sqrt{2x+1} = -3$

No solution since $\sqrt{2x+1} \geq 0$.

13. $y - \sqrt{y-3} = 5$

$y - 5 = \sqrt{y-3} \Rightarrow (y-5)^2 = \left(\sqrt{y-3}\right)^2$

$y^2 - 10y + 25 = y - 3$

$y^2 - 11y + 28 = 0$

$(y-7)(y-4) = 0$

$y = 7, \ y = -4$

check: $4 - \sqrt{4-3} \overset{?}{=} 5, \ 3 \neq 5$

$7 - \sqrt{7-3} \overset{?}{=} 5, \ 5 = 5$

$x = 7$ is the solution.

15. $\sqrt{y+1} - 1 = y$

$\sqrt{y+1} = y + 1$

$y + 1 = y^2 + 2y + 1$

$y^2 + y = 0$

$y(y+1) = 0$

$y = 0, \ y = -1$

15. check: $\sqrt{0+1} - 1 \overset{?}{=} 0, \ 0 = 0$

$\sqrt{-1+1} - 1 \overset{?}{=} -1, \ -1 = -1$

$y = 0, \ y = -1$ is the solution.

17. $x - 2\sqrt{x-3} = 3$

$x - 3 = 2\sqrt{x-3}$

$x^2 - 6x + 9 = 4x - 12$

$x^2 - 10x + 21 = 0$

$(x-7)(x-3) = 0$

$x = 7, \ x = 3$

check: $7 - 2\sqrt{7-3} \overset{?}{=} 3, \ 3 = 3$

$3 - 2\sqrt{3-3} \overset{?}{=} 3, \ 3 = 3$

$x = 7, \ x = 3$ is the solution.

19. $\sqrt{3x^2 - x} = x$

$3x^2 - x = x^2$

$2x^2 - x = 0$

$x(2x-1) = 0$

$x = 0, \ x = \dfrac{1}{2}$

check: $\sqrt{3(0)^2 - 0} \overset{?}{=} 0, \quad 0 = 0$

$\sqrt{3\left(\dfrac{1}{2}\right)^2 - \dfrac{1}{2}} \overset{?}{=} \dfrac{1}{2}, \ \dfrac{1}{2} = \dfrac{1}{2}$

$x = 0, \ x = \dfrac{1}{2}$ is the solution.

21. $\sqrt[3]{2x+3} = 2 \Rightarrow \left(\sqrt[3]{2x+3}\right)^3 = 2^3$

$2x + 3 = 8$

$2x = 5$

$x = \dfrac{5}{2}$

187

© 2006 Pearson Education, Inc., Upper Saddle River, NJ. All rights reserved. This material is protected under all copyright laws as they currently exist. No portion of this material may be reproduced, in any form or by any means, without permission in writing from the publisher.

21. check: $\sqrt[3]{2 \cdot \dfrac{5}{2} + 3} \overset{?}{=} 2, \; 2 = 2$

$x = \dfrac{5}{2}$ is the solution.

23. $\sqrt[3]{4x - 1} = 3$

$\qquad 4x - 1 = 27$

$\qquad 4x = 28$

$\qquad x = 7$

check: $\sqrt[3]{4(7) - 1} \overset{?}{=} 3, \; 3 = 3$

$x = 7$ is the solution.

25. $\sqrt{x + 4} = 1 + \sqrt{x - 3}$

$\qquad x + 4 = 1 + 2\sqrt{x - 3} + x - 3$

$\qquad 6 = 2\sqrt{x - 3} \Rightarrow 3 = \sqrt{x - 3}$

$\qquad 9 = x - 3$

$\qquad x = 12$

check: $\sqrt{12 + 4} \overset{?}{=} 1 + \sqrt{12 - 3}, \; 4 = 4$

$x = 12$ is the solution.

27. $\sqrt{5x + 1} = 1 + \sqrt{3x}$

$\qquad 5x + 1 = 1 + 2\sqrt{3x} + 3x$

$\qquad 2x = 2\sqrt{3x}$

$\qquad x = \sqrt{3x}$

$\qquad x^2 = 3x$

$\qquad x^2 - 3x = 0$

$\qquad x(x - 3) = 0$

$\qquad x = 0, \; x = 3$

check: $\sqrt{5(0) + 1} \overset{?}{=} 1 + \sqrt{3(0)}, \; 1 = 1$

$\qquad \sqrt{5(3) + 1} \overset{?}{=} 1 + \sqrt{3(3)}, \; 4 = 4$

$x = 0, \; x = 3$ is the solution.

29. $\sqrt{x + 6} = 1 + \sqrt{x + 2}$

$\qquad x + 6 = 1 + 2\sqrt{x + 2} + x + 2$

$\qquad 9 = 4(x + 2)$

$\qquad 4x + 8 = 9$

$\qquad 4x = 1$

$\qquad x = \dfrac{1}{4}$

check: $\sqrt{\dfrac{1}{4} + 6} \overset{?}{=} 1 + \sqrt{\dfrac{1}{4} + 2}, \; \dfrac{5}{2} = \dfrac{5}{2}$

$x = \dfrac{1}{4}$ is the solution.

31. $\sqrt{6x + 6} = 1 + \sqrt{4x + 5}$

$\qquad 6x + 6 = 1 + 2\sqrt{4x + 5} + 4x + 5$

$\qquad x^2 = 4x + 5$

$\qquad x^2 - 4x - 5 = 0$

$\qquad (x - 5)(x + 1) = 0$

$\qquad x = 5, \; x = -1$

check: $\sqrt{6(5) + 6} \overset{?}{=} 1 + \sqrt{4(5) + 5}, \quad 6 = 6$

$\qquad \sqrt{6(-1) + 6} \overset{?}{=} 1 + \sqrt{4(-1) + 5}, \; 0 \neq 2$

$x = 5$ is the solution.

33. $\sqrt{2x + 9} - \sqrt{x + 1} = 2$

$\qquad \sqrt{2x + 9} = 2 + \sqrt{x + 1}$

$\qquad 2x + 9 = 4 + 4\sqrt{x + 1} + x + 1$

$\qquad x + 4 = 4\sqrt{x + 1}$

$\qquad x^2 + 8x + 16 = 16x + 16$

$\qquad x^2 - 8x = 0$

$\qquad x(x - 8) = 0$

$\qquad x = 0, \; x = 8$

© 2006 Pearson Education, Inc., Upper Saddle River, NJ. All rights reserved. This material is protected under all copyright laws as they currently exist. No portion of this material may be reproduced, in any form or by any means, without permission in writing from the publisher.

33. check: $\sqrt{2(0)+9}-\sqrt{0+1} \overset{?}{=} 2,\ 2=2$

$\qquad\qquad \sqrt{2(8)+9}-\sqrt{8+1} \overset{?}{=} 2,\ 2=2$

$x=0,\ x=8$ is the solution.

35. $\sqrt{4x+6}=\sqrt{x+1}-\sqrt{x+5}$

$\qquad 4x+6=x+1-2\sqrt{x+1}\sqrt{x+5}+x+5$

$\qquad 2x=2\sqrt{x^2+6x+5}$

$\qquad x=\sqrt{x^2+6x+5}$

$\qquad x^2=x^2+6x+5$

$\qquad 6x+5=0$

$\qquad x=-\dfrac{5}{6}$

check:

$$\sqrt{4\left(-\dfrac{5}{6}\right)+6} \overset{?}{=} \sqrt{-\dfrac{5}{6}+1}-\sqrt{-\dfrac{5}{6}+5}$$

$$\dfrac{4\sqrt{6}}{6} \neq \dfrac{-4\sqrt{6}}{6}$$

No solution.

37. $\qquad 2\sqrt{x}-\sqrt{x-5}=\sqrt{2x-2}$

$\quad 4x-4\sqrt{x}\sqrt{x-5}+x-5=2x-2$

$\qquad 4\sqrt{x}\sqrt{x-5}=3x-3$

$\qquad 16x^2-80x=9x^2-18x+9$

$\qquad 7x^2-62x-9=0$

$\qquad (7x+1)(x-9)=0$

$\qquad\qquad x=-\dfrac{1}{7}\ \text{ or }\ x=9$

$x=-\dfrac{1}{7}$ does not check since it gives

the square root of a negative.

check: $2\sqrt{9}-\sqrt{9-5} \overset{?}{=} \sqrt{2(9)-2},\ 4=4$

$x=9$ is the solution.

39. $x=\sqrt{5.326x-1.983}$

$\quad x^2=5.326x-1.983$

$\quad x^2-5.326x+1.983=0$

$\quad x=0.40279\ \text{ or }\ x=4.92321$

check:

$0.40279 \overset{?}{=} \sqrt{5.326(0.40279)-1.983}$

$\quad 0.4028=0.4028$

$4.92321 \overset{?}{=} \sqrt{5.326(4.92321)-1.983}$

$\quad 4.9232=4.9232$

$x=4.9232,\ x=0.4028$ is the solution

to four decimal places.

41. (a) $V=2\sqrt{3S} \Rightarrow V^2=4(3S) \Rightarrow S=\dfrac{V^2}{12}$

(b) $S=\dfrac{18^2}{12}=27$ ft

43. $0.11y+1.25=\sqrt{3.7625+0.22x}$

$0.0121y^2+0.275y+1.5625=3.7625+0.22x$

$0.22x=0.0121y^2+0.275y-2.2$

$\quad x=0.055y^2+1.25y-10$

45. $\qquad \sqrt{x^2-4x+c}=x-1$

$\qquad \sqrt{4^2-4(4)+c}=4-1$

$\qquad\qquad \sqrt{c}=3 \Rightarrow c=9$

Cumulative Review

47. $(4^3x^6)^{\frac{2}{3}}=4^{3\cdot\frac{2}{3}}x^{6\cdot\frac{2}{3}}=4^2x^4=16x^4$

49. $\sqrt[3]{-216x^6y^9}=-6x^2y^3$

189

© 2006 Pearson Education, Inc., Upper Saddle River, NJ. All rights reserved. This material is protected under all copyright laws as they currently exist. No portion of this material may be reproduced, in any form or by any means, without permission in writing from the publisher.

51. $V = Ah = (4x^2 + 2x + 9)(2x + 3)$
$V = 8x^3 + 12x^2 + 4x^2 + 6x + 18x + 27$
$V = 8x^3 + 16x^2 + 24x + 27 \text{ cm}^3$

53. $w = $ speed of current
$(12 + w) \cdot 3 = (12 - w) \cdot 5$
$36 + 3w = 60 - 5w$
$8w = 24$
$w = 3$
The current flows at 3 miles per hour.

7.6 Exercises

1. No. There is no real number that, when squared, will equal -9.

3. No. To be equal, the real number parts must be equal, and the imaginary number parts must be equal. $2 \neq 3$ and $3i \neq 2i$.

5. $\sqrt{-25} = \sqrt{25}\sqrt{-1} = 5i$

7. $\sqrt{-50} = \sqrt{25 \cdot 2}\sqrt{-1} = 5i\sqrt{2}$

9. $\sqrt{\dfrac{-4}{49}} = \sqrt{\dfrac{4}{49}}\sqrt{-1} = \dfrac{2}{7}i$

11. $-\sqrt{-81} = -\sqrt{81}\sqrt{-1} = -9i$

13. $2 + \sqrt{-3} = 2 + \sqrt{3}\sqrt{-1} = 2 + i\sqrt{3}$

15. $-1.5 + \sqrt{-81} = -1.5 + \sqrt{81}\sqrt{-1}$
$= -1.5 + 9i$

17. $-3 + \sqrt{-24} = -3 + \sqrt{4 \cdot 6}\sqrt{-1}$
$= -3 + 2i\sqrt{6}$

19. $\left(\sqrt{-3}\right)\left(\sqrt{-2}\right) = \sqrt{3}\sqrt{-1}\sqrt{2}\sqrt{-1}$
$= i\sqrt{3} \cdot i\sqrt{2} = i^2\sqrt{6} = -\sqrt{6}$

21. $\left(\sqrt{-36}\right)\left(\sqrt{-4}\right) = \left(\sqrt{36}\sqrt{-1}\right)\left(\sqrt{4}\sqrt{-1}\right)$
$= (6i)(2i) = 12i^2 = -12$

23. $x - 3i = 5 + yi$
$x = 5$
$y = -3$

25. $1.3 - 2.5yi = x - 5i$
$x = 1.3$
$-2.5y = -5$
$y = 2$

27. $23 + yi = 17 - x + 3i$
$23 = 17 - x$
$x = -6$
$y = 3$

29. $(1 + 8i) + (-6 + 3i) = 1 + 8i - 6 + 3i$
$= -5 + 11i$

31. $\left(-\dfrac{3}{2} + \dfrac{1}{2}i\right) + \left(\dfrac{5}{2} - \dfrac{3}{2}i\right)$
$= -\dfrac{3}{2} + \dfrac{5}{2} + \left(\dfrac{1}{2} - \dfrac{3}{2}\right)i = 1 - i$

33. $(2.8 - 0.7i) - (1.6 - 2.8i)$
$= 2.8 - 1.6 + (-0.7 + 2.8)i$
$= 1.2 + 2.1i$

35. $(4i)(3i) = 12i^2 = 12(-1) = -12$

37. $(-7i)(6i) = -42i^2 = (-42)(-1) = 42$

190

© 2006 Pearson Education, Inc., Upper Saddle River, NJ. All rights reserved. This material is protected under all copyright laws as they currently exist. No portion of this material may be reproduced, in any form or by any means, without permission in writing from the publisher.

39. $(2+3i)(2-i) = 4-2i+6i-3i^2$
$$= 4+4i-3(-1)$$
$$= 4+4i+3$$
$$= 7+4i$$

41. $5i-2(-4+i) = 5i+8-2i = 8+3i$

43. $2i(5i-6) = 10i^2-12i = -10-12i$

45. $\left(\dfrac{1}{2}+i\right)^2 = \dfrac{1}{4}+i+i^2 = \dfrac{1}{4}+i-1 = -\dfrac{3}{4}+i$

47. $(i\sqrt{3})(i\sqrt{7}) = i^2\sqrt{21} = -\sqrt{21}$

49. $(3+\sqrt{-2})(4+\sqrt{-5})$
$$= (3+i\sqrt{2})(4+i\sqrt{5})$$
$$= 12+3i\sqrt{5}+4i\sqrt{2}+i^2\sqrt{10}$$
$$= 12+3i\sqrt{5}+4i\sqrt{2}-\sqrt{10}$$
$$= 12-\sqrt{10}+(3\sqrt{5}+4\sqrt{2})i$$

51. $i^{17} = (i^4)^4 \cdot i = 1^4 \cdot i = i$

53. $i^{24} = (i^4)^6 = 1^6 = 1$

55. $i^{46} = (i^4)^{11} \cdot i^2 = 1^{11}(-1) = -1$

57. $i^{37} = i^{36}i = (i^4)^9 i = 1^9 i = i$

59. $i^{30}+i^{28} = (i^4)^7 \cdot i^2 + (i^4)^7$
$$= 1^7(-1)+1^7 = -1+1 = 0$$

61. $i^{100}-i^7 = (i^4)^{25}-i^4i^3 = 1^{25}-1\cdot(-i)$
$$= 1+i$$

63. $\dfrac{2+i}{3-i} \cdot \dfrac{3+i}{3+i} = \dfrac{6+5i+i^2}{9+1} = \dfrac{6+5i-1}{10}$
$$= \dfrac{5(1+i)}{10} = \dfrac{1+i}{2}$$

65. $\dfrac{3i}{4+2i} \cdot \dfrac{4-2i}{4-2i} = \dfrac{12i-6i^2}{16+4} = \dfrac{6+12i}{20}$
$$= \dfrac{3+6i}{10}$$

67. $\dfrac{5-2i}{6i} \cdot \dfrac{-6i}{-6i} = \dfrac{-30i+12i^2}{36} = \dfrac{-12-30i}{36}$
$$= -\dfrac{2+5i}{6}$$

69. $\dfrac{2}{i} \cdot \dfrac{i}{i} = \dfrac{2i}{i^2} = \dfrac{2i}{-1} = -2i$

71. $\dfrac{7}{5-6i} \cdot \dfrac{5+6i}{5+6i} = \dfrac{35+42i}{25+36} = \dfrac{35+42i}{61}$

73. $\dfrac{5-2i}{3+2i} \cdot \dfrac{3-2i}{3-2i} = \dfrac{15-10i-6i+4i^2}{9+4}$
$$= \dfrac{15-16i-4}{13} = \dfrac{11-16i}{13}$$

75. $\sqrt{-98} = \sqrt{98}\sqrt{-1} = \sqrt{49}\sqrt{2}\sqrt{-1} = 7i\sqrt{2}$

77. $(4-7i)-(-2+5i) = 4-7i+2-5i$
$$= 6-12i$$

79. $(5i-4)(6i-2) = 30i^2-10i-24i+8$
$$= -30-34i+8$$
$$= -22-34i$$

191

© 2006 Pearson Education, Inc., Upper Saddle River, NJ. All rights reserved. This material is protected under all copyright laws as they currently exist.
No portion of this material may be reproduced, in any form or by any means, without permission in writing from the publisher.

81. $\dfrac{2-3i}{2+i} \cdot \dfrac{2-i}{2-i} = \dfrac{4-2i-6i+3i^2}{4+1}$

$\qquad = \dfrac{4-8i-3}{5} = \dfrac{1-8i}{5}$

83. $(29.3+56.2i)^2$

$\qquad = 858.49 + 3293.32i + 3158.44i^2$

$\qquad = 858.49 + 3293.32i - 3158.44$

$\qquad = -2299.95 + 3293.32i$

85. $Z = \dfrac{V}{I} = \dfrac{-9i-6i^2}{9} = \dfrac{6-9i}{9} = \dfrac{2-3i}{3}$

Cumulative Review

87. $x+3+2x-5+4x+2 = 105$

$\qquad\qquad\qquad\quad 7x = 105$

$\qquad\qquad\qquad\quad\; x = 15$

$\qquad\qquad\qquad\; x+3 = 18$

$\qquad\qquad\qquad 2x-5 = 25$

$\qquad\qquad\qquad 4x+2 = 62$

18 hours producing juice in glass bottles, 25 hours producing juice in cans, and 62 hours producing juice in plastic bottles.

7.7 Exercises

1. Answers may vary. A person's weekly paycheck varies as the number of hours worked, $y = kx$ where y is the weekly salary, k is the hourly salary, and x is the number of hours worked.

3. $y = \dfrac{k}{x}$

5. $y = kx,\ \ 15 = k \cdot 40,\ \ k = \dfrac{3}{8}$

$\qquad y = \dfrac{3}{8}x,\ \ y = \dfrac{3}{8} \cdot 64 = 24$

7. $p = kd,\ \ 21 = k \cdot 50,\ \ k = \dfrac{21}{50}$

$\qquad p = \dfrac{21}{50}d,\ \ p = \dfrac{21}{50} \cdot 170 = 71.4$

The pressure would be 71.4 psi.

9. $d = ks^2,\ \ 40 = k \cdot 30^2,\ \ k = \dfrac{2}{45}$

$\qquad d = \dfrac{2}{45}s^2,\ \ d = \dfrac{2}{45} \cdot 60^2 = 160$ ft to stop

11. $y = \dfrac{k}{x^2},\ \ 10 = \dfrac{k}{2^2},\ \ k = 40$

$\qquad y = \dfrac{40}{x^2},\ \ y = \dfrac{40}{0.5^2} = 160$

13. $g = \dfrac{k}{p},\ \ 3000 = \dfrac{k}{2.10},\ \ k = 6300$

$\qquad g = \dfrac{6300}{p},\ \ g = \dfrac{6300}{1.90} = 3316$ gal

15. $s = \dfrac{k}{t},\ \ 45 = \dfrac{k}{6},\ \ k = 270$

$\qquad s = \dfrac{270}{t},\ \ s = \dfrac{270}{9} = 30$ mph

17. $w = \dfrac{k}{l},\ \ 900 = \dfrac{k}{8},\ \ k = 7200$

$\qquad w = \dfrac{7200}{l},\ \ w = \dfrac{7200}{18} = 400$ lb

19. $s = kwt^2,\ \ 400 = k(5)(2)^2,\ \ k = 20$

$\qquad s = 20wt^2 = 20(4)(3.5)^2 = 980$ lb

21. $d = kav,\ \ 222 = k(37.8)(45),\ \ k \approx 0.1305$

$\qquad d \approx 0.1305av$

$\qquad 450 \approx 0.1305(55)v$

$\qquad v \approx 62.7$ mph

© 2006 Pearson Education, Inc., Upper Saddle River, NJ. All rights reserved. This material is protected under all copyright laws as they currently exist. No portion of this material may be reproduced, in any form or by any means, without permission in writing from the publisher.

Cumulative Review

23. $3x^2 - 8x + 4 = 0$

$(3x - 2)(x - 2) = 0$

$x = \dfrac{2}{3}$ or $x = 2$

25. $488.75 = 1.0625p$

$p = 460$

The original price was $460.

27. $x =$ number of gold leaf frames

$140x + 95(110 - x) = 13,375$

$140x + 10,450 - 95x = 13,375$

$45x = 2907$

$x = 64.6$

$110 - x = 45.4$

He can buy 65 gold leaf frames and 45 silver frames.

Putting Your Skills to Work

1. $\sqrt[12]{2} = 2^{\frac{1}{12}} = 1.059463094$

2. $440(1.059463094) = 466.1637615$ hertz

3. $\dfrac{440}{1.059463094} = 415.3046976$ hertz

4. $261.63\left(2^{\frac{1}{12}}\right)^{12} = 261.63(2) = 523.26$ hertz

5. The frequency of the higher note is twice the frequency of the lower note. Yes.

6. $\dfrac{261.63}{2} = 130.82$ hertz

7. $\dfrac{440}{2} = 220$ hertz

Chapter 7 Review Problems

1. $(3xy^{\frac{1}{2}})(5x^2y^{-3}) = 15x^3y^{-\frac{5}{2}} = \dfrac{15x^3}{y^{\frac{5}{2}}}$

2. $\dfrac{3x^{\frac{2}{3}}}{6x^{\frac{1}{6}}} = \dfrac{x^{\frac{2}{3}-\frac{1}{6}}}{2} = \dfrac{x^{\frac{1}{2}}}{2}$

3. $(25a^3b^4)^{\frac{1}{2}} = 25^{\frac{1}{2}}a^{3\cdot\frac{1}{2}}b^{4\cdot\frac{1}{2}} = 5a^{\frac{3}{2}}b^2$

4. $5^{\frac{1}{4}} \cdot 5^{\frac{1}{2}} = 5^{\frac{1}{4}+\frac{1}{2}} = 5^{\frac{3}{4}}$

5. $(2a^{\frac{1}{3}}b^{\frac{1}{4}})(-3a^{\frac{1}{2}}b^{\frac{1}{2}}) = -6a^{\frac{1}{3}+\frac{1}{2}}b^{\frac{1}{4}+\frac{1}{2}} = -6a^{\frac{5}{6}}b^{\frac{3}{4}}$

6. $\dfrac{6x^{\frac{2}{3}}y^{\frac{1}{10}}}{12x^{\frac{1}{6}}y^{-\frac{1}{5}}} = \dfrac{x^{\frac{2}{3}-\frac{1}{6}}y^{\frac{1}{10}+\frac{1}{5}}}{2} = \dfrac{x^{\frac{1}{2}}y^{\frac{3}{10}}}{2}$

7. $(2x^{-\frac{1}{5}}y^{\frac{1}{10}}z^{\frac{4}{5}})^{-5} = 2^{-5}x^{-\frac{1}{5}(-5)}y^{\frac{1}{10}(-5)}z^{\frac{4}{5}(-5)}$

$= \dfrac{xy^{-\frac{1}{2}}z^{-4}}{2^5} = \dfrac{x}{32y^{\frac{1}{2}}z^4}$

8. $\left(\dfrac{49a^3b^6}{a^{-7}b^4}\right)^{\frac{1}{2}} = \left(49a^{10}b^2\right)^{\frac{1}{2}} = 49^{\frac{1}{2}}a^{10(\frac{1}{2})}b^{2(\frac{1}{2})}$

$= 7a^5b$

9. $\dfrac{(x^{\frac{3}{4}}y^{\frac{2}{5}})^{\frac{1}{2}}}{x^{-\frac{1}{8}}} = x^{\frac{3}{4}\cdot\frac{1}{2}}x^{\frac{1}{8}}y^{\frac{2}{5}\cdot\frac{1}{2}} = x^{\frac{3}{8}+\frac{1}{8}}y^{\frac{1}{5}} = x^{\frac{1}{2}}y^{\frac{1}{5}}$

© 2006 Pearson Education, Inc., Upper Saddle River, NJ. All rights reserved. This material is protected under all copyright laws as they currently exist. No portion of this material may be reproduced, in any form or by any means, without permission in writing from the publisher.

10. $\left(\dfrac{27x^{5n}}{x^{2n-3}}\right)^{\frac{1}{3}} = \left(27x^{5n-(2n-3)}\right)^{\frac{1}{3}} = 27^{\frac{1}{3}}(x^{3n+3})^{\frac{1}{3}}$

$\qquad = 3x^{(3n+3)(\frac{1}{3})} = 3x^{n+1}$

11. $(5^{\frac{6}{5}})^{\frac{10}{7}} = 5^{\frac{6}{5}\cdot\frac{10}{7}} = 5^{\frac{12}{7}}$

12. $2x^{\frac{1}{3}} + x^{-\frac{2}{3}} = 2x^{\frac{1}{3}} + \dfrac{1}{x^{\frac{2}{3}}} = \dfrac{2x^{\frac{1}{3}+\frac{2}{3}}+1}{x^{\frac{2}{3}}} = \dfrac{2x+1}{x^{\frac{2}{3}}}$

13. $6x^{\frac{3}{2}} - 9x^{\frac{1}{2}} = 3x(2x^{\frac{1}{2}} - 3x^{-\frac{1}{2}})$

14. $-\sqrt{16} = -4$

15. $\sqrt[5]{-32} = \sqrt[5]{-1}\sqrt[5]{32} = -\sqrt[5]{2^5} = -2$

16. $\sqrt[6]{-20}$ not a real number.

17. $-\sqrt{\dfrac{1}{25}} = -\dfrac{1}{5}$

18. $\sqrt{0.04} = 0.2$

19. $\sqrt[4]{-256}$ not a real number.

20. $\sqrt[3]{-\dfrac{1}{8}} = -\dfrac{1}{2}$

21. $\sqrt[3]{\dfrac{27}{64}} = \dfrac{3}{4}$

22. $64^{\frac{2}{3}} = \left(4^3\right)^{\frac{2}{3}} = 4^{3\cdot\frac{2}{3}} = 4^2 = 16$

23. $125^{\frac{4}{3}} = \left(5^3\right)^{\frac{4}{3}} = 5^{3\cdot\frac{4}{3}} = 5^4 = 625$

24. $\sqrt{81x^2y^6z^{10}} = \sqrt{9^2x^2\left(y^3\right)^2\left(z^5\right)^2}$

$\qquad = 9xy^3z^5$

25. $\sqrt[3]{125a^9b^{60}} = \sqrt[3]{5^3\left(a^3\right)^3\left(b^{20}\right)^3} = 5a^3b^{20}$

26. $\sqrt[3]{-8a^{12}b^{15}c^{21}} = \sqrt[3]{(-2)^3\left(a^4\right)^3\left(b^5\right)^3\left(c^7\right)^3}$

$\qquad = -2a^4b^5c^7$

27. $\sqrt{49x^{22}y^2} = \sqrt{7^2\left(x^{11}\right)^2y^2} = 7x^{11}y$

28. $\sqrt[5]{a^2} = a^{\frac{2}{5}}$

29. $\sqrt[4]{y^3} = y^{\frac{3}{4}}$

30. $\sqrt{2b} = \left(2b\right)^{\frac{1}{2}}$

31. $\sqrt[3]{6c} = \left(6c\right)^{\frac{1}{3}}$

32. $\left(\sqrt[6]{ab}\right)^5 = \left(\left(ab\right)^{\frac{1}{6}}\right)^5 = \left(ab\right)^{\frac{5}{6}}$

33. $m^{\frac{1}{2}} = \sqrt[2]{m^1} = \sqrt{m}$

34. $n^{\frac{1}{4}} = \sqrt[4]{n^1} = \sqrt[4]{n}$

35. $y^{\frac{3}{5}} = \sqrt[5]{y^3}$

36. $\left(3z\right)^{\frac{2}{3}} = \sqrt[3]{\left(3z\right)^2} = \sqrt[3]{9z^2}$

37. $\left(2x\right)^{\frac{3}{7}} = \sqrt[7]{\left(2x\right)^3} = \sqrt[7]{8x^3}$

194

© 2006 Pearson Education, Inc., Upper Saddle River, NJ. All rights reserved. This material is protected under all copyright laws as they currently exist. No portion of this material may be reproduced, in any form or by any means, without permission in writing from the publisher.

38. $16^{\frac{3}{4}} = \left(2^4\right)^{\frac{3}{4}} = 2^{4 \cdot \frac{3}{4}} = 2^3 = 8$

39. $64^{\frac{5}{6}} = \left(2^6\right)^{\frac{5}{6}} = 2^{6 \cdot \frac{5}{6}} = 2^5 = 32$

40. $(-27)^{\frac{2}{3}} = \left((-3)^3\right)^{\frac{2}{3}} = (-3)^{3 \cdot \frac{2}{3}} = (-3)^2 = 9$

41. $(-8)^{\frac{1}{3}} = \left((-2)^3\right)^{\frac{1}{3}} = (-2)^{3 \cdot \frac{1}{3}} = (-2)^1 = -2$

42. $\left(\dfrac{1}{9}\right)^{\frac{1}{2}} = \left(3^{-2}\right)^{\frac{1}{2}} = 3^{-2 \cdot \frac{1}{2}} = 3^{-1} = \dfrac{1}{3^1} = \dfrac{1}{3}$

43. $(0.49)^{\frac{1}{2}} = \left((0.7)^2\right)^{\frac{1}{2}} = 0.7^{2 \cdot \frac{1}{2}} = 0.7^1 = 0.7$

44. $\left(\dfrac{1}{16}\right)^{-\frac{1}{4}} = \left(2^{-4}\right)^{-\frac{1}{4}} = 2^{-4 \cdot \frac{-1}{4}} = 2^1 = 2$

45. $\left(\dfrac{1}{36}\right)^{-\frac{1}{2}} = \left(6^{-2}\right)^{-\frac{1}{2}} = 6^{-2 \cdot \frac{-1}{2}} = 6^1 = 6$

46. $\left(25a^2b^4\right)^{\frac{3}{2}} = \left(5^2\right)^{\frac{3}{2}}\left(a^2\right)^{\frac{3}{2}}\left(b^4\right)^{\frac{3}{2}}$

$\quad = 5^{2 \cdot \frac{3}{2}} a^{2 \cdot \frac{3}{2}} b^{4 \cdot \frac{3}{2}} = 5^3 a^3 b^6$

$\quad = 125a^3b^6$

47. $\left(4a^6b^2\right)^{\frac{5}{2}} = \left(2^2\right)^{\frac{5}{2}}\left(a^6\right)^{\frac{5}{2}}\left(b^2\right)^{\frac{5}{2}}$

$\quad = 2^5 a^{6 \cdot \frac{5}{2}} b^{2 \cdot \frac{5}{2}} = 32a^{15}b^5$

48. $\sqrt{50} + 2\sqrt{32} - \sqrt{8} = 5\sqrt{2} + 8\sqrt{2} - 2\sqrt{2}$

$\quad = 11\sqrt{2}$

49. $\sqrt{28} - 4\sqrt{7} + 5\sqrt{63}$

$\quad = \sqrt{4 \cdot 7} - 4\sqrt{7} + 5\sqrt{9 \cdot 7}$

$\quad = 2\sqrt{7} - 4\sqrt{7} + 15\sqrt{7} = 13\sqrt{7}$

50. $3\sqrt{50} + 2\sqrt{75} - \sqrt{300}$

$\quad = 3\sqrt{25 \cdot 2} + 2\sqrt{25 \cdot 3} - \sqrt{100 \cdot 3}$

$\quad = 3 \cdot 5\sqrt{2} + 2 \cdot 5\sqrt{3} - 10\sqrt{3} = 15\sqrt{2}$

51. $\sqrt{40x^3} + x\sqrt{90x} = \sqrt{4x^2 \cdot 10x} + x\sqrt{9 \cdot 10x}$

$\quad = 2x\sqrt{10x} + 3x\sqrt{10x} = 5x\sqrt{10x}$

52. $2\sqrt{32x} - 5x\sqrt{2} + \sqrt{18x}$

$\quad = 2\sqrt{16 \cdot 2x} - 5x\sqrt{2} + \sqrt{9 \cdot 2x}$

$\quad = 8\sqrt{2x} - 5x\sqrt{2} + 3\sqrt{2x} = 11\sqrt{2x} - 5x\sqrt{2}$

53. $3\sqrt[3]{16} - 4\sqrt[3]{54} = 3\sqrt[3]{2^3 \cdot 2} - 4\sqrt[3]{3^3 \cdot 2}$

$\quad = 3 \cdot 2\sqrt[3]{2} - 4 \cdot 3\sqrt[3]{2}$

$\quad = 6\sqrt[3]{2} - 12\sqrt[3]{2} = -6\sqrt[3]{2}$

54. $(5\sqrt{12})(3\sqrt{6}) = 15\sqrt{72}$

$\quad = 15\sqrt{36 \cdot 2} = 90\sqrt{2}$

55. $\left(-2\sqrt{15}\right)\left(4x\sqrt{3}\right) = -8x\sqrt{45} = -8x\sqrt{9 \cdot 5}$

$\quad = -24x\sqrt{5}$

56. $3\sqrt{x}(2\sqrt{8x} - 3\sqrt{48}$

$\quad = 3\sqrt{x}(4\sqrt{2x} - 12\sqrt{3})$

$\quad = 12x\sqrt{2} - 36\sqrt{3x}$

57. $\sqrt{5a}\left(2 - \sqrt{15a}\right) = 2\sqrt{5a} - \sqrt{75a^2}$

$\quad = 2\sqrt{5a} - \sqrt{25a^2 \cdot 3}$

$\quad = 2\sqrt{5a} - 5a\sqrt{3}$

© 2006 Pearson Education, Inc., Upper Saddle River, NJ. All rights reserved. This material is protected under all copyright laws as they currently exist.
No portion of this material may be reproduced, in any form or by any means, without permission in writing from the publisher.

58. $-\sqrt{3xy}\left(\sqrt{2x}-\sqrt{6y}\right)$

$= -\sqrt{6x^2y} + \sqrt{18xy^2}$

$= -x\sqrt{6y} + \sqrt{9y^2 \cdot 2x}$

$= -x\sqrt{6y} + 3y\sqrt{2x}$

59. $2\sqrt{7b}\left(\sqrt{ab} - b\sqrt{3bc}\right)$

$= 2\sqrt{7ab^2} - 2b\sqrt{21b^2c}$

$= 2b\sqrt{7a} - 2b^2\sqrt{21c}$

60. $(5\sqrt{2} + \sqrt{3})(\sqrt{2} - 2\sqrt{3})$

$= 10 - 9\sqrt{6} - 6 = 4 - 9\sqrt{6}$

61. $(5\sqrt{6} - 2\sqrt{2})(\sqrt{6} - \sqrt{2}) = 30 - 7\sqrt{12} + 4$

$= 34 - 7\sqrt{4 \cdot 3} = 34 - 14\sqrt{3}$

62. $(2\sqrt{5} - 3\sqrt{6})^2 = 20 - 12\sqrt{30} + 54$

$= 74 - 12\sqrt{30}$

63. $(\sqrt[3]{2x} + \sqrt[3]{6})(\sqrt[3]{4x^2} - \sqrt[3]{y})$

$= \sqrt[3]{8x^3} - \sqrt[3]{2xy} + \sqrt[3]{24x^2} - \sqrt[3]{6y}$

$= 2x - \sqrt[3]{2xy} + 2\sqrt[3]{3x^2} - \sqrt[3]{6y}$

64. $f(x) = \sqrt{5x+20}$

(a) $f(16) = \sqrt{5(16)+20}$

$= \sqrt{100} = 10$

(b) domain: $5x + 20 \ge 0$

$5x \ge -20$

$x \ge -4$

65. $f(x) = \sqrt{36-4x}$

(a) $f(5) = \sqrt{36-4(5)} = \sqrt{16} = 4$

65. (b) domain: $36 - 4x \ge 0$

$4x \le 36$

$x \le 9$

66. $f(x) = \sqrt{\dfrac{3}{4}x - \dfrac{1}{2}}$

(a) $f(1) = \sqrt{\dfrac{3}{4}\cdot 1 - \dfrac{1}{2}} = \sqrt{\dfrac{1}{4}} = \dfrac{1}{2}$

(b) domain: $\dfrac{3}{4}x - \dfrac{1}{2} \ge 0$

$3x - 2 \ge 0$

$3x \ge 2$

$x \ge \dfrac{2}{3}$

67. $\sqrt{\dfrac{3x^2}{y} \cdot \dfrac{y}{y}} = \sqrt{\dfrac{3x^2y}{y^2}} = \dfrac{x\sqrt{3y}}{\sqrt{y^2}} = \dfrac{x\sqrt{3y}}{y}$

68. $\dfrac{2}{\sqrt{3y}} \cdot \dfrac{\sqrt{3y}}{\sqrt{3y}} = \dfrac{2\sqrt{3y}}{3y}$

69. $\dfrac{3\sqrt{7x}}{\sqrt{21x}} = \dfrac{3\sqrt{7x}}{\sqrt{3}\cdot\sqrt{7x}}$

$= \dfrac{3}{\sqrt{3}} \cdot \dfrac{\sqrt{3}}{\sqrt{3}} = \dfrac{3\sqrt{3}}{3} = \sqrt{3}$

70. $\dfrac{2}{\sqrt{6}-\sqrt{5}} \cdot \dfrac{\sqrt{6}+\sqrt{5}}{\sqrt{6}+\sqrt{5}}$

$= \dfrac{2\sqrt{6}+2\sqrt{5}}{6-5} = 2\sqrt{6}+2\sqrt{5}$

71. $\dfrac{\sqrt{x}}{3\sqrt{x}+\sqrt{y}} \cdot \dfrac{3\sqrt{x}-\sqrt{y}}{3\sqrt{x}-\sqrt{y}} = \dfrac{3x-\sqrt{xy}}{9x-y}$

© 2006 Pearson Education, Inc., Upper Saddle River, NJ. All rights reserved. This material is protected under all copyright laws as they currently exist.
No portion of this material may be reproduced, in any form or by any means, without permission in writing from the publisher.

72. $\dfrac{\sqrt{5}}{\sqrt{7}-3} \cdot \dfrac{\sqrt{7}+3}{\sqrt{7}+3} = \dfrac{\sqrt{35}+3\sqrt{5}}{7-9}$

$\qquad\qquad\qquad = -\dfrac{\sqrt{35}+3\sqrt{5}}{2}$

73. $\dfrac{2\sqrt{3}+\sqrt{6}}{\sqrt{3}+2\sqrt{6}} \cdot \dfrac{\sqrt{3}-2\sqrt{6}}{\sqrt{3}-2\sqrt{6}}$

$\quad = \dfrac{6-4\sqrt{18}+\sqrt{18}-12}{3-24}$

$\quad = \dfrac{-6-3\sqrt{9\cdot2}}{-21} = \dfrac{-6-9\sqrt{2}}{-21} = \dfrac{2+3\sqrt{2}}{7}$

74. $\dfrac{5\sqrt{2}-\sqrt{3}}{\sqrt{6}-\sqrt{3}} \cdot \dfrac{\sqrt{6}+\sqrt{3}}{\sqrt{6}+\sqrt{3}}$

$\quad = \dfrac{5\sqrt{12}+5\sqrt{6}-\sqrt{18}-3}{6-3}$

$\quad = \dfrac{5\sqrt{4\cdot3}+5\sqrt{6}-\sqrt{9\cdot2}-3}{3}$

$\quad = \dfrac{10\sqrt{3}+5\sqrt{6}-3\sqrt{2}-3}{3}$

75. $\dfrac{3\sqrt{x}+\sqrt{y}}{\sqrt{x}-\sqrt{y}} \cdot \dfrac{\sqrt{x}+\sqrt{y}}{\sqrt{x}+\sqrt{y}} = \dfrac{3x+4\sqrt{xy}+y}{x-y}$

76. $\dfrac{2xy}{\sqrt[3]{16xy^5}} \cdot \dfrac{\sqrt[3]{4x^2y}}{\sqrt[3]{4x^2y}} = \dfrac{2xy\sqrt[3]{4x^2y}}{4xy^2}$

$\qquad\qquad\qquad = \dfrac{\sqrt[3]{4x^2y}}{2y}$

77. $\sqrt{-16}+\sqrt{-45} = \sqrt{16}\sqrt{-1}+\sqrt{45}\sqrt{-1}$

$\qquad\qquad\qquad = 4i+i\sqrt{9\cdot5}$

$\qquad\qquad\qquad = 4i+3i\sqrt{5}$

78. $2x-3i+5 = yi-2+\sqrt{6}$

$\qquad\quad 2x+5 = -2+\sqrt{6}$

$\qquad\qquad 2x = -7+\sqrt{6}$

$\qquad\qquad\quad x = \dfrac{-7+\sqrt{6}}{2}$

$\qquad\qquad\quad y = -3$

79. $(-12-6i)+(3-5i) = -12-6i+3-5i$

$\qquad\qquad\qquad\qquad\quad = -9-11i$

80. $(2-i)-(12-3i) = 2-i-12+3i$

$\qquad\qquad\qquad\qquad = -10+2i$

81. $(7+3i)(2-5i) = 14-29i-15i^2$

$\qquad\qquad\qquad\quad = 14-29i+15$

$\qquad\qquad\qquad\quad = 29-29i$

82. $(8-4i)^2 = 64-64i+16i^2$

$\qquad\qquad\quad = 64-64i-16$

$\qquad\qquad\quad = 48-64i$

83. $2i(3+4i) = 6i+8i^2 = -8+6i$

84. $3-4(2+i) = 3-8-4i = -5-4i$

85. $i^{34} = (i^4)^8 \cdot i^2 = 1^8(-1) = -1$

86. $i^{65} = (i^4)^{16} \cdot i = 1^{16} \cdot i = i$

87. $\dfrac{7-2i}{3+4i} \cdot \dfrac{3-4i}{3-4i} = \dfrac{21-6i-28i+8i^2}{9+16}$

$\qquad\qquad\qquad = \dfrac{21-34i-8}{25}$

$\qquad\qquad\qquad = \dfrac{13-34i}{25}$

© 2006 Pearson Education, Inc., Upper Saddle River, NJ. All rights reserved. This material is protected under all copyright laws as they currently exist.
No portion of this material may be reproduced, in any form or by any means, without permission in writing from the publisher.

88. $\dfrac{5-2i}{1-3i} \cdot \dfrac{1+3i}{1+3i} = \dfrac{5-2i+15i-6i^2}{1+9}$

$\qquad\qquad\qquad = \dfrac{5+13i+6}{10}$

$\qquad\qquad\qquad = \dfrac{11+13i}{10}$

89. $\dfrac{4-3i}{5i} \cdot \dfrac{-5i}{-5i} = \dfrac{-20i+15i^2}{-25i^2} = \dfrac{-20i-15}{-25(-1)}$

$\qquad\qquad\quad = \dfrac{-15-20i}{25} = -\dfrac{5(3+4i)}{5\cdot 5}$

$\qquad\qquad\quad = -\dfrac{3+4i}{5}$

90. $\dfrac{12}{3-5i} \cdot \dfrac{3+5i}{3+5i} = \dfrac{36+60i}{9+25}$

$\qquad\qquad\qquad = \dfrac{36+60i}{34}$

$\qquad\qquad\qquad = \dfrac{18+30i}{17}$

91. $\dfrac{10-4i}{2+5i} \cdot \dfrac{2-5i}{2-5i} = \dfrac{20-58i+20i^2}{4+25}$

$\qquad\qquad\qquad = \dfrac{20-58i-20}{29}$

$\qquad\qquad\qquad = \dfrac{-58i}{29}$

$\qquad\qquad\qquad = -2i$

92. $\sqrt{3x-2} = 5$

$\qquad 3x-2 = 25$

$\qquad\quad 3x = 27$

$\qquad\qquad x = 3$

check: $\sqrt{3(9)-2} \overset{?}{=} 5,\ 5=5$

$x = 9$ is the solution.

93. $\sqrt[3]{3x-1} = 2$

$\qquad 3x-1 = 8$

$\qquad\quad 3x = 9$

$\qquad\qquad x = 3$

check: $\sqrt[3]{3(3)-1} \overset{?}{=} 2,\ 2=2$

$x = 3$ is the solution.

94. $\qquad \sqrt{2x+1} = 2x-5$

$\qquad\qquad 2x+1 = 4x^2-20x+25$

$\qquad 4x^2-22x+24 = 0$

$\qquad\quad 2x-11x+12 = 0$

$\qquad (x-4)(2x-3) = 0$

$\qquad\qquad\qquad x = 4,\ \ x = \dfrac{3}{2}$

check: $\sqrt{2(4)+1} \overset{?}{=} 2(4)-5,\ 3=3$

$\sqrt{2\left(\dfrac{3}{2}\right)+1} \overset{?}{=} 2\left(\dfrac{3}{2}\right)-5,\ \sqrt{4} \neq -2$

$x = 4$ is the solution.

95. $1+\sqrt{3x+1} = x$

$\qquad \sqrt{3x+1} = x-1$

$\qquad\quad 3x+1 = x^2-2x+1$

$\qquad\quad x^2-5x = 0$

$\qquad\quad x(x-5) = 0$

$\qquad\qquad x = 0,\ \ x = 5$

check: $1+\sqrt{3(0)+1} \overset{?}{=} 0,\ 2 \neq 0$

$1+\sqrt{3(5)+1} \overset{?}{=} 5,\ 5=5$

$x = 5$ is the solution.

© 2006 Pearson Education, Inc., Upper Saddle River, NJ. All rights reserved. This material is protected under all copyright laws as they currently exist.
No portion of this material may be reproduced, in any form or by any means, without permission in writing from the publisher.

96.

$$\sqrt{3x+1} = \sqrt{2x-1} + 1$$

$$\sqrt{3x+1} = \sqrt{2x-1} + 1$$

$$3x+1 = 2x-1 + 2\sqrt{2x-1} + 1$$

$$x+1 = 2\sqrt{2x-1}$$

$$x^2 + 2x + 1 = 8x - 4$$

$$x^2 - 6x + 5 = 0$$

$$(x-5)(x-1) = 0$$

$$x = 5, \ x = 1$$

check: $\sqrt{3(5)+1} - \sqrt{2(5)-1} \overset{?}{=} 1, \ 1 = 1$

$\sqrt{3(1)+1} - \sqrt{2(1)-1} \overset{?}{=} 1, \ 1 = 1$

$x = 5, \ x = 1$ is the solution.

97.

$$\sqrt{7x+2} = \sqrt{x+3} + \sqrt{2x-1}$$

$$7x+2 = x+3 + 2\sqrt{x+3}\sqrt{2x-1} + 2x-1$$

$$4x = 2\sqrt{x+3}\sqrt{2x-1}$$

$$2x = \sqrt{x+3}\sqrt{2x-1}$$

$$4x^2 = 2x^2 + 5x - 3$$

$$2x^2 - 5x + 3 = 0$$

$$(x-1)(2x-3) = 0$$

$$x = 1, \ x = \frac{3}{2}$$

check: $\sqrt{7(1)+2} \overset{?}{=} \sqrt{1+3} + \sqrt{2(1)-1}, \ 3 = 3$

$$\sqrt{7\left(\frac{3}{2}\right)+2} \overset{?}{=} \sqrt{\left(\frac{3}{2}\right)+3} + \sqrt{2\left(\frac{3}{2}\right)-1}$$

$$\frac{5}{\sqrt{2}} = \frac{5}{\sqrt{2}}$$

$x = 1, \ x = \frac{3}{2}$ is the solution.

98. $y = kx, \ 16 = k \cdot 5, \ k = \frac{16}{5}$

$$y = \frac{16}{5}x, \ y = \frac{16}{5} \cdot 3 = \frac{48}{5} = 9.6$$

99. $y = kx, \ 5 = k \cdot 20, \ k = \frac{1}{4}$

$$y = \frac{1}{4}x, \ y = \frac{1}{4} \cdot 50 = \frac{50}{4} = 12.5$$

100. $d = kv^2, \ 50 = k \cdot 30^2, \ k = \frac{1}{18}$

$$d = \frac{1}{18}v^2, \ d = \frac{1}{18} \cdot 55^2 \approx 168.1 \text{ ft}$$

101. $t = k\sqrt{d}, \ 2 = k\sqrt{64}, \ k = \frac{1}{4}$

$$t = \frac{1}{4}\sqrt{d}, \ t = \frac{1}{4}\sqrt{196} = \frac{14}{4} = 3.5 \text{ sec}$$

102. $y = \frac{k}{x}, \ 8 = \frac{k}{3}, \ k = 24$

$$y = \frac{24}{x}, \ y = \frac{24}{48} = 0.5$$

103. $V = \frac{k}{P}, \ 70 = \frac{k}{24}, \ k = 1680$

$$V = \frac{1680}{P}, \ 100 = \frac{1680}{P}, \ P = 16.8 \text{ lb/in}^2$$

104. $y = k\frac{x}{z^2}, \ 1 = k \cdot \frac{8}{4^2}, \ k = 2$

$$y = 2 \cdot \frac{x}{z^2}, \ y = 2 \cdot \frac{6}{3^2} = \frac{4}{3} = 1.3$$

105. $V = khr^2, \ 50 = k(5)(3)^2, \ k = \frac{10}{9}$

$$V = \frac{10}{9}r^2h, \ V = \frac{10}{9}(4)^2(9) = 160 \text{ cm}^3$$

© 2006 Pearson Education, Inc., Upper Saddle River, NJ. All rights reserved. This material is protected under all copyright laws as they currently exist. No portion of this material may be reproduced, in any form or by any means, without permission in writing from the publisher.

How Am I Doing? Chapter 7 Test

1. $(2x^{\frac{1}{2}}y^{\frac{1}{3}})(-3x^{\frac{1}{3}}y^{\frac{1}{6}}) = -6x^{\frac{1}{2}+\frac{1}{3}}y^{\frac{1}{3}+\frac{1}{6}}$

$$= -6x^{\frac{5}{6}}y^{\frac{1}{2}}$$

2. $\dfrac{7x^3}{4x^{\frac{3}{4}}} = \dfrac{7x^{3-\frac{3}{4}}}{4} = \dfrac{7x^{\frac{9}{4}}}{4}$

3. $(8x^{\frac{1}{3}})^{\frac{3}{2}} = 8^{\frac{3}{2}}x^{\frac{1}{3}\cdot\frac{3}{2}} = 8^{\frac{3}{2}}x^{\frac{1}{2}}$

4. $\left(\dfrac{4}{9}\right)^{\frac{3}{2}} = \left(\left(\dfrac{2}{3}\right)^2\right)^{\frac{3}{2}} = \left(\dfrac{2}{3}\right)^{2\cdot\frac{3}{2}} = \left(\dfrac{2}{3}\right)^3 = \dfrac{8}{27}$

5. $\sqrt[5]{-32} = \sqrt[5]{(-2)^5} = -2$

6. $8^{-\frac{2}{3}} = \dfrac{1}{\left(8^{\frac{1}{3}}\right)^2} = \dfrac{1}{2^2} = \dfrac{1}{4}$

7. $16^{\frac{5}{4}} = \left(16^{\frac{1}{4}}\right)^5 = 2^5 = 32$

8. $\sqrt{75a^4b^9} = \sqrt{25a^4b^8 \cdot 3b} = 5a^2b^4\sqrt{3b}$

9. $\sqrt{49a^4b^{10}} = \sqrt{7^2\left(a^2\right)^2\left(b^5\right)^2} = 7a^2b^5$

10. $\sqrt[3]{54m^3n^5} = \sqrt[3]{3^3\,m^3n^3 \cdot 2n^2} = 3mn\sqrt[3]{2n^2}$

11. $3\sqrt{24} - \sqrt{18} + \sqrt{50}$

$$= 3\sqrt{4\cdot6} - \sqrt{9\cdot2} + \sqrt{25\cdot2}$$
$$= 6\sqrt{6} - 3\sqrt{2} + 5\sqrt{2}$$
$$= 6\sqrt{6} + 2\sqrt{2}$$

12. $\sqrt{40x} - \sqrt{27x} + 2\sqrt{12x}$

$$= \sqrt{4\cdot10x} - \sqrt{9\cdot3x} + 2\sqrt{4\cdot3x}$$
$$= 2\sqrt{10x} - 3\sqrt{3x} + 4\sqrt{3x}$$
$$= 2\sqrt{10x} + \sqrt{3x}$$

13. $\left(-3\sqrt{2y}\right)\left(5\sqrt{10xy}\right) = -15\sqrt{20xy^2}$

$$= -15\sqrt{4y^2\cdot5x}$$
$$= -30y\sqrt{5x}$$

14. $2\sqrt{3}(3\sqrt{6} - 5\sqrt{2}) = 6\sqrt{18} - 10\sqrt{6}$

$$= 6\sqrt{9\cdot2} - 10\sqrt{6}$$
$$= 18\sqrt{2} - 10\sqrt{6}$$

15. $(5\sqrt{3} - \sqrt{6})(2\sqrt{3} + 3\sqrt{6})$

$$= 30 + 15\sqrt{18} - 2\sqrt{18} - 18$$
$$= 12 + 13\sqrt{9\cdot2}$$
$$= 12 + 39\sqrt{2}$$

16. $\dfrac{30}{\sqrt{5x}} \cdot \dfrac{\sqrt{5x}}{\sqrt{5x}} = \dfrac{30\sqrt{5x}}{5x} = \dfrac{6\sqrt{5x}}{x}$

17. $\sqrt{\dfrac{xy}{3}} = \dfrac{\sqrt{xy}}{\sqrt{3}} \cdot \dfrac{\sqrt{3}}{\sqrt{3}} = \dfrac{\sqrt{3xy}}{3}$

18. $\dfrac{1+2\sqrt{3}}{3-\sqrt{3}} \cdot \dfrac{3+\sqrt{3}}{3+\sqrt{3}} = \dfrac{3+\sqrt{3}+6\sqrt{3}+2(3)}{9-3}$

$$= \dfrac{9+7\sqrt{3}}{6}$$

© 2006 Pearson Education, Inc., Upper Saddle River, NJ. All rights reserved. This material is protected under all copyright laws as they currently exist. No portion of this material may be reproduced, in any form or by any means, without permission in writing from the publisher.

19.
$$\sqrt{3x-2} = x$$
$$3x-2 = x^2$$
$$x^2 - 3x + 2 = 0$$
$$(x-2)(x-1) = 0$$
$$x = 2, \quad x = 1$$

check: $\sqrt{3(2)-2} \stackrel{?}{=} 2, \ 2 = 2$

$\sqrt{3(1)-2} \stackrel{?}{=} 1, \ 1 = 1$

$x = 2, \ x = 1$ is the solution.

20.
$$5 + \sqrt{x+15} = x$$
$$\sqrt{x+15} = x - 5$$
$$x + 15 = x^2 - 10x + 25$$
$$x^2 - 11x + 10 = 0$$
$$(x-10)(x-11) = 0$$
$$x = 10, \quad x = 11$$

check: $5 + \sqrt{10+15} \stackrel{?}{=} 10, \ 10 = 10$

$5 + \sqrt{11+15} \stackrel{?}{=} 11, \ 5 + \sqrt{26} \neq 11$

$x = 10$ is the solution.

21.
$$5 - \sqrt{x-2} = \sqrt{x+3}$$
$$25 - 10\sqrt{x-2} + x - 2 = x + 3$$
$$20 = 10\sqrt{x-2}$$
$$2 = \sqrt{x-2}$$
$$4 = x - 2$$
$$x = 6$$

check: $5 - \sqrt{6-2} \stackrel{?}{=} \sqrt{6+3}, \ 3 = 3$

$x = 6$ is the solution.

22. $(8+2i) - 3(2-4i) = 8 + 2i - 6 + 12i$
$$= 2 + 14i$$

23. $i^{18} + \sqrt{-16} = (i^4)^4 \cdot i^2 + \sqrt{16}\sqrt{-1}$
$$= 1^4(-1) + 4i$$
$$= -1 + 4i$$

24. $(3-2i)(4+3i) = 12 + i - 6i^2 = 12 + i + 6$
$$= 18 + i$$

25. $\dfrac{2+5i}{1-3i} \cdot \dfrac{1+3i}{1+3i} = \dfrac{2+11i+15i^2}{1+9}$
$$= \dfrac{-13+11i}{10}$$

26. $(6+3i)^2 = 36 + 36i + 9i^2$
$$= 27 + 36i$$

27. $i^{43} = (i^4)^{10} \cdot i^3 = 1^{10} \cdot (-i) = -i$

28. $y = \dfrac{k}{x}, \ 9 = \dfrac{k}{2}, \ k = 18$

$y = \dfrac{18}{x}, \ y = \dfrac{18}{6} = 3$

29. $y = k \cdot \dfrac{x}{z^2}, \ 3 = k \cdot \dfrac{8}{4^2}, \ k = 6$

$y = 6 \cdot \dfrac{x}{z^2}, \ y = 6 \cdot \dfrac{5}{6^2} = \dfrac{5}{6}$

30. $d = kv^2, \ 30 = k \cdot 30^2, \ k = \dfrac{1}{30}$

$d = \dfrac{1}{30} \cdot v^2, \ d = \dfrac{1}{30} \cdot 50^2 \approx 83.3$ feet

Cumulative Test for Chapters 1-7

1. Associative property of addition.

© 2006 Pearson Education, Inc., Upper Saddle River, NJ. All rights reserved. This material is protected under all copyright laws as they currently exist. No portion of this material may be reproduced, in any form or by any means, without permission in writing from the publisher.

2. $-3a(2ab-a^3)+b(ab^2+4a^2)$

$= -6a^2b+3a^4+ab^3+4a^2b$

$= -2a^2b+3a^4+ab^3$

3. $7(12-14)^3-7+3\div(-3)$

$= 7(-2)^3-7-1$

$= 7(-8)-8$

$= -56-8$

$= -64$

4. $y = -\dfrac{3}{4}x+2$

$4y = -3x+8$

$3x = -4y+8$

$x = \dfrac{-4y+8}{3}$

5. $3x-5y=15$

x	y
5	0
0	-3

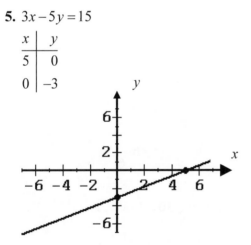

6. $16x^2+24x-16 = 8(2x^2+3x-2)$

$= 8(2x-1)(x+2)$

7. Multiply first equation by -3 and add to second equation; then multiply first equation by -2 and add to third equation.

$$
\begin{array}{rrrrr}
x & +4y & -z & = & 10 \\
3x & +2y & +z & = & 4 \\
2x & -3y & +2z & = & -7
\end{array}
$$

$$
\begin{array}{rrrr}
x & +4y & -z & = & 10 \\
 & -10y & +4z & = & -26 \\
 & -11y & +4z & = & -27
\end{array}
$$

Multiply the second equation by $-\dfrac{11}{10}$ and add to the third equation.

$$
\begin{array}{rrrr}
x & +4y & -z & = & 10 \\
 & -10y & +4z & = & -26 \\
 & & -\dfrac{2}{5}z & = & \dfrac{8}{5}
\end{array}
$$

$-\dfrac{2}{5}z = \dfrac{8}{5}$

$z = -4$, substitute in second equation

$-10y+4(-4) = -26$

$y = 1$, substitute in first equation

$x+4(1)-(-4) = 10$

$x = 2$

$x=2$, $y=1$, $z=-4$ is the solution.

8. $\dfrac{7x}{x^2-2x-15}-\dfrac{2}{x-5}$

$= \dfrac{7x}{(x-5)(x+3)}-\dfrac{2(x+3)}{(x-5)(x+3)}$

$= \dfrac{7x-2x-6}{(x-5)(x+3)}$

$= \dfrac{5x-6}{(x-5)(x+3)}$

© 2006 Pearson Education, Inc., Upper Saddle River, NJ. All rights reserved. This material is protected under all copyright laws as they currently exist. No portion of this material may be reproduced, in any form or by any means, without permission in writing from the publisher.

9. $P = 2L + 2W$

$48 = 2(2W + 3) + 2W$

$24 = 2W + 3 + W$

$3W = 21$

$W = 7$ m for the width

$L = 2W + 3 = 17$ m for the length

10. $2ax - 3b = y - 5ax$

$2ax + 5ax = y + 3b$

$7ax = y + 3b$

$a = \dfrac{y + 3b}{7x}$

11. $\dfrac{2x^{-3}y^{-4}}{4x^{-\frac{5}{2}}y^{\frac{7}{2}}} = \dfrac{1}{2}x^{-3-\left(-\frac{5}{2}\right)}y^{-4-\frac{7}{2}} = \dfrac{1}{2}x^{-\frac{1}{2}}y^{-\frac{15}{2}}$

$= \dfrac{1}{2x^{\frac{1}{2}}y^{\frac{15}{2}}}$

12. $(3x^{-\frac{1}{2}}y^2)^{-\frac{1}{3}} = 3^{-\frac{1}{3}}x^{-\frac{1}{2}\left(-\frac{1}{3}\right)}y^{2\left(-\frac{1}{3}\right)} = \dfrac{x^{\frac{1}{6}}}{3^{\frac{1}{3}}y^{\frac{2}{3}}}$

13. $64^{-\frac{1}{3}} = \dfrac{1}{64^{\frac{1}{3}}} = \dfrac{1}{4}$

14. $\sqrt[3]{40x^5y^9} = \sqrt[3]{8 \cdot 5x^3y^9x^2} = 2xy^3\sqrt[3]{5x^2}$

15. $\sqrt{80x} + 2\sqrt{45x} - 3\sqrt{20x}$

$= \sqrt{16 \cdot 5x} + 2\sqrt{9 \cdot 5x} - 3\sqrt{4 \cdot 5x}$

$= 4\sqrt{5x} + 6\sqrt{5x} - 6\sqrt{5x}$

$= 4\sqrt{5x}$

16. $(2\sqrt{3} - 5\sqrt{2})(\sqrt{3} + 4\sqrt{2})$

$= 6 + 3\sqrt{6} - 40$

$= -34 + 3\sqrt{6}$

17. $\dfrac{\sqrt{3} + 2}{2\sqrt{3} - 5} \cdot \dfrac{2\sqrt{3} + 5}{2\sqrt{3} + 5} = \dfrac{6 + 9\sqrt{3} + 10}{12 - 25}$

$= -\dfrac{16 + 9\sqrt{3}}{13}$

18. $i^{21} + \sqrt{-16} + \sqrt{-49}$

$= (i^4)^5 \cdot i + \sqrt{16}\sqrt{-1} + \sqrt{49}\sqrt{-1}$

$= 1^5 \cdot i + 4i + 7i$

$= 12i$

19. $(3 - 4i)^2 = 3^2 - 2(3)(4i) + (4i)^2$

$= 9 - 24i + 16i^2$

$= 9 - 24i - 16$

$= -7 - 24i$

20. $\dfrac{1 + 4i}{1 + 3i} \cdot \dfrac{1 - 3i}{1 - 3i} = \dfrac{1 + i - 12i^2}{1^2 + 3^2} = \dfrac{13 + i}{10}$

21.

$x - 3 = \sqrt{3x + 1}$

$x^2 - 6x + 9 = 3x + 1$

$x^2 - 9x + 8 = 0$

$(x - 1)(x - 8) = 0$

$x = 1, \quad x = 8$

check: $1 - 3 \overset{?}{=} \sqrt{3(1) + 1}, \quad -2 \neq 2$

$8 - 3 \overset{?}{=} \sqrt{3(8) + 1}, \quad 5 = 5$

$x = 8$ is the solution.

© 2006 Pearson Education, Inc., Upper Saddle River, NJ. All rights reserved. This material is protected under all copyright laws as they currently exist. No portion of this material may be reproduced, in any form or by any means, without permission in writing from the publisher.

22. $1 + \sqrt{x+1} = \sqrt{x+2}$

$1 + 2\sqrt{x+1} + x + 1 = x + 2$

$\sqrt{x+1} = 0$

$x + 1 = 0$

$x = -1$

check: $1 + \sqrt{-1+1} \overset{?}{=} \sqrt{-1+2}, \quad 1 = 1$

$x = -1$ is the solution.

23. $y = kx^2, \ 12 = k \cdot 2^2, \ k = 3$

$y = 3x^2, \ y = 3 \cdot 5^2 = 75$

24. $I = \dfrac{k}{d^2}, \ 120 = \dfrac{k}{10^2}, \ k = 12{,}000$

$I = \dfrac{12{,}000}{d^2}, \ I = \dfrac{12{,}000}{15^2} \approx 53.3 \text{ lumens}$

© 2006 Pearson Education, Inc., Upper Saddle River, NJ. All rights reserved. This material is protected under all copyright laws as they currently exist. No portion of this material may be reproduced, in any form or by any means, without permission in writing from the publisher.

Chapter 8

8.1 Exercises

1. $x^2 = 100$

$$x = \pm\sqrt{100}$$

$$x = \pm 10$$

3. $3x^2 - 45 = 0$

$$3x^2 = 45$$

$$x^2 = 15$$

$$x = \pm\sqrt{15}$$

5. $2x^2 - 80 = 0$

$$2x^2 = 80$$

$$x^2 = 40$$

$$x = \pm\sqrt{40} = \pm\sqrt{4 \cdot 10}$$

$$x = \pm 2\sqrt{10}$$

7. $x^2 = -81$

$$x = \pm 9i$$

9. $x^2 + 81 = 0$

$$x^2 = -81$$

$$x = \pm 9i$$

11. $(x-3)^2 = 12$

$$x - 3 = \pm\sqrt{12} = \pm\sqrt{4 \cdot 3}$$

$$x - 3 = \pm 2\sqrt{3}$$

$$x = 3 \pm 2\sqrt{3}$$

13. $(x+9)^2 = 21$

$$x + 9 = \pm\sqrt{21}$$

$$x = -9 \pm\sqrt{21}$$

15. $(2x+1)^2 = 7$

$$2x + 1 = \pm\sqrt{7}$$

$$2x = -1 \pm\sqrt{7}$$

$$x = \frac{-1 \pm\sqrt{7}}{2}$$

17. $(4x-3)^2 = 36$

$$4x - 3 = \pm 6$$

$$4x = 3 \pm 6$$

$$x = \frac{3 \pm 6}{4}$$

$$x = \frac{9}{4}, \ -\frac{3}{4}$$

19. $(2x+5)^2 = 49$

$$2x + 5 = \pm 7$$

$$2x = -5 \pm 7$$

$$x = \frac{-5 \pm 7}{2}$$

$$x = 1, \ x = -6$$

21. $3x^2 - 5 = 0$

$$x^2 = \frac{5}{3}$$

$$x = \pm\sqrt{\frac{5}{3}} = \pm\frac{\sqrt{15}}{3}$$

23. $\quad x^2 + 10x + 5 = 0$

$$x^2 + 10x + 25 = -5 + 25$$

$$(x+5)^2 = 20$$

$$x + 5 = \pm\sqrt{20} = \pm 2\sqrt{5}$$

$$x = -5 \pm 2\sqrt{5}$$

205

© 2006 Pearson Education, Inc., Upper Saddle River, NJ. All rights reserved. This material is protected under all copyright laws as they currently exist.
No portion of this material may be reproduced, in any form or by any means, without permission in writing from the publisher.

25. $x^2 - 8x = 17$

$x^2 - 8x + 16 = 17 + 16$

$(x - 4)^2 = 33$

$x - 4 = \pm\sqrt{33}$

$x = 4 \pm \sqrt{33}$

27. $x^2 - 14x + 49 = -48 + 49$

$(x - 7)^2 = 1$

$x - 7 = \pm 1$

$x = 7 \pm 1$

$x = 6, \ x = 8$

29. $\dfrac{x^2}{2} + \dfrac{5}{2}x = 2$

$x^2 + 5x + \dfrac{25}{4} = 4 + \dfrac{25}{4}$

$\left(x + \dfrac{5}{2}\right)^2 = \dfrac{41}{4}$

$x + \dfrac{5}{2} = \pm\dfrac{\sqrt{41}}{2}$

$x = \dfrac{-5 \pm \sqrt{41}}{2}$

31. $2y^2 + 10y = -11$

$y^2 + 5y = -\dfrac{11}{2}$

$y^2 + 5y + \dfrac{25}{4} = -\dfrac{11}{2} + \dfrac{25}{4}$

$\left(y + \dfrac{5}{2}\right)^2 = \dfrac{3}{4}$

$y + \dfrac{5}{2} = \pm\dfrac{\sqrt{3}}{2}$

$y = \dfrac{-5 \pm \sqrt{3}}{2}$

33. $3x^2 + 10x - 2 = 0$

$x^2 + \dfrac{10}{3}x - \dfrac{2}{3} = 0$

$x^2 + \dfrac{10}{3}x + \dfrac{25}{9} = \dfrac{2}{3} + \dfrac{25}{9}$

$\left(x + \dfrac{5}{3}\right)^2 = \dfrac{31}{9}$

$x + \dfrac{5}{3} = \pm\dfrac{\sqrt{31}}{3}$

$x = \dfrac{-5 \pm \sqrt{31}}{3}$

35. $2y^2 - y = 6$

$y^2 - \dfrac{1}{2}y = 3$

$y^2 - \dfrac{1}{2}y + \dfrac{1}{16} = 3 + \dfrac{1}{16}$

$\left(y - \dfrac{1}{4}\right)^2 = \dfrac{49}{16}$

$y - \dfrac{1}{4} = \pm\dfrac{7}{4}$

$y = \dfrac{1}{4} \pm \dfrac{7}{4}$

$y = 2, \ y = -\dfrac{3}{2}$

37. $x^2 + 2x - 5 = 0$

$x^2 + 2x + 1 = 5 + 1$

$(x + 1)^2 = 6$

$x + 1 = \pm\sqrt{6}$

$x = -1 \pm \sqrt{6}$

206

© 2006 Pearson Education, Inc., Upper Saddle River, NJ. All rights reserved. This material is protected under all copyright laws as they currently exist. No portion of this material may be reproduced, in any form or by any means, without permission in writing from the publisher.

39. $\dfrac{x^2}{2} - x = 4$

$$x^2 - 2x + 1 = 8 + 1$$
$$(x-1)^2 = 9$$
$$x - 1 = \pm 3$$
$$x = 1 \pm 3$$
$$x = 4,\ x = -2$$

41. $3x^2 + 1 = x$

$$x^2 - \dfrac{1}{3}x + \dfrac{1}{36} = -\dfrac{1}{3} + \dfrac{1}{36}$$
$$x^2 - \dfrac{1}{3}x + \dfrac{1}{36} = -\dfrac{11}{36}$$
$$\left(x - \dfrac{1}{6}\right)^2 = -\dfrac{11}{36}$$
$$x - \dfrac{1}{6} = \pm \dfrac{i\sqrt{11}}{6}$$
$$x = \dfrac{1 \pm i\sqrt{11}}{6}$$

43. $x^2 + 1 = x$

$$x^2 - x + 1 = 0$$
$$x^2 - x + \dfrac{1}{4} = -1 + \dfrac{1}{4}$$
$$\left(x - \dfrac{1}{2}\right)^2 = -\dfrac{3}{4}$$
$$x - \dfrac{1}{2} = \pm \dfrac{i\sqrt{3}}{2}$$
$$x = \dfrac{-1 \pm i\sqrt{3}}{2}$$

45. $2x^2 + 2 = 3x$

$$x^2 - \dfrac{3}{2}x + \dfrac{9}{16} = -1 + \dfrac{9}{16}$$
$$\left(x - \dfrac{3}{4}\right)^2 = -\dfrac{7}{16}$$
$$x - \dfrac{3}{4} = \pm \dfrac{i\sqrt{7}}{4}$$
$$x = \dfrac{3 \pm i\sqrt{7}}{4}$$

47. $x^2 + 2x - 5 = 0$

$$(-1 + \sqrt{6})^2 + 2(-1 + \sqrt{6}) - 5 \overset{?}{=} 0$$
$$1 - 2\sqrt{6} + 6 - 2 + 2\sqrt{6} - 5 \overset{?}{=} 0$$
$$0 = 0$$

49. $(x-7)^2 (8) = 648$

$$(x-7)^2 = 81$$
$$x - 7 = 9$$
$$x = 16$$

51. $L = 4t^2$

$$t = \sqrt{\dfrac{L}{4}}$$
$$t = \sqrt{\dfrac{3.1}{4}} \approx 0.88 \text{ second}$$

53. $D = 16t^2$

$$t = \sqrt{\dfrac{D}{16}}$$
$$t = \sqrt{\dfrac{3600}{16}} = 15 \text{ seconds}$$

Cumulative Review

55. $\sqrt{b^2 - 4ac} = \sqrt{4^2 - 4(3)(-4)} = \sqrt{64} = 8$

© 2006 Pearson Education, Inc., Upper Saddle River, NJ. All rights reserved. This material is protected under all copyright laws as they currently exist. No portion of this material may be reproduced, in any form or by any means, without permission in writing from the publisher.

57. $5x^2 - 6x + 8 = 5(-2)^2 - 6(-2) + 8$
$$= 20 + 12 + 8$$
$$= 40$$

8.2 Exercises

1. Place the quadratic in standard form. Find a, b, and c. Substitute these values into the quadratic formula.

3. If the discriminant in the quadratic formula is zero, then the quadratic equation will have <u>one real</u> solution.

5. $x^2 + x - 5 = 0$
$$a = 1, b = 1, c = -5$$
$$x = \frac{-b \pm \sqrt{b^2 - 4ac}}{2a}$$
$$x = \frac{-1 \pm \sqrt{(1)^2 - 4(1)(-5)}}{2(1)}$$
$$x = \frac{-1 \pm \sqrt{21}}{2}$$

7. $2x^2 + x - 4 = 0$
$$a = 2, b = 1, c = -4$$
$$x = \frac{-b \pm \sqrt{b^2 - 4ac}}{2a}$$
$$x = \frac{-1 \pm \sqrt{1^2 - 4(2)(-4)}}{2(2)}$$
$$x = \frac{-1 \pm \sqrt{33}}{4}$$

9. $\qquad x^2 = \frac{2}{3}x$
$$x^2 - \frac{2}{3}x = 0$$
$$3x^2 - 2x = 0$$
$$a = 3, b = -2, c = 0$$
$$x = \frac{-b \pm \sqrt{b^2 - 4ac}}{2a}$$
$$x = \frac{-(-2) \pm \sqrt{(-2)^2 - 4(3)(0)}}{2(3)}$$
$$x = \frac{2 \pm \sqrt{4}}{6} = \frac{2 \pm 2}{6}$$
$$x = 0, \; x = \frac{2}{3}$$

11. $3x^2 - x - 2 = 0$
$$a = 3, b = -1, c = -2$$
$$x = \frac{-b \pm \sqrt{b^2 - 4ac}}{2a}$$
$$x = \frac{-(-1) \pm \sqrt{(-1)^2 - 4(3)(-2)}}{2(3)}$$
$$x = \frac{1 \pm \sqrt{25}}{6} = \frac{1 \pm 5}{6}$$
$$x = 1, \; x = -\frac{2}{3}$$

13. $4x^2 + 3x - 2 = 0$
$$a = 4, b = 3, c = -2$$
$$x = \frac{-b \pm \sqrt{b^2 - 4ac}}{2a}$$
$$x = \frac{-(3) \pm \sqrt{(3)^2 - 4(4)(-2)}}{2(4)}$$
$$x = \frac{-3 \pm \sqrt{41}}{8}$$

208

© 2006 Pearson Education, Inc., Upper Saddle River, NJ. All rights reserved. This material is protected under all copyright laws as they currently exist. No portion of this material may be reproduced, in any form or by any means, without permission in writing from the publisher.

15. $3x^2 + 1 = 8$

$3x^2 - 7 = 0$

$a = 3, b = 0, c = -7$

$x = \dfrac{-b \pm \sqrt{b^2 - 4ac}}{2a}$

$x = \dfrac{0 \pm \sqrt{0^2 - 4(3)(-7)}}{2(3)}$

$x = \dfrac{\pm\sqrt{84}}{6} = \dfrac{\pm 2\sqrt{21}}{6}$

$x = \dfrac{\pm\sqrt{21}}{3}$

17. $2x(x+3) - 3 = 4x - 2$

$2x^2 + 6x - 4x - 1 = 0$

$2x^2 + 2x - 1 = 0$

$a = 2, b = 2, c = -1$

$x = \dfrac{-b \pm \sqrt{b^2 - 4ac}}{2a}$

$x = \dfrac{-(2) \pm \sqrt{(2)^2 - 4(2)(-1)}}{2(2)}$

$x = \dfrac{-2 \pm \sqrt{12}}{4} = \dfrac{-2 \pm 2\sqrt{3}}{4}$

$x = \dfrac{2(-1 \pm \sqrt{3})}{4} = \dfrac{-1 \pm \sqrt{3}}{2}$

19. $x(x+3) - 2 = 3x + 7$

$x^2 + 3x - 2 = 3x + 7$

$x^2 - 9 = 0$

$a = 1, b = 0, c = -9$

$x = \dfrac{-b \pm \sqrt{b^2 - 4ac}}{2a}$

19. $x = \dfrac{-(0) \pm \sqrt{(0)^2 - 4(1)(-9)}}{2(1)}$

$x = \dfrac{\pm\sqrt{36}}{2} = \dfrac{\pm 6}{2} = \pm 3$

21. $(x-2)(x+1) = \dfrac{2x+3}{2}$

$x^2 - x - 2 = \dfrac{2x+3}{2}$

$2x^2 - 2x - 4 = 2x + 3$

$2x^2 - 4x - 7 = 0$

$a = 2, b = -4, c = -7$

$x = \dfrac{-b \pm \sqrt{b^2 - 4ac}}{2a}$

$x = \dfrac{-(-4) \pm \sqrt{(-4)^2 - 4(2)(-7)}}{2(2)}$

$x = \dfrac{4 \pm \sqrt{72}}{4} = \dfrac{4 \pm 6\sqrt{2}}{4}$

$x = \dfrac{2(2 \pm 3\sqrt{2})}{4} = \dfrac{2 \pm 3\sqrt{2}}{2}$

23. $\dfrac{1}{x+2} + \dfrac{1}{x} = \dfrac{1}{3}$

$3x + 3(x+2) = x(x+2)$

$3x + 3x + 6 = x^2 + 2x$

$x^2 - 4x - 6 = 0$

$a = 1, b = -4, c = -6$

$x = \dfrac{-b \pm \sqrt{b^2 - 4ac}}{2a}$

$x = \dfrac{-(-4) \pm \sqrt{(-4)^2 - 4(1)(-6)}}{2(1)}$

$x = \dfrac{4 \pm \sqrt{40}}{2} = \dfrac{4 \pm 2\sqrt{10}}{2}$

$x = 2 \pm \sqrt{10}$

© 2006 Pearson Education, Inc., Upper Saddle River, NJ. All rights reserved. This material is protected under all copyright laws as they currently exist. No portion of this material may be reproduced, in any form or by any means, without permission in writing from the publisher.

25. $\dfrac{1}{15} + \dfrac{3}{y} = \dfrac{4}{y+1}$

$y(y+1) + 45(y+1) = 60y$

$y^2 + y + 45y + 45 = 60y$

$y^2 - 14y + 45 = 0$

$a = 1, b = -14, c = 45$

$y = \dfrac{-b \pm \sqrt{b^2 - 4ac}}{2a}$

$y = \dfrac{-(-14) \pm \sqrt{(-14)^2 - 4(1)(45)}}{2(1)}$

$y = \dfrac{14 \pm \sqrt{16}}{2} = \dfrac{14 \pm 4}{2}$

$y = 9, \ y = 5$

27. $x(x+4) = -12$

$x^2 + 4x + 12 = 0$

$a = 1, \ b = 4, \ c = 12$

$x = \dfrac{-b \pm \sqrt{b^2 - 4ac}}{2a}$

$x = \dfrac{-4 \pm \sqrt{4^2 - 4(1)(12)}}{2(1)}$

$x = \dfrac{-4 \pm \sqrt{-32}}{2} = \dfrac{-4 \pm 4i\sqrt{2}}{2}$

$x = -2 \pm 2i\sqrt{2}$

29. $2x^2 + 15 = 0$

$a = 2, \ b = 0, c = 15$

$x = \dfrac{-b \pm \sqrt{b^2 - 4ac}}{2a}$

$x = \dfrac{-(0) \pm \sqrt{(0)^2 - 4(2)(15)}}{2(2)}$

29. $x = \dfrac{\pm\sqrt{-120}}{4} = \dfrac{\pm\sqrt{4(30)}\sqrt{-1}}{4}$

$x = \dfrac{\pm 2i\sqrt{30}}{4} = \dfrac{\pm i\sqrt{30}}{2}$

31. $3x^2 - 8x + 7 = 0$

$a = 3, b = -8, c = 7$

$x = \dfrac{-b \pm \sqrt{b^2 - 4ac}}{2a}$

$x = \dfrac{-(-8) \pm \sqrt{(-8)^2 - 4(3)(7)}}{2(3)}$

$x = \dfrac{8 \pm \sqrt{-20}}{6} = \dfrac{8 \pm 2i\sqrt{5}}{6} = \dfrac{4 \pm i\sqrt{5}}{3}$

33. $3x^2 + 4x = 2$

$3x^2 + 4x - 2 = 0$

$a = 3, b = 4, c = -2$

$b^2 - 4ac = 4^2 - 4(3)(-2) = 40$

2 irrational roots

35. $2x^2 + 10x + 8 = 0$

$a = 2, b = 10, c = 8$

$b^2 - 4ac = 10^2 - 4(2)(8) = 36$

2 rational roots

37. $9x^2 + 4 = 12x$

$9x^2 - 12x + 4 = 0$

$a = 9, b = -12, c = 4$

$b^2 - 4ac = (-12)^2 - 4(9)(4) = 0$

1 rational root

39. $7x(x-1) + 15 = 10$

$7x^2 - 7x + 5 = 0$

$a = 7, \ b = -7, \ c = 5$

$b^2 - 4ac = (-7)^2 - 4(7)(5) = -91$

2 nonreal complex roots

210

© 2006 Pearson Education, Inc., Upper Saddle River, NJ. All rights reserved. This material is protected under all copyright laws as they currently exist. No portion of this material may be reproduced, in any form or by any means, without permission in writing from the publisher.

41. $13, -2$

$x = 13, \; x = -2$

$x - 13 = 0, \; x + 2 = 0$

$(x - 13)(x + 2) = 0$

$x^2 - 11x - 26 = 0$

43. $-5, -12$

$x = -5, \; x = -12$

$x + 5 = 0, \; x + 12 = 0$

$(x + 5)(x + 12) = 0$

$x^2 + 17x + 60 = 0$

45. $4i, -4i$

$x = 4i, \; x = -4i$

$x - 4i = 0, \; x + 4i = 0$

$(x - 4i)(x + 4i) = 0$

$x^2 + 16 = 0$

47. $3, -\dfrac{5}{2}$

$x = 3, \; x = -\dfrac{5}{2}$

$x - 3 = 0, \; 2x + 5 = 0$

$(x - 3)(2x + 5) = 0$

$2x^2 - x - 15 = 0$

49. $3x^2 + 5x - 9 = 0$

$x = \dfrac{-5 \pm \sqrt{5^2 - 4(3)(-9)}}{2(3)}$

$x = \dfrac{-5 \pm \sqrt{133}}{6}$

$x = 1.0888, \; x = -2.7554$

51. $0.162x^2 + 0.094x - 0.485 = 0$

$x = \dfrac{-0.094 \pm \sqrt{0.094^2 - 4(0.162)(-0.485)}}{2(0.162)}$

$x = \dfrac{-0.094 \pm \sqrt{0.323116}}{0.324}$

$x = 1.4643, \; x = -2.0445$

53. $p = -100x^2 + 4800x - 54{,}351 = 0$

$x = \dfrac{-4800 \pm \sqrt{4800^2 - 4(-100)(-54{,}351)}}{2(-100)}$

$x = \dfrac{-4800 \pm \sqrt{1{,}299{,}600}}{-200}$

$x = 18.3, \; x = 29.7$

Eighteen or thirty bikes per day will produce a zero profit.

55. $p_{max} = -100(24)^2 + 4800(24) - 54{,}351$

$p_{max} = \$3249$

The maximum profit is \$3249 per day. 24 is the average of 18 and 30.

Cumulative Review

55. $9x^2 - 6x + 3 - 4x - 12x^2 + 8$

$= -3x^2 - 10x + 11$

57. current: $2L + 2W = 50$

$L + W = 25 \Rightarrow L = 25 - W$

new: $2(2L) + 2(3W) = 118$

$4L + 6W = 118$

$4(25 - W) + 6W = 118$

$100 - 4W + 6W = 118$

$2W = 18$

$W = 9$ ft for the width

$L = 25 - W = 16$ ft for the length

211

© 2006 Pearson Education, Inc., Upper Saddle River, NJ. All rights reserved. This material is protected under all copyright laws as they currently exist. No portion of this material may be reproduced, in any form or by any means, without permission in writing from the publisher.

8.3 Exercises

1. $x^4 - 9x^2 + 20 = 0$

$y = x^2$

$y^2 - 9y + 20 = 0$

$(y - 5)(y - 4) = 0$

$y = 5, \ y = 4$

$x^2 = 5, \ x^2 = 4$

$x = \pm\sqrt{5}, \ x = \pm 2$

3. $x^4 + x^2 - 12 = 0$

$y = x^2$

$y^2 + y - 12 = 0$

$(y - 3)(y + 4) = 0$

$y = 3, \ y = -4$

$x^2 = 3, \ x^2 = -4$

$x = \pm\sqrt{3}, \ x = \pm 2i$

5. $3x^4 = 10x^2 + 8$

$3x^4 - 10x^2 - 8 = 0$

$y = x^2$

$3y^2 - 10y - 8 = 0$

$(3y + 2)(y - 4) = 0$

$y = -\dfrac{2}{3}, \ y = 4$

$x^2 = -\dfrac{2}{3}, \ x^2 = 4$

$x = \pm\dfrac{i\sqrt{6}}{3}, \ \ x = \pm 2$

7. $x^6 - 7x^3 - 8 = 0, \ y = x^3$

$y^2 - 7y - 8 = 0$

$(y - 8)(y + 1) = 0$

7. $y = 8, \ y = -1$

$x^3 = 8, \ x^3 = -1$

$x = 2, \ x = -1$

9. $x^6 - 3x^3 = 0$

$y = x^3$

$y^2 - 3y = 0$

$y(y - 3) = 0$

$y = 0, \ y = 3$

$x^3 = 0, \ x^3 = 3$

$x = 0, \ x = \sqrt[3]{3}$

11. $x^8 = 17x^4 - 16$

$x^8 - 17x^4 + 16 = 0$

$y = x^4$

$y^2 - 17y + 16 = 0$

$(y - 16)(y - 1) = 0$

$y = 16, \ y = 1$

$x^4 = 16, \ x^4 = 1$

$x = \pm 2, \ x = \pm 1$

13. $3x^8 + 13x^4 = 10$

$3x^8 + 13x^4 - 10 = 0$

$y = x^4$

$3y^2 + 13y - 10 = 0$

$(3y - 2)(y + 5) = 0$

$y = \dfrac{2}{3}, \ y = -5$

$x^4 = \dfrac{2}{3}, \ x^4 = -5$, no real roots

$x = \pm\dfrac{\sqrt[4]{54}}{3}$

© 2006 Pearson Education, Inc., Upper Saddle River, NJ. All rights reserved. This material is protected under all copyright laws as they currently exist. No portion of this material may be reproduced, in any form or by any means, without permission in writing from the publisher.

15. $x^{\frac{2}{3}} + 2x^{\frac{1}{3}} - 12 = 0$

$y = x^{\frac{1}{3}}$

$y^2 + y - 12 = 0$

$(y+4)(y-3) = 0$

$y = -4, \ y = 3$

$x^{\frac{1}{3}} = -4, \ x^{\frac{1}{3}} = 3$

$x = (-4)^3 = -64, \ x = 3^3 = 27$

$x = -64, \ x = 27$

17. $12x^{\frac{2}{3}} + 5x^{\frac{1}{3}} - 2 = 0$

$y = x^{\frac{1}{3}}$

$12y^2 + 5y - 2 = 0$

$(4y-1)(3y+2) = 0$

$y = \frac{1}{4}, \ y = -\frac{2}{3}$

$x^{\frac{1}{3}} = \frac{1}{4}, \ x^{\frac{1}{3}} = -\frac{2}{3}$

$x = \left(\frac{1}{4}\right)^3, \ x = \left(-\frac{2}{3}\right)^3$

$x = \frac{1}{64}, \ x = -\frac{8}{27}$

19. $2x^{\frac{1}{2}} - 5x^{\frac{1}{4}} - 3 = 0$

$y = x^{\frac{1}{4}}$

$2y^2 - 5y - 3 = 0$

$(2y+1)(y-3) = 0$

$y = -\frac{1}{2}, \ y = 3$

$x^{\frac{1}{4}} = -\frac{1}{2}, \ x = \frac{1}{16}$ (extraneous)

$x^{\frac{1}{4}} = 3, \ x = 3^4 = 81$

21. $2x^{\frac{1}{2}} - x^{\frac{1}{4}} - 6 = 0$

$y = x^{\frac{1}{4}}$

$2y^2 - y - 6 = 0$

$(y-2)(2y+3) = 0$

$y = 2, \ y = -\frac{3}{2}$

$x^{\frac{1}{4}} = 2, \ x^{\frac{1}{4}} = -\frac{3}{2}$

$x = \left(-\frac{3}{2}\right)^4 = \frac{81}{16}$ (extraneous)

$x = 2^4 = 16$

23. $x^{\frac{2}{5}} + x^{\frac{1}{5}} - 2 = 0$

$y = x^{\frac{1}{5}}$

$y^2 + y - 2 = 0$

$(y+2)(y-1) = 0$

$y = -2, \ y = 1$

$x^{\frac{1}{5}} = -2, \ x^{\frac{1}{5}} = 1$

$x = (-2)^5 = -32, \ x = 1^5 = 1$

25. $x^6 - 5x^3 = 14$

$y = x^3$

$y^2 - 5y - 14 = 0$

$(y-7)(y+2) = 0$

$y = 7, \ y = -2$

$x^3 = 7, \ x^3 = -2$

$x = \sqrt[3]{7}, \ x = \sqrt[3]{-2}$

© 2006 Pearson Education, Inc., Upper Saddle River, NJ. All rights reserved. This material is protected under all copyright laws as they currently exist.
No portion of this material may be reproduced, in any form or by any means, without permission in writing from the publisher.

27. $(x^2 + x)^2 - 5(x^2 + x) = -6$

$(x^2 + x)^2 - 5(x^2 + x) + 6 = 0$

$y = (x^2 + x)$

$y^2 - 5y + 6 = 0$

$(y - 2)(y - 3) = 0$

$y = 2, \ y = 3$

$(x^2 + x) = 2, \ (x^2 + x) = 3$

$x^2 + x - 2 = 0, \ x^2 + x - 3 = 0$

$(x + 2)(x - 1) = 0, \ x = \dfrac{-1 \pm \sqrt{1^2 - 4(1)(-3)}}{2(1)}$

$x = -2, \ x = 1, \ x = \dfrac{-1 \pm \sqrt{13}}{2}$

29. $x - 5x^{\frac{1}{2}} + 6 = 0$

$y = x^{\frac{1}{2}}$

$y^2 - 5y + 6 = 0$

$(y - 3)(y - 2) = 0$

$y = 3, \ y = 2$

$x^{\frac{1}{2}} = 3, \ x^{\frac{1}{2}} = 2$

$x = 9, \quad x = 4$

31. $x^{-2} + 3x^{-1} = 0$

$y = x^{-1}$

$y^2 + 3y = 0$

$y(y + 3) = 0$

$y = 0, \ y = -3$

$x^{-1} = -3, \ x^{-1} = 0 \, \text{extraneous}$

$x = -\dfrac{1}{3}$

33. $15 - \dfrac{2x}{x - 1} = \dfrac{x^2}{x^2 - 2x + 1}$

$15 - \dfrac{2x}{x - 1} = \dfrac{x^2}{(x - 1)(x - 1)}$

$15(x - 1)^2 - 2x(x - 1) = x^2$

$15x^2 - 30x + 15 - 2x^2 + 2x = x^2$

$12x^2 - 28x + 15 = 0$

$(6x - 5)(2x - 3) = 0$

$x = \dfrac{5}{6}, \ x = \dfrac{3}{2}$

Cumulative Review Problems

35. $2x + 3y = 5 \overset{\times 5}{\rightarrow} 10x + 15y = 25$

$-5x - 2y = 4 \overset{\times 2}{\rightarrow} \underline{-10x - 4y = \ \ 8}$

$11y = 33$

$y = 3$

$2x + 3(3) = 5$

$2x = -4$

$x = -2$

$(-2, 3)$ is the solution.

37. $3\sqrt{2}(\sqrt{5} - 2\sqrt{6}) = 3\sqrt{10} - 6\sqrt{12}$

$= 3\sqrt{10} - 6\sqrt{4 \cdot 3}$

$= 3\sqrt{10} - 12\sqrt{3}$

39. $\dfrac{28.3 - 16.9}{16.9} = 0.674556213\ldots$

High school graduate: 67.5%

$\dfrac{36.4 - 24.0}{24.0} = 0.51\overline{6}$

Associate's degree: 51.7%

© 2006 Pearson Education, Inc., Upper Saddle River, NJ. All rights reserved. This material is protected under all copyright laws as they currently exist. No portion of this material may be reproduced, in any form or by any means, without permission in writing from the publisher.

39. $\dfrac{50.1-30.1}{30.1}=0.6644518272...$

Bachelor's degree: 66.4%

$\dfrac{87.4-51.1}{51.1}=0.71037182...$

Doctorate: 71.0%

41. $\dfrac{281,500,000-109,000,000}{4063}$

$=42,456.31307$

The average profit per performance was \$42,456.31.

43. $(42,456.31)(7451)$

$=316,341,965.8$

The total profit of *Cats* was \$316,341,965.80.

How Am I Doing? Sections 8.1-8.3

1. $2x^2+3=39$

$2x^2=36$

$x^2=18$

$x=\pm\sqrt{18}$

$x=\pm\sqrt{9\cdot2}$

$x=\pm3\sqrt{2}$

2. $(3x+4)^2=20$

$3x+4=\pm\sqrt{20}$

$3x+4=\pm2\sqrt{5}$

$3x=-4\pm2\sqrt{5}$

$x=\dfrac{-4\pm2\sqrt{5}}{3}$

3. $x^2-8x=-12$

$x^2-8x+16=-12+16$

$(x-4)^2=4$

$x-4=\pm2$

$x=4\pm2$

$x=2,\ x=6$

4. $2x^2-4x-3=0$

$x^2-2x+1=\dfrac{3}{2}+1$

$(x-1)^2=\dfrac{5}{2}$

$x-1=\pm\sqrt{\dfrac{5}{2}\cdot\dfrac{2}{2}}$

$x-1=\pm\sqrt{\dfrac{10}{4}}$

$x-1=\pm\dfrac{\sqrt{10}}{2}$

$x=1\pm\dfrac{\sqrt{10}}{2}=\dfrac{2\pm\sqrt{10}}{2}$

5. $8x^2-2x-7=0$

$x=\dfrac{-b\pm\sqrt{b^2-4ac}}{2a}$

$x=\dfrac{-(-2)\pm\sqrt{(-2)^2-4(8)(-7)}}{2(8)}$

$x=\dfrac{2\pm\sqrt{228}}{16}$

$x=\dfrac{2\pm\sqrt{4\cdot57}}{16}$

$x=\dfrac{2\pm2\sqrt{57}}{16}$

$x=\dfrac{1\pm\sqrt{57}}{8}$

215

© 2006 Pearson Education, Inc., Upper Saddle River, NJ. All rights reserved. This material is protected under all copyright laws as they currently exist. No portion of this material may be reproduced, in any form or by any means, without permission in writing from the publisher.

6. $(x-1)(x+5) = 2$

$x^2 + 4x - 5 = 2$

$x^2 + 4x - 7 = 0$

$x = \dfrac{-b \pm \sqrt{b^2 - 4ac}}{2a}$

$x = \dfrac{-4 \pm \sqrt{4^2 - 4(1)(-7)}}{2(1)}$

$x = \dfrac{-4 \pm \sqrt{44}}{2}$

$x = \dfrac{-4 \pm \sqrt{4 \cdot 11}}{2}$

$x = \dfrac{-4 \pm 2\sqrt{11}}{2}$

$x = -2 \pm \sqrt{11}$

7. $4x^2 = -12x - 17$

$4x^2 + 12x + 17 = 0$

$x = \dfrac{-b \pm \sqrt{b^2 - 4ac}}{2a}$

$x = \dfrac{-12 \pm \sqrt{12^2 - 4 \cdot 4 \cdot 17}}{2 \cdot 4}$

$x = \dfrac{-12 \pm \sqrt{-128}}{8}$

$x = \dfrac{-12 \pm \sqrt{64 \cdot 2}\sqrt{-1}}{8}$

$x = \dfrac{-12 \pm 8i\sqrt{2}}{8}$

$x = \dfrac{-3 \pm 2i\sqrt{2}}{2}$

8. $5x^2 + 4x - 12 = 0$

$x = \dfrac{-b \pm \sqrt{b^2 - 4ac}}{2a}$

$x = \dfrac{-4 \pm \sqrt{4^2 - 4(5)(-12)}}{2(5)}$

$x = \dfrac{-4 \pm \sqrt{256}}{10}$

$x = \dfrac{-4 \pm 16}{10}$

$x = -2, \; x = \dfrac{6}{5}$

9. $7x^2 + 9x = 14x^2 - 3x$

$7x^2 - 12x = 0$

$x = \dfrac{-b \pm \sqrt{b^2 - 4ac}}{2a}$

$x = \dfrac{-(-12) \pm \sqrt{(-12)^2 - 4(7)(0)}}{2(7)}$

$x = \dfrac{12 \pm 12}{14}$

$x = 0, \; \dfrac{12}{7}$

10. $4x^2 - 3x = -6$

$4x^2 - 3x + 6 = 0$

$x = \dfrac{-b \pm \sqrt{b^2 - 4ac}}{2a}$

$x = \dfrac{-(-3) \pm \sqrt{(-3)^2 - 4(4)(6)}}{2(4)}$

$x = \dfrac{3 \pm \sqrt{-87}}{8}$

$x = \dfrac{3 \pm i\sqrt{87}}{8}$

216

© 2006 Pearson Education, Inc., Upper Saddle River, NJ. All rights reserved. This material is protected under all copyright laws as they currently exist. No portion of this material may be reproduced, in any form or by any means, without permission in writing from the publisher.

11. $\dfrac{18}{x} + \dfrac{12}{x+1} = 9$

$18x + 18 + 12x = 9x^2 + 9x$

$9x^2 - 21x - 18 = 0$

$3x^2 - 7x - 6 = 0$

$x = \dfrac{-b \pm \sqrt{b^2 - 4ac}}{2a}$

$x = \dfrac{-(-7) \pm \sqrt{(-7)^2 - 4(3)(-6)}}{2(3)}$

$x = \dfrac{7 \pm \sqrt{121}}{6}$

$x = \dfrac{7 \pm 11}{6}$

$x = 3,\ x = -\dfrac{2}{3}$

12. $\quad x^6 - 7x^3 - 8 = 0$

$(x^3)^2 - 7x^3 - 8 = 0$

$(x^3 - 8)(x^3 + 1) = 0$

$x^3 - 8 = 0,\ x^3 + 1 = 0$

$x^3 = 8 \qquad x^3 = -1$

$x = 2 \qquad x = -1$

13. $w^{\frac{4}{3}} - 6w^{\frac{2}{3}} + 8 = 0$

$(w^{\frac{2}{3}})^2 - 6w^{\frac{2}{3}} + 8 = 0$

$(w^{\frac{2}{3}} - 4)(w^{\frac{2}{3}} - 2) = 0$

$w^{\frac{2}{3}} - 4 = 0, \qquad w^{\frac{2}{3}} - 2 = 0$

$w^2 = 64 \qquad\quad w^2 = 8$

$w = \pm 8 \qquad\quad w^2 = 8$

$\qquad\qquad\qquad\quad w = \pm 2\sqrt{2}$

14. $x^8 = 7x^4 - 12$

$y = x^4$

$y^2 - 7y + 12 = 0$

$(y - 4)(y - 3) = 0$

$y = 4,\ y = 3$

$x^4 = 4,\ x^4 = 3$

$(x^2)^2 = 4,\ (x^2)^2 = 3$

$x^2 = \pm 2,\ x^2 = \pm\sqrt{3}$

$x^2 = 2,\ x^2 = \sqrt{3}$

$x = \pm\sqrt{2},\ x = \pm\sqrt{\sqrt{3}} = \pm\sqrt[4]{3}$

15. $2x^{\frac{2}{5}} = 7x^{\frac{1}{5}} - 3$

$y = x^{\frac{1}{5}}$

$2y^2 - 7y + 3 = 0$

$(2y - 1)(y - 3) = 0$

$y = \dfrac{1}{2},\ y = 3$

$x^{\frac{1}{5}} = \dfrac{1}{2},\ x^{\frac{1}{5}} = 3$

$x = \dfrac{1}{32},\ x = 243$

8.4 Exercises

1. $S = 16t^2$

$t^2 = \dfrac{S}{16}$

$t = \pm\sqrt{\dfrac{S}{16}} = \pm\dfrac{\sqrt{S}}{4}$

© 2006 Pearson Education, Inc., Upper Saddle River, NJ. All rights reserved. This material is protected under all copyright laws as they currently exist. No portion of this material may be reproduced, in any form or by any means, without permission in writing from the publisher.

3. $S = 4\pi r^2$

$$r^2 = \frac{S}{4\pi}$$

$$r = \pm\sqrt{\frac{S}{4\pi}}$$

5. $3H = \frac{1}{2}ax^2$

$$ax^2 = 6H$$

$$x^2 = \frac{6H}{a}$$

$$x = \pm\sqrt{\frac{6H}{a}}$$

7. $4(y^2 + w) - 5 = 7R$

$$4(y^2 + w) = 5 + 7R$$

$$4y^2 + 4w = 5 + 7R$$

$$y^2 = \frac{7R - 4w + 5}{4}$$

$$y = \pm\frac{\sqrt{7R - 4w + 5}}{2}$$

9. $Q = \frac{3mwM^2}{2c}, \quad M^2 = \frac{2Qc}{3mw}$

$$M = \pm\sqrt{\frac{2Qc}{3mw}}$$

11. $V = \pi(r^2 + R^2)h$

$$V = \pi r^2 h + \pi R^2 h$$

$$\pi r^2 h = V - \pi R^2 h$$

$$r^2 = \frac{V - \pi R^2 h}{\pi h}$$

$$r = \pm\sqrt{\frac{V - \pi R^2 h}{\pi h}}$$

13. $7bx^2 - 3ax = 0$

$$x(7bx - 3a) = 0$$

$$x = 0, \; x = \frac{3a}{7b}$$

15. $P = EI - RI^2$

$$RI^2 - EI + P = 0$$

$$a = R, \; b = -E, \; c = P$$

$$I = \frac{-(-E) \pm \sqrt{(-E)^2 - 4RP}}{2R}$$

$$I = \frac{E \pm \sqrt{E^2 - 4RP}}{2R}$$

17. $10w^2 - 3qw - 4 = 0$

$$a = 10, \; b = -3q, \; c = -4$$

$$w = \frac{-(-3q) \pm \sqrt{(-3q)^2 - 4(10)(-4)}}{2(10)}$$

$$w = \frac{3q \pm \sqrt{9q^2 + 160}}{20}$$

19. $S = 2\pi rh + \pi r^2$

$$\pi r^2 + 2\pi hr - S = 0$$

$$a = \pi, \; b = 2\pi h, \; c = -S$$

$$r = \frac{-2\pi h \pm \sqrt{(2\pi h)^2 - 4\pi(-S)}}{2\pi}$$

$$r = \frac{-2\pi h \pm \sqrt{4\pi^2 h^2 + 4\pi S}}{2\pi}$$

$$r = \frac{-2\pi h \pm \sqrt{4\pi^2 h^2 + 4\pi S}}{2\pi}$$

$$r = \frac{-2\pi h \pm 2\sqrt{\pi^2 h^2 + \pi S}}{2\pi}$$

$$r = \frac{-\pi h \pm \sqrt{\pi^2 h^2 + \pi S}}{\pi}$$

© 2006 Pearson Education, Inc., Upper Saddle River, NJ. All rights reserved. This material is protected under all copyright laws as they currently exist. No portion of this material may be reproduced, in any form or by any means, without permission in writing from the publisher.

21. $(a+1)x^2 + 5x + 2w = 0$

$$x = \frac{-5 \pm \sqrt{5^2 - 4(a+1)(2w)}}{2(a+1)}$$

$$x = \frac{-5 \pm \sqrt{25 - 8aw - 8w}}{2a+2}$$

23. $c^2 = a^2 + b^2$

$6^2 = 4^2 + b^2$

$b^2 = 36 - 16 = 20$

$b = \sqrt{20} = 2\sqrt{5}$

25. $c^2 = a^2 + b^2$

$\sqrt{34}^2 = a^2 + \sqrt{19}^2$

$a^2 = 34 - 19$

$a^2 = 15$

$a = \sqrt{15}$

27. $c^2 = a^2 + b^2$

$144 = a^2 + 4a^2 = 5a^2$

$a^2 = \frac{144}{5}$

$a = \sqrt{\frac{144}{5}}$

$a = \frac{12}{\sqrt{5}}$

$a = \frac{12\sqrt{5}}{5}$

$b = 2a = \frac{24\sqrt{5}}{5}$

29. $x^2 + x^2 = 10^2 = 100$

$x^2 = 50$

$x = 5\sqrt{2}$ in. for each leg

31. $W(W + 0.07) = 0.026$

$W^2 + 0.07W - 0.026 = 0$

$$W = \frac{-0.07 + \sqrt{0.07^2 - 4(1)(-0.026)}}{2}$$

$W = 0.13$ mi for the width

$L = W + 0.07 = 0.2$ mi for the length

33. $(2W + 4)W = 126$

$2W^2 + 4W - 126 = 0$

$W^2 + 2w - 63 = 0$

$(W - 7)(W + 9) = 0$

$W = 7$ ft for the width

$L = 2W + 4 = 18$ ft for the length

35. $b =$ base of triangle

$$A = \frac{1}{2}bh = \frac{1}{2}b(2b + 2) = 72$$

$2b^2 + 2b = 144$

$b^2 + b - 72 = 0$

$(b - 8)(b + 9) = 0$

$b - 8 = 0, \ b + 9 = 0, b = -9,$ reject, $b > 0$

$b = 8$ cm, base

$2b + 2 = 18$ cm, altitude

37. $v =$ speed in rain

$$s = vt, \ t = \frac{s}{v} \Rightarrow \frac{225}{v} + \frac{150}{v+5} 8$$

$225(v + 5) + 150v = 8v(v + 5)$

$225v + 1125v + 150v = 8v^2 + 40v$

$8v^2 - 335v - 1125 = 0$

$(v - 45)(8v + 25) = 0$

$v = 45$ mph in the rain

$v + 5 = 50$ mph without the rain

© 2006 Pearson Education, Inc., Upper Saddle River, NJ. All rights reserved. This material is protected under all copyright laws as they currently exist. No portion of this material may be reproduced, in any form or by any means, without permission in writing from the publisher.

39. $t =$ time from home to work

$$1 \text{ hr } 16 \text{ min } = 1 + \frac{16}{60} = \frac{19}{15} \text{ hr}$$

$\dfrac{19}{15} - t =$ time from work to home

The distance from home to work and the distance from work to home are the same.

$$50t = 45\left(\frac{19}{15} - t\right)$$

$$50t = 57 - 45t$$

$$95t = 57$$

$$t = \frac{57}{95} = \frac{3}{5}$$

$$50 \cdot \frac{3}{5} = 30$$

Bob lives 30 miles from his job.

41. $2003 - 1980 = 23$

$$N = 1.11x^2 + 33.39x + 304.09$$

$$N = 1.11(23)^2 + 33.39(23) + 304.09$$

$$N = 1659.25 \text{ thousands}$$

$$N = 1,659,250 \text{ inmates in 2003}$$

43. $N = 1.11x^2 + 33.39x + 304.09$

$1,744,800 = 1744.8 \text{ thousands}$

$$1.11x^2 + 33.39x + 304.09 = 1744.8$$

$$1.11x^2 + 33.39x - 1440.71 = 0$$

$$x = \frac{-33.39 + \sqrt{33.39^2 - 4(1.11)(-1440.71)}}{2(1.11)}$$

$$x = 23.99988462$$

$1980 + 24 = 2004$

The number of inmates will reach 1,744,800 in the year 2004.

45. $w = \dfrac{12b^2}{\dfrac{5}{2}w + \dfrac{7}{2}b + \dfrac{21}{2}}$

$$\frac{5}{2}w^2 + w\left(\frac{7}{2}b + \frac{21}{2}\right) - 12b^2 = 0$$

$$5w^2 + (7b + 21)w - 24b^2 = 0$$

$$w = \frac{-(7b+21) \pm \sqrt{(7b+21)^2 - 4(5)(-24b^2)}}{2(5)}$$

$$w = \frac{-7b - 21 \pm \sqrt{49b^2 + 294b + 441 + 480b^2}}{10}$$

$$w = \frac{-7b - 21 \pm \sqrt{529b^2 + 294b + 441}}{10}$$

Cumulative Review

47. $\dfrac{4}{\sqrt{3x}} \cdot \dfrac{\sqrt{3x}}{\sqrt{3x}}$

$$= \frac{4\sqrt{3x}}{3x}$$

49. $\dfrac{3}{\sqrt{x} + \sqrt{y}} \cdot \dfrac{\sqrt{x} - \sqrt{y}}{\sqrt{x} - \sqrt{y}}$

$$= \frac{3(\sqrt{x} - \sqrt{y})}{x - y}$$

51. $\dfrac{3ab}{\sqrt[3]{8ab^2}} \cdot \dfrac{\sqrt[3]{a^2b}}{\sqrt[3]{a^2b}}$

$$= \frac{3ab\sqrt[3]{a^2b}}{2ab}$$

$$= \frac{3\sqrt[3]{a^2b}}{2}$$

© 2006 Pearson Education, Inc., Upper Saddle River, NJ. All rights reserved. This material is protected under all copyright laws as they currently exist. No portion of this material may be reproduced, in any form or by any means, without permission in writing from the publisher.

8.5 Exercises

1. $f(x) = x^2 - 2x - 8$

$x_{\text{vertex}} = \dfrac{-b}{2a}$

$x_{\text{vertex}} = \dfrac{-(-2)}{2(1)}$

$x_{\text{vertex}} = 1$

$f(x_{\text{vertex}}) = 1^2 - 2(1) - 8$

$y_{\text{vertex}} = -9$

$V(1, -9)$

$f(0) = 0^2 - 2(0) - 8$

$f(0) = -8$

$x^2 - 2x - 8 = 0$

$(x - 4)(x + 2) = 0$

$x = 4, \ x = -2$

$I(0, -8); \ (4, 0); \ (-2, 0)$

3. $f(x) = -x^2 - 4x + 12$

$x_{\text{vertex}} = \dfrac{-b}{2a}$

$x_{\text{vertex}} = \dfrac{-(-4)}{2(-1)}$

$x_{\text{vertex}} = -2$

$f(x_{\text{vertex}}) = -(-2)^2 - 4(-2) + 12$

$f(x_{\text{vertex}}) = 16$

$V(-2, 16)$

$f(0) = -0^2 - 4(0) + 12 = 12$

$-x^2 - 4x + 12 = 0$

$x^2 + 4x - 12 = 0$

$(x - 2)(x + 6) = 0$

$x = 2, \ x = -6$

$I(0, 12); \ (2, 0); \ (-6, 0)$

5. $p(x) = 3x^2 + 12x + 3$

$x_{\text{vertex}} = \dfrac{-b}{2a} = \dfrac{-(12)}{2(3)} = -2$

$f(x_{\text{vertex}}) = 3(-2)^2 + 12(-2) + 3 = -9$

$V(-2, -9)$

$f(0) = 3(0)^2 + 12(0) + 3 = 3$

$3x^2 + 12x + 3 = 0$

$x^2 + 4x + 1 = 0$

$a = 1, \ b = 4, \ c = 1$

$x = \dfrac{-4 \pm \sqrt{4^2 - 4(1)(1)}}{2(1)}$

$x = -0.3, \ x = -3.7$

$I(0, 3); \ (-0.3, 0); \ (-3.7, 0)$

7. $r(x) = -3x^2 - 2x - 6$

$x_{\text{vertex}} = \dfrac{-b}{2a}$

$x_{\text{vertex}} = \dfrac{-(-2)}{2(-3)}$

$x_{\text{vertex}} = -\dfrac{1}{3}$

$f(x_{\text{vertex}}) = -3\left(-\dfrac{1}{3}\right)^2 - 2\left(-\dfrac{1}{3}\right) - 6$

$f(x_{\text{vertex}}) = -\dfrac{17}{3}$

$V\left(-\dfrac{1}{3}, -\dfrac{17}{3}\right)$

$f(0) = -3(0)^2 - 2(0) - 6 = -6$

$-3x^2 - 2x - 6 = 0$

$a = -3, b = -2, c = -6$

$b^2 - 4ac = -68 < 0 \Rightarrow$ no x-intercepts

$I(0, -6)$

© 2006 Pearson Education, Inc., Upper Saddle River, NJ. All rights reserved. This material is protected under all copyright laws as they currently exist. No portion of this material may be reproduced, in any form or by any means, without permission in writing from the publisher.

9. $f(x) = 2x^2 + 2x - 4$

$x_{\text{vertex}} = \dfrac{-b}{2a}$

$x_{\text{vertex}} = \dfrac{-(2)}{2(2)}$

$x_{\text{vertex}} = -\dfrac{1}{2}$

$f(x_{\text{vertex}}) = 2\left(-\dfrac{1}{2}\right)^2 + 2\left(-\dfrac{1}{2}\right) - 4$

$y_{\text{vertex}} = -\dfrac{9}{2}$

$V\left(-\dfrac{1}{2}, -\dfrac{9}{2}\right)$

$f(0) = 2(0)^2 + 2(0) - 4$

$f(0) = -4$

$2x^2 + 2x - 4 = 0$

$x^2 + x - 2 = 0$

$(x-1)(x+2) = 0$

$x = 1, \;\; x = -2$

$I(0,-4); \;\; (1,0); \;\; (-2,0)$

11. $f(x) = x^2 - 6x + 8$

$\dfrac{-b}{2a} = \dfrac{-(-6)}{2(1)} = 3$

$f(3) = 3^2 - 6(3) + 8 = -1$

$V(3,-1)$

$f(0) = 0^2 - 6(0) + 8 = 8$

y-intercept: $(0,8)$

$x^2 - 6x + 8 = 0$

$(x-4)(x-2) = 0$

$x = 4, \;\; x = 2$

x-intercepts: $(4,0), \; (2,0)$

11.

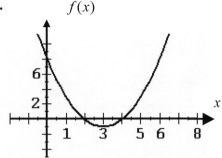

13. $g(x) = x^2 + 2x - 8$

$\dfrac{-b}{2a} = \dfrac{-2}{2} = -1$

$g(-1) = (-1)^2 + 2(-1) - 8 = -9$

$V(-1,-9)$

$g(0) = 0^2 + 2(0) - 8 = -8$

y-intercept: $(0,-8)$

$x^2 + 2x - 8 = 0$

$(x+4)(x-2) = 0$

$x = -4, \;\; x = 2$

x-intercepts: $(-4,0), \; (2,0)$

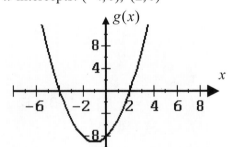

15. $p(x) = -x^2 + 4x - 3$

$\dfrac{-b}{2a} = \dfrac{-4}{2(-1)} = 2$

$p(2) = -2^2 + 4(2) - 3 = 1$

$V(2,1)$

© 2006 Pearson Education, Inc., Upper Saddle River, NJ. All rights reserved. This material is protected under all copyright laws as they currently exist.
No portion of this material may be reproduced, in any form or by any means, without permission in writing from the publisher.

15. $p(0) = -0^2 + 4(0) - 3 = -3$

y-intercept: $(0, -3)$

$-x^2 + 4x - 3 = 0$

$x^2 - 4x + 3 = 0$

$(x - 3)(x - 1) = 0$

$x = 3, \ x = 1$

x-intercepts: $(3, 0), \ (1, 0)$

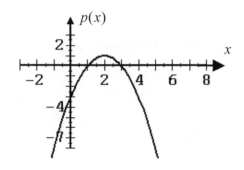

17. $r(x) = 3x^2 + 6x + 4$

$\dfrac{-b}{2a} = \dfrac{-6}{2(3)} = -1$

$r(-1) = 3(-1)^2 + 6(-1) + 4 = 1$

$V(-1, 1)$

$r(0) = 3 \cdot 0^2 + 6(0) + 4 = 4$

y-intercept: $(0, 4)$

$3x^2 + 6x + 4 = 0$

$a = 4, \ b = 6, \ c = 4$

$b^2 - 4ac = 6^2 - 4(4)(4) = -28 < 0$

x-intercepts: none

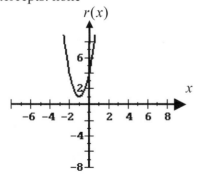

19. $f(x) = x^2 - 6x + 5$

$\dfrac{-b}{2a} = \dfrac{-(-6)}{2(1)} = 3$

$f(3) = 3^2 - 6(3) + 5 = -4$

$V(3, -4)$

$f(0) = 0^2 - 6(0) + 5 = 5$

y-intercept: $(0, 5)$

$x^2 - 6x + 5 = 0$

$(x - 5)(x - 1) = 0$

$x = 5, \ x = 1$

x-intercept: $(5, 0), \ (1, 0)$

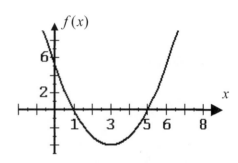

21. $f(x) = x^2 - 4x + 4$

$\dfrac{-b}{2a} = \dfrac{-(-4)}{2(1)} = 2$

$f(2) = 2^2 - 4(2) + 4 = 0$

$V(2, 0)$

$f(0) = 0^2 - 4(0) + 4 = 4$

y-intercept: $(0, 4)$

$x^2 - 4x + 4 = 0$

$(x - 2)(x - 2) = 0$

$x = 2, \ x = 2$

x-intercept: $(2, 0)$

© 2006 Pearson Education, Inc., Upper Saddle River, NJ. All rights reserved. This material is protected under all copyright laws as they currently exist. No portion of this material may be reproduced, in any form or by any means, without permission in writing from the publisher.

21.

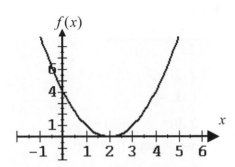

23. $f(x) = x^2 - 4$

$$\frac{-b}{2a} = \frac{-0}{2(1)} = 0$$

$f(0) = 0^2 - 4 = -4$

$V(0, -4)$

$f(0) = 0^2 - 4 = -4$

y-intercept: $(0, -4)$

$x^2 - 4 = 0$

$x^2 = 4$

$x = \pm 2$

x-intercept: $(\pm 2, 0)$

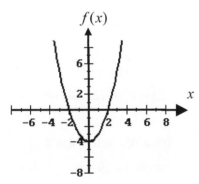

25. $N(x) = 0.18x^2 - 3.18x + 102.25$

$N(20) = 0.18(20)^2 - 3.18(20) + 102.25$

$= 110.65$ thousands

$= 110,650$

25. $N(40) = 0.18(40)^2 - 3.18(40) + 102.25$

$= 263.05$ thousands

$= 263,050$

$N(60) = 0.18(60)^2 - 3.18(60) + 102.25$

$= 559.45$ thousands

$= 559,450$

$N(80) = 0.18(80)^2 - 3.18(80) + 102.25$

$= 999.85$ thousands

$= 999,850$

$N(100) = 0.18(100)^2 - 3.18(100) + 102.25$

$= 1584.25$ thousands

$= 1,584,250$

27. From the graph, $N(70) \approx 750,000$ who scuba dive and have $70,000 mean income.

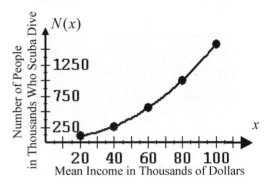

29. From the graph, $N(x) = 390$ for $x \approx 50$. This means that 390,000 people who scuba dive have a mean income of $50,000.

224

© 2006 Pearson Education, Inc., Upper Saddle River, NJ. All rights reserved. This material is protected under all copyright laws as they currently exist. No portion of this material may be reproduced, in any form or by any means, without permission in writing from the publisher.

31. $P(x) = -6x^2 + 312x - 3672$

$P(16) = -6(16)^2 + 312(16) - 3672 = -216$

$P(20) = -6(20)^2 + 312(20) - 3672 = 168$

$P(24) = -6(24)^2 + 312(24) - 3672 = 360$

$P(30) = -6(30)^2 + 312(30) - 3672 = 288$

$P(35) = -6(35)^2 + 312(35) - 3672 = -102$

33. $\dfrac{-b}{2a} = \dfrac{-312}{2(-6)} = 26$

$-6(26)^2 + 312(26) - 3672 = \$384$

26 tablets per day will give a maximum profit of \$384 per day.

35. $P(x) = -6x^2 + 312x - 3672 = 0$

$6x^2 - 312x + 3672 = 0$

$x^2 - 52x + 612 = 0$

$(x - 18)(x - 34) = 0$

$x = 18, \quad x = 34$

18 or **34** tablets per day will give a daily profit of zero dollars.

37. $d(t) = -16t^2 + 32t + 40$

$\dfrac{-b}{2a} = \dfrac{-32}{2(-16)} = 1$

$d(1) = -16(1^2) + 32(1) + 40 = 56$

$-16t^2 + 32t + 40 = 0$

$t = \dfrac{-32 - \sqrt{32^2 - 4(-16)(40)}}{2(-16)}$

$t = 2.870828693...$

The maximum height is 56 feet and the ball will reach the ground about 2.9 seconds after being thrown upward.

39. $y = x^2 - 4.4x + 7.59$

$\dfrac{-b}{2a} = \dfrac{-(-4.4)}{2(1)} = 2.2$

$2.2^2 - 4.4(2.2) + 7.59 = 2.75$

$V(2.2, 2.75)$

$0^2 - 4.4(0) + 7.59$

y-intercept: $(0, 7.59)$

$a = 1, \ b = -4.4, \ c = 7.59$

$b^2 - 4ac = (-4.4)^2 - 4(2)(7.59)$

$b^2 - 4ac = -41.36 < 0$

x-intercepts: none

41. $y = 2.3x^2 - 5.4x - 1.6$

x-intercepts: $(-0.3, 0), \ (2.6, 0)$

© 2006 Pearson Education, Inc., Upper Saddle River, NJ. All rights reserved. This material is protected under all copyright laws as they currently exist. No portion of this material may be reproduced, in any form or by any means, without permission in writing from the publisher.

43. $y = ax^2 + bx + c$

$(0,2) \Rightarrow a(0)^2 + b(0) + c = 2 \Rightarrow c = 2$

$(2,10) \Rightarrow a(2)^2 + b(2) + 2 = 10$

$4a + 2b = 8$ (1)

$(-2,34) \Rightarrow a(-2)^2 + b(-2) + 2 = 34$

$4a - 2b = 32$ (2)

Adding (1) and (2) gives

$8a = 40,\ a = 5$

$4(5) + 2b = 8 \Rightarrow 2b = -12 \Rightarrow b = -6$

$a = 5,\ b = -6,\ c = 2$

Cumulative Review

45. $9x + 5y = 6$

$\underline{2x - 5y = -17}$

$11x \qquad = -11$

$\qquad x = -1$

$9(-1) + 5y = 6$

$\qquad 5y = 15$

$\qquad y = 3$

$(-1, 3)$ is the solution.

47. $3x - y + 2z = 12$

$2x - 3y + z = 5$

$x + 3y + 8z = 22$

Multiply the first equation by $-\dfrac{2}{3}$ and add to the second equation, then

multiply the first equation by $-\dfrac{1}{3}$ and add to the third equation.

47. $3x - y + 2z = 12$

$-\dfrac{7}{3}y - \dfrac{1}{3}z = -3$

$\dfrac{10}{3}y + \dfrac{22}{3}z = 18$

Multiply the second equation

by $\dfrac{10}{7}$ and add to the third quation

$3x - y + 2z = 12$

$-\dfrac{7}{3}y - \dfrac{1}{3}z = -3$

$\dfrac{48}{7}z = \dfrac{96}{7},\ z = 2$

Substitute $z = 2$ into second equation.

$-\dfrac{7}{3}y - \dfrac{1}{3}(2) = -3,\ y = 1$

Substitute $y = 1,\ z = 2$ into first equation.

$3x - 1 + 2(2) = 12,\ x = 3$

$(3, 1, 2)$ is the solution.

8.6 Exercises

1. The critical points divide the number line into regions. All values of x in a given region produce results that are greater than zero, or else all the values of x in a given region produce results that are less than zero.

3. $x^2 + x - 12 < 0$

$x^2 + x - 12 = 0$

$(x + 4)(x - 3) = 0$

$x = -4,\ x = 3$

Critical points: $-4, 3$

© 2006 Pearson Education, Inc., Upper Saddle River, NJ. All rights reserved. This material is protected under all copyright laws as they currently exist. No portion of this material may be reproduced, in any form or by any means, without permission in writing from the publisher.

3. Test: $x^2 + x - 12$

Region	Test	Result
I	−5	$8 > 0$
II	0	$-12 < 0$
III	4	$8 > 0$

$$-4 < x < 3$$

5. $x^2 \geq 4$

$x^2 - 4 \geq 0$

$x^2 - 4 = 0$

$(x+2)(x-2) = 0$

$x = -2, \ x = 2$

Critical points: $-2, 2$

Test: $x^2 - 4$

Region	Test	Result
I	−3	$5 > 0$
II	0	$-4 < 0$
III	3	$5 > 0$

$$x \leq -2 \quad \text{or} \quad x \geq 2$$

7. $2x^2 + x - 3 < 0$

$2x^2 + x - 3 = 0$

$(2x+3)(x-1) = 0$

$x = -\dfrac{3}{2}, \ x = 1$

Critical points: $-\dfrac{3}{2}, 1$

Test: $2x^2 + x - 3$

Region	Test	Result
I	−2	$3 > 0$
II	0	$-3 < 0$
III	2	$7 > 0$

7.

$$-\dfrac{3}{2} < x < 1$$

9. $x^2 + x - 20 > 0$

$x^2 + x - 20 = 0$

$(x+5)(x-4) = 0$

$x = -5, \ x = 4$

Critical points: $-5, 4$

Test: $x^2 + x - 20$

Region	Test	Result
I	−6	$10 > 0$
II	0	$-20 < 0$
III	5	$10 > 0$

$x < -5 \ \text{or} \ x > 4$

11. $8x^2 \leq 2x + 3$

$8x^2 - 2x - 3 \leq 0$

$8x^2 - 2x - 3 = 0$

$(2x+1)(4x-3) = 0$

$x = -\dfrac{1}{2}, \ x = \dfrac{3}{4}$

Critical points: $-\dfrac{1}{2}, \dfrac{3}{4}$

Test: $8x^2 - 2x - 3$

Region	Test	Result
I	−1	$7 > 0$
II	0	$-3 < 0$
III	1	$3 > 0$

$-\dfrac{1}{2} \leq x \leq \dfrac{3}{4}$

227

© 2006 Pearson Education, Inc., Upper Saddle River, NJ. All rights reserved. This material is protected under all copyright laws as they currently exist. No portion of this material may be reproduced, in any form or by any means, without permission in writing from the publisher.

13. $6x^2 - 5x > 6$

$6x^2 - 5x - 6 > 0$

$6x^2 - 5x - 6 = 0$

$(2x - 3)(3x + 2) = 0$

$x = \dfrac{3}{2}, \quad x = -\dfrac{2}{3}$

Critical points: $\dfrac{3}{2}, -\dfrac{2}{3}$

Test: $6x^2 - 5x - 6$

Region	Test	Result
I	-1	$5 > 0$
II	0	$-6 < 0$
III	2	$8 > 0$

$x < -\dfrac{2}{3} \ \text{ or } \ x > \dfrac{3}{2}$

15. $-2x + 30 \geq x(x + 5)$

$-2x + 30 \geq x^2 + 5x$

$0 \geq x^2 + 7x - 30$

$x^2 + 7x - 30 \leq 0$

$x^2 + 7x - 30 = 0$

$(x + 10)(x - 3) = 0$

$x = -10, \quad x = 3$

Critical points: $-10, 3$

Test: $x^2 + 7x - 30$

Region	Test	Result
I	-12	$30 > 0$
II	0	$-30 < 0$
III	5	$30 > 0$

$-10 \leq x \leq 3$

17. $x^2 - 2x \geq -1$

$x^2 - 2x + 1 \geq 0$

$(x - 1)^2 \geq 0$

All real numbers satisfy this inequality.

19. $x^2 - 4x \leq -4$

$x^2 - 4x + 4 \leq 0$

$x^2 - 4x + 4 = 0$

$(x - 2)(x - 2) = 0$

Critical point: 2

Test: $x^2 - 4x + 4$

Region	Test	Result
I	0	$4 > 0$
II	3	$1 > 0$

$x = 2$

21. $x^2 - 2x > 4$

$x^2 - 2x - 4 > 0$

$x^2 - 2x - 4 = 0$

$a = 1, \ b = -2, \ c = -4$

$x = \dfrac{-(-2) \pm \sqrt{(-2)^2 - 4(1)(-4)}}{2(1)}$

$x = \dfrac{2 \pm \sqrt{20}}{2} = 1 \pm \sqrt{5}$

$x \approx 3.2, -1.2$

Approximate critical points: $3.2, -1.2$

Test: $x^2 - 2x - 4$

Region	Test	Result
I	-2	$4 > 0$
II	0	$-4 < 0$
III	4	$4 > 0$

$x < 1 - \sqrt{5} \approx -1.2 \ \text{ or } \ x > 1 + \sqrt{5} \approx 3.2$

© 2006 Pearson Education, Inc., Upper Saddle River, NJ. All rights reserved. This material is protected under all copyright laws as they currently exist. No portion of this material may be reproduced, in any form or by any means, without permission in writing from the publisher.

23. $x^2 - 6x < -7$

$x^2 - 6x + 7 < 0$

$x^2 - 6x + 7 = 0$

$a = 1, \ b = -6, \ c = 7$

$x = \dfrac{-(-6) \pm \sqrt{(-6)^2 - 4(1)(7)}}{2(1)}$

$x = \dfrac{6 \pm \sqrt{8}}{2}$

$x \approx 4.4, \ 1.6$

Approximate critical points: 4.4, 1.6

Test: $x^2 - 6x + 7$

Region	Test	Result
I	0	$7 > 0$
II	2	$-1 < 0$
III	5	$2 > 0$

$1.6 \approx 3 - \sqrt{2} < x < 3 + \sqrt{2} \approx 4.4$

25. $2x^2 \geq x^2 - 4$

$x^2 \geq -4$

All real numbers satisfy this inequality.

27. $5x^2 \leq 4x^2 - 1$

$x^2 \leq -1$

No real number satisfies this inequality.

29. $s = -16t^2 + 640t$

$-16t^2 + 640t > 6000$

$t^2 - 40t + 375 < 0$

$t^2 - 40t + 375 = 0$

$(t - 15)(t - 25) = 0$

$t = 15, \ t = 25$

29. Critical points: 15, 25

Test: $t^2 - 40t + 375$

Region	Test	Result
I	0	$375 > 0$
II	20	$-25 < 0$
III	30	$75 > 0$

$15 < t < 25$

The height will be greater than 6000 feet for times between 15 and 25 seconds.

31. Profit $= -20(x^2 - 220x + 2400)$

$-20(x^2 - 220x + 2400) > 0$

$x^2 - 220x + 2400 < 0$

$x^2 - 220x + 2400 = 0$

$x = \dfrac{220 \pm \sqrt{38,800}}{2} \approx 208.5, \ 11.5$

Approximate critical points: 208.4, 11.5

Test: $x^2 - 220x + 2400$

Region	Test	Result
I	0	$2400 > 0$
II	20	$-1600 < 0$
III	300	$26,400 > 0$

$\approx 11.5 < x < 208.5$

(a) The profit will be greater than zero for production levels between approximately 11.5 and 208.5 units.

(b) $-20(50^2 - 220(50) + 2400)$

$= 122,000$

The daily profit is \$122,000 when 50 units are manufactured.

(c) $-20(60^2 - 220(60) + 2400)$

$= 144,000$

The daily profit is \$144,000 when 60 units are manufactured.

© 2006 Pearson Education, Inc., Upper Saddle River, NJ. All rights reserved. This material is protected under all copyright laws as they currently exist. No portion of this material may be reproduced, in any form or by any means, without permission in writing from the publisher.

Cumulative Review

33. $\dfrac{0+81+92+80+\ E5\ +\ E6}{6} \geq 70$

E5 + E6 ≥ 420 − 253

E5 + E6 ≥ 167

She must score a combined total of 167 points on the two remaining tests. Any two scores that total 167 will be sufficient to participate in synchronized swimming.

35. $10(18)+14(10)+5(16)=\$400$, 2-hr trip

$10(22)+14(12)+5(19)=\$483$, 4-hr trip

Putting Your Skills to Work

1. $P(x)=0.046x^2+1.58x+150.4$

$P(0)=0.046(0)^2+1.58(0)+150.4$

$P(0)=150.4$

$P(15)=0.046(15)^2+1.58(15)+150.4$

$P(15)=184.45$

2. $P(x)=0.046x^2+1.58x+150.4$

$P(10)=0.046(10)^2+1.58(10)+150.4$

$P(10)=170.8$

$P(20)=0.046(20)^2+1.58(20)+150.4$

$P(20)=200.4$

3.

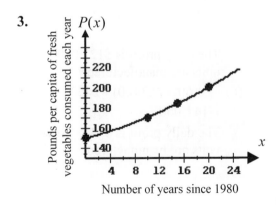

Number of years since 1980

4. $P(15)\approx184$

5. $P(22)-P(10)$

$=0.046(22)^2+1.58(22)+150.4$

$\quad-(0.046(10)^2+1.58(10)+150.4)$

$=36.62$ lb

6. $P(18)-P(0)$

$=0.046(18)^2+1.58(18)+150.4$

$\quad-(0.046(0)^2+1.58(0)+150.4)$

$=43.34$ lb

7. $P(x)=0.046x^2+1.58x+150.4$

$0.046x^2+1.58x+150.4=230.7$

$0.046x^2+1.58x-80.3=0$

$x=\dfrac{-1.58+\sqrt{1.58^2-4(0.046)(-80.3)}}{2(0.046)}$

$x=28$

$1980+28=2008$ when level is 230.7 lb

8. $P(x)=0.046x^2+1.58x+150.4$

$0.046x^2+1.58x+150.4=239.2$

$0.046x^2+1.58x-88.8=0$

$x=\dfrac{-1.58+\sqrt{1.58^2-4(0.046)(-88.8)}}{2(0.046)}$

$x=30$

$1980+30=2010$ when level is 239.2 lb

Chapter 8 Review Problems

1. $6x^2=24$

$x^2=4$

$x=\pm2$

230

© 2006 Pearson Education, Inc., Upper Saddle River, NJ. All rights reserved. This material is protected under all copyright laws as they currently exist. No portion of this material may be reproduced, in any form or by any means, without permission in writing from the publisher.

2. $(x+8)^2 = 81$

$$x+8 = \pm 9$$
$$x = -8 \pm 9$$
$$x = 1, \; x = -17$$

3. $x^2 + 8x + 13 = 0$

$$x^2 + 8x + 16 = -13 + 16$$
$$(x+4)^2 = 3$$
$$x + 4 = \pm\sqrt{3}$$
$$x = -4 \pm \sqrt{3}$$

4. $4x^2 - 8x + 1 = 0$

$$x^2 - 2x + 1 = -\frac{1}{4} + 1$$
$$(x-1)^2 = \frac{3}{4}$$
$$x - 1 = \pm\frac{\sqrt{3}}{2}$$
$$x = 1 \pm \frac{\sqrt{3}}{2}$$

5. $3x^2 - 10x + 6 = 0$

$$a = 3, \; b = -10, \; c = 6$$
$$x = \frac{-(-10) \pm \sqrt{(-10)^2 - 4(3)(6)}}{2(3)}$$
$$x = \frac{10 \pm \sqrt{28}}{6}$$
$$x = \frac{10 \pm \sqrt{4 \cdot 7}}{6}$$
$$x = \frac{5 \pm \sqrt{7}}{3}$$

6. $x^2 - 6x - 4 = 0$

$$a = 1, \; b = -6, \; c = -4$$
$$x = \frac{-(-6) \pm \sqrt{(-6)^2 - 4(1)(-4)}}{2(1)}$$
$$x = \frac{6 \pm \sqrt{52}}{2} = \frac{6 \pm \sqrt{4 \cdot 13}}{2}$$
$$x = 3 \pm \sqrt{13}$$

7. $4x^2 - 12x + 9 = 0$

$$(2x-3)^2 = 0$$
$$2x - 3 = 0$$
$$x = \frac{3}{2}$$

8. $\quad x^2 - 14 = 5x$

$$x^2 - 5x - 14 = 0$$
$$(x-7)(x+2) = 0$$
$$x = 7, \; x = -2$$

9. $6x^2 - 23x = 4x$

$$6x^2 - 27x = 0$$
$$3x(2x - 9) = 0$$
$$3x = 0, \; 2x - 9 = 0$$
$$x = 0, \; x = \frac{9}{2}$$

10. $\quad 2x^2 = 5x - 1$

$$2x^2 - 5x + 1 = 0$$
$$x = \frac{-b \pm \sqrt{b^2 - 4ac}}{2a}$$
$$x = \frac{-(-5) \pm \sqrt{(-5)^2 - 4(2)(1)}}{2(2)}$$
$$x = \frac{5 \pm \sqrt{17}}{4}$$

231

© 2006 Pearson Education, Inc., Upper Saddle River, NJ. All rights reserved. This material is protected under all copyright laws as they currently exist. No portion of this material may be reproduced, in any form or by any means, without permission in writing from the publisher.

11. $x^2 - 3x - 23 = 5$

$x^2 - 3x - 28 = 0$

$(x - 7)(x + 4) = 0$

$x - 7 = 0, \ x + 4 = 0$

$x = 7, \ x = -4$

12. $5x^2 - 10 = 0$

$5x^2 = 10$

$x^2 = 2$

$x = \pm\sqrt{2}$

13. $3x^2 - 2x = 15x - 10$

$3x^2 - 17x + 10 = 0$

$(3x - 2)(x - 5) = 0$

$3x - 2 = 0, \ x - 5 = 0$

$3x - 2 = 0, \ x - 5 = 0$

$x = \dfrac{2}{3}, \ x = 5$

14. $6x^2 + 12x - 24 = 0$

$x^2 + 2x - 4 = 0$

$a = 1, \ b = 2, \ c = -4$

$x = \dfrac{-2 \pm \sqrt{2^2 - 4(1)(-4)}}{2(1)}$

$x = \dfrac{-2 \pm \sqrt{20}}{2} = \dfrac{-2 \pm \sqrt{4 \cdot 5}}{2}$

$x = -1 \pm \sqrt{5}$

15. $7x^2 + 24 = 5x^2$

$2x^2 = -24$

$x^2 = -12$

$x = \pm i \sqrt{4 \cdot 3}$

$x = \pm 2i\sqrt{3}$

16. $3x^2 + 5x + 1 = 0$

$a = 3, \ b = 5, \ c = 1$

$x = \dfrac{-5 \pm \sqrt{5^2 - 4(3)(1)}}{2(3)}$

$x = \dfrac{-5 \pm \sqrt{13}}{6}$

17. $3x(3x + 2) - 2 = 3x$

$9x^2 + 6x - 2 - 3x = 0$

$9x^2 + 3x - 2 = 0$

$(3x + 2)(3x - 1) = 0$

$3x + 2 = 0, \ 3x - 1 = 0$

$x = -\dfrac{2}{3}, \ x = \dfrac{1}{3}$

18. $10x(x - 2) + 10 = 2x$

$10x^2 - 20x + 10 - 2x = 0$

$10x^2 - 22x + 10 = 0$

$5x^2 - 11x + 5 = 0$

$a = 5, \ b = -11, \ c = 5$

$x = \dfrac{-(-11) \pm \sqrt{(-11)^2 - 4(5)(5)}}{2(5)}$

$x = \dfrac{11 \pm \sqrt{21}}{10}$

19. $\dfrac{x - 5}{x} + 9x = 1$

$x - 5 + 9x^2 = x$

$9x^2 = 5$

$x^2 = \dfrac{5}{9}$

$x = \pm\sqrt{\dfrac{5}{9}} = \pm\dfrac{\sqrt{5}}{3}$

© 2006 Pearson Education, Inc., Upper Saddle River, NJ. All rights reserved. This material is protected under all copyright laws as they currently exist. No portion of this material may be reproduced, in any form or by any means, without permission in writing from the publisher.

20. $\dfrac{4}{5}x^2 + x + \dfrac{1}{5} = 0$

$4x^2 + 5x + 1 = 0$

$(4x+1)(x+1) = 0$

$4x+1 = 0, \; x+1 = 0$

$x = -\dfrac{1}{4}, \; x = -1$

21. $y + \dfrac{5}{3y} + \dfrac{17}{6} = 0$

$6y^2 + 10 + 17y = 0$

$6y^2 + 17y + 10 = 0$

$(6y+5)(y+2) = 0$

$6y+5 = 0, \; y+2 = 0$

$y = -\dfrac{5}{6}, \; y = -2$

22. $\dfrac{19}{y} - \dfrac{15}{y^2} + 10 = 0$

$19y - 15 + 10y^2 = 0$

$10y^2 + 19y - 15 = 0$

$(2y+5)(5y-3) = 0$

$2y+5 = 0, \; 5y-3 = 0$

$y = -\dfrac{5}{2}, \; y = \dfrac{3}{5}$

23. $\dfrac{15}{y^2} - \dfrac{2}{y} = 1$

$15 - 2y = y^2$

$y^2 + 2y - 15 = 0$

$(y+5)(y-3) = 0$

$y+5 = 0, \; y-3 = 0$

$y = -5, \; y = 3$

24. $y - 18 + \dfrac{81}{y} = 0$

$y^2 - 18y + 81 = 0$

$(y-9)^2 = 0$

$y - 9 = 0$

$y = 9$

25. $(3y+2)(y-1) = 7(-y+1)$

$3y^2 - y - 2 = -7y + 7$

$3y^2 + 6y - 9 = 0$

$y^2 + 2y - 3 = 0$

$(y+3)(y-1) = 0$

$y+3 = 0, \; y-1 = 0$

$y = -3, \; y = 1$

26. $y(y+1) + (y+2)^2 = 4$

$y^2 + y + y^2 + 4y + 4 = 4$

$2y^2 + 5y = 0$

$y(2y+5) = 0$

$y = 0, \; 2y+5 = 0$

$y = 0, \; y = -\dfrac{5}{2}$

27. $\dfrac{2x}{x+3} + \dfrac{3x-1}{x+1} = 3$

$2x(x+1) + (3x-1)(x+3) = 3(x+3)(x+1)$

$2x^2 + 2x + 3x^2 + 8x - 3 = 3x^2 + 12x + 9$

$2x^2 - 2x - 12 = 0$

$x^2 - x - 6 = 0$

$(x-3)(x+2) = 0$

$x-3 = 0, \; x+2 = 0$

$x = 3, \; x = -2$

© 2006 Pearson Education, Inc., Upper Saddle River, NJ. All rights reserved. This material is protected under all copyright laws as they currently exist.
No portion of this material may be reproduced, in any form or by any means, without permission in writing from the publisher.

28. $\dfrac{4x+1}{2x+5} + \dfrac{3x}{x+4} = 2$

$(4x+1)(x+4) + 3x(2x+5) = 2(2x+5)(x+4)$

$4x^2 + 17x + 4 + 6x^2 + 15x = 4x^2 + 26x + 40$

$6x^2 + 6x - 36 = 0$

$x^2 + x - 6 = 0$

$(x+3)(x-2) = 0$

$x + 3 = 0,\ x - 2 = 0$

$x = -3,\ x = 2$

29. $2x^2 + 5x - 3 = 0$

$a = 2,\ b = 5,\ c = -3$

$b^2 - 4ac = 5^2 - 4(2)(-3) = 49 = 7^2$

Two rational solutions.

30. $3x^2 - 7x - 12 = 0$

$a = 3, b = -7, c = -12$

$b^2 - 4ac = (-7)^2 - 4(3)(-12) = 193$

Two irrational solutions.

31. $3x^2 - 5x + 6 = 0$

$a = 3,\ b = -5,\ c = 6$

$b^2 - 4ac = (-5)^2 - 4(3)(6) = -4$

Two nonreal complex solutions.

32. $25x^2 - 20x + 4 = 0$

$a = 25, b = -20, c = 4$

$b^2 - 4ac = (-20)^2 - 4(25)(4) = 0$

One rational solution.

33. $5,\ -5$

$x = 5,\ x = -5$

$x - 5 = 0,\ x + 5 = 0$

$(x-5)(x+5) = 0$

$x^2 - 25 = 0$

34. $3i,\ -3i$

$x = 3i,\ x = -3i$

$x - 3i = 0,\ x + 3i = 0$

$(x - 3i)(x + 3i) = 0$

$x^2 - 9i^2 = 0$

$x^2 + 9 = 0$

35. $4\sqrt{2},\ -4\sqrt{2}$

$x = 4\sqrt{2},\ x = -4\sqrt{2}$

$x - 4\sqrt{2} = 0,\ x + 4\sqrt{2} = 0$

$(x - 4\sqrt{2})(x + 4\sqrt{2}) = 0$

$x^2 - (4\sqrt{2})(4\sqrt{2}) = 0$

$x^2 - 32 = 0$

36. $-\dfrac{3}{4},\ -\dfrac{1}{2}$

$x = -\dfrac{3}{4},\ x = -\dfrac{1}{2}$

$4x = -3,\ 2x = -1$

$4x + 3 = 0,\ 2x + 1 = 0$

$(4x + 3)(2x + 1) = 0$

$8x^2 + 10x + 3 = 0$

37. $x^4 - 6x^2 + 8 = 0$

$y = x^2$

$y^2 - 6y + 8 = 0$

$(y - 4)(y - 2) = 0$

$y - 4 = 0, y - 2 = 0$

$y = 4,\ y = 2,$

$x^2 = 4,\ x^2 = 2$

$x = \pm 2,\ x = \pm\sqrt{2}$

© 2006 Pearson Education, Inc., Upper Saddle River, NJ. All rights reserved. This material is protected under all copyright laws as they currently exist. No portion of this material may be reproduced, in any form or by any means, without permission in writing from the publisher.

38. $2x^6 - 5x^3 - 3 = 0$

$y = x^3$

$2y^2 - 5y - 3 = 0$

$(2y + 1)(y - 3) = 0$

$2y + 1 = 0, \ y - 3 = 0$

$y = -\dfrac{1}{2}, \ y = 3$

$x^3 = -\dfrac{1}{2}, \ x^2 = 3$

$x = -\sqrt[3]{\dfrac{1}{2}} = -\dfrac{\sqrt[3]{4}}{2}, \ x = \sqrt[3]{3}$

39. $x^{\frac{2}{3}} - 3 = 2x^{\frac{1}{3}}$

$x^{\frac{2}{3}} - 2x^{\frac{1}{3}} - 3 = 0$

$y = x^{\frac{1}{3}}$

$y^2 - 2y - 3 = 0$

$(y - 3)(y + 1) = 0$

$y = 3, \ y = -1$

$x^{\frac{1}{3}} = 3, \ x^{\frac{1}{3}} = -1$

$x = 27, \ x = -1$

40. $3x - x^{\frac{1}{2}} = 2$

$3x - x^{\frac{1}{2}} - 2 = 0$

$y = x^{\frac{1}{2}}$

$3y^2 - y - 2 = 0$

$(3y + 2)(y - 1) = 0$

$y = -\dfrac{2}{3}, \ y = 1$

$x^{\frac{1}{2}} = 1, \ x^{\frac{1}{2}} = -\dfrac{2}{3}$ extraneous

$x = 1$

41. $(2x - 5)^2 + 4(2x - 5) + 3 = 0$

$y = 2x - 5$

$y^2 + 4y + 3 = 0$

$(y + 3)(y + 1) = 0$

$y + 3 = 0, \ y + 1 = 0$

$y = -3, \ y = -1$

$2x - 5 = -3, \ 2x - 5 = -1$

$2x = 2, \ 2x = 4$

$x = 1, \ x = 2$

42. $1 + 4x^{-8} = 5x^{-4}$

$x^8 + 4 = 5x^4$

$x^8 - 5x^4 + 4 = 0$

$y = x^4$

$y^2 - 5y + 4 = 0$

$(y - 4)(y - 1) = 0$

$y - 4 = 0, \ y - 1 = 0$

$y = 4, \ y = 1$

$x^4 = 4, \ x^4 = 1$

$x = \pm 4^{\frac{1}{4}} = \pm (2^2)^{\frac{1}{4}}, \ x = \pm 1$

$x = \pm \sqrt{2}, \ x = \pm 1$

43. $3M = \dfrac{2A^2}{N}$

$A^2 = \dfrac{3MN}{2}$

$A = \pm \sqrt{\dfrac{3MN}{2}}$

44. $3t^2 + 4b = t^2 + 6ay$

$2t^2 = 6ay - 4b$

$t^2 = 3ay - 2b$

$t = \pm \sqrt{3ay - 2b}$

© 2006 Pearson Education, Inc., Upper Saddle River, NJ. All rights reserved. This material is protected under all copyright laws as they currently exist. No portion of this material may be reproduced, in any form or by any means, without permission in writing from the publisher.

45. $yx^2 - 3x - 7 = 0$

$a = y, \ b = -3, \ c = -7$

$x = \dfrac{-(-3) \pm \sqrt{(-3)^2 - 4(y)(-7)}}{2y}$

$x = \dfrac{3 \pm \sqrt{9 + 28y}}{2y}$

46. $20d^2 - xd - x^2 = 0$

$(4d - x)(5d + x) = 0$

$4d - x = 0, \ 5d + x = 0$

$d = \dfrac{x}{4}, \ d = -\dfrac{x}{5}$

47. $3y^2 - 4ay + 2a = 0$

$y = \dfrac{-(-4a) \pm \sqrt{(-4a)^2 - 4(3)(2a)}}{2(3)}$

$y = \dfrac{4a \pm \sqrt{16a^2 - 24a}}{6}$

$y = \dfrac{4a \pm \sqrt{4(4a^2 - 6a)}}{6}$

$y = \dfrac{4a \pm 2\sqrt{4a^2 - 6a}}{6}$

$y = \dfrac{2a \pm \sqrt{4a^2 - 6a}}{3}$

48. $PV = 5x^2 + 3y^2 + 2x$

$5x^2 + 2x + 3y^2 - PV = 0$

$a = 5, \ b = 2, \ c = 3y^2 - PV$

$x = \dfrac{-2 \pm \sqrt{2^2 - 4(5)(3y^2 - PV)}}{2(5)}$

$x = \dfrac{-2 \pm \sqrt{4(1 - 15y^2 + 5PV)}}{10}$

48. $x = \dfrac{-2 \pm 2\sqrt{1 - 15y^2 + 5PV}}{10}$

$x = \dfrac{-1 \pm \sqrt{1 - 15y^2 + 5PV}}{5}$

49. $c^2 = a^2 + b^2 = (3\sqrt{2})^2 + 2^2$

$c^2 = 18 + 4 = 22$

$c = \sqrt{22}$

50. $c^2 = a^2 + b^2$

$16^2 = a^2 + 4^2$

$a^2 = 256 - 16 = 240 = 16(15)$

$a = 4\sqrt{15}$

51. $c^2 = a^2 + b^2$

$6^2 = 5^2 + b^2$

$b^2 = 36 - 25 = 11$

$b = \sqrt{11} \approx 3.3$

The car is approximately 3.3 miles from the observer.

52. $A = \dfrac{1}{2}bh = 70$

$b(2b + 6) = 140$

$2b^2 + 6b - 140 = 0$

$b^2 + 3b - 70 = 0$

$(b - 7)(b + 10) = 0$

$b - 7 = 0, \ b + 10 = 0$

$b = 7, \ b = -10$ reject, $b > 0$

$h = 2b + 6 = 20$

The base is 7 cm and the altitude is 20 cm.

© 2006 Pearson Education, Inc., Upper Saddle River, NJ. All rights reserved. This material is protected under all copyright laws as they currently exist. No portion of this material may be reproduced, in any form or by any means, without permission in writing from the publisher.

53. $A = LW = 203$

$(4W + 1)W = 203$

$4W^2 + W - 203 = 0$

$(W - 7)(4W + 29) = 0$

$W - 7 = 0, \ 4W + 29 = 0$

$W = 7, \ W = -\dfrac{29}{4}$ reject, $W > 0$

$L = 4W + 1 = 29$

The width is 7 m and the length is 29 m.

54. $v = $ cruising speed

$60 = vt_1 \Rightarrow t_1 = \dfrac{60}{v}$

$5 = (v - 15)t_2 \Rightarrow t_2 = \dfrac{5}{v - 15}$

$t_1 + t_2 = \dfrac{60}{v} + \dfrac{5}{v - 15} = 4$

$60(v - 15) + 5v = 4v(v - 15)$

$60v - 900 + 5v = 4v^2 - 60v$

$4v^2 - 125v + 900 = 0$

$(v - 20)(4v - 45) = 0$

$v - 20 = 0, \ 4v - 45 = 0$

$v = 20, \ v = \dfrac{45}{4} = 11.25$ reject, $v > 15$

$v - 15 = 5$

The cruising speed is 20 mph and the trolling speed is 5 mph.

55. $v = $ speed with no rain

$200 = vt_1 \Rightarrow t_1 = \dfrac{200}{v}$

$90 = (v - 5)t_2 \Rightarrow t_2 = \dfrac{90}{v - 5}$

$t_1 + t_2 = \dfrac{200}{v} + \dfrac{90}{v - 5} = 6$

$200(v - 5) + 90v = 6v(v - 5)$

$200v - 1000 + 90v = 6v^2 - 30v$

55. $6v^2 - 320v + 1000 = 0$

$(v - 50)(6v - 20) = 0$

$v - 50 = 0, \ 6v - 20 = 0$

$v = 50, \ v = \dfrac{10}{3}$ reject, $v > 5$

$v - 5 = 45$

The speed before the rain was 50 mph and 45 mph in the rain.

56. $(10 + 2x)(6 + 2x) - 10(6) = 100$

$60 + 32x + 4x^2 - 60 = 100$

$4x^2 + 32x - 100 = 0$

$x^2 + 8x - 25 = 0$

$x = \dfrac{-8 + \sqrt{8^2 - 4(1)(-25)}}{2} \approx 2.4$

The walkway should be approximately 2.4 feet wide.

57. $(40 + 2x)(30 + 2x) - 40(3) = 296$

$1200 + 140x + 4x^2 - 1200 = 296$

$4x^2 + 140x - 296 = 0$

$x^2 + 35x - 74 = 0$

$(x - 2)(x + 37) = 0$

$x = 2, \ x = -37$ reject, $x > 0$

The walkway should be 2 feet wide.

58. $g(x) = -x^2 + 6x - 11$

$\dfrac{-b}{2a} = \dfrac{-6}{2(-1)} = 3$

$g(3) = -3^2 + 6(3) - 11 = -2$

$V(3, -2)$

$g(0) = -0^2 + 6(0) - 11 = -11$

y-intercept: $(0, -11)$

$b^2 - 4ac = 6^2 - 4(-1)(-11) = -8 < 0$

x-intercepts: none

© 2006 Pearson Education, Inc., Upper Saddle River, NJ. All rights reserved. This material is protected under all copyright laws as they currently exist. No portion of this material may be reproduced, in any form or by any means, without permission in writing from the publisher.

59. $f(x) = x^2 + 10x + 25$

$\dfrac{-b}{2a} = \dfrac{-10}{2(1)} = -5$

$f(-5) = (-5)^2 + 10(-5) + 25 = 0$

$V(-5, 0)$

$f(0) = 25$

y-intercept: $(0, 25)$

$x^2 + 10x + 25 = 0$

$(x+5)^2 = 0$

$x = -5$

x-intercept: $(-5, 0)$

60. $f(x) = x^2 + 4x + 3$

$\dfrac{-b}{2a} = \dfrac{-4}{2(1)} = -2$

$f(-2) = (-2)^2 + 4(-2) + 3 = -1$

$V(-2, -1)$

$f(0) = 3$

y-intercept: $(0, 3)$

$x^2 + 4x + 3 = 0$

$(x+3)(x+1) = 0$

$x = -3, \; x = -1$

x-intercepts: $(-3, 0), \; (-1, 0)$

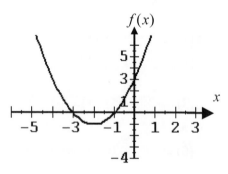

61. $f(x) = x^2 + 6x + 5$

$\dfrac{-b}{2a} = \dfrac{-6}{2(1)} = -3$

$f(-3) = (-3)^2 + 6(-3) + 5 = -4$

$V(-3, -4)$

$f(0) = 5$

y-intercept: $(0, 5)$

$x^2 + 6x + 5 = 0$

$(x+5)(x+1) = 0$

$x = -5, \; x = -1$

x-intercepts: $(-5, 0), \; (-1, 0)$

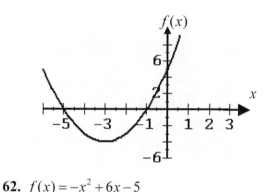

62. $f(x) = -x^2 + 6x - 5$

$\dfrac{-b}{2a} = \dfrac{-6}{2(-1)} = 3$

$f(3) = -3^2 + 6(3) - 5 = 4$

$V(3, 4)$

$f(0) = -5$

y-intercept: $(0, -5)$

$-x^2 + 6x - 5 = 0$

$x^2 - 6x + 5 = 0$

$(x-1)(x-5) = 0$

$x = 1, \; x = 5$

x-intercepts: $(1, 0), \; (5, 0)$

© 2006 Pearson Education, Inc., Upper Saddle River, NJ. All rights reserved. This material is protected under all copyright laws as they currently exist. No portion of this material may be reproduced, in any form or by any means, without permission in writing from the publisher.

62.

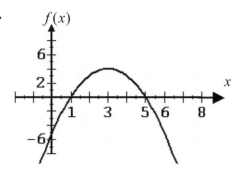

63. $h(t) = -16t^2 + 400t + 40$

$$\frac{-b}{2a} = \frac{-400}{2(-16)} = 12.5$$

$$h(1.25) = -16(1.25)^2 + 400(12.5) + 40$$

$$h(12.5) = 2540$$

$$-16t^2 + 400t + 40 = 0$$

$$t = \frac{-400 - \sqrt{400^2 - 4(-16)(40)}}{2(-16)}$$

$$t = 25.09960317...$$

The maximum height is 2540 feet. The amount of time for the complete flight is 25.1 seconds.

64. $R(x) = x(1200 - x) = -x^2 + 1200x$

$$\frac{-b}{2a} = \frac{-1200}{2(-1)} = \$600 \text{ for max revenue}$$

65. $x^2 + 7x - 18 < 0$

$$x^2 + 7x - 18 = 0$$

$$(x + 9)(x - 2) = 0$$

$$x = -9, \; x = 2$$

Critical points: $-9, \; 2$

Test: $x^2 + 7x - 18$

Region	Test	Results
I	-10	$12 > 0$
II	0	$-18 < 0$
III	3	$12 > 0$

65.

$$-9 < x < 2$$

66. $x^2 + 4x - 21 < 0$

$$x^2 + 4x - 21 = 0$$

$$(x + 7)(x - 3) = 0$$

$$x = -7, \; x = 3$$

Critical points: $-7, \; 3$

Test: $x^2 + 4x - 21$

Region	Test	Results
I	-8	$11 > 0$
II	0	$-21 < 0$
III	4	$11 > 0$

$$-7 < x < 3$$

67. $x^2 - 9x + 20 > 0$

$$x^2 - 9x + 20 = 0$$

$$(x - 5)(x - 4) = 0$$

$$x = 5, \; x = 4$$

Critical points: $4, \; 5$

Test: $x^2 - 9x + 20$

Region	Test	Results
I	0	$20 > 0$
II	4.5	$-0.25 < 0$
III	6	$2 > 0$

$$x < 4 \quad \text{or} \quad x > 5$$

239

© 2006 Pearson Education, Inc., Upper Saddle River, NJ. All rights reserved. This material is protected under all copyright laws as they currently exist.
No portion of this material may be reproduced, in any form or by any means, without permission in writing from the publisher.

68. $x^2 - 11x + 28 > 0$

$x^2 - 11x + 28 = 0$

$(x - 7)(x - 4) = 0$

$x = 7, \ x = 4$

Critical points: 7, 4

Test: $x^2 - 11x + 28$

Region	Test	Results
I	0	$28 > 0$
II	6	$-2 < 0$
III	8	$4 > 0$

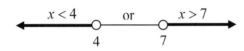

$x < 4$ or $x > 7$

69. $3x^2 - 5x - 2 \le 0$

$3x^2 - 5x - 2 = 0$

$(3x + 1)(x - 2) = 0$

$x = -\dfrac{1}{3}, \ x = 2$

Critical points: $-\dfrac{1}{3}, \ 2$

Test: $3x^2 - 5x - 2$

Region	Test	Results
I	-1	$6 > 0$
II	0	$-2 < 0$
III	3	$10 > 0$

$-\dfrac{1}{3} \le x \le 2$

70. $2x^2 - 5x - 3 \le 0$

$2x^2 - 5x - 3 = 0$

$(2x + 1)(x - 3) = 0$

$x = -\dfrac{1}{2}, \ x = 3$

70. Critical points: $-\dfrac{1}{2}, \ 3$

Test: $2x^2 - 5x - 3$

Region	Test	Results
I	-1	$4 > 0$
II	0	$-3 < 0$
III	4	$9 > 0$

$-\dfrac{1}{2} \le x \le 3$

71. $9x^2 - 4 > 0$

$9x^2 - 4 = 0$

$x^2 = \dfrac{4}{9}$

$x = \pm\dfrac{2}{3}$

Critical points: $-\dfrac{2}{3}, \ \dfrac{2}{3}$

Test: $9x^2 - 4$

Region	Test	Results
I	-2	$32 > 0$
II	0	$-4 < 0$
III	2	$32 > 0$

$x < -\dfrac{2}{3} \text{ or } x > \dfrac{2}{3}$

72. $16x^2 - 25 > 0$

$16x^2 - 25 = 0$

$x^2 = \dfrac{25}{16}$

$x = \pm\dfrac{5}{4}$

Critical points: $-\dfrac{5}{4}, \ \dfrac{5}{4}$

© 2006 Pearson Education, Inc., Upper Saddle River, NJ. All rights reserved. This material is protected under all copyright laws as they currently exist. No portion of this material may be reproduced, in any form or by any means, without permission in writing from the publisher.

72.   Test: $16x^2 - 25$

Region	Test	Results
I	−2	$39 > 0$
II	0	$-25 < 0$
III	2	$39 > 0$

$$x < -\frac{5}{4} \text{ or } x > \frac{5}{4}$$

73. $4x^2 - 8x \le 12 + 5x^2$

$-x^2 - 8x - 12 \le 0$

$x^2 + 8x + 12 \ge 0$

$x^2 + 8x + 12 = 0$
$(x+6)(x+2) = 0$

$x = -6, \ x = -2$

Critical points: $-6, \ -2$

Test: $x^2 + 8x + 12$

Region	Test	Results
I	−8	$12 > 0$
II	−4	$-4 < 0$
III	0	$12 > 0$

$x \le -6 \text{ or } x \ge -2$

74. $x^2 - 9x > 4 - 7x$

$x^2 - 2x - 4 = 0$

$$x = \frac{-(-2) \pm \sqrt{(-2)^2 - 4(1)(-4)}}{2}$$

$x = 1 \pm \sqrt{5}$

Critical points: $1 - \sqrt{5}, \ 1 + \sqrt{5}$

Test: $x^2 - 2x - 4$

Region	Test	Results
I	−2	$4 > 0$
II	0	$-4 < 0$
III	4	$4 > 0$

$x < 1 - \sqrt{5} \approx -1.2 \text{ or } x > 1 + \sqrt{5} \approx 3.2$

75. $x^2 + 13x > 16 + 7x$

$x^2 + 6x - 16 > 0$

$x^2 + 6x - 16 = 0$

$(x+8)(x-2) = 0$

$x + 8 = 0, \ x - 2 = 0$

$x = -8, \ x = 2$

Critical points: $-8, \ 2$

Test: $x^2 + 6x - 16$

Region	Test	Results
I	−10	$24 > 0$
II	0	$-16 < 0$
III	4	$24 > 0$

$x < -8 \text{ or } x > 2$

76. $3x^2 - 12x > -11$

$3x^2 - 12x + 11 > 0$

$3x^2 - 12x + 11 = 0$

$$x = \frac{12 \pm \sqrt{(-12)^2 - 4(3)(11)}}{2(3)} = 1.4, \ 2.6$$

Critical points: $1.4, \ 2.6$

Test: $3x^2 - 12x + 11$

Region	Test	Results
I	0	$11 > 0$
II	2	$-1 < 0$
III	3	$2 > 0$

$x < 1.4 \text{ or } x > 2.6$

77. $4x^2 + 12x + 9 < 0$

$(2x + 3)^2 < 0$

No real solution

© 2006 Pearson Education, Inc., Upper Saddle River, NJ. All rights reserved. This material is protected under all copyright laws as they currently exist. No portion of this material may be reproduced, in any form or by any means, without permission in writing from the publisher.

78. $-2x^2 + 7x + 12 \le -3x^2 + x$

$x^2 + 6x + 12 \le 0$

$a = 1,\ b = 6,\ c = 12$

$b^2 - 4ac = 6^2 - 4(1)(12) = -12 < 0$

No real solution.

79. $(x+4)(x-2)(3-x) > 0$

$(x+4)(x-2)(3-x) = 0$

$x = -4,\ x = 2,\ x = 3$

Critical points: $-4,\ 2,\ 3$

Test: $(x+4)(x-2)(3-x)$

Region	Test	Result
I	-5	$56 > 0$
II	0	$-24 < 0$
III	2.5	$\dfrac{13}{8} > 0$
IV	4	$-16 < 0$

$x < -4$ or $2 < x < 3$

80. $(x+1)(x+4)(2-x) < 0$

$(x+1)(x+4)(2-x) = 0$

$x = -1,\ x = -4,\ x = 2$

Critical points: $-1,\ -4,\ 2$

Test: $(x+1)(x+4)(2-x)$

Region	Test	Result
I	-5	$28 > 0$
II	-2	$-8 < 0$
III	0	$8 > 0$
IV	3	$-28 < 0$

$-4 < x < -1$ or $x > 2$

How Am I Doing? Chapter 8 Test

1. $8x^2 + 9x = 0$

$x(8x + 9) = 0$

$x = 0,\ 8x + 9 = 0$

$x = 0,\ x = -\dfrac{9}{8}$

2. $6x^2 - 3x = 1$

$6x^2 - 3x - 1 = 0$

$x = \dfrac{-b \pm \sqrt{b^2 - 4ac}}{2a}$

$x = \dfrac{-(-3) \pm \sqrt{(-3)^2 - 4(6)(-1)}}{2(6)}$

$x = \dfrac{3 \pm \sqrt{33}}{12}$

3. $\dfrac{3x}{2} - \dfrac{8}{3} = \dfrac{2}{3x}$

$9x^2 - 16x - 4 = 0$

$(9x + 2)(x - 2) = 0$

$9x + 2 = 0,\ x - 2 = 0$

$x = -\dfrac{2}{9},\ x = 2$

4. $x(x-3) - 30 = 5(x-2)$

$x^2 - 3x - 30 = 5x - 10$

$x^2 - 8x - 20 = 0$

$(x - 10)(x + 2) = 0$

$x - 10 = 0,\ x + 2 = 0$

$x = 10,\ x = -2$

5. $7x^2 - 4 = 52$

$7x^2 = 56$

$x^2 = 8$

$x = \pm\sqrt{8} = \pm\sqrt{4 \cdot 2}$

$x = \pm 2\sqrt{2}$

242

© 2006 Pearson Education, Inc., Upper Saddle River, NJ. All rights reserved. This material is protected under all copyright laws as they currently exist. No portion of this material may be reproduced, in any form or by any means, without permission in writing from the publisher.

6.

$$\frac{2x}{2x+1} - \frac{6}{4x^2-1} = \frac{x+1}{2x-1}$$

$$\frac{2x}{2x+1} - \frac{6}{(2x+1)(2x-1)} = \frac{x+1}{2x-1}$$

$$2x(2x-1)-6 = (x+1)(2x+1)$$

$$4x^2 - 2x - 6 = 2x^2 + 3x + 1$$

$$2x^2 - 5x - 7 = 0$$

$$(2x-7)(x+1) = 0$$

$$2x-7 = 0, \ x+1 = 0$$

$$x = \frac{7}{2}, \ x = -1$$

7. $2x^2 - 6x + 5 = 0$

$a = 2, \ b = -6, \ c = 5$

$$x = \frac{-(-6) \pm \sqrt{(-6)^2 - 4(2)(5)}}{2(2)}$$

$$x = \frac{6 \pm \sqrt{-4}}{4}$$

$$x = \frac{6 \pm \sqrt{4}\sqrt{-1}}{4}$$

$$x = \frac{6 \pm 2i}{4}$$

$$x = \frac{3 \pm i}{2}$$

8. $2x(x-3) = -3$

$$2x^2 - 6x + 3 = 0$$

$$a = 2, \ b = -6, \ c = 3$$

$$x = \frac{-(-6) \pm \sqrt{(-6)^2 - 4(2)(3)}}{2(2)}$$

$$x = \frac{6 \pm \sqrt{12}}{4} = \frac{6 \pm \sqrt{4 \cdot 3}}{4}$$

$$x = \frac{3 \pm \sqrt{3}}{2}$$

9. $x^4 - 11x^2 + 18 = 0$

$$y = x^2$$

$$y^2 - 11y + 18 = 0$$

$$(y-9)(y-2) = 0$$

$$y - 9 = 0, \ y - 2 = 0$$

$$y = 9, \ y = 2$$

$$x^2 = 9, \ x^2 = 2$$

$$x = \pm 3, \ x = \pm\sqrt{2}$$

10. $3x^{-2} - 11x^{-1} - 20 = 0$

$$3 - 11x - 20x^2 = 0$$

$$20x^2 + 11x - 3 = 0$$

$$(5x-1)(4x+3) = 0$$

$$5x - 1 = 0, \ 4x + 3 = 0$$

$$x = \frac{1}{5}, \ x = -\frac{3}{4}$$

11. $x^{\frac{2}{3}} - 3x^{\frac{1}{3}} - 4 = 0$

$$y = x^{\frac{1}{3}}$$

$$y^2 - 3y - 4 = 0$$

$$(y-4)(y+1) = 0$$

$$y = 4, \ y = -1$$

$$x^{\frac{1}{3}} = 4, \ x^{\frac{1}{3}} = -1$$

$$x = 64, \ x = -1$$

12. $B = \dfrac{xyw}{z^2}$

$$z^2 = \frac{xyw}{B}$$

$$z = \pm\sqrt{\frac{xyw}{B}}$$

243

© 2006 Pearson Education, Inc., Upper Saddle River, NJ. All rights reserved. This material is protected under all copyright laws as they currently exist. No portion of this material may be reproduced, in any form or by any means, without permission in writing from the publisher.

13. $5y^2 + 2by + 6w = 0$

$$y = \frac{-2b \pm \sqrt{(2b)^2 - 4(5)(6w)}}{2(5)}$$

$$y = \frac{-2b \pm \sqrt{4(b^2 - 30w)}}{10}$$

$$y = \frac{-b \pm \sqrt{b^2 - 30w}}{5}$$

14. $A = LW = (3W + 1)W = 80$

$3W^2 + W - 80 = 0$

$(W - 5)(3W + 16) = 0$

$W = 5, \ W = -\dfrac{16}{3}$ reject, $W > 0$

$W = 5$ mi for the width

$L = 3W + 1 = 16$ mi for the length

15. $c^2 = a^2 + b^2$

$c^2 = 6^2 + (2\sqrt{3})^2$

$c^2 = 36 + 12 = 48$

$c = \sqrt{48} = \sqrt{16 \cdot 3}$

$c = 4\sqrt{3}$

16. $6 = vt_1 \Rightarrow t_1 = \dfrac{6}{v}$

$3 = (v + 1)t_2 \Rightarrow t_2 = \dfrac{3}{v + 1}$

$t_1 + t_2 = 4 \Rightarrow \dfrac{6}{v} + \dfrac{3}{v + 1} = 4$

$6(v + 1) + 3v = 4v(v + 1)$

$6v + 6 + 3v = 4v^2 + 4v$

$4v^2 - 5v - 6 = 0$

$(v - 2)(4v + 3) = 0$

$v = 2$ mph first part

$v + 1 = 3$ mph second part

17. $f(x) = -x^2 - 6x - 5$

$\dfrac{-b}{2a} = \dfrac{-(-6)}{2(-1)} = -3$

$f(-3) = -(-3)^2 - 6(-3) - 5$

$f(-3 = 4$

$V(-3, 4)$

$f(0) = -5$

y-intercept: $(0, -5)$

$x^2 + 6x + 5 = 0$

$(x + 1)(x + 5) = 0$

$x + 1 = 0, \ x + 5 = 0$

$x = -1, \ x = -5$

x-intercepts: $(-1, 0), \ (-5, 0)$

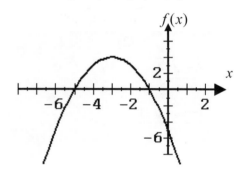

18. $2x^2 + 3x \geq 27$

$2x^2 + 3x - 27 \geq 0$

$2x^2 + 3x - 27 = 0$

$(2x + 9)(x - 3) = 0$

$2x - 9 = 0, \ x - 3 = 0$

$2x = 9, \ x = 3$

$x = -\dfrac{9}{2}, \ x = 3$

Critical Points: $-\dfrac{9}{2}, \ 3$

© 2006 Pearson Education, Inc., Upper Saddle River, NJ. All rights reserved. This material is protected under all copyright laws as they currently exist. No portion of this material may be reproduced, in any form or by any means, without permission in writing from the publisher.

18. Test: $2x^2 + 3x - 27$

Region	Test	Result
I	−5	$8 > 0$
II	0	$-27 < 0$
III	4	$17 > 0$

$x \le -\dfrac{9}{2}$ or $x \ge 3$

19. $x^2 - 5x - 14 < 0$

$x^2 - 5x - 14 = 0$

$(x+2)(x-7) = 0$

$x + 2 = 0,\ x - 7 = 0$

$x = -2,\ x = 7$

Critical points: $-2,$

Test: $x^2 - 5x - 14$

Region	Test	Result
I	−3	$10 > 0$
II	0	$-14 < 0$
III	8	$10 > 0$

$-2 < x < 7$

20. $x^2 + 3x - 7 > 0$

$x = \dfrac{-3 \pm \sqrt{3^2 - 4(1)(-7)}}{2}$

$x = -4.5,\ x = 1.5$

Critical points: $-4.5,\ 1.5$

Test: $x^2 + 3x - 7$

Region	Test	Result
I	−5	$3 > 0$
II	0	$-7 < 0$
III	2	$3 > 0$

$x < -4.5$ or $x > 1.5$

Cumulative Test for Chapters 1-8

1. $(-3x^{-2}y^3)^4 = (-3)^4 x^{-2 \cdot 4} y^{3 \cdot 4}$

$\qquad = \dfrac{81y^{12}}{x^8}$

2. $\dfrac{1}{2}a^3 - 2a^2 + 3a - \dfrac{1}{4}a^3 - 6a + a^2$

$\qquad = \dfrac{1}{4}a^3 - a^2 - 3a$

3. $\dfrac{1}{3}(x-3) + 1 = \dfrac{1}{2}x - 2$

$\qquad 2x - 6 + 6 = 3x - 12$

$\qquad\qquad x = 12$

4. $6x - 3y = -12$

x	y
0	4
−2	0

5. $2y + x = 8$

$y = -\dfrac{1}{2}x + 4 \Rightarrow m = -\dfrac{1}{2} \Rightarrow m_P = -\dfrac{1}{2}$

$y - y_1 = m_P(x - x_1)$

$y - (-1) = -\dfrac{1}{2}(x - 6)$

$2y + 2 = -x + 6$

$x + 2y = 4$

© 2006 Pearson Education, Inc., Upper Saddle River, NJ. All rights reserved. This material is protected under all copyright laws as they currently exist. No portion of this material may be reproduced, in any form or by any means, without permission in writing from the publisher.

6. $7x - 3y = 1 \xrightarrow{\times 5} 35x - 15y = 5$

$-5x + 4y = 3 \xrightarrow{\times 7} \underline{-35x + 28y = 21}$

$\qquad\qquad\qquad\qquad\quad 13y = 26$

$\qquad\qquad\qquad\qquad\qquad y = 2$

$7x - 3(2) = 1,\ 7x = 7,\ x = 1$

$(1, 2)$ is the solution.

7. $125x^3 - 27y^2$

$\quad = (5x - 3y)(25x^2 + 15xy + 9y^2)$

8. $\sqrt{72x^3 y^6} = \sqrt{36x^2 y^6 \cdot 2x}$

$\qquad\qquad\ = 6xy^3 \sqrt{2x}$

9. $(3 + \sqrt{2})(\sqrt{6} + \sqrt{3})$

$\quad = 3\sqrt{6} + 3\sqrt{3} + \sqrt{12} + \sqrt{6}$

$\quad = 4\sqrt{6} + 3\sqrt{3} + \sqrt{4 \cdot 3}$

$\quad = 4\sqrt{6} + 3\sqrt{3} + 2\sqrt{3}$

$\quad = 4\sqrt{6} + 5\sqrt{3}$

10. $\dfrac{3x}{\sqrt{6}} \cdot \dfrac{\sqrt{6}}{\sqrt{6}} = \dfrac{3x\sqrt{6}}{6} = \dfrac{x\sqrt{6}}{2}$

11. $3x^2 + 12x = 26x$

$\quad 3x^2 - 14x = 0$

$\quad x(3x - 14) = 0$

$\qquad\qquad x = 0,\ x = \dfrac{14}{3}$

12. $\qquad\quad 12x^2 = 11x - 2$

$\quad 12x^2 - 11x + 2 = 0$

$\quad (4x - 1)(3x - 2) = 0$

$\qquad 4x - 1 = 0,\ 3x - 2 = 0$

$\qquad\qquad x = \dfrac{1}{4},\ x = \dfrac{2}{3}$

13. $\qquad 44 = 3(2x - 3)^2 + 8$

$\quad 3(2x - 3)^2 = 36$

$\quad (2x - 3)^2 = 12$

$\qquad 2x - 3 = \pm\sqrt{12}$

$\qquad 2x - 3 = \pm\sqrt{4 \cdot 3}$

$\qquad 2x - 3 = \pm 2\sqrt{3}$

$\qquad\quad 2x = 3 \pm 2\sqrt{3}$

$\qquad\quad x = \dfrac{3 \pm 2\sqrt{3}}{2}$

14. $3 - \dfrac{4}{x} + \dfrac{5}{x^2} = 0$

$\quad 3x^2 - 4x + 5 = 0$

$\quad x = \dfrac{-(-4) \pm \sqrt{(-4)^2 - 4(3)(5)}}{2(3)}$

$\quad x = \dfrac{4 \pm \sqrt{-44}}{6} = \dfrac{4 \pm \sqrt{4 \cdot 11}\sqrt{-1}}{6}$

$\quad x = \dfrac{4 \pm 2i\sqrt{11}}{6}$

$\quad x = \dfrac{2 \pm i\sqrt{11}}{3}$

15. $\sqrt{3x + 7} - 1 = x$

$\quad \sqrt{3x + 7} = x + 1$

$\quad 3x + 7 = x^2 + 2x + 1$

$\quad x^2 - x + 6 = 0$

$\quad (x - 3)(x - 2) = 0$

$\quad x = 3,\ x = 2$

check: $\sqrt{3(3) + 7} - 1 \overset{?}{=} 3,\ 3 = 3$

$\qquad\quad \sqrt{3(2) + 7} - 1 \overset{?}{=} 2,\ \sqrt{13} - 1 \neq 2$

$x = 3$ is the solution.

© 2006 Pearson Education, Inc., Upper Saddle River, NJ. All rights reserved. This material is protected under all copyright laws as they currently exist.
No portion of this material may be reproduced, in any form or by any means, without permission in writing from the publisher.

16. $x^{\frac{2}{3}} + 9x^{\frac{1}{3}} + 18 = 0$

$y = x^{\frac{1}{3}}$

$y^2 + 9y + 18 = 0$

$(y+6)(y+3) = 0$

$y = -6, \ y = -3$

$x^{\frac{1}{3}} = -6, \ x^{\frac{1}{3}} = -3$

$x = -216, \ x = -27$

check: $(-216)^{\frac{2}{3}} + 9(-216)^{\frac{1}{3}} + 18 \overset{?}{=} 0, \ 0 = 0$

$\qquad (-27)^{\frac{2}{3}} + 9(-27)^{\frac{1}{3}} + 18 \overset{?}{=} 0, \ 0 = 0$

$x = -216, \ x = -27$ is the solution.

17. $2y^2 + 5wy - 7z = 0$

$y = \dfrac{-5w \pm \sqrt{(5w)^2 - 4(2)(-7z)}}{2(2)}$

$y = \dfrac{-5w \pm \sqrt{25w^2 + 56z}}{4}$

18. $3y^2 + 16z^2 = 5w$

$3y^2 = 5w - 16z^2$

$y^2 = \dfrac{5w - 16z^2}{3}$

$y = \pm \sqrt{\dfrac{5w - 16z^2}{3} \cdot \dfrac{3}{3}}$

$y = \pm \dfrac{\sqrt{15w - 48z^2}}{3}$

19. $\qquad c^2 = a^2 + b^2$

$\left(\sqrt{31}\right)^2 = 4^2 + b^2$

$31 = 16 + b^2$

$b^2 = 15$

$b = \sqrt{15}$

20. $A = \dfrac{1}{2}bh$

$A = \dfrac{1}{2}b(3b+3)$

$45 = \dfrac{1}{2}b(3b+3)$

$90 = 3b^2 + 3b$

$b^2 + b - 30 = 0$

$(b-5)(b+6) = 0$

$b - 5 = 0, \ b + 6 = 0$

$b = 5, \ b = -6$ reject, $b > 0$

$h = 3b + 3$

$h = 18$

The base of the triangle is 5 meters and the altitude of the triangle is 18 meters.

21. $f(x) = -x^2 + 8x - 12$

$a = -1, \ b = 8, \ c = -12$

$x_{\text{vertex}} = \dfrac{-b}{2a}$

$x_{\text{vertex}} = \dfrac{-8}{2(-1)}$

$x_{\text{vertex}} = 4$

$y_{\text{vertex}} = f(x_{\text{vertex}})$

$y_{\text{vertex}} = f(4) = -4^2 + 8(4) - 12$

$y_{\text{vertex}} = 4$

$V(4,4)$

$f(0) = -12$

y-intercept: $(0, -12)$

$-x^2 + 8x - 12 = 0$

$x^2 - 8x + 12 = 0$

$(x-6)(x-2) = 0$

$x - 6 = 0, \ x - 2 = 0$

$x = 6, \ x = 2$

x-intercepts: $(6,0), \ (2,0)$

© 2006 Pearson Education, Inc., Upper Saddle River, NJ. All rights reserved. This material is protected under all copyright laws as they currently exist. No portion of this material may be reproduced, in any form or by any means, without permission in writing from the publisher.

22.

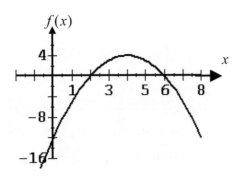

23. $6x^2 - x \leq 2$

$6x^2 - x - 2 \leq 0$

$6x^2 - x - 2 = 0$

$(3x - 2)(2x + 1) = 0$

$3x - 2 = 0, \ 2x + 1 = 0$

$x = \dfrac{2}{3}, \ x = -\dfrac{1}{2}$

Critical points: $\dfrac{2}{3}, \ -\dfrac{1}{2}$

Test: $6x^2 - x - 2$

Region	Test	Results
I	-1	$5 > 0$
II	0	$-2 < 0$
III	1	$3 > 0$

$-\dfrac{1}{2} \leq x \leq \dfrac{2}{3}$

24. $x^2 > -2x + 15$

$x^2 + 2x - 15 > 0$

$x^2 + 2x - 15 = 0$

$(x + 5)(x - 3) = 0$

$x + 5 = 0, \ x - 3 = 0$

$x = -5, \ x = 3$

Critical points: $-5, \ 3$

Test: $x^2 + 2x - 15$

Region	Test	Results
I	-6	$9 > 0$
II	0	$-15 < 0$
III	5	$20 > 0$

$x < -5$ or $x > 3$

© 2006 Pearson Education, Inc., Upper Saddle River, NJ. All rights reserved. This material is protected under all copyright laws as they currently exist.
No portion of this material may be reproduced, in any form or by any means, without permission in writing from the publisher.

Chapter 9

9.1 Exercises

1. Subtract the value of the points and use the absolute value: $|-2-4| = |-6| = 6$.

3. The equation, $(x-1)^2 + (y+2)^2 = 9 = 3^2$, is in standard form. The center is $(1,-2)$ and the radius is 3.

5. $d = \sqrt{(x_2 - x_1)^2 + (y_2 - y_1)^2}$

$d = \sqrt{(1-2)^2 + (6-4)^2}$

$d = \sqrt{1+4} = \sqrt{5}$

7. $d = \sqrt{(x_2 - x_1)^2 + (y_2 - y_1)^2}$

$d = \sqrt{(0-(-4))^2 + (-3-1)^2}$

$d = \sqrt{16+16} = \sqrt{32}$

$d = 4\sqrt{2}$

9. $d = \sqrt{(x_2 - x_1)^2 + (y_2 - y_1)^2}$

$d = \sqrt{(4-(-2))^2 + (-5-(-13))^2}$

$d = \sqrt{36+64} = \sqrt{100} = 10$

11. $d = \sqrt{(x_2 - x_1)^2 + (y_2 - y_1)^2}$

$d = \sqrt{\left(\dfrac{5}{4} - \dfrac{1}{4}\right)^2 + \left(-\dfrac{1}{3} - \left(-\dfrac{2}{3}\right)\right)^2}$

$d = \sqrt{1 + \dfrac{1}{9}} = \sqrt{\dfrac{10}{9}} = \dfrac{\sqrt{10}}{\sqrt{9}}$

$d = \dfrac{\sqrt{10}}{3}$

13. $d = \sqrt{(x_2 - x_1)^2 + (y_2 - y_1)^2}$

$d = \sqrt{\left(\dfrac{7}{3} - \dfrac{1}{3}\right)^2 + \left(\dfrac{1}{5} - \dfrac{3}{5}\right)^2}$

$d = \sqrt{4 + \dfrac{4}{25}} = \sqrt{\dfrac{104}{25}} = \dfrac{\sqrt{4 \cdot 26}}{\sqrt{25}}$

$d = \dfrac{2\sqrt{26}}{5}$

15. $d = \sqrt{(x_2 - x_1)^2 + (y_2 - y_1)^2}$

$d = \sqrt{(1.3-(-5.7))^2 + (2.6-1.6)^2}$

$d = \sqrt{50}$

$d = 5\sqrt{2}$

17.

$d = \sqrt{(x_2 - x_1)^2 + (y_2 - y_1)^2}$

$10 = \sqrt{(y-6)^2 + (1-7)^2}$

$100 = y^2 - 4y + 40$

$y^2 - 4y - 60 = 0$

$(y-10)(y+6) = 0$

$y - 10 = 0, \; y + 6 = 0$

$y = 10, \; y = -6$

19.

$d = \sqrt{(x_2 - x_1)^2 + (y_2 - y_1)^2}$

$2.5 = \sqrt{(0-1.5)^2 + (y-2)^2}$

$6.25 = 2.25 + y^2 - 4y + 4$

$y^2 - 4y = 0$

$y(y-4) = 0$

$y = 0, \; y - 4 = 0$

$y = 0, \; y = 4$

© 2006 Pearson Education, Inc., Upper Saddle River, NJ. All rights reserved. This material is protected under all copyright laws as they currently exist. No portion of this material may be reproduced, in any form or by any means, without permission in writing from the publisher.

21.

$$d = \sqrt{(x_2 - x_1)^2 + (y_2 - y_1)^2}$$

$$\sqrt{10} = \sqrt{(x-7)^2 + (6-3)^2}$$

$$10 = x^2 - 14x + 49 + 9$$

$$x^2 - 14x + 48 = 0$$

$$(x-6)(x-8) = 0$$

$$x - 6 = 0, \ x - 8 = 0$$

$$x = 6, \ x = 8$$

23.

$$d = \sqrt{(x_2 - x_1)^2 + (y_2 - y_1)^2}$$

$$4 = \sqrt{(2-5)^2 + (y-7)^2}$$

$$16 = 9 + y^2 - 14y + 49$$

$$y^2 - 14y + 42 = 0$$

$$y = \frac{14 \pm \sqrt{14^2 - 4(1)(42)}}{2(1)}$$

$$y = \frac{14 \pm \sqrt{28}}{2} \approx \begin{cases} 9.6 \\ 4.4 \end{cases}$$

$$y \approx 4.4 \text{ miles}$$

25. $\quad (x-h)^2 + (y-k)^2 = r^2$

$$(x - (-3))^2 + (y-7)^2 = 6^2$$

$$(x+3)^2 + (y-7)^2 = 36$$

27. $\quad (x-h)^2 + (y-k)^2 = r^2$

$$(x - (-1.8))^2 + (y-0)^2 = \left(\frac{2}{5}\right)^2$$

$$(x+1.8)^2 + y^2 = \frac{4}{25}$$

29. $\ (x-h)^2 + (y-k)^2 = r^2$

$$\left(x - \frac{3}{8}\right)^2 + (y-0)^2 = \sqrt{3}^2$$

$$\left(x - \frac{3}{8}\right)^2 + y^2 = 3$$

31. $\ x^2 + y^2 = 25$

$\quad C(0,0), \ r = 5$

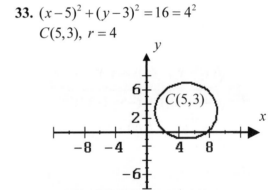

33. $\ (x-5)^2 + (y-3)^2 = 16 = 4^2$

$\quad C(5,3), \ r = 4$

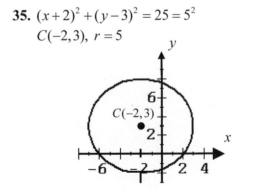

35. $\ (x+2)^2 + (y-3)^2 = 25 = 5^2$

$\quad C(-2,3), \ r = 5$

250

© 2006 Pearson Education, Inc., Upper Saddle River, NJ. All rights reserved. This material is protected under all copyright laws as they currently exist. No portion of this material may be reproduced, in any form or by any means, without permission in writing from the publisher.

37. $x^2 + y^2 + 8x - 6y - 24 = 0$

$x^2 + 8x + 16 + y^2 - 6y + 9 = 24 + 16 + 9$

$(x+4)^2 + (y-3)^2 = 49 = 7^2$

$C(-4, 3), \ r = 7$

39. $x^2 + y^2 - 12x + 2y - 12 = 0$

$x^2 - 12x + 36 + y^2 + 2y + 1 = 12 + 36 + 1$

$(x-6)^2 + (y+1)^2 = 49 = 7^2$

$C(6, -1), \ r = 7$

41. $x^2 + y^2 + 3x - 2 = 0$

$x^2 + 3x + y^2 = 2$

$x^2 + 3x + \dfrac{9}{4} + y^2 = 2 + \dfrac{9}{4} = \dfrac{17}{4}$

$\left(x + \dfrac{3}{2}\right)^2 + y^2 = \left(\dfrac{\sqrt{17}}{2}\right)^2$

$C\left(-\dfrac{3}{2}, 0\right), \ r = \dfrac{\sqrt{17}}{2}$

43. $(x - 44.8)^2 + (y - 31.8)^2 = 25.3^2 = 640.09$

45. $(x - 5.32)^2 + (y + 6.54)^2 = 47.28$

$(y + 6.54)^2 = 47.28 - (x - 5.32)^2$

$y + 6.54 = \pm\sqrt{47.28 - (x - 5.32)^2}$

$y_1 = -6.54 + \sqrt{47.28 - (x - 5.32)^2}$

$y_2 = -6.54 - \sqrt{47.28 - (x - 5.32)^2}$

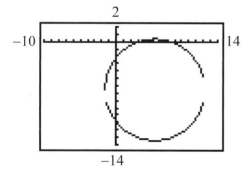

Cumulative Review Problems

47. $9 + \dfrac{3}{x} = \dfrac{2}{x^2}$

$9x^2 + 3x - 2 = 0$

$(3x + 2)(3x - 1) = 0$

$3x + 2 = 0, \ 3x - 1 = 0$

$x = -\dfrac{2}{3}, \ x = \dfrac{1}{3}$

49. $4x^2 + 2x = 1 \Rightarrow 4x^2 + 2x - 1 = 0$

$x = \dfrac{-2 \pm \sqrt{2^2 - 4(4)(-1)}}{2(4)}$

$x = \dfrac{-2 \pm \sqrt{20}}{8} = \dfrac{-2 \pm \sqrt{4(5)}}{8} = \dfrac{-2 \pm 2\sqrt{5}}{8}$

$x = \dfrac{-1 \pm \sqrt{5}}{4}$

51. $V = Ah$

$V = 20 \ \text{mi}^2 (150 \ \text{ft}) \left(\dfrac{5280^2 \ \text{ft}^2}{\text{mi}^2} \right)$

$V = 8.364 \times 10^{10} \ \text{ft}^3$

9.2 Exercises

1. The graph of $y = x^2$ is symmetric about the _y-axis_ . The graph of $x = y^2$ is symmetric about the _x-axis_ .

3. Since $y = 2(x - 3)^2 + 4$ is in standard form, $y = a(x - h)^2 + k$, the vertex is $(h, k) = (3, 4)$.

5. $y = -4x^2$

$V(0, 0)$

$y\text{-intercept} = (0, 0)$

© 2006 Pearson Education, Inc., Upper Saddle River, NJ. All rights reserved. This material is protected under all copyright laws as they currently exist. No portion of this material may be reproduced, in any form or by any means, without permission in writing from the publisher.

5.

x	-2	-1	0	1	2
y	-16	-4	0	-4	-16

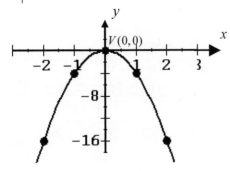

7. $y = x^2 - 6$

$V(0, -6)$

y-intercept: $(0, -6)$

x	-3	-2	0	2	3
y	3	-2	-6	-2	6

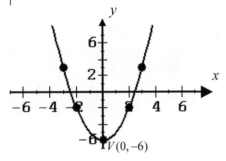

9. $y = \frac{1}{2}x^2 - 2$

$V(0, -2)$

y-intercept: $(0, -2)$

x	-4	-2	0	2	4
y	6	0	-2	0	6

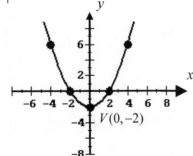

11. $y = (x-3)^2 - 2$

$V(3, -2)$

y-intercept: $(0, 7)$

x	1	2	3	4	5
y	2	-1	-2	-1	2

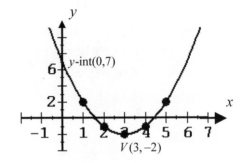

13. $y = 2(x-1)^2 + \frac{3}{2}$

$V\left(1, \frac{3}{2}\right)$

y-intercept: $\left(0, \frac{7}{2}\right)$

x	-1	0	1	2	3
y	$\frac{19}{2}$	$\frac{7}{2}$	$\frac{3}{2}$	$\frac{7}{2}$	$\frac{19}{2}$

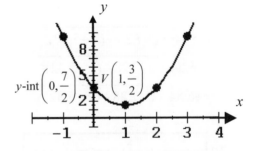

252

© 2006 Pearson Education, Inc., Upper Saddle River, NJ. All rights reserved. This material is protected under all copyright laws as they currently exist. No portion of this material may be reproduced, in any form or by any means, without permission in writing from the publisher.

15. $y = -4\left(x + \dfrac{3}{2}\right)^2 + 5$

$V\left(-\dfrac{3}{2}, 5\right)$

y-intercept: $(0, -4)$

x	-3	-2	$-\dfrac{3}{2}$	-1	0
y	-4	4	5	4	-4

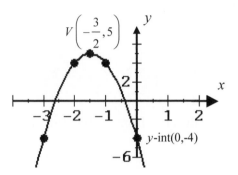

17. $x = \dfrac{1}{2}y^2$

$V(0, 0)$

x-intercept: $(0, 0)$

x	0	2	2	4	4
y	0	2	-2	-8	8

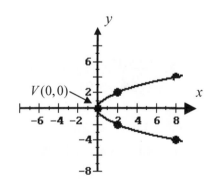

19. $x = \dfrac{1}{4}y^2 - 2$

$V(-2, 0)$

x-intercept: $(-2, 0)$

x	-2	-1	-1	2	2
y	0	-2	2	-4	4

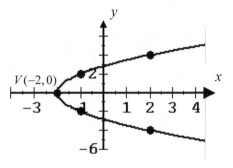

21. $x = -y^2 + 2$

$V(2, 0)$

x-intercept: $(2, 0)$

x	2	-2	-2	-7	-7
y	0	-2	2	-3	3

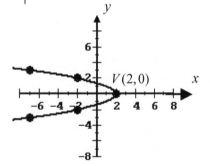

23. $x = (y - 2)^2 + 3$

$V(3, 2)$

x-intercept: $(7, 0)$

x	3	4	4	7	7
y	2	1	3	4	0

© 2006 Pearson Education, Inc., Upper Saddle River, NJ. All rights reserved. This material is protected under all copyright laws as they currently exist.
No portion of this material may be reproduced, in any form or by any means, without permission in writing from the publisher.

23.

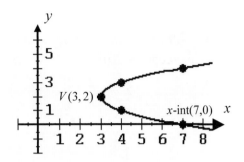

25. $x = -3(y+1) - 2$

$V(-2, -1)$

x-intercept: $(-5, 0)$

x	-2	-5	-5
y	-1	0	-2

27. $y = x^2 - 4x - 1$

$y = x^2 - 4x + 4 - 4 - 1$

$y = (x-2)^2 - 5$

(a) Vertical

(b) Opens upward

(c) $V(2, -5)$

29. $y = -2x^2 + 4x + 5 = -2x^2 + 4x - 2 + 7$

$y = (-2x^2 + 4x - 2) + 7$

$y = -2(x^2 - 2x + 1) + 7$

$y = -2(x-1)^2 + 7$

(a) Vertical

(b) Downward

(c) $V(1, 7)$

31. $x = y^2 + 8y + 9$

$x = y^2 + 8y + 16 - 7$

$x = (y+4)^2 - 7$

(a) Horizontal

(b) Opens right

(c) $V(-7, -4)$

33. $y = ax^2, \ 8 = a(16)^2, \ a = \dfrac{1}{32}$

$y = \dfrac{1}{32}x^2$

35. $a = \dfrac{1}{4p} = \dfrac{1}{32} \Rightarrow p = 8$

The distance from $(0,0)$ to the focus point is 8 inches.

37. $y = 2x^2 + 6.48x - 0.1312$

$y = 2(x^2 + 3.24x + 2.6244) - 0.1312 - 5.2488$

$y = 2(x+1.62)^2 - 5.38$

$V(-1.62, -5.38)$

y-intercept: $(0, -0.1312)$

$$\dfrac{-6.48 \pm \sqrt{6.48^2 - 4(2)(-0.1312)}}{2(2)}$$

$$= \begin{cases} 0.020121947 \\ -3.260121947 \end{cases}$$

x-intercepts: $(0.020121947, 0)$

$\qquad\qquad\qquad (-3.26012194, 0)$

39. $P = -3x^2 + 240x + 31,200$

$P = -3(x^2 - 80x + 600) + 31,200 + 4800$

$P = -3(x - 40)^2 + 36,000$

The maximum profit is \$36,000 and the number of items needed is 40.

© 2006 Pearson Education, Inc., Upper Saddle River, NJ. All rights reserved. This material is protected under all copyright laws as they currently exist. No portion of this material may be reproduced, in any form or by any means, without permission in writing from the publisher.

41. $E = x(900 - x) = -x^2 + 900x$

$E = -(x^2 - 900x + 202,500) + 202,500$

$E = -(x - 450)^2 + 202,500$

The maximum yield is 202,500 and the number of trees per acre is 450.

Cumulative Review

43. $\sqrt{50x^3} = \sqrt{25x^2 \cdot 2x}$

$\qquad = 5x\sqrt{2x} \text{ for } x \geq 0$

45. $\sqrt{98x} + x\sqrt{8} - 3\sqrt{50x}$

$= \sqrt{49 \cdot 2x} + x\sqrt{4 \cdot 2} - 3\sqrt{25 \cdot 2x}$

$= 7\sqrt{2x} + 2x\sqrt{2} - 15\sqrt{2x}$

$= 2x\sqrt{2} - 8\sqrt{2x}$

47. $\quad d = rt$

$\quad d = 30t_1$

$\quad t_1 = \dfrac{d}{30}$

$\quad d = 50t_2$

$\quad t_2 = \dfrac{d}{50}$

$t_1 + t_2 = \dfrac{d}{30} + \dfrac{d}{50} = 2.25$

$\dfrac{80d}{1500} = 2.25$

$\quad d = \dfrac{1500(2.25)}{80}$

$\quad d = 42.1875$

It is approximately 42.2 miles from the farm to the supermarket warehouse.

49. $8(1050)(0.88) = 7392$

Sir George can expect 7392 blooms if there is heavy rainfall this year.

9.3 Exercises

1. $\dfrac{(x+2)^2}{4} + \dfrac{(y-3)}{9} = 1$ is in the form

$\dfrac{(x-h)^2}{a^2} + \dfrac{(y-k)^2}{b^2} = 1$ where (h, k) is the

center of the ellipse. Therefore, the center of the ellipse is $(-2, 3)$.

3. $\dfrac{x^2}{36} + \dfrac{y^2}{4} = 1 \Rightarrow \dfrac{x^2}{6^2} + \dfrac{y^2}{2^2} = 1$

$a = 6, \ b = 2$

Intercepts: $(\pm 6, 0), \ (0, \pm 2)$

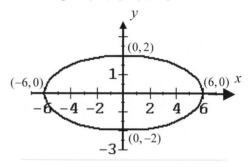

5. $\dfrac{x^2}{81} + \dfrac{y^2}{100} = 1 \Rightarrow \dfrac{x^2}{9^2} + \dfrac{y^2}{10^2} = 1$

$a = 9, \ b = 10$

Intercepts: $(\pm 9, 0), \ (0, \pm 10)$

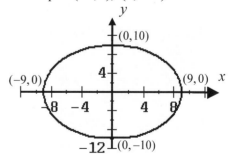

255

© 2006 Pearson Education, Inc., Upper Saddle River, NJ. All rights reserved. This material is protected under all copyright laws as they currently exist. No portion of this material may be reproduced, in any form or by any means, without permission in writing from the publisher.

7. $4x^2 + y^2 - 36 = 0$

$$\frac{x^2}{9} + \frac{y^2}{36} = 1 \Rightarrow \frac{x^2}{3^2} + \frac{y^2}{6^2} = 1$$

$a = 3, \ b = 6$

Intercepts: $(\pm 3, 0), \ (0, \pm 6)$

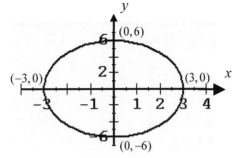

9. $x^2 + 9y^2 = 81 \Rightarrow \frac{x^2}{81} + \frac{y^2}{9} = 1$

$$\frac{x^2}{9^2} + \frac{y^2}{3^2} = 1$$

$a = 9, \ b = 3$

Intercepts: $(\pm 9, 0), \ (0, \pm 3)$

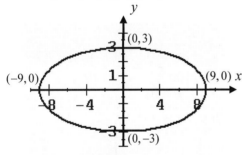

11. $x^2 + 12y^2 = 36$

$$\frac{x^2}{36} + \frac{y^2}{3} = 1 \Rightarrow \frac{x^2}{6^2} + \frac{y^2}{\sqrt{3}^2} = 1$$

$a = 6, \ b = \sqrt{3}$

Intercepts: $(\pm 6, 0), \ (0, \pm \sqrt{3})$

11.

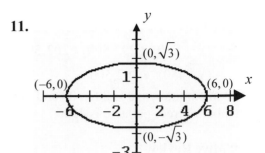

13. $\frac{x^2}{25} + \frac{y^2}{16} = 1 \Rightarrow \frac{x^2}{\left(\frac{5}{2}\right)^2} + \frac{y^2}{\left(\frac{4}{3}\right)^2} = 1$

$a = \frac{5}{2}, \ b = \frac{4}{3}$

Intercepts: $\left(\pm \frac{5}{2}, 0\right), \left(0, \pm \frac{4}{3}\right)$

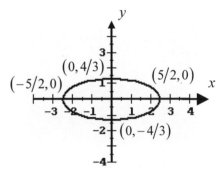

15. $121x^2 + 64y^2 = 7744$

$$\frac{x^2}{64} + \frac{y^2}{121} = 1 \Rightarrow \frac{x^2}{8^2} + \frac{y^2}{11^2} = 1$$

$a = 8, \ b = 11, \ C(0, 0)$

Intercepts: $(0, \pm 11), (\pm 8, 0)$

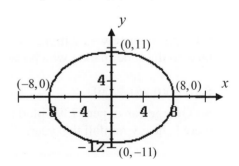

© 2006 Pearson Education, Inc., Upper Saddle River, NJ. All rights reserved. This material is protected under all copyright laws as they currently exist. No portion of this material may be reproduced, in any form or by any means, without permission in writing from the publisher.

17. $\dfrac{(x-h)^2}{a^2}+\dfrac{(y-k)^2}{b^2}=1$

$C(0,0) \Rightarrow (h,k)=(0,0)$

$x\text{-int}(13,0) \Rightarrow a=13$

$y\text{-int}(0,-12) \Rightarrow b=12$

$\dfrac{x^2}{13^2}+\dfrac{y^2}{12^2}=1$

$\dfrac{x^2}{169}+\dfrac{y^2}{144}=1$

19. $\dfrac{(x-h)^2}{a^2}+\dfrac{(y-k)^2}{b^2}=1$

$C(0,0) \Rightarrow (h,k)=(0,0)$

$x\text{-int}(9,0) \Rightarrow a=9$

$y\text{-int}(0,3\sqrt{2}) \Rightarrow b=3\sqrt{2}$

$\dfrac{x^2}{9^2}+\dfrac{y^2}{(3\sqrt{2})^2}=1$

$\dfrac{x^2}{81}+\dfrac{y^2}{18}=1$

21. $\dfrac{x^2}{5013}+\dfrac{y^2}{4970}=1 \Rightarrow a^2=5013$

$a=\sqrt{5013}$

$d=2a=2\sqrt{5013} \approx 142$

The largest possible distance across the ellipse is 142 million miles.

23. $\dfrac{(x-h)^2}{a^2}+\dfrac{(y-k)^2}{b^2}=1$

$\dfrac{(x-5)^2}{9}+\dfrac{(y-2)^2}{1}=1$

$\dfrac{(x-5)^2}{3^2}+\dfrac{(y-2)^2}{1^2}=1$

$a=3,\ b=1,\ C(5,2)$

Vertices: $(2,2),\ (8,2),\ (5,1),\ (5,3)$

23.

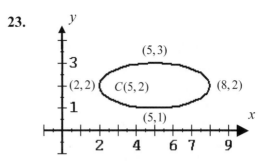

25. $\dfrac{(x-h)^2}{a^2}+\dfrac{(y-k)^2}{b^2}=1$

$\dfrac{x^2}{25}+\dfrac{(y-4)^2}{16}=1 \Rightarrow \dfrac{x^2}{5^2}+\dfrac{(y-4)^2}{4^2}=1$

$a=5,\ b=4,\ C(0,4)$

Vertices: $(5,4),\ (0,8),\ (-5,4),\ (0,0)$

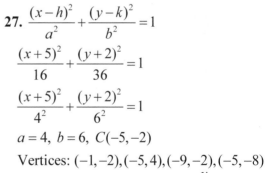

27. $\dfrac{(x-h)^2}{a^2}+\dfrac{(y-k)^2}{b^2}=1$

$\dfrac{(x+5)^2}{16}+\dfrac{(y+2)^2}{36}=1$

$\dfrac{(x+5)^2}{4^2}+\dfrac{(y+2)^2}{6^2}=1$

$a=4,\ b=6,\ C(-5,-2)$

Vertices: $(-1,-2),(-5,4),(-9,-2),(-5,-8)$

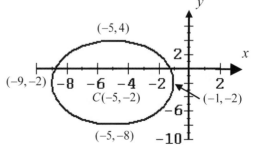

257

© 2006 Pearson Education, Inc., Upper Saddle River, NJ. All rights reserved. This material is protected under all copyright laws as they currently exist. No portion of this material may be reproduced, in any form or by any means, without permission in writing from the publisher.

29. $\left(\dfrac{2+6}{2}, \dfrac{3+3}{2}\right) = (4,3)$

$a = |6-4| = 2$

$b = |7-3| = 4$

$\dfrac{(x-4)^2}{2^2} + \dfrac{(y-3)^2}{4^2} = 1$

$\dfrac{(x-4)^2}{4} + \dfrac{(y-3)^2}{16} = 1$

31. $C\left(\dfrac{0+60}{2}, \dfrac{0+40}{2}\right) = C(30,20)$

$2a = 60$

$a = 30$

$2b = 40$

$b = 20$

$\dfrac{(x-30)^2}{30^2} + \dfrac{(y-20)^2}{20^2} = 1$

$\dfrac{(x-30)^2}{900} + \dfrac{(y-20)^2}{400} = 1$

33. $\dfrac{(x-3.6)^2}{14.98} + \dfrac{(y-5.3)^2}{28.98} = 1$

$\dfrac{(0-3.6)^2}{14.98} + \dfrac{(y-5.3)^2}{28.98} = 1$

$(y-5.3)^2 = 28.98\left(1 - \dfrac{12.96}{14.98}\right)$

$y = \pm\sqrt{28.98\left(1 - \dfrac{12.967}{14.98}\right)} + 5.3$

$y = \begin{cases} 7.2768 \\ 3.3232 \end{cases}$

$\dfrac{(x-3.6)^2}{14.98} + \dfrac{(0-5.3)^2}{28.98} = 1$

$(x-3.6)^2 = 14.98\left(1 - \dfrac{28.09}{28.98}\right)$

33. $x = \pm\sqrt{14.98\left(1 - \dfrac{28.09}{28.98}\right)} + 3.6$

$x = \begin{cases} 4.2783 \\ 2.9217 \end{cases}$

x-intercepts: $(4.2783, 0),\ (2.9217, 0)$

y-intercepts: $(0, 7.2768),\ (0, 3.3232)$

35. $A = \pi ab$

$A = 3.1416\left(\dfrac{185}{2}\right)\left(\dfrac{154}{2}\right)$

$A = 22{,}376.0$ square meters

Cumulative Review

37. $(2\sqrt{3} + 4\sqrt{2})(5\sqrt{6} - \sqrt{2})$

$= 10\sqrt{18} - 2\sqrt{6} + 20\sqrt{12} - 8$

$= 10\sqrt{9 \cdot 2} - 2\sqrt{6} + 20\sqrt{4 \cdot 3} - 8$

$= 30\sqrt{2} - 2\sqrt{6} + 40\sqrt{3} - 8$

39. $\dfrac{1224\text{ feet}}{1850\text{ steps}} \cdot \dfrac{12\text{ inches}}{\text{foot}} = 7.9\dfrac{\text{inches}}{\text{step}}$

How Am I Doing? Sections 9.1-9.3

1. $(x-h)^2 + (y-k)^2 = r^2$

$(x-8)^2 + (y-(-2))^2 = \sqrt{7}^2$

$(x-8)^2 + (y+2)^2 = 7$

2. $(x_1, y_1) = (-6, -2),\ (x_2, y_2) = (-3, 4)$

$d = \sqrt{(x_2 - x_1)^2 + (y_2 - y_1)^2}$

$d = \sqrt{(-3-(-6))^2 + (4-(-2))^2}$

$d = \sqrt{45} = \sqrt{9(5)}$

$d = 3\sqrt{5}$

© 2006 Pearson Education, Inc., Upper Saddle River, NJ. All rights reserved. This material is protected under all copyright laws as they currently exist. No portion of this material may be reproduced, in any form or by any means, without permission in writing from the publisher.

3. $x^2 + y^2 - 2x - 4y + 1 = 0$

$x^2 - 2x + 1 + y^2 - 4y + 4 = -1 + 1 + 4$

$(x-1)^2 + (y-2)^2 = 4 = 2^2$

Center $= (1, 2)$

radius $= 2$

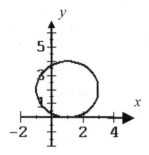

4. $y = a(x-h)^2 + k$ has $x = h$ as its axis of symmetry. $y = 4(x-3)^2 + 5$ has $x = 3$ as its axis of symmetry.

5. $y = a(x-h)^2 + k$ has $V(h,k)$. Therefore,

$y = \dfrac{1}{3}(x+4)^2 + 6 = \dfrac{1}{3}(x-(-4))^2 + 6$

has $V(-4, 6)$.

6. $x = (y+1)^2 + 2$

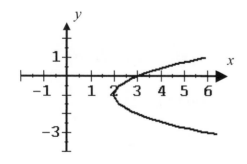

7. $x^2 = y - 4x - 1$

$y = x^2 + 4x + 1$

$y = x^2 + 4x + 4 - 3$

$y = (x+2)^2 - 2$

7.

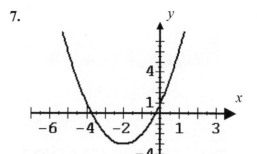

8. $C(0,0) \Rightarrow h = 0,\ k = 0$

x-intercept: $(-10, 0) \Rightarrow a = 10$

y-intercept: $(0, 7) \Rightarrow b = 7$

$\dfrac{(x-h)^2}{a^2} + \dfrac{(y-k)^2}{b^2} = 1$

$\dfrac{x^2}{10^2} + \dfrac{y^2}{7^2} = 1 \Rightarrow \dfrac{x^2}{100} + \dfrac{y^2}{49} = 1$

9. $4x^2 + y^2 - 36 = 0$

$4x^2 + y^2 = 36$

$\dfrac{x^2}{9} + \dfrac{y^2}{36} = 1$

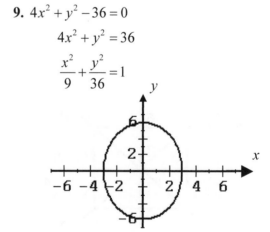

10. $\dfrac{(x+3)^2}{25} + \dfrac{(y-1)^2}{16} = 1$

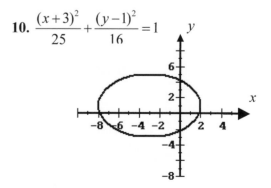

259

© 2006 Pearson Education, Inc., Upper Saddle River, NJ. All rights reserved. This material is protected under all copyright laws as they currently exist. No portion of this material may be reproduced, in any form or by any means, without permission in writing from the publisher.

9.4 Exercises

1. $\dfrac{x^2}{a^2} - \dfrac{y^2}{b^2} = 1$ where $a, b > 0$.

3. $\dfrac{x^2}{16} - \dfrac{y^2}{4} = 1$ is a horizontal hyperbola centered at the origin with vertices at $(4,0)$ and $(-4,0)$. Draw a fundamental rectangle with corners at $(4,2)$, $(4,-2)$, $(-4,2)$, $(-4,-2)$. Extend the diagonals through the rectangle as asymptotes of the hyperbola. Construct each branch of the hyperbola passing through the vertex and approaching the asymptotes.

5. $\dfrac{x^2}{4} - \dfrac{y^2}{25} = 1 \Rightarrow \dfrac{x^2}{2^2} - \dfrac{y^2}{5^2} = 1$

$a = 2, \ b = 5$

$V(\pm 2, 0), \ y_{\text{asymptote}} = \pm \dfrac{5}{2} x$

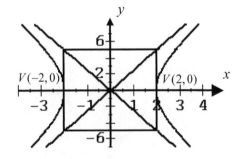

7. $\dfrac{y^2}{25} - \dfrac{x^2}{16} = 1 \Rightarrow \dfrac{y^2}{5^2} - \dfrac{x^2}{4^2} = 1$

$a = 4, \ b = 5$

$V(0, \pm 5)$

$y_{\text{asymptote}} = \pm \dfrac{5}{4} x$

7.

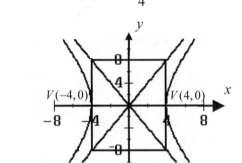

9. $4x^2 - y^2 = 64, \ \dfrac{x^2}{16} - \dfrac{y^2}{64} = 1$

$\dfrac{x^2}{4^2} - \dfrac{y^2}{8^2} = 1, \ a = 4, \ b = 8$

$V(\pm 4, 0), \ y_{\text{asymptote}} = \pm \dfrac{8}{4} x$

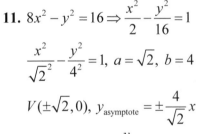

11. $8x^2 - y^2 = 16 \Rightarrow \dfrac{x^2}{2} - \dfrac{y^2}{16} = 1$

$\dfrac{x^2}{\sqrt{2}^2} - \dfrac{y^2}{4^2} = 1, \ a = \sqrt{2}, \ b = 4$

$V(\pm\sqrt{2}, 0), \ y_{\text{asymptote}} = \pm \dfrac{4}{\sqrt{2}} x$

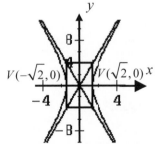

© 2006 Pearson Education, Inc., Upper Saddle River, NJ. All rights reserved. This material is protected under all copyright laws as they currently exist. No portion of this material may be reproduced, in any form or by any means, without permission in writing from the publisher.

13.

$$4y^2 - 3x^2 = 48$$

$$\frac{y^2}{12} - \frac{x^2}{16} = 1$$

$$\frac{y^2}{(2\sqrt{3})^2} - \frac{x^2}{4^2} = 1$$

$$b = 2\sqrt{3}$$

$$a = 4$$

$$V(0, \pm 2\sqrt{3}), \; y_{asymptote} = \pm \frac{\sqrt{3}}{4} x$$

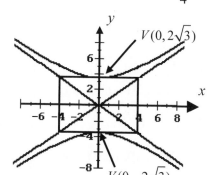

15. $V(\pm 3, 0) \Rightarrow a = 3, \; a^2 = 9$

$$y_{asymptote} = \pm \frac{4}{3} x$$

$$b = 4, \; b^2 = 16$$

$$\frac{x^2}{9} - \frac{y^2}{16} = 1$$

17. $V(0, \pm 11)$

$$b = 11, \; b^2 = 121$$

$$y_{asymptote} = \pm \frac{11}{13} x$$

$$a = 13, \; a^2 = 169$$

$$\frac{y^2}{121} - \frac{x^2}{169} = 1$$

19. $\dfrac{x^2}{a^2} - \dfrac{y^2}{b^2} = 1, \;$ from graph, $a = 120.$

$$y_{asymptote} = \frac{3}{1} x$$

$$\frac{b}{a} = \frac{3}{1}$$

$$\frac{b}{120} = \frac{3}{1}$$

$$b = 360$$

$$\frac{x^2}{120^2} - \frac{y^2}{360^2} = 1$$

$$\frac{x^2}{14,400} - \frac{y^2}{129,600} = 1$$

21. $\dfrac{(x-1)^2}{4} - \dfrac{(y+2)^2}{9} = 1$

$$\frac{(x-1)^2}{2^2} - \frac{(y+2)^2}{3^2} = 1$$

$$C(1, -2)$$

$$a = 2, \; b = 3$$

$$V(1 \pm 2, -2) = (3, -2), \; (-1, -2)$$

$$y_{asymptote} = \pm \frac{3}{2}(x-1) - 2$$

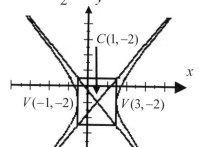

© 2006 Pearson Education, Inc., Upper Saddle River, NJ. All rights reserved. This material is protected under all copyright laws as they currently exist. No portion of this material may be reproduced, in any form or by any means, without permission in writing from the publisher.

23. $\dfrac{(y+2)^2}{36} - \dfrac{(x+1)^2}{81} = 1$

$\dfrac{(y+2)^2}{6^2} - \dfrac{(x+1)^2}{9^2} = 1$

$C(-1,-2)$

$a = 6,\ b = 9$

$V(-1,-2\pm6) = (-1,4),\ (-1,-8)$

$y_{\text{asymptote}} = \pm\dfrac{6}{9}(x-(-1)) + (-2)$

$y_{\text{asymptote}} = \pm\dfrac{2}{3}(x+1) - 2$

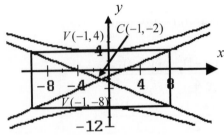

25. $\dfrac{(x+6)^2}{7} - \dfrac{y^2}{3} = 1$

$\dfrac{(x-(-6))^2}{\sqrt{7}^2} - \dfrac{(y-0)^2}{\sqrt{3}^2} = 1$

$C(-6,0)$

$V(-6\pm\sqrt{7},0)$

27. $C\left(4,\dfrac{0-14}{2}\right) = (4,-7)$

$y_{\text{asymptote}} = \dfrac{-7}{4}x = \dfrac{b}{a}x \Rightarrow a = 4,\ b = 7$

$\dfrac{(y-(-7))^2}{7^2} - \dfrac{(x-4)^2}{4^2} = 1$

$\dfrac{(y+7)^2}{49} - \dfrac{(x-4)^2}{16} = 1$

29. $8x^2 - y^2 = 16\big|_{x=3.5}$

$8(3.5)^2 - y^2 = 16$

$y^2 = 8(3.5)^2 - 16$

$y = \pm\sqrt{8(3.5)^2 - 16} = \pm9.055385138$

Cumulative Review

31. $12x^2 + x - 6 = (4x+3)(3x-2)$

33. $\dfrac{3}{x^2 - 5x + 6} + \dfrac{2}{x^2 - 4}$

$= \dfrac{3(x+2)}{(x-3)(x-2)(x+2)} + \dfrac{2(x-3)}{(x-2)(x+2)(x-3)}$

$= \dfrac{3x+6+2x-6}{(x-3)(x-2)(x+2)}$

$= \dfrac{5x}{(x-3)(x-2)(x+2)}$

35. $(x-4)d = 240 \Rightarrow d = \dfrac{240}{x-4}$

$x(d-2) = 240$

$x\left(\dfrac{240}{x-4} - 2\right) = 240$

$x(240 - 2(x-4)) = 240(x-4)$

$240x - 2x^2 + 8x = 240x - 960$

$2x^2 - 8x - 960 = 0$

$x^2 - 4x - 480 = 0$

$(x-24)(x+20) = 0$

$\qquad x = 24$ total on the team

$\qquad x - 4 = 20$ actually contributed

37. $\dfrac{(2.1\times10^9 + I)\ \text{pencils}}{274\times10^6\ \text{people}} = \dfrac{10\ \text{pencils}}{\text{person}}$

$I = 10(274\times10^6) - 2.1\times10^9$

$I = 640,000,000$ pencils were imported

© 2006 Pearson Education, Inc., Upper Saddle River, NJ. All rights reserved. This material is protected under all copyright laws as they currently exist. No portion of this material may be reproduced, in any form or by any means, without permission in writing from the publisher.

9.5 Exercises

1. $y^2 = 2x$

$y = -2x + 2$, substitute into first equation

$(-2x + 2)^2 = 2x$

$4x^2 - 8x + 4 = 2x$

$4x^2 - 10x + 4 = 0$

$2x^2 - 5x + 2 = 0$

$(2x - 1)(x - 2) = 0$

$x = \begin{cases} \dfrac{1}{2}, \; y = -2\left(\dfrac{1}{2}\right) + 2 = 1 \\ 2, \; y = -2(2) + 2 = -2 \end{cases}$

$(2, -2)$, $\left(\dfrac{1}{2}, 1\right)$ is the solution.

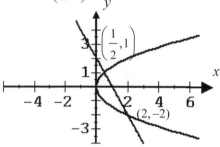

3. $x + 2y = 0 \Rightarrow x = -2y$

$x^2 + 4y^2 = 32$

$(-2y)^2 + 4y^2 = 32$

$4y^2 + 4y^2 = 8y^2 = 32 \Rightarrow y^2 = 4$

$y = \begin{cases} 2, \; x = -2(2) = -4 \\ -2, \; x = -2(-2) = 4 \end{cases}$

$(-4, 2)$, $(4, -2)$ is the solution.

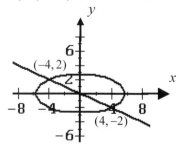

5. $\dfrac{x^2}{1} - \dfrac{y^2}{3} = 1 \Rightarrow 3x^2 - y^2 = 3$

$x + y = 1 \Rightarrow y = 1 - x$

$3x^2 - (1 - x)^2 = 3$

$3x^2 - 1 + 2x - x^2 = 3$

$2x^2 + 2x - 4 = 0$

$x^2 + x - 2 = 0$

$(x + 2)(x - 1) = 0$

$x + 2 = 0, \; x - 1 = 0$

$x = -2, \; x = 1$

$y = 1 - x = \begin{cases} 1 - (-2) = 3 \\ 1 - 1 = 0 \end{cases}$

$(-2, 3)$, $(1, 0)$ is the solution

7. $x^2 + y^2 - 25 = 0$

$3y = x + 5 \Rightarrow x = 3y - 5$

$(3y - 5)^2 + y^2 - 25 = 0$

$9y^2 - 30y + 25 + y^2 - 25 = 0$

$10y^2 - 30y = 0$

$10y(y - 3) = 0$

$10y = 0, \; y - 3 = 0$

$y = 0, \; y = 3$

$x = 3y - 5 = \begin{cases} 3(0) - 5 = -5 \\ 3(3) - 5 = 4 \end{cases}$

$(-5, 0)$, $(4, 3)$ is the solution

9. $x^2 + 2y^2 = 4$

$y = -x + 2$

$x^2 + 2(-x + 2)^2 = 4$

$x^2 + 2x^2 - 8x + 8 = 4$

$3x^2 - 8x + 4 = 0$

$(3x - 2)(x - 2) = 0$

© 2006 Pearson Education, Inc., Upper Saddle River, NJ. All rights reserved. This material is protected under all copyright laws as they currently exist. No portion of this material may be reproduced, in any form or by any means, without permission in writing from the publisher.

9. $3x - 2 = 0,\ x - 2 = 2$

$x = \dfrac{2}{3},\ x = 2$

$y = -x + 2 = \begin{cases} -\dfrac{2}{3} + 2 = \dfrac{4}{3} \\ -2 + 2 = 0 \end{cases}$

$\left(\dfrac{2}{3}, \dfrac{4}{3}\right),\ (2, 0)$ is the solution

11. $\dfrac{x^2}{4} - \dfrac{y^2}{4} = 1 \Rightarrow x^2 - y^2 = 4$

$x + y - 4 = 0 \Rightarrow x = 4 - y$

$(4 - y)^2 - y^2 = 4$

$16 - 8y + y^2 - y^2 = 4$

$8y = 12$

$y = \dfrac{3}{2}$

$x = 4 - y = 4 - \dfrac{3}{2} = \dfrac{5}{2}$

$\left(\dfrac{5}{2}, \dfrac{3}{2}\right)$ is the solution

13. $2x^2 - 5y^2 = -2 \overset{\times 2}{\rightarrow} 4x^2 - 10y^2 = -4$

$3x^2 + 2y^2 = 35 \overset{\times 5}{\rightarrow} \underline{15x^2 + 10y^2 = 175}$

$\qquad\qquad\qquad\quad 19x^2 \qquad\quad = 171$

$x = \pm 3$

$y^2 = \dfrac{35 - 3x^2}{2}$

$y = \pm\sqrt{\dfrac{35 - 3x^2}{2}}\Bigg|_{x = \pm 3} = \pm\sqrt{\dfrac{35 - 3(\pm 3)^2}{2}}$

$y = \pm 2$

$(3, \pm 2),\ (-3, \pm 2)$ is the solution

13.

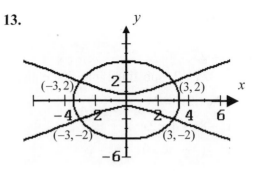

15. $x^2 + y^2 = 9$

$\underline{2x^2 - y^2 = 3}$

$3x^2 \qquad = 12$

$x^2 = 4$

$x = \pm 2$

$(\pm 2)^2 + y^2 = 9$

$y^2 = 5$

$y = \pm\sqrt{5}$

$(2, \pm\sqrt{5}), (-2, \pm\sqrt{5})$ is the solution.

17. $x^2 + 2y^2 = 8 \rightarrow x^2 + 2y^2 = 8$

$x^2 - y^2 = 1 \overset{\times -1}{\rightarrow} \underline{-x^2 + y^2 = -1}$

$\qquad\qquad\qquad\qquad\quad 3y^2 = 7$

$y = \pm\dfrac{\sqrt{21}}{3}$

$x^2 = 1 + y^2 = 1 + \dfrac{7}{3} = \dfrac{10}{3}$

$x = \pm\dfrac{\sqrt{30}}{3}$

$\left(\dfrac{\sqrt{30}}{3}, \pm\dfrac{\sqrt{21}}{3}\right), \left(-\dfrac{\sqrt{30}}{3}, \pm\dfrac{\sqrt{21}}{3}\right)$

is the solution

© 2006 Pearson Education, Inc., Upper Saddle River, NJ. All rights reserved. This material is protected under all copyright laws as they currently exist. No portion of this material may be reproduced, in any form or by any means, without permission in writing from the publisher.

19. $x^2 + y^2 = 7 \rightarrow \quad x^2 + y^2 = 7$

$\dfrac{x^2}{3} - \dfrac{y^2}{9} = 1 \rightarrow \dfrac{3x^2 - y^2 = 9}{}$

$ 4x^2 = 16$

$x^2 = 4$

$x = \pm 2$

$y^2 = 7 - x^2 = 7 - 4 = 3$

$y = \pm\sqrt{3}$

$(2, \pm\sqrt{3}), \ (-2, \pm\sqrt{3})$ is the solution

21. $2xy = 5 \Rightarrow x = \dfrac{5}{2y}$

$x - 4y = 3 \Rightarrow \dfrac{5}{2y} - 4y = 3$

$8y^2 + 6y - 5 = 0$

$(2y - 1)(4y + 5) = 0$

$y = \dfrac{1}{2}, \ y = -\dfrac{5}{4}$

$y = \dfrac{1}{2}, \ x = \dfrac{5}{2 \cdot \dfrac{1}{2}} = 5$

$y = -\dfrac{5}{4}, \ x = \dfrac{5}{2 \cdot \dfrac{-5}{4}} = -2$

$\left(5, \dfrac{1}{2}\right), \left(-2, -\dfrac{5}{4}\right)$ is the solution.

23. $xy = -6$

$2x + y = -4 \Rightarrow y = -4 - 2x$

$x(-4 - 2x) = -6$

$2x^2 + 4x - 6 = 0 \Rightarrow x^2 + 2x - 3 = 0$

$(x + 3)(x - 1) = 0$

$x = -3, \ x = 1$

$x = -3, \ y = -4 - 2(-3) = 2$

$x = 1, \ y = -4 - 2(1) = -6$

$(-3, 2), \ (1, -6)$ is the solution.

25. $x + y = 5 \Rightarrow x = 5 - y$

$x^2 + y^2 = 4 \Rightarrow (5 - y)^2 + y^2 = 4$

$25 - 10y + y^2 + y^2 = 4$

$2y^2 - 10y + 21 = 0$

$y = \dfrac{-(-10) \pm \sqrt{(-10)^2 - 4(2)(21)}}{2(2)}$

$y = \dfrac{10 \pm \sqrt{-68}}{4}$

No real solution, line does not intersect the circle.

27. $y = 2x - 6$

$\dfrac{x^2}{49} + \dfrac{y^2}{36} = 1 \Rightarrow \dfrac{x^2}{49} + \dfrac{(2x - 6)^2}{36} = 1$

$36x^2 + 49(4x^2 - 24x + 36) = 1764$

$36x^2 + 196x^2 - 1176x + 1764 = 1764$

$232x^2 - 1176x = 0$

$x(232x - 1176) = 0$

$x = 0, \ y = 2(0) - 6 = -6$

$x = \dfrac{1176}{232} = \dfrac{147}{29}, \ y = 2\left(\dfrac{147}{29}\right) - 6 = \dfrac{120}{29}$

$(0, -6), \ \left(\dfrac{147}{29}, \dfrac{120}{29}\right)$ are the points of crossing

© 2006 Pearson Education, Inc., Upper Saddle River, NJ. All rights reserved. This material is protected under all copyright laws as they currently exist. No portion of this material may be reproduced, in any form or by any means, without permission in writing from the publisher.

29. $x^2 + y^2 = 16,000,000 \Rightarrow$

$y^2 = 16,000,000 - x^2$

$25,000,000x^2 - 9,000,000y^2$

$= 2.25 \times 10^{14}$

$25x^2 - 9y^2 = 2.25 \times 10^8$

$25x^2 - 9(16,000,000 - x^2) = 2.25 \times 10^8$

$34x^2 = 369,000,000$

$x^2 = 10,852,941.18$

$x = 3294.380242$

$y^2 = 16,000,000 - 10,852,941.18$

$y^2 = 5,147,058.824$

$y = 2268.713032$

The hyperbola intersects the circle when $(x, y) \approx (3290, 2270)$

Cumulative Review

31. $(3x^3 - 8x^2 - 33x - 10) \div (3x + 1)$

$$\begin{array}{r} x^2 - 3x - 10 \\ 3x+1\overline{)3x^3 - 8x^2 - 33x - 10} \\ \underline{3x^3 + \ x^2} \\ -9x^2 - 33x \\ \underline{-9x^2 - \ 3x} \\ -30x - 10 \\ \underline{-30x - 10} \end{array}$$

$(3x^3 - 8x^2 - 33x - 10) \div (3x + 1) = x^2 - 3x - 10$

33. $P = 11.5n - 290,000 = \$1,187,750$

$11.5n = 1,477,750$

$n = 128,500$

Putting Your Skills to Work

1. $\dfrac{(x-h)^2}{a^2} + \dfrac{(y-k)^2}{b^2} = 1$

$(h,k) = (0,0),\ a = 30,\ b = 6$

$\dfrac{x^2}{30^2} + + \dfrac{y^2}{6^2} = 1 \Rightarrow \dfrac{x^2}{900} + + \dfrac{y^2}{36} = 1$

2. $t = \dfrac{d}{r} = \dfrac{1\ \text{mi}}{9.8\dfrac{\text{ft}}{\text{min}} \cdot \dfrac{\text{mi}}{5280\ \text{ft}} \cdot \dfrac{60\ \text{min}}{\text{hr}}}$

$t = 9\ \text{hr}$

3. $t = \dfrac{d}{r} = \dfrac{6\ \text{mi}}{9.8\dfrac{\text{ft}}{\text{min}} \cdot \dfrac{\text{mi}}{5280\ \text{ft}} \cdot \dfrac{60\ \text{min}}{\text{hr}} \cdot \dfrac{24\ \text{hr}}{\text{day}}}$

$t = 2.25\ \text{days}$

4. $11:36\ \text{A.M.} + \dfrac{40\ \text{min}}{\text{day}} \cdot 3\ \text{day}$

$= 1:36\ \text{P.M.}$

5. $\dfrac{40\ \text{min}}{\text{day}} \cdot \dfrac{1\ \text{hr}}{60\ \text{min}} \cdot n = 24\ \text{hr}$

$n = 36\ \text{day}$

6. $\dfrac{40\ \text{min}}{\text{day}} \cdot \dfrac{1\ \text{hr}}{60\ \text{min}} \cdot 92\ \text{day} = 61.3\ \text{hr}$

7. $61.3\ \text{hr} \cdot \dfrac{\text{day}}{24\ \text{hr}} = 2.6\ \text{day}$

Chapter 9 Review Problems

1. $d = \sqrt{(0 - (-3))^2 + (-6 - 2)^2} = \sqrt{73}$

2. $d = \sqrt{(-2 - (-7))^2 + (-1 - 3)^2} = \sqrt{41}$

266

© 2006 Pearson Education, Inc., Upper Saddle River, NJ. All rights reserved. This material is protected under all copyright laws as they currently exist. No portion of this material may be reproduced, in any form or by any means, without permission in writing from the publisher.

3. $(x-h)^2 + (y-k)^2 = r^2$

  $(x-(-6))^2 + (y-3)^2 = \sqrt{15}^2$

  $(x+6)^2 + (y-3)^2 = 15$

4. $(x-h)^2 + (y-k)^2 = r^2$

  $(x-0)^2 + (y-(-7))^2 = 5^2$

  $x^2 + (y+7)^2 = 25$

5. $x^2 + y^2 + 2x - 6y + 5 = 0$

  $x^2 + 2x + 1 + y^2 - 6y + 9 = -5 + 1 + 9$

  $(x+1)^2 + (y-3)^2 = 5 = \sqrt{5}^2$

  $C(-1,3),\ r = \sqrt{5}$

6. $x^2 + y^2 - 10x + 12y + 52 = 0$

  $x^2 - 10x + 25 + y^2 + 12y + 36$

  $\qquad\qquad\qquad = -52 + 25 + 36$

  $(x-5)^2 + (y+6)^2 = 9 = 3^2$

  $C(5,-6),\ r = 3$

7. $x = \dfrac{1}{3}y$

x	y
0	0	$V(0,0)$
3	3	y-intercept: $(0,0)$
3	-3

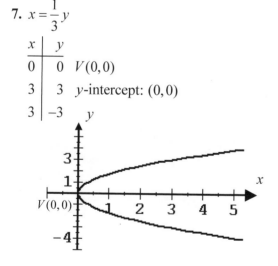

8. $x = \dfrac{1}{2}(y-2)^2 + 4$

x	y
4	2	$V(4,2)$
6	0	y-intercept: $(6,0)$
6	4

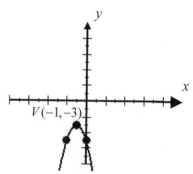

9. $y = -2(x+1)^2 - 3$

x	y
-2	-5	$V(-1,-3)$
-1	-3	y-intercept: $(0,-5)$
0	-5

10. $x^2 + 6x = y - 4$

  $y = x^2 + 6x + 9 - 9 + 4$

  $y = (x+3)^2 - 5$

  $V(-3,-5)$

  Opens upward.

© 2006 Pearson Education, Inc., Upper Saddle River, NJ. All rights reserved. This material is protected under all copyright laws as they currently exist.
No portion of this material may be reproduced, in any form or by any means, without permission in writing from the publisher.

11. $x + 8y = y^2 + 10$

$x = y^2 - 8y + 16 - 6$

$x = (y-4)^2 - 6$

$V(-6, 4)$

Opens to right.

12. $\dfrac{x^2}{4} + \dfrac{y^2}{1} = 1 \Rightarrow \dfrac{x^2}{2^2} + \dfrac{y^2}{1^2} = 1$

$a = 2, \ b = 1, \ C(0,0)$

Vertices: $(0,1), \ (0,-1), \ (-2,0), \ (2,0)$

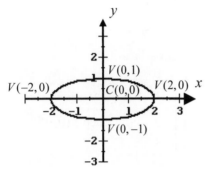

13. $16x^2 + y^2 - 32 = 0 \Rightarrow \dfrac{x^2}{2} + \dfrac{y^2}{32} = 1$

$\dfrac{x^2}{\sqrt{2}^2} + \dfrac{y^2}{(4\sqrt{2})^2} = 1$

$a = \sqrt{2}, \ b = 4\sqrt{2}$

$C(0,0)$

Vertices: $(0, 4\sqrt{2}), \ (0, -4\sqrt{2})$

$(-\sqrt{2}, 0), \ (\sqrt{2}, 0)$

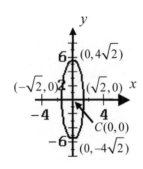

14. $\dfrac{(x+5)^2}{4} + \dfrac{(y+3)^2}{25} = 1$

$\dfrac{(x-(-5))^2}{2^2} + \dfrac{(y-(-3))^2}{5^2} = 1$

$C(-5, -3)$

$a = 2, \ b = 5$

Vertices: $(-3, -3), \ (-7, -3)$

$\qquad\quad (-5, 2), \ (-5, -8)$

15. $\dfrac{(x+1)^2}{9} + \dfrac{(y-2)^2}{16} = 1$

$\dfrac{(x-(-1))^2}{3^2} + \dfrac{(y-2)^2}{4^2} = 1$

$C(-1, 2)$

$a = 3, \ b = 4$

Vertices: $(2, 2), \ (-4, 2)$

$\qquad\quad (-1, 6), \ (-1, -2)$

16. $x^2 - 4y^2 - 16 = 0 \Rightarrow \dfrac{x^2}{16} - \dfrac{y^2}{4} = 1$

$\dfrac{x^2}{4^2} - \dfrac{y^2}{2^2} = 1, \ C(0,0), \ a = 4, \ b = 2$

Vertices: $(-4, 0), \ (4, 0)$

$y_{\text{asymptote}} = \pm\dfrac{2}{4}x = \pm\dfrac{1}{2}x$

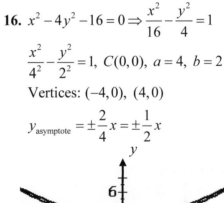

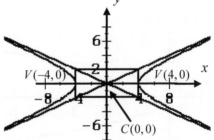

© 2006 Pearson Education, Inc., Upper Saddle River, NJ. All rights reserved. This material is protected under all copyright laws as they currently exist.
No portion of this material may be reproduced, in any form or by any means, without permission in writing from the publisher.

17. $3y^2 - x^2 = 27$

$\dfrac{y^2}{9} - \dfrac{x^2}{27} = 1 \Rightarrow \dfrac{y^2}{3^2} - \dfrac{x^2}{\sqrt{27}^2} = 1$

$a = 3,\ b = \sqrt{27},\ C(0,0)$

Vertices: $(0,3),\ (0,-3)$

$y_{\text{asymptote}} = \pm \dfrac{3}{\sqrt{27}} x = \pm \dfrac{\sqrt{3}}{3} x$

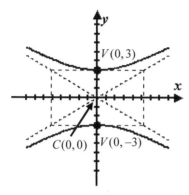

18. $\dfrac{(x-2)^2}{4} - \dfrac{(y+3)^2}{25} = 1$

$\dfrac{(x-2)^2}{2^2} - \dfrac{(y-(-3))^2}{5^2} = 1$

$C(2,-3),\ a = 2,\ b = 5$

Vertices: $(0,-3),\ (4,-3)$

19. $9(y-2)^2 - (x+5)^2 - 9 = 0$

$\dfrac{(y-2)^2}{1^2} - \dfrac{(x-(-5))^2}{3^3} = 0$

$C(-5,2),\ a = 3,\ b = 1$

Vertices: $(-5,3),\ (-5,1)$

20. $x^2 + y = 9 \rightarrow x^2 + y = 9$

$y - x = 3 \xrightarrow{\times -1} \underline{\quad x - y = -3\quad}$

$\ x^2 - x\ \ = 6$

20. $(x+3)(x-2) = 0$

$x + 3 = 0,\ x - 2 = 0$

$x = -3,\ x = 2$

$y = x + 3 = \begin{cases} -3 + 3 = 0 \\ 2 + 3 = 5 \end{cases}$

$(-3,0),\ (2,5)$ is the solution.

21. $x^2 + y^2 = 4$

$x + y = 2 \Rightarrow y = 2 - x$

$x^2 + (2-x)^2 = 4$

$x^2 + x^2 - 4x + 4 = 4$

$x^2 - 2x = 0 \Rightarrow x(x-2) = 0$

$x = 0,\ x = 2$

$x = 0,\ y = 2 - 0 = 2$

$x = 2,\ y = 2 - 2 = 0$

$(0,2),\ (2,0)$ is the solution.

22. $2x^2 + y^2 = 17 \Rightarrow y^2 = 17 - 2x^2$

$x^2 + 2y^2 = 22$

$x^2 + 2(17 - 2x^2) = 22$

$x^2 + 34 - 4x^2 = 22$

$3x^2 = 12$

$x^2 = 4$

$x = \pm 2$

$y = \pm\sqrt{17 - 2x^2}$

$y = \pm\sqrt{17 - 2(4)}$

$y = \pm 3$

$(2,\pm 3),\ (-2,\pm 3)$ is the solution.

23. $xy = -2 \Rightarrow y = \dfrac{-2}{x}$

$x^2 + y^2 = 5 \Rightarrow x^2 + \left(\dfrac{-2}{x}\right)^2 = 5$

© 2006 Pearson Education, Inc., Upper Saddle River, NJ. All rights reserved. This material is protected under all copyright laws as they currently exist.
No portion of this material may be reproduced, in any form or by any means, without permission in writing from the publisher.

23. $x^4 + 4 = 5x^2$

$x^4 - 5x^2 + 4 = 0$

$(x^2 - 4)(x^2 - 1) = 0$

$x^2 - 4 = 0, \ x^2 - 1 = 0$

$x^2 = 4, \ x^2 = 1$

$x = \pm 2, \ x = \pm 1$

$$y = \frac{-2}{x} = \begin{cases} \dfrac{-2}{2} = -1 \\[6pt] \dfrac{-2}{-2} = 1 \\[6pt] \dfrac{-2}{1} = -2 \\[6pt] \dfrac{-2}{-1} = 2 \end{cases}$$

$(2,-1), \ (-2,1), \ (1,-2), \ (-1,2)$ is the solution.

24. $3x^2 - 4y^2 = 12$

$7x^2 - y^2 = 8 \Rightarrow y^2 = 7x^2 - 8$

$3x^2 - 4(7x^2 - 8) = 12$

$3x^2 - 28x^2 + 32 = 12$

$25x^2 = 20 \Rightarrow x^2 = \dfrac{20}{25}$

$y^2 = 7x^2 - 8 = 7 \cdot \dfrac{20}{25} - 8 = -\dfrac{12}{5}$

$y^2 > 0 \Rightarrow$ No real solution, hyperbolas do not intersect.

25. $y = x^2 + 1 \Rightarrow x^2 = y - 1$

$x^2 + y^2 - 8y + 7 = 0$

$y - 1 + y^2 - 8y + 7 = 0 \Rightarrow y^2 - 7y + 6 = 0$

$(y-1)(y-6) = 0$

$y - 1 = 0, \ y - 6 = 0$

$y = 1, \ y = 6$

25. $x^2 = y - 1 = \begin{cases} 1 - 1 = 0 \\ 6 - 1 = 5 \end{cases}$

$x = \begin{cases} 0 \\ \pm\sqrt{5} \end{cases}$

$(0,1), \ (\sqrt{5},6), \ (-\sqrt{5},6)$ is the solution.

26. $2x^2 + y^2 = 18$

$xy = 4 \Rightarrow y = \dfrac{4}{x}$

$2x^2 + \left(\dfrac{4}{x}\right)^2 = 18$

$2x^4 + 16 = 18x^2$

$x^4 - 9x^2 + 8 = 0$

$(x^2 - 8)(x^2 - 1) = 0$

$x^2 = 8, \ x^2 = 1$

$x = \pm 2\sqrt{2}, \ x = \pm 1$

$$y = \frac{4}{x} = \begin{cases} \dfrac{4}{2\sqrt{2}} = \sqrt{2} \\[6pt] \dfrac{4}{-2\sqrt{2}} = -\sqrt{2} \\[6pt] \dfrac{4}{1} = 4 \\[6pt] \dfrac{4}{-1} = -4 \end{cases}$$

$(2\sqrt{2}, \sqrt{2}), \ (-2\sqrt{2}, -\sqrt{2}),$

$(1,4), \ (-1,-4)$ is the solution.

27. $y^2 - 2x^2 = 2 \xrightarrow{\times -2} -2y^2 + 4x^2 = -4$

$2y^2 - 3x^2 = 5 \rightarrow \underline{\ 2y^2 - 3x^2 = 5\ }$

$ \quad x^2 = 1, \ x = \pm 1$

$y^2 = 2x^2 + 2 = 2(1) + 2 = 4$

$y = \pm 2$

$(1, \pm 2), \ (-1, \pm 2)$ is the solution.

© 2006 Pearson Education, Inc., Upper Saddle River, NJ. All rights reserved. This material is protected under all copyright laws as they currently exist. No portion of this material may be reproduced, in any form or by any means, without permission in writing from the publisher.

28. $y^2 = 2x$

$y = \frac{1}{2}x + 1 \Rightarrow x = 2y - 2$

$y^2 = 2(2y - 2) = 4y - 4$

$y^2 - 4y + 4 = 0$

$(y - 2)^2 = 0$

$y = 2$

$x = 2y - 2 = 2(2) - 2 = 4 - 2 = 2$

$x = 2$

$(2, 2)$ is the solution.

29. $y^2 = \frac{1}{2}x$

$y = x - 1 \Rightarrow x = y + 1$

$y^2 = \frac{1}{2}(y + 1)$

$2y^2 - y - 1 = 0$

$(2y + 1)(y - 1) = 0$

$2y + 1 = 0, \ y - 1 = 0$

$y = -\frac{1}{2}, \ y = 1$

$x = y + 1 = \begin{cases} -\frac{1}{2} + 1 = \frac{1}{2} \\ 1 + 1 = 2 \end{cases}$

$\left(\frac{1}{2}, -\frac{1}{2}\right)$, $(2, 1)$ is the solution.

30. $y^2 = 4px$

$y^2 = 4(2)x = 8x$

$y^2 = 8x$

$2.5^2 = 8x$

$x = 0.78125$

The searchlight should be 0.78 feet deep.

31. $y^2 = 4px$

$5^2 = 4p(4)$

$p = \frac{25}{16} = 1.5625$

The receiver should be placed 1.56 feet from the center of the dish.

How Am I Doing? Chapter 9 Test

1. $d = \sqrt{(-2 - (-6))^2 + (5 - (-8))^2}$

$d = \sqrt{185}$

2. $y^2 - 6y - x + 13 = 0$

$x - 13 + 9 = y^2 - 6y + 9$

$x = (y - 3)^2 + 4$

Parabola: $V(4, 3)$

x-int: $(13, 0)$

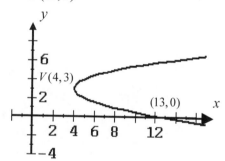

3. $x^2 + y^2 + 6x - 4y + 9 = 0$

$x^2 + 6x + 9 + y^2 - 4y + 4 = -9 + 9 + 4$

$(x + 3)^2 + (y - 2)^2 = 4 = 2^2$

Circle: $C(-3, 2)$, $r = 2$

x-int: $(-3, 0)$

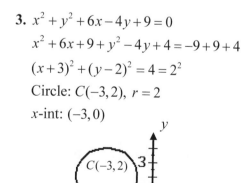

© 2006 Pearson Education, Inc., Upper Saddle River, NJ. All rights reserved. This material is protected under all copyright laws as they currently exist. No portion of this material may be reproduced, in any form or by any means, without permission in writing from the publisher.

4. $\dfrac{x^2}{25} + \dfrac{y^2}{1} = 1 \Rightarrow \dfrac{x^2}{5^2} + \dfrac{y^2}{1^2} = 1$

Ellipse: $C(0,0)$

$a = 5, \ b = 1$

Vertices: $(5,0),(-5,0),(0,1),(0,-1)$

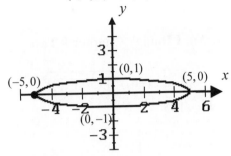

5. $\dfrac{x^2}{10} - \dfrac{y^2}{9} = 1$

Hyperbola:

Center: $C(0,0)$

Vertices: $V(\pm\sqrt{10},0)$

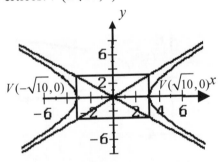

6. $y = -2(x+3)^2 + 4$

Parabola: $V(-3,4)$

y-intercept: $(0,-14)$

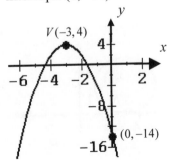

7. $\dfrac{(x+2)^2}{16} + \dfrac{(y-5)^2}{4} = 1$

$\dfrac{(x-(-2))^2}{4^2} + \dfrac{(y-5)^2}{2^2} = 1$

Ellipse: $C(-2,5), \ a = 4, \ b = 2$

Vertices: $(-2,7),(-2,3),(-6,5),(2,5)$

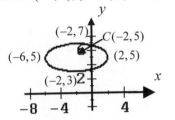

8. $7y^2 - 7x^2 = 28$

$\dfrac{y^2}{2^2} - \dfrac{x^2}{2^2} = 1,$ Hyperbola: $C(0,0)$

Vertices: $(0,2), \ (0,-2), \ a = 2, \ b = 2$

$y_{\text{asymptote}} = \pm\dfrac{2}{2}x = \pm x$

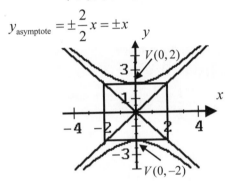

9. $(x-h)^2 + (y-k)^2 = r^2$

$(x-3)^2 + (y-(-5))^2 = \sqrt{8}^2$

$(x-3)^2 + (y+5)^2 = 8$

10. $C(h,k) = C(0,0) \Rightarrow h = 0, \ k = 0$

$(3,0) \Rightarrow a = 3, \ (0,5) \Rightarrow b = 5$

$\dfrac{(x-h)^2}{a^2} + \dfrac{(y-k)^2}{b^2} = 1$

$\dfrac{x^2}{9} + \dfrac{y^2}{25} = 1$

© 2006 Pearson Education, Inc., Upper Saddle River, NJ. All rights reserved. This material is protected under all copyright laws as they currently exist.
No portion of this material may be reproduced, in any form or by any means, without permission in writing from the publisher.

11. $x = (y-k)^2 + h, \ (h,k) = (-7,3)$

$x = (y-3)^2 + (-7)$

$x = (y-3)^2 - 7$

12. $C(h,k) = C(0,0) \Rightarrow h = 0, \ k = 0$

$V(\pm 3, 0) \Rightarrow a = 3$

$y_{\text{asymptote}} = \pm \dfrac{b}{a} x = \dfrac{5}{3} x \Rightarrow b = 5$

$\dfrac{(x-h)^2}{a^2} - \dfrac{(y-k)^2}{b^2} = 1$

$\dfrac{x^2}{9} - \dfrac{y^2}{25} = 1$

13. $-2x + y = 5 \Rightarrow y = 2x + 5$

$x^2 + y^2 - 25 = 0$

$x^2 + (2x+5)^2 - 25 = 0$

$x^2 + 4x^2 + 20x + 25 - 25 = 0$

$5x^2 + 20x = 0$

$5x(x+4) = 0$

$x = 0, \ x = -4$

$y = 2x + 5 = 2(0) + 5 = 5$

$y = 2(-4) + 5 = -3$

$(0,5), \ (-4,-3)$ is the solution.

14. $x^2 + y^2 = 9$

$y = x - 3$

$x^2 + (x-3)^2 = 9$

$x^2 + x^2 - 6x + 9 = 9$

$x^2 - 3x = 0$

$x(x-3) = 0$

$x = 0, \ x = 3$

$y = x - 3 = 0 - 3 = -3$

$y = x - 3 = 3 - 3 = 0$

$(0,-3), \ (3,0)$ is the solution.

15. $4x^2 + y^2 - 4 = 0 \Rightarrow y^2 = 4 - 4x^2$

$9x^2 - 4y^2 - 9 = 0$

$9x^2 - 4(4 - 4x^2) - 9 = 0$

$9x^2 - 16 + 16x^2 - 9 = 0$

$25x^2 = 25$

$x^2 = 1$

$x = \pm 1$

$y^2 = 4 - 4x^2 = 4 - 4(1) = 0 \Rightarrow y = 0$

$(1,0), \ (-1,0)$ is the solution.

16. $x^2 + 2y^2 = 15$

$\underline{x^2 - y^2 = 6} \ \text{subtract}$

$3y^2 = 9 \Rightarrow y^2 = 3 \Rightarrow y = \pm\sqrt{3}$

$x^2 = 6 + y^2 = 6 + 3 = 9 \Rightarrow x = \pm 3$

$(\sqrt{3}, \pm\sqrt{3}), \ (-\sqrt{3}, \pm\sqrt{3})$ is the solution.

Cumulative Test for Chapters 1-9

1. $5(-3) = -3(5)$ illustrates the commutative property of multiplication.

2. $2\{x - 3[x - 2(x+1)]\}$

$= 2\{x - 3[x - 2x - 2]\}$

$= 2\{x - 3[-x - 2]\}$

$= 2\{x + 3x + 6\}$

$= 2\{4x + 6\}$

$= 8x + 12$

3. $3(4-6)^3 + \sqrt{25} = 3(-2)^3 + \sqrt{25}$

$= 3(-8) + 5$

$= -24 + 5$

$= -19$

© 2006 Pearson Education, Inc., Upper Saddle River, NJ. All rights reserved. This material is protected under all copyright laws as they currently exist. No portion of this material may be reproduced, in any form or by any means, without permission in writing from the publisher.

4. $A = 3bt + prt$

$prt = A - 3bt$

$$p = \frac{A - 3bt}{rt}$$

5. $4x^3 - 16x = 4x(x^2 - 4)$

$$= 4x(x + 2)(x - 2)$$

6. $\dfrac{3x}{x-2} + \dfrac{5}{x-1} = \dfrac{3x(x-1) + 5(x-2)}{(x-2)(x-1)}$

$$= \frac{3x^2 - 3x + 5x - 10}{(x-2)(x-1)}$$

$$= \frac{3x^2 - 2x - 10}{(x-2)(x-1)}$$

7. $\dfrac{3}{2x+3} = \dfrac{1}{2x-3} + \dfrac{2}{4x^2 - 9}$

$$\frac{3}{(2x+3)} = \frac{1}{2x-3} + \frac{2}{(2x+3)(2x-3)}$$

$$3(2x-3) = 2x + 3 + 2$$

$$6x - 9 = 2x + 5$$

$$4x = 14$$

$$x = \frac{7}{2}$$

8. $3x - 2y - 9z = 9$

$$x - y + z = 8$$

$$2x + 3y - z = -2$$

Switch the first and second equation.

$$x - y + z = 8$$

$$3x - 2y - 9z = 9$$

$$2x + 3y - z = -2$$

Multiply the first equation by -3 and add to the second equation and multiply the first equation by -2 and add to the third equation

8. $x - y + z = 8$

$$y - 12z = -15$$

$$5y - 3z = -18$$

Multiply the second equation by -5 and add to the third equation

$$x - y + z = 8$$

$$y - 12z = -15$$

$$57z = 57$$

$$z = 1$$

$$y = 12z - 15 = 12(1) - 15$$

$$y = -3$$

$$x - y + z = 8$$

$$x - (-3) + 1 = 8$$

$$x = 4$$

$(4, -3, 1)$ is the solution.

9. $(\sqrt{2} + \sqrt{3})(2\sqrt{6} - \sqrt{3})$

$$= 2\sqrt{12} - \sqrt{6} + 2\sqrt{18} - 3$$

$$= 2\sqrt{4 \cdot 3} + 2\sqrt{9 \cdot 2} - \sqrt{6} - 3$$

$$= 4\sqrt{3} + 6\sqrt{2} - \sqrt{6} - 3$$

10. $\sqrt{12x^2} + 2x\sqrt{27} - \sqrt{18x}$

$$= \sqrt{4x^2 \cdot 3} + 2x\sqrt{9 \cdot 3} - \sqrt{9 \cdot 2x}$$

$$= 2x\sqrt{3} + 6x\sqrt{3} - 3\sqrt{2x}$$

$$= 8x\sqrt{3} - 3\sqrt{2x}$$

11. $x + 4(x + 2) > 7x + 8$

$$x + 4x + 8 > 7x + 8$$

$$-2x > 0$$

$$x < 0$$

© 2006 Pearson Education, Inc., Upper Saddle River, NJ. All rights reserved. This material is protected under all copyright laws as they currently exist. No portion of this material may be reproduced, in any form or by any means, without permission in writing from the publisher.

12. $\dfrac{6(x-4)}{5} \ge \dfrac{3(x+2)}{4}$

$24(x-4) \ge 15(x+2)$

$24x-96 \ge 15x+30$

$9x \ge 126$

$x \ge 14$

13. $d = \sqrt{(-3-6)^2+(-4-(-1))^2}$

$d = \sqrt{90}$

$d = \sqrt{9 \cdot 10}$

$d = 3\sqrt{10}$

14. $y = -\dfrac{1}{2}(x+2)^2-3$, Parabola: $V(-2,-3)$

y-intercept: $(0,-5)$

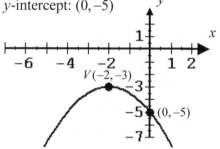

15. $25x^2+25y^2=125$

$x^2+y^2 = 5 = \sqrt{5}^2$

Circle: $C(0,0)$, $r = \sqrt{5}$

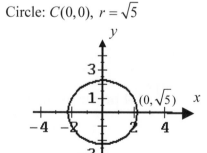

16. $16x^2-4y^2=64 \Rightarrow \dfrac{x^2}{4}-\dfrac{y^2}{16}=1$

$\dfrac{x^2}{2^2}-\dfrac{y^2}{4^2}=1$

Hyperbola: $C(0,0)$

$a = 2$, $b = 4$

Vertices: $(-2,0)$, $(2,0)$

$y_{\text{asymptote}} = \pm\dfrac{4}{2}x = \pm 2x$

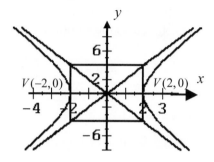

17. $\dfrac{(x-2)^2}{25}+\dfrac{(y-3)^2}{16}=1$

$\dfrac{(x-2)^2}{5^2}+\dfrac{(y-3)^2}{4^2}=1$

Ellipse: $C(2,3)$

$a = 5$, $b = 4$

Vertices: $(2,7),(-3,3),(2,-1),(7,3)$

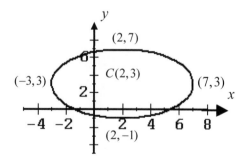

© 2006 Pearson Education, Inc., Upper Saddle River, NJ. All rights reserved. This material is protected under all copyright laws as they currently exist. No portion of this material may be reproduced, in any form or by any means, without permission in writing from the publisher.

18.
$$y = 2x^2$$
$$y = 2x + 4$$
$$2x^2 = 2x + 4$$
$$x^2 - x - 2 = 0$$
$$(x-2)(x+1) = 0$$
$$x - 2 = 0, \ x + 1 = 0$$
$$x = 2, \ x = -1$$
$$y = 2x^2 = 2(2)^2 = 8$$
$$y = 2(-1)^2 = 2$$
$(2, 8), \ (-1, 2)$ is the solution.

19. $y = x^2 + 1 \Rightarrow x^2 = y - 1$
$$4y^2 = 4 - x^2 = 4 - (y - 1)$$
$$4y^2 = 4 - y + 1$$
$$4y^2 + y - 5 = 0$$
$$(y-1)(4y+5) = 0$$
$$y = 1, \ y = -\frac{5}{4}$$
$$x = \pm\sqrt{y-1} = \begin{cases} \pm\sqrt{1-1} = 0 \\ \pm\sqrt{1-\dfrac{5}{4}} = \pm\dfrac{i}{2} \end{cases}$$

$(0, 1)$ is the solution.

20. $x^2 + y^2 = 25$
$$x - 2y = -5 \Rightarrow x = 2y - 5$$
$$(2y - 5)^2 + y^2 = 25$$
$$4y^2 - 20y + 25 + y^2 = 25$$
$$5y^2 - 20y = 0$$
$$5y(y - 4) = 0$$
$$5y = 0, \ y - 4 = 0$$
$$y = 0, \ y = 4$$
$$x = 2y - 5 = 2(0) - 5 = -5$$
$$x - 2y - 5 = 2(4) - 5 = 3$$
$(3, 4), \ (-5, 0)$ is the solution

21. $xy = -15 \Rightarrow y = -\dfrac{15}{x}$
$$4x + 3y = 3$$
$$4x + 3\left(-\frac{15}{x}\right) = 3$$
$$4x^2 - 45 = 3x$$
$$4x^2 - 3x - 45 = 0$$
$$(x + 3)(4x - 15) = 0$$
$$x + 3 = 0, \ 4x - 15 = 0$$
$$x = -3, \ x = \frac{15}{4}$$
$$y = -\frac{15}{x} = -\frac{15}{-3} = 5$$
$$y = -\frac{15}{x} = -\frac{15}{\frac{15}{4}} = -4$$
$(-3, 5), \ \left(\dfrac{15}{4}, -4\right)$ is the solution

276

© 2006 Pearson Education, Inc., Upper Saddle River, NJ. All rights reserved. This material is protected under all copyright laws as they currently exist. No portion of this material may be reproduced, in any form or by any means, without permission in writing from the publisher.

Chapter 10

10.1 Exercises

1. $f(x) = 3x - 5$

$$f\left(-\frac{2}{3}\right) = 3\left(-\frac{2}{3}\right) - 5$$

$$f\left(-\frac{2}{3}\right) = -7$$

3. $f(x) = 3x - 5$

$$f(a - 4) = 3(a - 4) - 5$$

$$f(a - 4) = 3a - 12 - 5$$

$$f(a - 4) = 3a - 17$$

5. $g(x) = \frac{1}{2}x - 3$

$$g(4) + g(a) = \frac{1}{2}(4) - 3 + \frac{1}{2}a - 3$$

$$= \frac{1}{2}a - 4$$

7. $g(x) = \frac{1}{2}x - 3$

$$g(4a) - g(a) = \frac{1}{2}(4a) - 3 - \left[\frac{1}{2}a - 3\right]$$

$$g(4a) - g(a) = 2a - 3 - \frac{1}{2}a + 3$$

$$g(4a) - g(a) = \frac{3}{2}a$$

9. $g(x) = \frac{1}{2}x - 3$

$$g(2a - 4) = \frac{1}{2}(2a - 4) - 3$$

$$g(2a - 4) = a - 2 - 3$$

$$g(2a - 4) = a - 5$$

11. $g(x) = \frac{1}{2}x - 3$

$$g(a^2) - g\left(\frac{2}{5}\right) = \frac{1}{2}a^2 - 3 - \left(\frac{1}{2} \cdot \frac{2}{5} - 3\right)$$

$$= \frac{1}{2}a^2 - 3 - \frac{1}{5} + 3$$

$$= \frac{1}{2}a^2 - \frac{1}{5}$$

13. $p(x) = 3x^2 + 4x - 2$

$$p(-2) = 3(-2)^2 + 4(-2) - 2$$

$$p(-2) = 2$$

15. $p(x) = 3x^2 + 4x - 2$

$$p\left(\frac{1}{2}\right) = 3\left(\frac{1}{2}\right)^2 + 4\left(\frac{1}{2}\right) - 2$$

$$p\left(\frac{1}{2}\right) = \frac{3}{4}$$

17. $p(x) = 3x^2 + 4x - 2$

$$p(a + 1) = 3(a + 1)^2 + 4(a + 1) - 2$$

$$p(a + 1) = 3a^2 + 6a + 3 + 4a + 4 - 2$$

$$p(a + 1) = 3a^2 + 10a + 5$$

19. $p(x) = 3x^2 + 4x - 2$

$$p\left(-\frac{2a}{3}\right) = 3\left(-\frac{2a}{3}\right)^2 + 4\left(-\frac{2a}{3}\right) - 2$$

$$p\left(-\frac{2a}{3}\right) = \frac{4a^2}{3} - \frac{8a}{3} - 2$$

21. $h(x) = \sqrt{x + 5}$

$$h(4) = \sqrt{4 + 5} = \sqrt{9} = 3$$

© 2006 Pearson Education, Inc., Upper Saddle River, NJ. All rights reserved. This material is protected under all copyright laws as they currently exist. No portion of this material may be reproduced, in any form or by any means, without permission in writing from the publisher.

23. $h(x) = \sqrt{x+5}$

$h(7) = \sqrt{7+5} = \sqrt{12} = \sqrt{4 \cdot 3}$

$h(7) = 2\sqrt{3}$

25. $h(x) = \sqrt{x+5}$

$h(a^2 - 1) = \sqrt{a^2 - 1 + 5} = \sqrt{a^2 + 4}$

27. $h(x) = \sqrt{x+5}$

$h(-2b) = \sqrt{-2b + 5}$

29. $h(x) = \sqrt{x+5}$

$h(4a - 1) = \sqrt{4a - 1 + 5}$

$= \sqrt{4a + 4}$

$= \sqrt{4(a+1)}$

$= 2\sqrt{a+1}$

31. $h(x) = \sqrt{x+5}$

$h(b^2 + b) = \sqrt{b^2 + b + 5}$

33. $r(x) = \dfrac{7}{x-3}$

$r(7) = \dfrac{7}{7-3}$

$r(7) = \dfrac{7}{4}$

35. $r(x) = \dfrac{7}{x-3}$

$r(3.5) = \dfrac{7}{3.5 - 3} = 14$

37. $r(x) = \dfrac{7}{x-3}$

$r(a^2) = \dfrac{7}{a^2 - 3}$

39. $r(x) = \dfrac{7}{x-3}$

$r(a+2) = \dfrac{7}{a+2-3}$

$r(a+2) = \dfrac{7}{a-1}$

41. $r(x) = \dfrac{7}{x-3}$

$r\left(\dfrac{1}{2}\right) + r(8) = \dfrac{7}{\dfrac{1}{2} - 3} + \dfrac{7}{8-3}$

$= -\dfrac{7}{5}$

43. $f(x) = 2x - 3$

$\dfrac{f(x+h) - f(x)}{h}$

$= \dfrac{2(x+h) - 3 - (2x-3)}{h}$

$= \dfrac{2x + 2h - 3 - 2x + 3}{h}$

$= \dfrac{2h}{h}$

$= 2$

45. $f(x) = x^2 - x$

$\dfrac{f(x+h) - f(x)}{h}$

$= \dfrac{(x+h)^2 - (x+h) - (x^2 - x)}{h}$

$= \dfrac{x^2 + 2xh + h^2 - x - h - x^2 + x}{h}$

$= \dfrac{2xh + h^2 - h}{h}$

$= \dfrac{h(2x + h - 1)}{h}$

$= 2x + h - 1$

278

© 2006 Pearson Education, Inc., Upper Saddle River, NJ. All rights reserved. This material is protected under all copyright laws as they currently exist. No portion of this material may be reproduced, in any form or by any means, without permission in writing from the publisher.

47. $P = 2.5w^2$

(a) $P(w) = 2.5w^2$

(b) $P(20) = 2.5(20)^2 = 1000$ kilowatts

(c) $P = 2.5(20 + e)^2 = 2.5(400 + 40e + e^2)$

$P(e) = 2.5e^2 + 100e + 1000$

(d) $P(2) = 2.5(2)^2 + 100(2) + 1000$

$= 1210$ kilowatts

49. The function values associated with $p(x) - 13$ would be the function values of $p(x)$ decreased by 13.

$p(3) - 13 \approx 39 - 13 = 26$

51. $f(x) = 3x^2 - 4.6x + 1.23$

$f(0.026a) = 3(0.026a)^2 - 4.6(0.026a) + 1.23$

$f(0.026a) = 0.002a^2 - 0.120a + 1.23$

53. $f(x) = 3x^2 - 4.6x + 1.23$

$f(a + 2.23)$

$= 3(a + 2.23)^2 - 4.6(a + 2.23) + 1.23$

$= 3a^2 + 13.380a + 14.919 - 4.6a - 10.258 + 1.23$

$= 3a^2 + 8.780a + 5.891$

55. $A(x) = \left(\dfrac{x}{4}\right)^2 + \left(\dfrac{20-x}{4}\right)^2$

$= \dfrac{x^2 + 400 - 40x + x^2}{16}$

$= \dfrac{2x^2 - 40x + 400}{16}$

$A(2) = \dfrac{2(2)^2 - 40(2) + 400}{16} = 20.5$

$A(5) = \dfrac{2(5)^2 - 40(5) + 400}{16} = 15.625$

$A(8) = \dfrac{2(8)^2 - 40(8) + 400}{16} = 13$

Cumulative Review

57. $\dfrac{7}{6} + \dfrac{5}{x} = \dfrac{3}{2x}$

$7x + 30 = 9$

$7x = -21$

$x = -3$

59. $\dfrac{V_{\text{Earth}}}{V_{\text{Mercury}}} = \dfrac{\dfrac{4}{3}\pi\left(\dfrac{7927}{2}\right)^3}{\dfrac{4}{3}\pi\left(\dfrac{3031}{2}\right)^3}$

$V_{\text{Earth}} = 17.88828747...(V_{\text{Mercury}})$

The volume of the Earth is approximately 17.9 times greater than the volume of Mercury.

10.2 Exercises

1. No, $f(x + 2)$ means substitute $x + 2$ for x in the function, $f(x)$. $f(x) + f(2)$ means evaluate $f(x)$ and $f(2)$ and then add the two results. One example is $f(x) = 2x + 1$

$f(x + 2) = 2(x + 2) + 1 = 2x + 5$

$f(x) + f(2) = 2x + 1 + 2(2) + 1 = 2x + 6$

3. To obtain the graph of $f(x) + k$, shift the graph of $f(x)$ <u>up</u> k units.

5. Graph fails vertical line test and does not represent a function.

7. Graph passes vertical line test and does represent a function.

9. Graph passes vertical line test and does represent a function.

© 2006 Pearson Education, Inc., Upper Saddle River, NJ. All rights reserved. This material is protected under all copyright laws as they currently exist.
No portion of this material may be reproduced, in any form or by any means, without permission in writing from the publisher.

11. Graph fails vertical line test and does not represent a function.

13. Graph passes vertical line test and does represent a function.

For Exercises 15, 17, and 19:

x	$f(x) = x^2$
-2	4
-1	1
0	0
1	1
2	4

15. $f(x) = x^2$, $h(x) = x^2 - 3$
Shift $f(x)$ down 3 units.

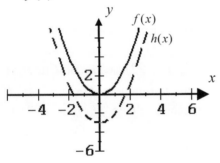

17. $f(x) = x^2$, $p(x) = (x+1)^2$
Shift $f(x)$ left 1 unit.

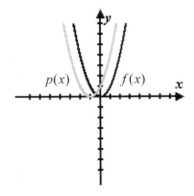

19. $f(x) = x^2$, $g(x) = (x-2)^2 + 1$
Shift $f(x)$ right 2 and up 1 units.

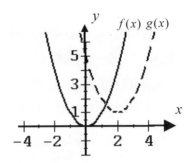

21. $f(x) = x^3$, $r(x) = x^3 - 1$
Shift $f(x)$ down 1 unit.

x	$f(x) = x^2$
-1	-1
0	0
1	1

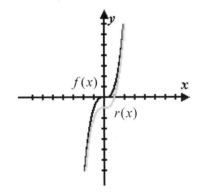

For Exercises 23 and 25:

x	$f(x) = |x|$
-2	2
-1	1
0	0
1	1
2	2

280

© 2006 Pearson Education, Inc., Upper Saddle River, NJ. All rights reserved. This material is protected under all copyright laws as they currently exist. No portion of this material may be reproduced, in any form or by any means, without permission in writing from the publisher.

23. $f(x) = |x|$, $s(x) = |x+4|$

Shift $f(x)$ left 4 units.

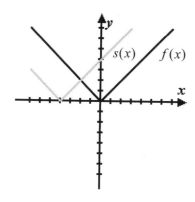

25. $f(x) = |x|$, $t(x) = |x-3|-4$

Shift right 3 and down 4 units.

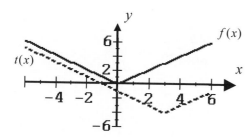

27. $f(x) = x^3$, $j(x) = (x-3)^3 + 3$

Shift $f(x)$ right 3 and up 3 units.

x	$f(x) = x^3$
-2	-8
-1	-1
0	0
1	1
2	8

29. $f(x) = \dfrac{3}{x}$, $g(x) = \dfrac{3}{x} - 2$

Shift $f(x)$ down 2 units.

x	$f(x) = \dfrac{3}{x}$
-3	-1
-1	-3
0	undefined
1	3
3	1

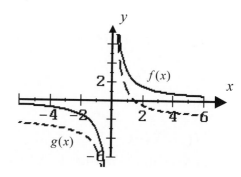

31. $f(x) = x^4$, $f(x) = (x-3.2)^4 - 2.6$

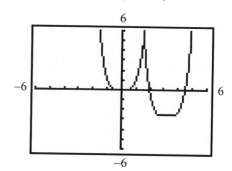

Cumulative Review

33. $\sqrt{12} + 3\sqrt{50} - 4\sqrt{27}$

$= \sqrt{4 \cdot 3} + 3\sqrt{25 \cdot 2} - 4\sqrt{9 \cdot 3}$

$= 2\sqrt{3} + 15\sqrt{2} - 12\sqrt{3}$

$= 15\sqrt{2} - 10\sqrt{3}$

281

© 2006 Pearson Education, Inc., Upper Saddle River, NJ. All rights reserved. This material is protected under all copyright laws as they currently exist. No portion of this material may be reproduced, in any form or by any means, without permission in writing from the publisher.

35. $\dfrac{\sqrt{5}-2}{\sqrt{5}+1} \cdot \dfrac{\sqrt{5}-1}{\sqrt{5}-1} = \dfrac{5-3\sqrt{5}+2}{5-1}$

$\qquad\qquad\qquad = \dfrac{7-3\sqrt{5}}{4}$

37. $\dfrac{\$13,623,120}{28,560} - 250 = \$227$

They overcharged each student $227.

How Am I Doing? Sections 10.1-10.2

1. $f(x) = 2x - 6$

$\quad f(-3) = 2(-3) - 6 = -12$

2. $f(x) = 2x - 6$

$\quad f(a) = 2a - 6$

3. $f(x) = 2x - 6$

$\quad f(2a) = 2(2a) - 6 = 4a - 6$

4. $f(x) = 2x - 6$

$\quad f(a+2) = 2(a+2) - 6 = 2a - 2$

5. $f(x) = 5x^2 + 2x - 3$

$\quad f(-2) = 5(-2)^2 + 2(-2) - 3 = 13$

6. $f(x) = 5x^2 + 2x - 3$

$\quad f(a) = 5a^2 + 2a - 3$

7. $f(x) = 5x^2 + 2x - 3$

$\quad f(a+1) = 5(a+1)^2 + 2(a+1) - 3$

$\qquad\qquad = 5(a^2 + 2a + 1) + 2a + 2 - 3$

$\qquad\qquad = 5a^2 + 10a + 5 + 2a - 1$

$\qquad\qquad = 5a^2 + 12a + 4$

8. $f(x) = 5x^2 + 2x - 3$

$\quad f(3a) = 5(3a)^2 + 2(3a) - 3$

$\qquad\qquad = 45a^2 + 6a - 3$

9. $f(x) = \dfrac{3x}{x+2}$

$\quad f(a) + f(a-2)$

$\quad = \dfrac{3a}{a+2} + \dfrac{3(a-2)}{a-2+2}$

$\quad = \dfrac{3a^2 + 3(a+2)(a-2)}{a(a+2)}$

$\quad = \dfrac{3a^2 + 3a^2 - 12}{a(a+2)}$

$\quad = \dfrac{6a^2 - 12}{a(a+2)}$

$\quad = \dfrac{6(a^2 - 2)}{a(a+2)}$

10. $\quad f(x) = \dfrac{3x}{x+2}$

$\quad f(3a) - f(3) = \dfrac{3(3a)}{3a+2} - \dfrac{3(3)}{3+2}$

$\qquad\qquad = \dfrac{9a}{3a+2} - \dfrac{9}{5}$

$\qquad\qquad = \dfrac{45a - 9(3a+2)}{5(3a+2)}$

$\qquad\qquad = \dfrac{45a - 27a - 18}{5(3a+2)}$

$\qquad\qquad = \dfrac{18(a-1)}{5(3a+2)}$

11. Graph passes vertical line test and therefore represents a function.

12. Graph does not pass vertical line test and hence does not represent a function.

© 2006 Pearson Education, Inc., Upper Saddle River, NJ. All rights reserved. This material is protected under all copyright laws as they currently exist. No portion of this material may be reproduced, in any form or by any means, without permission in writing from the publisher.

13. $f(x) = |x|$, $s(x) = |x-3|$

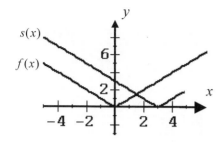

14. $f(x) = x^2$, $h(x) = (x+2)^2 + 3$

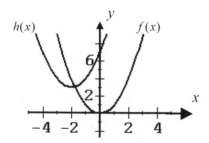

15. $f(x) = \dfrac{4}{x+2}$

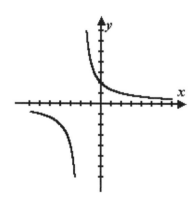

16. The graph of $g(x) = \dfrac{4}{x+2} - 2$ is the

graph of $f(x) = \dfrac{4}{x+2}$ shifted down 2

units.

10.3 Exercises

1. $f(x) = -2x+3$, $g(x) = 2+4x$
  (a) $(f+g)(x) = f(x) + g(x)$
$$= -2x+3+2+4x$$
$$= 2x+5$$
  (b) $(f-g)(x) = f(x) - g(x)$
$$= -2x+3-(2+4x)$$
$$= -2x+3-2-4x$$
$$= -6x+1$$
  (c) $(f+g)(2) = 2(2)+5$
$$= 9$$
  (d) $(f-g)(-1) = -6(-1)+1$
$$= 7$$

3. $f(x) = 3x^2 - x$, $g(x) = 5x+2$
  (a) $(f+g)(x) = f(x) + g(x)$
$$= 3x^2 - x + 5x + 2$$
$$= 3x^2 + 4x + 2$$
  (b) $(f-g)(x) = f(x) - g(x)$
$$= 3x^2 - x - (5x+2)$$
$$= 3x^2 - 6x - 2$$
  (c) $(f+g)(2) = 3(2)^2 + 4(2) + 2 = 22$
  (d) $(f-g)(-1) = 3(-1)^2 - 6(-1) - 2 = 7$

5. $f(x) = x^3 - \dfrac{1}{2}x^2 + x$, $g(x) = x^2 - \dfrac{x}{4} - 5$
  (a) $(f+g)(x) = f(x) + g(x)$
$$= x^3 - \frac{1}{2}x^2 + x + x^2 - \frac{x}{4} - 5$$
$$= x^3 + \frac{1}{2}x^2 + \frac{3x}{4} - 5$$

283

© 2006 Pearson Education, Inc., Upper Saddle River, NJ. All rights reserved. This material is protected under all copyright laws as they currently exist. No portion of this material may be reproduced, in any form or by any means, without permission in writing from the publisher.

5. (b) $(f - g)(x) = f(x) - g(x)$

$$= x^3 - \frac{1}{2}x^2 + x - (x^2 - \frac{x}{4} - 5)$$

$$= x^3 - \frac{1}{2}x^2 + x - x^2 + \frac{x}{4} + 5$$

$$= x^3 - \frac{3}{2}x^2 + \frac{5x}{4} + 5$$

(c) $(f + g)(2) = (2)^3 + \frac{1}{2}(2)^2 + \frac{3(2)}{4} - 5$

$$= \frac{13}{2}$$

(d) $(f - g)(-1) = (-1)^3 - \frac{3}{2}(-1)^2 + \frac{5(-1)}{4} + 5$

$$= \frac{5}{4}$$

7. $f(x) = -5\sqrt{x+6}, \ g(x) = 8\sqrt{x+6}$

(a) $f(x) + g(x) = f(x) + g(x)$

$$= -5\sqrt{x+6} + 8\sqrt{x+6}$$

$$= 3\sqrt{x+6}$$

(b) $f(x) - g(x) = -5\sqrt{x+6} - 8\sqrt{x+6}$

$$= -13\sqrt{x+6}$$

(c) $(f + g)(2) = 3\sqrt{2+6} = 3\sqrt{8} = 6\sqrt{2}$

(d) $(f - g)(-1) = -13\sqrt{-1+6} = -13\sqrt{5}$

9. $f(x) = 2x - 3, \ g(x) = -2x^2 - 3x + 1$

(a) $(fg)(x) = f(x)g(x)$

$$= (2x - 3)(-2x^2 - 3x + 1)$$

$$= -4x^3 - 6x^2 + 2x + 6x^2 + 9x - 3$$

$$= -4x^3 + 11x - 3$$

(b) $(fg)(-3)$

$$= -4(-3)^3 + 11(-3) - 3$$

$$= 72$$

11. $f(x) = \frac{2}{x^2}, \ g(x) = x^2 - x$

(a) $(fg)(x) = f(x)g(x) = \frac{2}{x^2}(x^2 - x)$

$$= 2 - \frac{2}{x} = \frac{2(x-1)}{x}$$

(b) $(fg)(-3) = \frac{2(-3-1)}{-3} = \frac{8}{3}$

13. $f(x) = \sqrt{-2x+1}, \ g(x) = -3x$

(a) $(fg)(x) = f(x)g(x) = \sqrt{-2x+1}(-3x)$

$$= -3x\sqrt{-2x+1}$$

(b) $(fg)(-3) = -3(-3)\sqrt{-2(-3)+1} = 9\sqrt{7}$

15. $f(x) = x - 6, \ g(x) = 3x$

(a) $\left(\dfrac{f}{g}\right)(x) = \dfrac{f(x)}{g(x)} = \dfrac{x-6}{3x}, \ x \neq 0$

(b) $\left(\dfrac{f}{g}\right)(2) = \dfrac{2-6}{3(2)} = -\dfrac{2}{3}$

17. $f(x) = x^2 - 1, \ g(x) = x - 1$

(a) $\left(\dfrac{f}{g}\right)(x) = \dfrac{f(x)}{g(x)} = \dfrac{x^2-1}{x-1}$

$$= \frac{(x-1)(x+1)}{x-1}$$

$$= x + 1, \ x \neq 1$$

(b) $\left(\dfrac{f}{g}\right)(2) = 2 + 1 = 3$

19. $f(x) = x^2 + 10x + 25, \ g(x) = x + 5$

(a) $\left(\dfrac{f}{g}\right)(x) = \dfrac{f(x)}{g(x)} = \dfrac{x^2+10x+25}{x+5}$

$$= \frac{(x+5)(x+5)}{(x+5)}$$

$$= x + 5, \ x \neq -5$$

© 2006 Pearson Education, Inc., Upper Saddle River, NJ. All rights reserved. This material is protected under all copyright laws as they currently exist.
No portion of this material may be reproduced, in any form or by any means, without permission in writing from the publisher.

19. (b) $\left(\dfrac{f}{g}\right)(2) = 2 + 5 = 7$

21. $f(x) = 4x - 1$, $g(x) = 4x^2 + 7x - 2$

(a) $\left(\dfrac{f}{g}\right)(x) = \dfrac{f(x)}{g(x)} = \dfrac{4x - 1}{4x^2 + 7x - 2}$

$= \dfrac{(4x - 1)}{(4x - 1)(x + 2)}$

$= \dfrac{1}{x + 2}, \; x \neq -2, \dfrac{1}{4}$

(b) $\left(\dfrac{f}{g}\right)(2) = \dfrac{1}{2 + 2} = \dfrac{1}{4}$

23. $f(x) = 3x + 2$, $g(x) = x^2 - 2x$

$(f - g)(x) = f(x) - g(x)$

$= 3x + 2 - (x^2 - 2x)$

$= -x^2 + 5x + 2$

25. $g(x) = x^2 - 2x$, $h(x) = \dfrac{x - 2}{3}$

$\left(\dfrac{g}{h}\right)(x) = \dfrac{g(x)}{h(x)} = \dfrac{x^2 - 2x}{\dfrac{x - 2}{3}}$

$= \dfrac{3x(x - 2)}{x - 2} = 3x, \; x \neq 2$

27. $(fg)(x) = 3x^3 - 4x^2 - 4x$

$(fg)(-1) = 3(-1)^3 - 4(-1)^2 - 4(-1) = -3$

29. $g(x) = x^2 - 2x$, $f(x) = 3x + 2$

$\left(\dfrac{g}{f}\right)(-1) = \dfrac{g(-1)}{f(-1)}$

$= \dfrac{(-1)^2 - 2(-1)}{3(-1) + 2} = -3$

31. $f(x) = 2 - 3x$, $g(x) = 2x + 5$

$f[g(x)] = f[2x + 5]$

$= 2 - 3(2x + 5)$

$= 2 - 6x - 15$

$= -6x - 13$

33. $f(x) = 2x^2 + 5$, $g(x) = x - 1$

$f[g(x)] = f[x - 1]$

$= 2(x - 1)^2 + 5$

$= 2(x^2 - 2x + 1) + 5$

$= 2x^2 - 4x + 7$

35. $f(x) = 8 - 5x$, $g(x) = x^2 + 3$

$f[g(x)] = f[x^2 + 3]$

$= 8 - 5(x^2 + 3)$

$= 8 - 5x^2 - 15$

$= -5x^2 - 7$

37. $f(x) = \dfrac{7}{2x - 3}$, $g(x) = x + 2$

$f[g(x)] = f(x + 2)$

$= \dfrac{7}{2(x + 2) - 3}$

$= \dfrac{7}{2x + 1}, \; x \neq -\dfrac{1}{2}$

39. $f(x) = |x + 3|$, $g(x) = 2x - 1$

$f[g(x)] = f[2x - 1]$

$= |2x - 1 + 3|$

$= |2x + 2|$ or

$= |2(x + 1)|$

$= |2||x + 1|$

$= 2|x + 1|$

© 2006 Pearson Education, Inc., Upper Saddle River, NJ. All rights reserved. This material is protected under all copyright laws as they currently exist. No portion of this material may be reproduced, in any form or by any means, without permission in writing from the publisher.

41. $f(x) = x^2 + 2,\ g(x) = 3x + 5$

$$f[g(x)] = f(3x + 5)$$
$$= (3x + 5)^2 + 2$$
$$= 9x^2 + 30x + 25 + 2$$
$$= 9x^2 + 30x + 27$$

43. $f(x) = x^2 + 2,\ g(x) = 3x + 5$

$$g[f(x)] = g[x^2 + 2]$$
$$= 3(x^2 + 2) + 5$$
$$= 3x^2 + 6 + 5$$
$$= 3x^2 + 11$$

45. From Exercise 43,

$$g[f(x)] = 3x^2 + 11$$
$$g[f(0)] = 3(0)^2 + 11$$
$$= 11$$

47. $p(x) = \sqrt{x - 1},\ f(x) = x^2 + 2$

$$(p \circ f)(x) = p[f(x)]$$
$$= p[x^2 + 2]$$
$$= \sqrt{x^2 + 2 - 1}$$
$$= \sqrt{x^2 + 1}$$

49. $g(x) = 3x + 5,\ h(x) = \dfrac{1}{x}$

$$(g \circ h)(\sqrt{2}) = g[h(\sqrt{2})]$$
$$= g\left[\frac{1}{\sqrt{2}}\right]$$
$$= 3 \cdot \frac{1}{\sqrt{2}} \cdot \frac{\sqrt{2}}{\sqrt{2}} + 5$$
$$= \frac{3\sqrt{2}}{2} + 5$$

51. $p(x) = \sqrt{x - 1},\ f(x) = x^2 + 2$

$$(p \circ f)(-5) = p[f(-5)]$$
$$= p\left[(-5)^2 + 2\right]$$
$$= p(27)$$
$$= \sqrt{27 - 1} = \sqrt{26}$$

53. $K[C(F)] = K\left[\dfrac{5F - 160}{9}\right]$

$$= \frac{5F - 160}{9} + 273$$
$$= \frac{5F - 160 + 9(273)}{9}$$
$$= \frac{5F + 2297}{9}$$

55. $v[r(h)] = v[3.5h]$

$$= 31.4(3.5h)^2$$
$$= 384.65h^2$$
$$384.65h^2\big|_{h=8} = 24{,}617.6 \text{ ft}^3$$

Cumulative Review

57. $36x^2 - 12x + 1 = (6x - 1)^2$

59. $x^4 - 10x^2 + 9 = (x^2 - 9)(x^2 - 1)$
$$= (x + 3)(x - 3)(x + 1)(x - 1)$$

61. $x = $ number of 60 sec commercials

$$60x + 30(20 - x) = 14(60)$$
$$60x + 600 - 30x = 840$$
$$30x = 240$$
$$x = 8$$
$$20 - x = 12$$

She should play eight commercials that are 60 sec long and twelve that are 30 sec long.

© 2006 Pearson Education, Inc., Upper Saddle River, NJ. All rights reserved. This material is protected under all copyright laws as they currently exist. No portion of this material may be reproduced, in any form or by any means, without permission in writing from the publisher.

10.4 Exercises

1. A one-to-one function is a function in which no ordered pairs <u>have the same second coordinate</u>.

3. The graphs of a function f and its inverse f^{-1} are symmetric about the line <u>$y = x$</u>.

5. The graph of a horizontal line is the graph of a function because it passes the vertical line test. A horizontal line is not the graph of a one-to-one function because it fails the horizontal line test.

7. $B = \{(0,1),(1,0),(10,0)\}$ is not one-to-one since two ordered pairs, $(1,0)$ and $(10,0)$, have the same second coordinate.

9. $F = \left\{\left(\dfrac{2}{3},2\right),\left(3,-\dfrac{4}{5}\right),\left(-\dfrac{2}{3},-2\right),\left(-3,\dfrac{4}{5}\right)\right\}$

is a one-to-one function since no two ordered pairs have the same second coordinate.

11.

$E = \left\{(1,1.28),\left(\dfrac{1}{2},-5\right),(-1,-2.8),\left(2.8,\dfrac{1}{2}\right)\right\}$

is a one-to-one function since no two ordered pairs have the same second coordinate.

13. Graph of function passes the horizontal line test and therefore, function is one-to-one.

15. Graph of function fails the horizontal line test and therefore, function is not one-to-one.

17. Graph of function fails the horizontal line test and therefore, function is not one-to-one.

19. $J = \{(8,2),(1,1),(0,0),(-8,-2)\}$

$J^{-1} = \{(2,8),(1,1),(0,0),(-2,-8)\}$

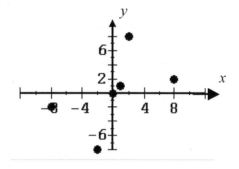

21. $f(x) = 4x - 5,\ f(x) \rightarrow y$

$y = 4x - 5,\ x \leftrightarrow y$

$x = 4y - 5$

$4y = x + 5$

$y = \dfrac{x+5}{4},\ y \rightarrow f^{-1}(x)$

$f^{-1}(x) = \dfrac{x+5}{4}$

23. $f(x) = x^3 - 2,\ f(x) \rightarrow y$

$y = x^3 + 7,\ x \leftrightarrow y$

$x = y^3 + 7$

$y^3 = x - 7$

$y = \sqrt[3]{x-7},\ y \rightarrow f^{-1}(x)$

$f^{-1}(x) = \sqrt[3]{x-7}$

© 2006 Pearson Education, Inc., Upper Saddle River, NJ. All rights reserved. This material is protected under all copyright laws as they currently exist. No portion of this material may be reproduced, in any form or by any means, without permission in writing from the publisher.

25. $f(x) = -\dfrac{4}{x},\ f(x) \to y$

$\quad y = -\dfrac{4}{x},\ x \leftrightarrow y$

$\quad y = -\dfrac{4}{x},\ y \to f^{-1}(-x)$

$\quad f^{-1}(x) = -\dfrac{4}{x}$

27. $f(x) = \dfrac{4}{x-5},\ f(x) \to y$

$\quad y = \dfrac{4}{x-5},\ x \leftrightarrow y$

$\quad x = \dfrac{4}{y-5}$

$\quad y - 5 = \dfrac{4}{x}$

$\quad y = \dfrac{4}{x} + 5,\ y \to f^{-1}(x)$

$\quad f^{-1}(x) = \dfrac{4}{x} + 5$

29. $g(x) = 2x + 5,\ g(x) \to y$

$\quad y = 2x + 5,\ x \leftrightarrow y$

$\quad x = 2y + 5$

$\quad 2y = x - 5$

$\quad y = \dfrac{x-5}{2}$

$\quad g^{-1}(x) = \dfrac{x-5}{2}$

31. $h(x) = \dfrac{1}{2}x - 2,\ h(x) \to y$

$\quad y = \dfrac{1}{2}x - 2,\ x \leftrightarrow y$

$\quad x = \dfrac{1}{2}y - 2$

$\quad 2x = y - 4$

$\quad y = 2x + 4$

$\quad h^{-1}(x) = 2x + 4$

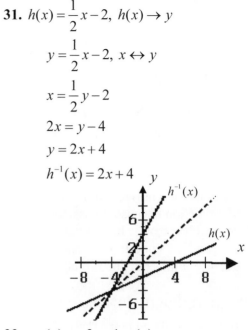

33. $r(x) = -3x - 1,\ r(x) \to y$

$\quad y = -3x - 1,\ x \leftrightarrow y$

$\quad x = -3y - 1$

$\quad 3y = -x - 1$

$\quad y = -\dfrac{x+1}{3},\ y \to r^{-1}(x)$

$\quad r^{-1}(x) = -\dfrac{x+1}{3}$

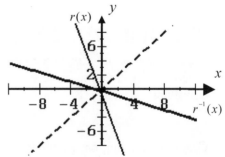

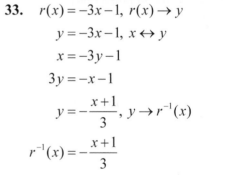

© 2006 Pearson Education, Inc., Upper Saddle River, NJ. All rights reserved. This material is protected under all copyright laws as they currently exist.
No portion of this material may be reproduced, in any form or by any means, without permission in writing from the publisher.

35. $f(x) = 1.437x - 4, \; f(x) \to y$

$y = 1.437x - 4, \; x \leftrightarrow y$

$x = 1.437y - 4$

$1.437y = x + 4$

$y = \dfrac{x+4}{1.437}, \; y \to f^{-1}(x)$

$f^{-1}(x) = \dfrac{x+4}{1.437}$

The inverse function tells how many Irish pounds were given by the bank for x dollars. No, because of the bank fee the inverse function will not work for Sean's transaction.

37. No. $f(x) = 2x^2 + 3$ is vertical parabola and fails the horizontal line test; it is not one-to-one and therefore, does not have an inverse.

39. $f\left[f^{-1}(x)\right] = f\left(\dfrac{1}{2}x - \dfrac{3}{4}\right)$

$= 2\left(\dfrac{1}{2}x - \dfrac{3}{4}\right) + \dfrac{3}{2}$

$= x - \dfrac{3}{2} + \dfrac{3}{2}$

$= x$

$f^{-1}\left[f(x)\right] = f^{-1}\left(2x + \dfrac{3}{2}\right)$

$= \dfrac{1}{2}\left(2x + \dfrac{3}{2}\right) - \dfrac{3}{4}$

$= x + \dfrac{3}{4} - \dfrac{3}{4}$

$= x$

Cumulative Review

41. $\qquad x = \sqrt{15 - 2x}$

$x^2 = 15 - 2x$

$x^2 + 2x - 15 = 0$

$(x + 5)(x - 3) = 0$

$\qquad\qquad x = -5, \; x = 3$

$x = -5$ does not check,

The solution is $x = 3$.

43. ratio $= \dfrac{4.6}{4.2} = \dfrac{23}{21}$

45. $\dfrac{1}{16}(12,800,000) = 800,000$ people

Putting Your Skills to Work

1. $\dfrac{1800 - 700}{700} = \dfrac{x - 120}{120}$

$x = 309$ lb

2. $\dfrac{3100 - 700}{700} = \dfrac{x - 200}{200}$

$x = 886$ lb

3. $P(x) = 0.027x^4 - 1.88x^3 + 41.25x^2$
$\qquad\qquad\qquad\qquad - 178.89x + 700$

$P(9) = 0.027 \cdot 9^4 - 1.88 \cdot 9^3 + 41.25 \cdot 9^2$
$\qquad\qquad\qquad\qquad - 178.89 \cdot 9 + 700$

$P(9) = 1238$ lb

4. $P(x) = 0.027x^4 - 1.88x^3 + 41.25x^2$
$\qquad\qquad\qquad\qquad - 178.89x + 700$

$P(9) = 0.027 \cdot 15^4 - 1.88 \cdot 15^3 + 41.25 \cdot 15^2$
$\qquad\qquad\qquad\qquad - 178.89 \cdot 15 + 700$

$P(9) = 2320$ lb

© 2006 Pearson Education, Inc., Upper Saddle River, NJ. All rights reserved. This material is protected under all copyright laws as they currently exist. No portion of this material may be reproduced, in any form or by any means, without permission in writing from the publisher.

5. $P(x) = 0.027x^4 - 1.88x^3 + 41.25x^2$
$$-178.89x + b$$

$P(21) = 0.027 \cdot 21^4 - 1.88 \cdot 21^3$
$$+41.25 \cdot 21^2 - 178.89 \cdot 21 + 400$$

$P(21) = 2675$ lb

6. $P(x) = 0.027x^4 - 1.88x^3 + 41.25x^2$
$$-178.89x + 1100$$

$P(28) = 0.027 \cdot 28^4 - 1.88 \cdot 28^3$
$$+41.25 \cdot 28^2 - 178.89 \cdot 28 + 1100$$

$P(28) = 3757$ lb

7. $P(x) = 0.027x^4 - 1.88x^3 + 41.25x^2$
$$-178.89x + 2000$$

$P(10) = 0.027 \cdot 10^4 - 1.88 \cdot 10^3$
$$+41.25 \cdot 10^2 - 178.89 \cdot 10 + 2000$$

$P(10) = 2726$ lb

8. $P(x) = 0.027x^4 - 1.88x^3 + 41.25x^2$
$$-178.89x + 2500$$

$P(11) = 0.027 \cdot 11^4 - 1.88 \cdot 11^3 + 41.25 \cdot 11^2$
$$-178.89 \cdot 11 + 2500$$

$P(11) = 3416$ lb

Chapter 10 Review Problems

1. $f(x) = \dfrac{1}{2}x + 3$

$f(a-1) = \dfrac{1}{2}(a-1) + 3 = \dfrac{1}{2}a + \dfrac{5}{2}$

2. $f(x) = \dfrac{1}{2}x + 3$

$f(a+2) = \dfrac{1}{2}(a+2) + 3 = \dfrac{1}{2}a + 4$

3. $\qquad f(x) = \dfrac{1}{2}x + 3$

$f(a-1) - f(a) = \dfrac{1}{2}(a-1) + 3 - \left(\dfrac{1}{2}a + 3\right)$

$$= \dfrac{1}{2}a - \dfrac{1}{2} + 3 - \dfrac{1}{2}a - 3$$

$$= -\dfrac{1}{2}$$

4. $\qquad f(x) = \dfrac{1}{2}x + 3$

$f(a+2) - f(a) = \dfrac{1}{2}(a+2) + 3 - \left(\dfrac{1}{2}a + 3\right)$

$$= \dfrac{1}{2}a + 1 + 3 - \dfrac{1}{2}a - 3$$

$$= 1$$

5. $\qquad f(x) = \dfrac{1}{2}x + 3$

$f(b^2 - 3) = \dfrac{1}{2}(b^2 - 3) + 3$

$$= \dfrac{1}{2}b^2 - \dfrac{3}{2} + 3$$

$$= \dfrac{1}{2}b^2 + \dfrac{3}{2}$$

6. $\qquad f(x) = \dfrac{1}{2}x + 3$

$f(4b^2 + 1) = \dfrac{1}{2}(4b^2 + 1) + 3$

$$= 2b^2 + \dfrac{1}{2} + 3$$

$$= 2b^2 + \dfrac{7}{2}$$

7. $p(x) = -2x^2 + 3x - 1$

$p(-3) = -2(-3)^2 + 3(-3) - 1$

$$= -28$$

290

© 2006 Pearson Education, Inc., Upper Saddle River, NJ. All rights reserved. This material is protected under all copyright laws as they currently exist.
No portion of this material may be reproduced, in any form or by any means, without permission in writing from the publisher.

8. $p(x) = -2x^2 + 3x - 1$

$p(-1) = -2(-1)^2 + 3(-1) - 1 = -6$

9. $p(x) = -2x^2 + 3x - 1$

$p(2a) + p(-2)$

$= -2(2a)^2 + 3(2a) - 1 + (-2(-2)^2 + 3(-2) - 1)$

$= -8a^2 + 6a - 1 + (-8 - 6 - 1)$

$= -8a^2 + 6a - 16$

10. $p(x) = -2x^2 + 3x - 1$

$p(-3a) + p(1)$

$= -2(-3a)^2 + 3(-3a) - 1 + (-2(1)^2$

$\qquad\qquad\qquad\qquad\quad + 3(1) - 1)$

$= -18a^2 - 9a - 1 + (-2 + 3 - 1)$

$= -18a^2 - 9a - 1$

11. $p(x) = -2x^2 + 3x - 1$

$p(a + 2) = -2(a + 2)^2 + 3(a + 2) - 1$

$\qquad\quad = -2(a^2 + 4a + 4) + 3(a + 2) - 1$

$\qquad\quad = -2a^2 - 8a - 8 + 3a + 6 - 1$

$\qquad\quad = -2a^2 - 5a - 3$

12. $p(x) = -2x^2 + 3x - 1$

$p(a - 3) = -2(a - 3)^2 + 3(a - 3) - 1$

$\qquad\quad = -2(a^2 - 6a + 9) + 3a - 9 - 1$

$\qquad\quad = -2a^2 + 12a - 18 + 3a - 10$

$\qquad\quad = -2a^2 + 15a - 28$

13. $h(x) = |2x - 1|$

$h(0) = |2(0) - 1| = |-1| = 1$

14. $h(x) = |2x - 1|$

$h(-5) = |2(-5) - 1| = |-11| = 11$

15. $h(x) = |2x - 1|$

$h\left(\dfrac{1}{4}a\right) = \left|2\left(\dfrac{1}{4}a\right) - 1\right|$

$\qquad\quad = \left|\dfrac{1}{2}a - 1\right|$

16. $h(x) = |2x - 1|$

$h\left(\dfrac{3}{2}a\right) = \left|2\left(\dfrac{3}{2}a\right) - 1\right| = |3a - 1|$

17. $h(x) = |2x - 1|$

$h(a^2 + a) = |2(a^2 + a) - 1| = |2a^2 + 2a - 1|$

18. $h(x) = |2x - 1|$

$h(2a^2 - 3a) = |2(2a^2 - 3a) - 1|$

$h(2a^2 - 3a) = |4a^2 - 6a - 1|$

19. $r(x) = \dfrac{3x}{x + 4}, \ x \neq -4$

$r(5) = \dfrac{3(5)}{5 + 4} = \dfrac{15}{9} = \dfrac{5}{3}$

20. $r(x) = \dfrac{3x}{x + 4}, \ x \neq -4$

$r(-6) = \dfrac{3(-6)}{-6 + 4}$

$\qquad = \dfrac{-18}{-2} = 9$

21. $r(x) = \dfrac{3x}{x + 4}, \ x \neq -4$

$r(2a - 5) = \dfrac{3(2a - 5)}{2a - 5 + 4} = \dfrac{6a - 15}{2a - 1}$

© 2006 Pearson Education, Inc., Upper Saddle River, NJ. All rights reserved. This material is protected under all copyright laws as they currently exist. No portion of this material may be reproduced, in any form or by any means, without permission in writing from the publisher.

22. $r(x) = \dfrac{3x}{x+4},\ x \neq -4$

$r(1-a) = \dfrac{3(1-a)}{1-a+4} = \dfrac{3-3a}{5-a}$

23. $r(x) = \dfrac{3x}{x+4},\ x \neq -4$

$r(3) + r(a) = \dfrac{3(3)}{3+4} + \dfrac{3(a)}{a+4}$

$= \dfrac{9}{7} + \dfrac{3a}{a+4}$

$= \dfrac{9(a+4) + 7(3a)}{7(a+4)}$

$= \dfrac{9a + 36 + 21a}{7a + 28}$

$= \dfrac{30a + 36}{7a + 28}$

24. $r(x) = \dfrac{3x}{x+4},\ x \neq -4$

$r(a) + r(-2) = \dfrac{3a}{a+4} + \dfrac{3(-2)}{-2+4}$

$= \dfrac{3a}{a+4} + \dfrac{-6}{2}$

$= \dfrac{3a}{a+4} - 3$

$= \dfrac{3a - 3(a+4)}{a+4}$

$= -\dfrac{12}{a+4}$

25. $f(x) = 7x - 4$

$\dfrac{f(x+h) - f(x)}{h} = \dfrac{7(x+h) - 4 - (7x-4)}{h}$

$= \dfrac{7x + 7h - 4 - 7x + 4}{h}$

$= 7$

26. $f(x) = 6x - 5$

$\dfrac{f(x+h) - f(x)}{h} = \dfrac{6(x+h) - 5 - (6x-5)}{h}$

$= \dfrac{6x + 6h - 5 - 6x + 5}{h}$

$= 6$

27. $f(x) = 2x^2 - 5x$

$\dfrac{f(x+h) - f(x)}{h}$

$= \dfrac{2(x+h)^2 - 5(x+h) - (2x^2 - 5x)}{h}$

$= \dfrac{2x^2 + 4xh + 2h^2 - 5x - 5h - 2x^2 + 5x}{h}$

$= \dfrac{4xh + 2h^2 - 5h}{h}$

$= 4x + 2h - 5$

28. $f(x) = 2x - 3x^2$

$\dfrac{f(x+h) - f(x)}{h}$

$= \dfrac{2(x+h) - 3(x+h)^2 - (2x - 3x^2)}{h}$

$= \dfrac{2x + 2h - 3x^2 - 6xh - 3h^2 - 2x + 3x^2}{h}$

$= \dfrac{2h - 6xh - 3h^2}{h}$

$= 2 - 6x - 3h$

$= -6x - 3h + 2$

29. (a) Yes, the graph passes the vertical line test and therefore represents a function.
(b) Yes, the graph passes the horizontal line test and therefore represents a one-to-one function.

© 2006 Pearson Education, Inc., Upper Saddle River, NJ. All rights reserved. This material is protected under all copyright laws as they currently exist. No portion of this material may be reproduced, in any form or by any means, without permission in writing from the publisher.

30. (a) No, the graph fails the vertical line test and therefore does not represent a function.

(b) No, unless the graph represents a function first it cannot represent a one-to-one function.

31. (a) Yes, the graph passes the vertical line test and therefore represents a function.

(b) No, the graph fails the horizontal line test and therefore does not represent a one-to-one function.

32. (a) Yes, the graph passes the vertical line test and therefore represents a function.

(b) No, the graph fails the horizontal line test and therefore does not represent a one-to-one function.

33. (a) No, the graph fails the vertical line test and therefore does not represent a function.

(b) No, unless the graph represents a function first it cannot represent a one-to-one function.

34. (a) Yes, the graph passes the vertical line test and therefore represents a function.

(b) Yes, the graph passes the horizontal line test and therefore represents a one-to-one function.

35. $f(x) = x^2$

$g(x) = (x+2)^2 + 4$ is $f(x)$ shifted left 2 units and up 4 units.

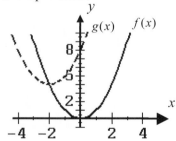

36. $f(x) = |x|$

$g(x) = |x+3|$ is $f(x)$ shifted left 3 units.

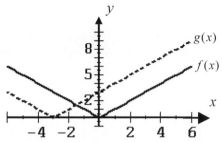

37. $f(x) = |x|$

$g(x) = |x-4|$ is $f(x)$ shifted right 4 units.

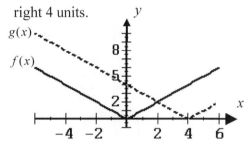

38. $f(x) = |x|$

$h(x) = |x| + 3$ is $f(x)$ shifted up 3 units.

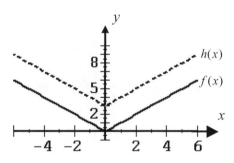

39. $f(x) = |x|$

$h(x) = |x| - 2$ is $f(x)$ shifted down 2 units.

© 2006 Pearson Education, Inc., Upper Saddle River, NJ. All rights reserved. This material is protected under all copyright laws as they currently exist. No portion of this material may be reproduced, in any form or by any means, without permission in writing from the publisher.

39.

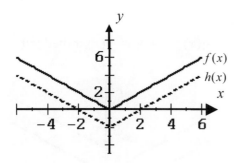

40. $f(x) = x^3$

$r(x) = (x+3)^3 + 1$ is $f(x)$ shifted left
3 units and up 1 unit.

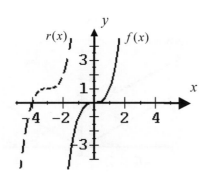

41. $f(x) = x^3$

$r(x) = (x-1)^3 + 5$ is $f(x)$ shifted right 1
unit and up 5 units.

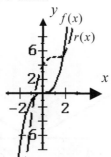

42. $f(x) = \dfrac{2}{x},\ x \neq 0$

$r(x) = \dfrac{2}{x+3} - 2,\ x \neq -3$ is $f(x)$ shifted
left 3 units and down 2 units.

42.

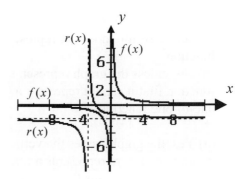

43. $f(x) = \dfrac{4}{x},\ x \neq 0$

$r(x) = \dfrac{4}{x+2},\ x \neq 2$ is $f(x)$ shifted
left 2 units.

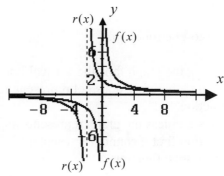

In Exercises 44-63,

$$f(x) = 3x + 5;\ g(x) = \frac{2}{x},\ x \neq 0$$

$$s(x) = \sqrt{x-2},\ x \geq 2;\ h(x) = \frac{x+1}{x-4},\ x \neq 4$$

$$p(x) = 2x^2 - 3x + 4;\ t(x) = -\frac{1}{2}x - 3$$

44. $(f+t)(x) = f(x) + t(x)$

$$= 3x + 5 + \left(-\frac{1}{2}x - 3\right)$$

$$= \frac{5}{2}x + 2$$

© 2006 Pearson Education, Inc., Upper Saddle River, NJ. All rights reserved. This material is protected under all copyright laws as they currently exist.
No portion of this material may be reproduced, in any form or by any means, without permission in writing from the publisher.

45. $(f+p)(x) = f(x) + p(x)$

$$= 3x + 5 + 2x^2 - 3x + 4$$
$$= 2x^2 + 9$$

46. $(p-f)(x) = p(x) - f(x)$

$$= 2x^2 - 3x + 4 - (3x + 5)$$
$$= 2x^2 - 3x + 4 - 3x - 5$$
$$= 2x^2 - 6x - 1$$

47. $(t-f)(x) = t(x) - f(x)$

$$= -\frac{1}{2}x - 3 - (3x + 5)$$
$$= -\frac{7}{2}x - 8$$

48. From Exercise 46,

$$(p-f)(x) = 2x^2 - 6x - 1$$
$$(p-f)(2) = 2(2)^2 - 6(2) - 1$$
$$= 2(4) - 12 - 1$$
$$= 8 - 13$$
$$= -5$$

49. From Exercise 47,

$$(t-f)(x) = -\frac{7}{2}x - 8$$
$$(t-f)(-3) = -\frac{7}{2}(-3) - 8$$
$$= \frac{5}{2}$$

50. $(fg)(x) = f(x)g(x)$

$$= (3x + 5)\left(\frac{2}{x}\right)$$
$$= \frac{6x + 10}{x}, \; x \neq 0$$

51. $(tp)(x) = t(x)p(x)$

$$= \left(-\frac{1}{2}x - 3\right)(2x^2 - 3x + 4)$$
$$= -x^3 + \frac{3x^2}{2} - 2x - 6x^2 + 9x - 12$$
$$= -x^3 - \frac{9}{2}x^2 + 7x - 12$$

52. $\left(\dfrac{g}{h}\right)(x) = \dfrac{g(x)}{h(x)} = \dfrac{\dfrac{2}{x}}{\dfrac{x+1}{x+4}}$

$$= \frac{2}{x} \cdot \frac{x-4}{x+1}$$
$$= \frac{2x - 8}{x^2 + x}, \; x \neq 0, 4, -1$$

53. $\left(\dfrac{g}{f}\right)(x) = \dfrac{g(x)}{f(x)} = \dfrac{\dfrac{2}{x}}{3x + 5}$

$$= \frac{2}{x} \cdot \frac{1}{3x + 5}$$
$$= \frac{2}{3x^2 + 5x}, \; x \neq 0, -\frac{5}{3}$$

54. From Exercise 52,

$$\left(\frac{g}{h}\right)(x) = \frac{2x - 8}{x^2 + x}, \; x \neq -1, 0, 4$$
$$\left(\frac{g}{h}\right)(-2) = \frac{2(-2) - 8}{(-2)^2 + (-2)} = -6$$

55. From Exercise 53,

$$\left(\frac{g}{f}\right)(x) = \frac{2}{3x^2 + 5x}, \; x \neq 0, -\frac{5}{3}$$
$$\left(\frac{g}{f}\right)(-3) = \frac{2}{3(-3)^2 + 5(-3)} = \frac{1}{6}$$

© 2006 Pearson Education, Inc., Upper Saddle River, NJ. All rights reserved. This material is protected under all copyright laws as they currently exist.
No portion of this material may be reproduced, in any form or by any means, without permission in writing from the publisher.

56. $p[f(x)] = p[3x + 5]$
$$= 2(3x + 5)^2 - 3(3x + 5) + 4$$
$$= 18x^2 + 60x + 50 - 9x - 15 + 4$$
$$= 18x^2 + 51x + 39$$

57. $t[s(x)] = t(\sqrt{x - 2})$
$$= -\frac{1}{2}\sqrt{x - 2} - 3$$

58. $s[p(x)] = s\left[2x^2 - 3x + 4\right]$
$$= \sqrt{2x^2 - 3x + 4 - 2}$$
$$= \sqrt{2x^2 - 3x + 2}$$

59. $s[t(x)] = s\left[-\frac{1}{2}x - 3\right]$
$$= \sqrt{-\frac{1}{2}x - 3 - 2}$$
$$= \sqrt{-\frac{1}{2}x - 5}, \ x \le -10$$

60. From Exercise 58,
$$s[p(x)] = \sqrt{2x^2 - 3x + 2}$$
$$s[p(2)] = \sqrt{2(2)^2 - 3(2) + 2} = 2$$

61. From Exercise 59,
$$s[t(x)] = \sqrt{-\frac{1}{2}x - 5}, \ x \le 10$$
$$s[t(-18)] = \sqrt{-\frac{1}{2}(-18) - 5} = 2$$

62. $f[g(x)] = f\left[\frac{2}{x}\right], \ x \ne 0$
$$= 3\left(\frac{2}{x}\right) + 5 = \frac{6}{x} + 5$$
$$= \frac{6 + 5x}{x}$$
$$g[f(x)] = g[3x + 5]$$
$$= \frac{2}{3x + 5}$$
$$f[g(x)] \ne g[f(x)]$$

63. $p[g(x)] = p\left[\frac{2}{x}\right]$
$$= 2\left(\frac{2}{x}\right)^2 - 3\left(\frac{2}{x}\right) + 4$$
$$= \frac{8 - 6x + 4x^2}{x^2}$$
$$g[p(x)] = g\left[2x^2 - 3x + 4\right]$$
$$= \frac{2}{2x^2 - 3x + 4}$$
$$p[g(x)] \ne g[p(x)]$$

64. $B = \{(3, 7), (7, 3), (0, 8), (0, -8)\}$
   (a) $D = \{0, 3, 7\}$
   (b) $R = \{-8, 3, 7, 8\}$
   (c) No, the set does not define a function since two of the ordered pairs have the same first coordinate.
   (d) No, since the set does not define a function it cannot define a one-to-one function.

65. $A = \{(100, 10), (200, 20), (300, 30), (400, 10)\}$
   (a) $D = \{100, 200, 300, 400\}$
   (b) $R = \{10, 20, 30\}$

© 2006 Pearson Education, Inc., Upper Saddle River, NJ. All rights reserved. This material is protected under all copyright laws as they currently exist. No portion of this material may be reproduced, in any form or by any means, without permission in writing from the publisher.

65. (c) Yes, the set defines a function since no two of the ordered pairs have the same first coordinate.
(d) No, the set does not define a one-to-one function since two of the ordered pairs have the same second coordinate.

66. $D = \left\{\left(\frac{1}{2}, 2\right), \left(\frac{1}{4}, 4\right), \left(-\frac{1}{3}, -3\right), \left(4, \frac{1}{4}\right)\right\}$

(a) domain $= \left\{\frac{1}{2}, \frac{1}{4}, -\frac{1}{3}, 4\right\}$

(b) $R = \left\{2, 4, -3, \frac{1}{4}\right\}$

(c) Yes, the set defines a function since no two of the ordered pairs have the same first coordinate.
(d) Yes, the set defines a one-to-one function since it is a function and no two ordered pairs have the same second coordinate.

67. $C = \{(12, 6), (0, 6), (0, -1), (-6, -12)\}$

(a) $D = \{12, 0, -6\}$

(b) $R = \{-1, -12, 6\}$

(c) No, the set does not define a function since two of the ordered pairs have the same first coordinate.
(d) No, since the set does not define a function it cannot define a one-to-one function.

68. $F = \{(3, 7), (2, 1), (0, -3), (1, 1)\}$

(a) $D = \{0, 1, 2, 3\}$

(b) $R = \{-3, 1, 7\}$

(c) Yes, the set defines a function since no two of the ordered pairs have the same first coordinate.
(d) No, the set does not define a

68. one-to-one function since two of the ordered pairs have the same second coordinate.

69. $E = \{(0, 1), (1, 2), (2, 9), (-1, -2)\}$

(a) $D = \{-1, 0, 1, 2\}$

(b) $R = \{-2, 1, 2, 9\}$

(c) Yes, the set defines a function since no two of the ordered pairs have the same first coordinate.
(d) Yes, the set defines a one-to-one function since it is a function and no two ordered pairs have the same second coordinate.

70. $A = \left\{\left(3, \frac{1}{3}\right), \left(-2, -\frac{1}{2}\right), \left(-4, -\frac{1}{4}\right), \left(5, \frac{1}{5}\right)\right\}$

$A^{-1} = \left\{\left(\frac{1}{3}, 3\right), \left(-\frac{1}{2}, -2\right), \left(-\frac{1}{4}, -4\right), \left(\frac{1}{5}, 5\right)\right\}$

71. $B = \{(1, 10), (3, 7), (12, 15), (10, 1)\}$

$B^{-1} = \{(10, 1), (7, 3), (15, 12), (1, 10)\}$

72. $f(x) = -\frac{3}{4}x + 2,\ f(x) \to y$

$y = -\frac{3}{4}x + 2,\ x \leftrightarrow y$

$x = -\frac{3}{4}y + 2$

$y = -\frac{4}{3}x + \frac{8}{3},\ y \to f^{-1}(x)$

$f^{-1}(x) = -\frac{4}{3}x + \frac{8}{3}$

© 2006 Pearson Education, Inc., Upper Saddle River, NJ. All rights reserved. This material is protected under all copyright laws as they currently exist.
No portion of this material may be reproduced, in any form or by any means, without permission in writing from the publisher.

73. $g(x) = -8 - 4x$, $g(x) \rightarrow y$

$\qquad y = -8 - 4x$, $x \leftrightarrow y$

$\qquad x = -8 - 4y$

$\qquad y = -\dfrac{1}{4}x - 2$, $y \rightarrow g^{-1}(x)$

$\qquad g^{-1}(x) = -\dfrac{1}{4}x - 2$

74. $h(x) = \dfrac{6}{x+5}$, $h(x) \rightarrow y$

$\qquad y = \dfrac{6}{x+5}$, $x \leftrightarrow y$

$\qquad x = \dfrac{6}{y+5}$

$\qquad y + 5 = \dfrac{6}{x}$, $y \rightarrow h^{-1}(x)$

$\qquad h^{-1}(x) = \dfrac{6}{x} - 5$

75. $j(x) = \dfrac{-7}{2-x}$, $j(x) \rightarrow y$

$\qquad y = \dfrac{-7}{2-x}$, $x \leftrightarrow y$

$\qquad x = \dfrac{-7}{2-y}$

$\qquad 2 - y = -\dfrac{7}{x}$, $y \rightarrow j^{-1}(x)$

$\qquad j^{-1}(x) = \dfrac{7}{x} + 2$

76. $p(x) = \sqrt[3]{x+1}$, $p(x) \rightarrow y$

$\qquad y = \sqrt[3]{x+1}$, $x \leftrightarrow y$

$\qquad x = \sqrt[3]{y+1}$

$\qquad y = x^3 - 1$, $y \rightarrow p^{-1}(x)$

$\qquad p^{-1}(x) = x^3 - 1$

77. $r(x) = x^3 + 2$, $r(x) \rightarrow y$

$\qquad y = x^3 + 2$, $x \leftrightarrow y$

$\qquad x = y^3 + 2$

$\qquad y = \sqrt[3]{x-2}$, $y \rightarrow r^{-1}(x)$

$\qquad r^{-1}(x) = \sqrt[3]{x-2}$

78. $f(x) = \dfrac{-x-2}{3}$, $f(x) \rightarrow y$

$\qquad y = \dfrac{-x-2}{3}$, $x \leftrightarrow y$

$\qquad x = \dfrac{-y-2}{3}$

$\qquad y = -3x - 2$, $y \rightarrow f^{-1}(x)$

$\qquad f^{-1}(x) = -3x - 2$

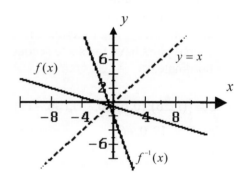

79. $f(x) = -\dfrac{3}{4}x + 1$, $f(x) \rightarrow y$

$\qquad y = -\dfrac{3}{4}x + 1$, $x \leftrightarrow y$

$\qquad x = -\dfrac{3}{4}y + 1$

$\qquad y = -\dfrac{4}{3}x + \dfrac{4}{3}$, $y \rightarrow f^{-1}(x)$

$\qquad f^{-1}(x) = -\dfrac{4}{3}x + \dfrac{4}{3}$

© 2006 Pearson Education, Inc., Upper Saddle River, NJ. All rights reserved. This material is protected under all copyright laws as they currently exist. No portion of this material may be reproduced, in any form or by any means, without permission in writing from the publisher.

79.

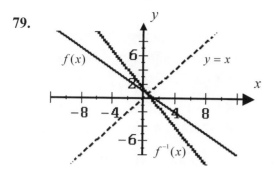

How Am I Doing? Chapter 10 Test

1. $f(x) = \dfrac{3}{4}x - 2$

$f(-8) = \dfrac{3}{4}(-8) - 2 = -8$

2. $f(x) = \dfrac{3}{4}x - 2$

$f(3a) = \dfrac{3}{4}(3a) - 2 = \dfrac{9}{4}a - 2$

3. $f(x) = \dfrac{3}{4}x - 2$

$f(a) - f(2) = \dfrac{3}{4}a - 2 - \left(\dfrac{3}{4}(2) - 2\right)$

$= \dfrac{3}{4}a - 2 - \dfrac{3}{2} + 2$

$= \dfrac{3}{4}a - \dfrac{3}{2}$

4. $f(x) = 3x^2 - 2x + 4$

$f(-6) = 3(-6)^2 - 2(-6) + 4 = 124$

5. $f(x) = 3x^2 - 2x + 4$

$f(a+1) = 3(a+1)^2 - 2(a+1) + 4$

$= 3a^2 + 6a + 3 - 2a - 2 + 4$

$= 3a^2 + 4a + 5$

6. $f(x) = 3x^2 - 2x + 4$

$f(a) + f(1) = 3a^2 - 2a + 4 + 3(1)^2 - 2(1) + 4$

$= 3a^2 - 2a + 9$

7. $f(x) = 3x^2 - 2x + 4$

$f(-2a) - 2 = 3(-2a)^2 - 2(-2a) + 4 - 2$

$= 12a^2 + 4a + 2$

8. (a) Graph passes vertical line test and therefore represents a function.
(b) Graph fails horizontal line test and does not represent a one-to-one function.

9. (a) Graph passes vertical line test and therefore represents a function.
(b) Graph passes horizontal line test and therefore represents a one-to-one function.

10. $f(x) = x^2$

$g(x) = (x-1)^2 + 3$ is $f(x)$ shifted right 1 unit and up 3 units.

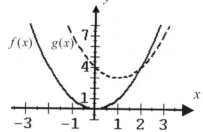

11. $f(x) = |x|$

$g(x) = |x+1| + 2$ is $f(x)$ shifted left 1 unit and up 2 units.

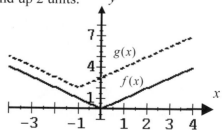

299

© 2006 Pearson Education, Inc., Upper Saddle River, NJ. All rights reserved. This material is protected under all copyright laws as they currently exist. No portion of this material may be reproduced, in any form or by any means, without permission in writing from the publisher.

12. $f(x) = 3x^2 - x - 6,\ g(x) = -2x^2 + 5x + 7$

(a)
$$(f + g)(x) = f(x) + g(x)$$
$$= 3x^2 - x - 6 + (-2x^2 + 5x + 7)$$
$$= 3x^2 - x - 6 - 2x^2 + 5x + 7$$
$$= x^2 + 4x + 1$$

(b)
$$(f - g)(x) = f(x) - g(x)$$
$$= 3x^2 - x - 6 - (-2x^2 + 5x + 7)$$
$$= 3x^2 - x - 6 + 2x^2 - 5x - 7$$
$$= 5x^2 - 6x - 13$$

(c) From (b)
$$(f - g)(x) = 5x^2 - 6x - 13$$
$$(f - g)(-2) = 5(-2)^2 - 6(-2) - 13 = 19$$

(a) $(f \circ g)(x) = f[g(x)]$
$$= f[4x + 5]$$
$$= \frac{1}{2}(4x + 5) - 3$$
$$= 2x - \frac{1}{2}$$

(b) $(g \circ f)(x) = g[f(x)]$
$$= g\left[\frac{1}{2}x - 3\right]$$
$$= 4\left(\frac{1}{2}x - 3\right) + 5$$
$$= 2x - 7$$

(c) $(f \circ g)\left(\frac{1}{4}\right) = 2 \cdot \frac{1}{4} - \frac{1}{2} = 0$

13. $f(x) = \frac{3}{x},\ x \neq 0;\ g(x) = 2x - 1$

(a) $(fg)(x) = f(x)g(x)$
$$= \frac{3}{x}(2x - 1)$$
$$= \frac{6x - 3}{x},\ x \neq 0$$

(b) $\left(\dfrac{f}{g}\right)(x) = \dfrac{f(x)}{g(x)}$
$$= \frac{\dfrac{3}{x}}{2x - 1}$$
$$= \frac{3}{2x^2 - x},\ x \neq 0, \frac{1}{2}$$

(c) $f[g(x)] = f[2x - 1]$
$$= \frac{3}{2x - 1},\ x \neq \frac{1}{2}$$

14. $f(x) = \frac{1}{2}x - 3,\ g(x) = 4x + 5$

15. $B = \{(1,8), (8,1), (9,10), (-10,9)\}$

(a) Yes, the function is one-to-one since no two ordered pairs have the same second coordinate.

(b) $B^{-1} = \{(8,1), (1,8), (10,9), (9,-10)\}$

16. $A = \{(1,5), (2,1), (4,-7), (0,7), (3,5)\}$

(a) The function is not one-to-one since two ordered pairs have the same second coordinate.

(b) A has no inverse.

17. $f(x) = \sqrt[3]{2x - 1},\ f(x) \to y$
$$y = \sqrt[3]{2x - 1},\ x \leftrightarrow y$$
$$x = \sqrt[3]{2y - 1}$$
$$y = \frac{x^3 + 1}{2},\ y \to f^{-1}(x)$$
$$f^{-1}(x) = \frac{x^3 + 1}{2}$$

© 2006 Pearson Education, Inc., Upper Saddle River, NJ. All rights reserved. This material is protected under all copyright laws as they currently exist. No portion of this material may be reproduced, in any form or by any means, without permission in writing from the publisher.

18. $f(x) = -3x + 2, \ f(x) \to y$

$\qquad y = -3x + 2, \ x \leftrightarrow y$

$\qquad x = -3y + 2$

$\qquad y = -\dfrac{1}{3}x + \dfrac{2}{3}, \ y \to f^{-1}(x)$

$\qquad f^{-1}(x) = -\dfrac{1}{3}x + \dfrac{2}{3}$

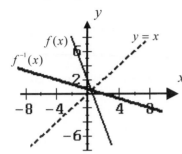

19. $f(x) = \dfrac{3}{7}x + \dfrac{1}{2}, \ f^{-1}(x) = \dfrac{14x - 7}{6}$

$f^{-1}\left[f(x)\right] = f^{-1}\left[\dfrac{3}{7}x + \dfrac{1}{2}\right]$

$\qquad = \dfrac{14\left[\dfrac{3}{7}x + \dfrac{1}{2}\right] - 7}{6}$

$\qquad = \dfrac{6x + 7 - 7}{6} = \dfrac{6x}{6}$

$\qquad = x$

20. $f(x) = 7 - 8x$

$\dfrac{f(x+h) - f(x)}{h}$

$= \dfrac{7 - 8(x+h) - (7 - 8x)}{h}$

$= \dfrac{7 - 8x - 8h - 7 + 8x}{h}$

$= -8$

Cumulative Test for Chapters 1-10

1. $3x\{2y - 3[x + 2(x + 2y)]\}$

$= 3x\{2y - 3[x + 2x + 4y]\}$

$= 3x\{2y - 3[3x + 4y]\}$

$= 3x\{2y - 9x - 12y\}$

$= 3x\{-10y - 9x\}$

$= -30xy - 27x^2$

2. $3y - 2xy - x^2 = 3(3) - 2(-1)(3) - (-1)^2$

$\qquad\qquad\qquad = 14$

3. $\dfrac{1}{2}(x - 2) = \dfrac{1}{3}(x + 10) - 2x$

$\qquad 3(x - 2) = 2(x + 10) - 12x$

$\qquad 3x - 6 = 2x + 20 - 12x$

$\qquad 13x = 26$

$\qquad x = 2$

4. $16x^4 - 1 = (4x^2 + 1)(4x^2 - 1)$

$\qquad\qquad = (4x^2 + 1)(2x + 1)(2x - 1)$

5. $(x - 1)(2x^2 + x - 5)$

$\qquad = 2x^3 + x^2 - 5x - 2x^2 - x + 5$

$\qquad = 2x^3 - x^2 - 6x + 5$

6. $\dfrac{3x}{x^2 - 4} = \dfrac{2}{x + 2} + \dfrac{4}{2 - x}$

$\dfrac{3x}{(x + 2)(x - 2)} = \dfrac{2}{x + 2} - \dfrac{4}{x - 2}$

$\qquad 3x = 2(x - 2) - 4(x + 2)$

$\qquad 3x = 2x - 4 - 4x - 8$

$\qquad 5x = -12$

$\qquad x = -\dfrac{12}{5}$

301

© 2006 Pearson Education, Inc., Upper Saddle River, NJ. All rights reserved. This material is protected under all copyright laws as they currently exist. No portion of this material may be reproduced, in any form or by any means, without permission in writing from the publisher.

7. $y - y_1 = m(x - x_1)$

$\quad y - (-1) = -3(x - 2)$

$\quad\quad y + 1 = -3x + 6$

$\quad\quad\quad y = -3x + 5$

8. $3x + 2y = 5 \Rightarrow y = \dfrac{5 - 3x}{2}$

$\quad\quad 7x + 5y = 11$

$\quad\quad 7x + 5 \cdot \dfrac{5 - 3x}{2} = 11$

$\quad\quad 14x + 25 - 15x = 22$

$\quad\quad\quad\quad -x = -3$

$\quad\quad\quad\quad\quad x = 3$

$\quad\quad y = \dfrac{5 - 3x}{2} = \dfrac{5 - 3(3)}{2} = -2$

$\quad\quad$ (3, -2) is the solution.

9. $\sqrt{18x^5 y^6 z^3} = \sqrt{9x^4 y^6 z^2 \cdot 2xz}$

$\quad\quad\quad\quad = 3x^2 y^3 z \sqrt{2xz}$

10. $(\sqrt{2} + \sqrt{3})(2\sqrt{2} - 4\sqrt{3})$

$\quad = 2(2) - 4\sqrt{6} + 2\sqrt{6} - 4(3)$

$\quad = 4 - 2\sqrt{6} - 12$

$\quad = -2\sqrt{6} - 8$

11. $d = \sqrt{(x_2 - x_1)^2 + (y_2 - y_1)^2}$

$\quad d = \sqrt{(-3 - 6)^2 + (-4 - (-1))^2} = \sqrt{90}$

$\quad d = 3\sqrt{10}$

12. $12x^2 - 11x + 2 = (4x - 1)(3x - 2)$

13. $x^3 - 5x^2 - 14x = x(x^2 - 5x - 14)$

$\quad\quad\quad\quad\quad\quad\quad = x(x - 7)(x + 2)$

14. $\quad (x - h)^2 + (y - k)^2 = r^2$

$\quad\quad (x - 0)^2 + (y - (-5))^2 = (2\sqrt{2})^2$

$\quad\quad\quad\quad x^2 + (y + 5)^2 = 8$

15. $f(x) = 3x^2 - 2x + 1$

$\quad$ (a) $f(-2) = 3(-2)^2 - 2(-2) + 1 = 17$

$\quad$ (b) $f(a - 2) = 3(a - 2)^2 - 2(a - 2) + 1$

$\quad\quad\quad\quad\quad = 3a^2 - 12a + 12 - 2a + 4 + 1$

$\quad\quad\quad\quad\quad = 3a^2 - 14a + 17$

$\quad$ (c) $f(a) + f(-2) = 3a^2 - 2a + 1 + 17$

$\quad\quad\quad\quad\quad\quad = 3a^2 - 2a + 18$

16. $f(x) = x^3$, $g(x) = (x + 2)^3 + 4$ is $f(x)$ shifted right 2 units and up 4 units.

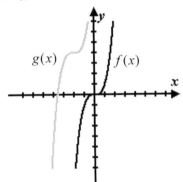

17. $f(x) = 2x^2 - 5x - 6$, $g(x) - 5x + 3$

$\quad$ (a) $(fg)(x) = f(x)g(x)$

$\quad\quad\quad = (2x^2 - 5x - 6)(5x + 3)$

$\quad\quad\quad = 10x^3 + 6x^2 - 25x^2 - 15x - 30x - 18$

$\quad\quad\quad = 10x^3 - 19x^2 - 45x - 18$

$\quad$ (b) $\left(\dfrac{f}{g}\right)(x) = \dfrac{f(x)}{g(x)}$

$\quad\quad\quad = \dfrac{2x^2 - 5x - 6}{5x + 3}, \; x \neq -\dfrac{3}{5}$

© 2006 Pearson Education, Inc., Upper Saddle River, NJ. All rights reserved. This material is protected under all copyright laws as they currently exist. No portion of this material may be reproduced, in any form or by any means, without permission in writing from the publisher.

17.

(c) $f[g(x)] = f[5x+3]$

$$= 2(5x+3)^2 - 5(5x+3) - 6$$
$$= 50x^2 + 60x + 18 - 25x - 15 - 6$$
$$= 50x^2 + 35x - 3$$

18. $A = \{(3,6),(1,8),(2,7),(4,4)\}$

(a) Yes, A is a function; no two ordered pairs have the same first coordinate.

(b) Yes, A is a one-to-one function since no two ordered pairs have the same second coordinate.

(c) $A^{-1} = \{(6,3),(8,1),(7,2),(4,4)\}$

19. $f(x) = \sqrt[3]{7x-3}, \ f(x) \to y$

$$y = \sqrt[3]{7x-3}, \ x \leftrightarrow y$$
$$x = \sqrt[3]{7y-3}$$
$$y = \frac{x^3+3}{7}, \ y \to f^{-1}(x)$$
$$f^{-1}(x) = \frac{x^3+3}{7}$$

20. $f(x) = 5x^3 - 3x^2 - 6$

(a) $f(5) = 5(5)^3 - 3(5)^2 - 6 = 544$

(b) $f(-3) = 5(-3)^3 - 3(-3)^2 - 6 = -168$

(c) $f(2a) = 5(2a)^3 - 3(2a)^2 - 6$
$$= 40a^3 - 12a^{-2} - 6$$

21. (a) $f(x) = -\frac{2}{3}x + 2, \ f(x) \to y$

$$y = -\frac{2}{3}x + 2, \ x \leftrightarrow y$$
$$x = -\frac{2}{3}y + 2$$
$$y = -\frac{3}{2}x + 3, \ y \to f^{-1}(x)$$
$$f^{-1}(x) = -\frac{3}{2}x + 3$$

(b)

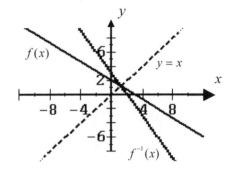

22. From Exercise 21,

$$f[f^{-1}(x)] = f\left[-\frac{3}{2}x + 3\right]$$
$$= -\frac{2}{3}\left[-\frac{3}{2}x + 3\right] + 2$$
$$= x - 2 + 2$$
$$= x$$

© 2006 Pearson Education, Inc., Upper Saddle River, NJ. All rights reserved. This material is protected under all copyright laws as they currently exist. No portion of this material may be reproduced, in any form or by any means, without permission in writing from the publisher.

Chapter 11

11.1 Exercises

1. The exponential function is an equation of the form

$\underline{f(x) = b^x \text{ where } b > 0, \ b \neq 1, \text{ and } x}$

$\underline{\text{is a real number.}}$

3. $f(x) = 3^x$

x	$y = f(x) = 3^x$
-2	$\dfrac{1}{9}$
-1	$\dfrac{1}{3}$
0	1
1	3
2	9

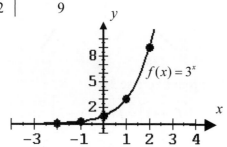

5. $f(x) = 2^{-x}$

x	$y = f(x) = 2^{-x}$
-2	4
-1	2
0	1
1	$\dfrac{1}{2}$
2	$\dfrac{1}{4}$

5.

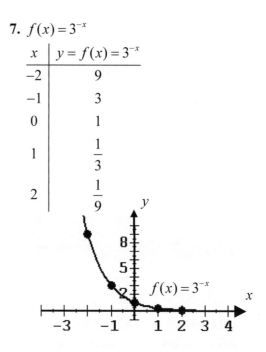

7. $f(x) = 3^{-x}$

x	$y = f(x) = 3^{-x}$
-2	9
-1	3
0	1
1	$\dfrac{1}{3}$
2	$\dfrac{1}{9}$

9. $f(x) = 2^{x+3}$

x	$y = f(x) = 2^{x+3}$
-3	1
-2	2
-1	4

304

© 2006 Pearson Education, Inc., Upper Saddle River, NJ. All rights reserved. This material is protected under all copyright laws as they currently exist. No portion of this material may be reproduced, in any form or by any means, without permission in writing from the publisher.

9.

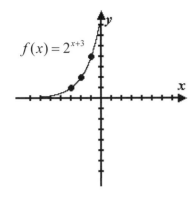

$f(x) = 2^{x+3}$

13.

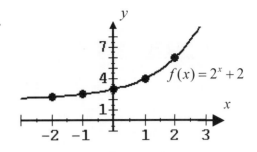

$f(x) = 2^x + 2$

11. $f(x) = 3^{x-3}$

x	$y = f(x) = 3^{x-3}$
2	$\dfrac{1}{3}$
3	1
4	3

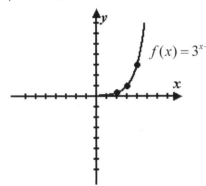

$f(x) = 3^{x-3}$

15. $f(x) = e^{x-1}$

x	$y = e^{x-1}$
-2	0.05
-1	0.14
0	0.37
1	1
2	2.7

$f(x) = e^{x-1}$

17. $f(x) = 2e^x$

x	$y = f(x) = 2e^x$
-2	0.27
-1	0.74
0	2
1	5.44
2	14.8

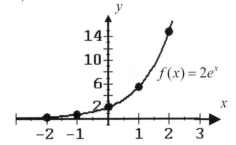

$f(x) = 2e^x$

13. $f(x) = 2^x + 2$

x	$y = f(x) = 2^x + 2$
-2	$\dfrac{9}{4}$
-1	$\dfrac{5}{2}$
0	3
1	4
2	6

305

© 2006 Pearson Education, Inc., Upper Saddle River, NJ. All rights reserved. This material is protected under all copyright laws as they currently exist. No portion of this material may be reproduced, in any form or by any means, without permission in writing from the publisher.

19. $f(x) = e^{1-x}$

x	$y = f(x) = e^{1-x}$
-2	20.1
-1	7.39
0	2.72
1	0.37
2	0.14

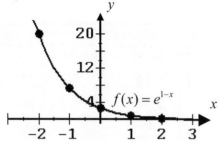

21. $2^x = 4$

$2^x = 2^2$

$x = 2$

23. $2^x = 1$

$2^x = 2^0$

$x = 0$

25. $2^x = \dfrac{1}{2}$

$2^x = \dfrac{1}{2^1} = 2^{-1}$

$x = -1$

27. $3^x = 81$

$3^x = 3^4$

$x = 4$

29. $3^x = 1$

$3^x = 3^0$

$x = 0$

31. $3^{-x} = \dfrac{1}{9} = \dfrac{1}{3^2}$

$3^{-x} = 3^{-2}$

$-x = -2$

$x = 2$

33. $4^x = 256$

$4^x = 4^4$

$x = 4$

35. $5^{x+1} = 125$

$5^{x+1} = 5^3$

$x + 1 = 3$

$x = 2$

37. $8^{3x-1} = 64 = 8^2$

$3x - 1 = 2$

$3x = 3$

$x = 1$

39. $A = P\left(1 + \dfrac{r}{n}\right)^{nt}$

$A = 2000\left(1 + \dfrac{0.063}{1}\right)^{1(3)} = 2402.314094$

Alicia will have $2402.31 after 3 years.

41. $A = P\left(1 + \dfrac{r}{n}\right)^{nt}$

$A = 3000\left(1 + \dfrac{0.032}{4}\right)^{4(6)} = \$3632.34$

$A = 3000\left(1 + \dfrac{0.032}{12}\right)^{12(6)} = \$3634.08$

She will have $3632.34 if it is compounded quarterly and $3634.08 if it is compounded monthly.

© 2006 Pearson Education, Inc., Upper Saddle River, NJ. All rights reserved. This material is protected under all copyright laws as they currently exist. No portion of this material may be reproduced, in any form or by any means, without permission in writing from the publisher.

43. $B(t) = 4000(2^t)$

$B(3) = 4000(2^3) = 32,000$

$B(9) = 4000(2^9) = 2,048,000$

At the end of 3 hours there will be 32,000 bacteria in the culture and at the end of 9 hours there will be 2,048,000 bacteria in the culture.

45. $S(f) = (1 - 0.18)^{f/4} = 0.82^{f/4}$

$S(20) = 0.82^{20/4} = 37\%$ at 20 ft

$S(48) = 0.82^{48/4} = 9\% < 10\%,$ yes

spotlights will be needed.

47. $A = Ce^{-0.0004297t}$

$A = 6e^{-0.0004297(1000)} \approx 3.91$

There will be approximately 3.91 mg of radium in the container after 1000 years.

49. $P = 14.7e^{-0.21d}$

$P = 14.7e^{-0.21(10)} \approx 1.80$ lb/in^2

51. $N = 0.00472e^{0.11596t}$

$N = 0.00472e^{0.11596(80)} \approx 50.4$

$N = 0.00472e^{0.11596(90)} \approx 160.8$

$\dfrac{160.8 - 50.4}{50.4} \approx 2.19$

About 50.4 million stocks were traded in 1980 and about 160.8 million stocks were traded in 1990, an increase of about 219%.

53. From the graph the world's population reached three billion people sometime in 1955.

55. $5.68(1.017)^{10} \approx 6.7$. The world's population would be about 6.7 billion people in 2005.

57. $f(x) = \dfrac{e^x + e^{-x}}{2}$

$$f(x) = \frac{e^x + e^{-x}}{2} = \cosh x$$

Cumulative Review

59. $5 - 2(3 - x) = 2(2x + 5) + 1$

$5 - 6 + 2x = 4x + 10 + 1$

$2x = -12$

$x = -6$

11.2 Exercises

1. A logarithm is an <u>exponent</u> .

3. In the equation $y = \log_b x$, the domain (the permitted values of x) is $\underline{x > 0.}$

5. $81 = 3^4 \Leftrightarrow \log_3 81 = 4$

7. $36 = 6^2 \Leftrightarrow \log_6 36 = 2$

9. $0.001 = 10^{-3} \Leftrightarrow \log_{10} 0.001 = -3$

© 2006 Pearson Education, Inc., Upper Saddle River, NJ. All rights reserved. This material is protected under all copyright laws as they currently exist. No portion of this material may be reproduced, in any form or by any means, without permission in writing from the publisher.

11. $\dfrac{1}{32} = 2^{-5} \Leftrightarrow \log_2 \dfrac{1}{32} = -5$

13. $y = e^5 \Leftrightarrow \log_e y = 5$

15. $2 = \log_3 9 \Leftrightarrow 3^2 = 9$

17. $0 = \log_{17} 1 \Leftrightarrow 17^0 = 1$

19. $\dfrac{1}{2} = \log_{16} 4 \Leftrightarrow 16^{1/2} = 4$

21. $-2 = \log_{10}(0.01) \Leftrightarrow 10^{-2} = 0.01$

23. $-4 = \log_3\left(\dfrac{1}{81}\right) \Leftrightarrow 3^{-4} = \dfrac{1}{81}$

25. $-\dfrac{3}{2} = \log_e x \Leftrightarrow e^{-3/2} = x$

27. $\log_2 x = 4 \Leftrightarrow 2^4 = x$
$$x = 16$$

29. $\log_{10} x = -3 \Leftrightarrow 10^{-3} = x$
$$x = \dfrac{1}{1000}$$

31. $\log_4 64 = y \Leftrightarrow 4^y = 64 = 4^3$
$$y = 3$$

33. $\log_8\left(\dfrac{1}{64}\right) = y \Leftrightarrow 8^y = \dfrac{1}{64} = \dfrac{1}{8^2} = 8^{-2}$
$$y = -2$$

35. $\log_a 121 = 2 \Leftrightarrow a^2 = 121 = 11^2$
$$a = 11$$

37. $\log_a 1000 = 3 \Leftrightarrow a^3 = 1000 = 10^3$
$$a = 10$$

39. $\log_{25} 5 = w \Leftrightarrow 25^w = 5$
$$(5^2)^w = 5^{2w} = 5^1$$
$$2w = 1$$
$$w = \dfrac{1}{2}$$

41. $\log_3\left(\dfrac{1}{3}\right) = w$
$$3^w = \dfrac{1}{3} = \dfrac{1}{3^1} = 3^{-1}$$
$$w = -1$$

43. $\log_{15} w = 0 \Leftrightarrow 15^0 = w$
$$w = 1$$

45. $\log_w 3 = \dfrac{1}{2} \Leftrightarrow w^{1/2} = 3$
$$w = 9$$

47. $\log_{10}(0.001) = x \Leftrightarrow 10^x = 0.001 = 10^{-3}$
$$x = -3$$

49. $\log_2 128 = x \Leftrightarrow 2^x = 128 = 2^7$
$$x = 7$$

51. $\log_{23} 1 = x \Leftrightarrow 23^x = 1 = 23^0$
$$x = 0$$

53. $\log_6 \sqrt{6} = x \Leftrightarrow 6^x = \sqrt{6} = 6^{1/2}$
$$x = \dfrac{1}{2}$$

55. $\log_{57} 1 = x \Leftrightarrow 57^x = 1 = 57^0$
$$x = 0$$

© 2006 Pearson Education, Inc., Upper Saddle River, NJ. All rights reserved. This material is protected under all copyright laws as they currently exist.
No portion of this material may be reproduced, in any form or by any means, without permission in writing from the publisher.

57. $\log_3 x = y \Leftrightarrow 3^y = x$

$x = 3^y$	y
1	0
3	1
9	2

$y = \log_3 x$

59. $\log_{1/4} x = y \Leftrightarrow (1/4)^y = x$

$x = (1/4)^y$	y
1	0
4	−1
16	−2

$y = \log_{1/4} x$

61. $\log_{10} x = y \Leftrightarrow 10^y = x$

$x = 10^y$	y
1/100	−2
1/10	−1
1	0
10	1
100	2

61.

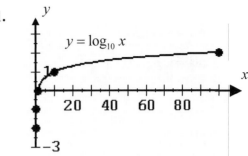

$y = \log_{10} x$

63. $f(x) = \log_3 x, \ f(x) \to y$

$y = \log_3 x \Leftrightarrow 3^y = x$

$x = 3^y$	y
1/9	−2
1/3	−1
1	0
3	1
9	2

$f^{-1}(x) = 3^x, \ f^{-1}(x) \to y$

$y = 3^x$

x	$y = 3^x$
−2	1/9
−1	1/3
0	1
1	3
2	9

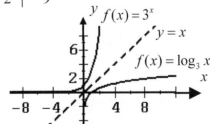

$f(x) = 3^x$

$y = x$

$f(x) = \log_3 x$

309

© 2006 Pearson Education, Inc., Upper Saddle River, NJ. All rights reserved. This material is protected under all copyright laws as they currently exist. No portion of this material may be reproduced, in any form or by any means, without permission in writing from the publisher.

65. $\text{pH} = -\log_{10}\left[\text{H}^+\right]$

$\text{pH} = -\log_{10}\left[10^{-2}\right]$

$-\text{pH} = \log_{10}\left[10^{-2}\right]$

$10^{-\text{pH}} = 10^{-2}$

$-\text{pH} = -2$

$\text{pH} = 2$

67. $\text{pH} = -\log_{10}\left[\text{H}^+\right]$

$8 = -\log_{10}\left[\text{H}^+\right]$

$-8 = \log_{10}\left[\text{H}^+\right]$

$10^{-8} = \text{H}^+$

69. $\text{pH} = -\log_{10}\left[\text{H}^+\right]$

$\text{pH} = -\log_{10}\left[1.103\times10^{-3}\right]$

$\text{pH} = -\log_{10}\left[0.001103\right]$

$\text{pH} = -(-2.957424488)$

$\text{pH} = 2.957$

71. $N = 1200 + (2500)(\log_{10} d)$

$\log_{10} d = \dfrac{N - 1200}{2500}$

$\log_{10} 10,000 = \dfrac{N - 1200}{2500}$

$10^{\frac{N-1200}{2500}} = 10,000 = 10^4$

$\dfrac{N - 1200}{2500} = 4$

$N - 1200 = 10,000$

$N = 11,200 \text{ sets}$

73. $N = 1200 + (2500)(\log_{10} d)$

$\log_{10} d = \dfrac{18,700 - 1200}{2500}$

$\log_{10} d = 7 \Leftrightarrow d = 10^7$

$d = \$10,000,000 \text{ should be spent}$

75. $5^{\log_5 4} = y \Leftrightarrow \log_5 4 = \log_5 y \rightarrow y = 4$

Cumulative Review

77. $y = -\dfrac{2}{3}x + 5$,

x	y
0	5
3	3

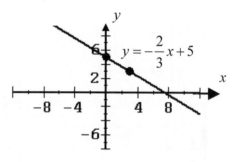

79. $y = -\dfrac{2}{3}x + 4$ has $m = -\dfrac{2}{3} \Rightarrow m_\perp = \dfrac{3}{2}$

$y - 1 = \dfrac{3}{2}(x - (-4)) = \dfrac{3}{2}(x + 4)$

$y - 1 = \dfrac{3}{2}x + 6$

$y = \dfrac{3}{2}x + 7$

81. (a) $A(t) = 9000(2)^t$

$A(2) = 9000(2)^2 = 36,000 \text{ cells}$

(b) $A(t) = 9000(2)^t$

$A(12) = 9000(2)^{12} = 36,864,000 \text{ cells}$

© 2006 Pearson Education, Inc., Upper Saddle River, NJ. All rights reserved. This material is protected under all copyright laws as they currently exist.
No portion of this material may be reproduced, in any form or by any means, without permission in writing from the publisher.

83. Cost for train:
$98 + 0.75(2)(23) = 132.5$
Cost to drive:
$2.50(23) + 120 + 1(23) = 200.50$
$200.5 - 132.5 = 68$
It is cheaper to take the train. He would save $68 per month by using the train.

11.3 Exercises

1. $\log_3 AB = \log_3 A + \log_3 B$

3. $\log_5 (7 \cdot 11) = \log_5 7 + \log_5 11$

5. $\log_b 9f = \log_b 9 + \log_b f$

7. $\log_9 \left(\dfrac{2}{7} \right) = \log_9 2 - \log_9 7$

9. $\log_b \left(\dfrac{H}{10} \right) = \log_b H - \log_b 10$

11. $\log_a \left(\dfrac{E}{F} \right) = \log_a E - \log_a F$

13. $\log_8 a^7 = 7 \log_8 a$

15. $\log_b A^{-2} = -2 \log_b A$

17. $\log_5 \sqrt{w} = \log_5 w^{1/2}$
$= \dfrac{1}{2} \log_5 w$

19. $\log_8 x^2 y = \log_8 x^2 + \log_8 y$
$= 2 \log_8 x + \log_8 y$

21. $\log_{11} \left(\dfrac{6M}{N} \right) = \log_{11} (6M) - \log_{11} N$
$= \log_{11} 6 + \log_{11} M - \log_{11} N$

23. $\log_2 \left(\dfrac{5xy^4}{\sqrt{z}} \right)$
$= \log_2 (5xy^4) - \log_2 \sqrt{z}$
$= \log_2 5 + \log_2 x + \log_2 y^4 - \log_2 z^{1/2}$
$= \log_2 5 + \log_2 x + 4 \log_2 y - \dfrac{1}{2} \log_2 z$

25. $\log_a \sqrt[3]{\dfrac{x^4}{y}} = \log_a \left(\dfrac{x^4}{y} \right)^{1/3} = \dfrac{1}{3} \log_a \left(\dfrac{x^4}{y} \right)$
$= \dfrac{1}{3} \left[\log_a x^4 - \log_b y \right]$
$= \dfrac{1}{3} \left[4 \log_a x - \log_b y \right]$
$= \dfrac{4}{3} \log_a x - \dfrac{1}{3} \log_a y$

27. $\log_4 13 + \log_4 y + \log_4 3$
$= \log_4 (13 \cdot y \cdot 3) = \log_4 (39y)$

29. $5 \log_3 x - \log_3 7 = \log_3 x^5 - \log_3 7$
$= \log_3 \dfrac{x^5}{7}$

31. $2 \log_b 7 + 3 \log_b y - \dfrac{1}{2} \log_b z$
$= \log_b 7^2 + \log_b y^3 - \log_b z^{1/2}$
$= \log_b 49 + \log_b y^3 - \log_b \sqrt{z}$
$= \log_b \dfrac{49 y^3}{\sqrt{z}}$

© 2006 Pearson Education, Inc., Upper Saddle River, NJ. All rights reserved. This material is protected under all copyright laws as they currently exist. No portion of this material may be reproduced, in any form or by any means, without permission in writing from the publisher.

33. $\log_3 3 = 1$

35. $\log_e e = 1$

37. $\log_9 1 = 0$

39. $3\log_7 7 + 4\log_7 1 = 3(1) + 4(0) = 3$

41. $\log_8 x = \log_8 7 \Rightarrow x = 7$

43. $\log_5(2x+7) = \log_5(29)$
$$2x + 7 = 29$$
$$2x = 22$$
$$x = 11$$

45. $\log_3 1 = x \Rightarrow x = 0$

47. $\log_7 7 = x \Rightarrow x = 1$

49. $\log_{10} x + \log_{10} 25 = 2$
$$\log_{10}(25x) = 2 \Leftrightarrow 10^2 = 25x$$
$$25x = 100 \rightarrow x = 4$$

51. $\log_2 7 = \log_2 x - \log_2 3$
$$\log_2 7 = \log_2 \frac{x}{3}$$
$$\frac{x}{3} = 7$$
$$x = 21$$

53. $3\log_5 x = \log_5 8$
$$\log_5 x^3 = \log_5 8$$
$$x^3 = 8$$
$$x = 2$$

55. $\log_e x = \log_e 5 + 1$
$$\log_e \frac{x}{5} = 1 \Leftrightarrow e^1 = \frac{x}{5} \Rightarrow x = 5e$$

57. $\log_6(5x+21) - \log_6(x+3) = 1$
$$\log_6 \frac{5x+21}{x+3} = 1 \Rightarrow \frac{5x+21}{x+3} = 6$$
$$5x + 21 = 6x + 18$$
$$x = 3$$

59. $5^{\log_5 4} + 3^{\log_3 2} = 4 + 2 = 6$

61. Let $\log_b M = x,\ \log_b N = y \Leftrightarrow$
$$b^x = M,\ b^y = N$$
$$\frac{M}{N} = \frac{b^x}{b^y} \Rightarrow \frac{M}{N} = b^{x-y}$$
$$\log_b \frac{M}{N} = \log_b b^{x-y} (x-y)\log_b b$$
$$\log_b \frac{M}{N} = (x-y)(1) = x - y$$
$$\log_b \frac{M}{N} = \log_b M - \log_b N$$

Cumulative Review

63. $V = \pi r^2 h = \pi(2)^2 5 \approx 62.83 \text{ m}^3$

65. $5x + 3y = 9 \overset{\times 2}{\rightarrow}\ 10x + 6y = 18$
$$7x - 2y = 25 \overset{\times 3}{\rightarrow} \underline{21x - 6y = 75}$$
$$31x \qquad = 93$$
$$x = 3$$
$$5(3) + 3y = 9$$
$$3y = -6$$
$$y = -2$$
$(3, -2)$ is the solution.

© 2006 Pearson Education, Inc., Upper Saddle River, NJ. All rights reserved. This material is protected under all copyright laws as they currently exist. No portion of this material may be reproduced, in any form or by any means, without permission in writing from the publisher.

67. $\dfrac{9.30\times10^8 - 8.01\times10^8}{8.01\times10^8} = 0.161048...$

$\dfrac{E - 9.3\times10^8}{9.3\times10^8} = 0.161048...$

$E \approx 1.08\times10^9$

Emissions increased 16.1% from 1996 to 2000. Emissions in 2004 will be 1.08×10^9 metric tons.

69. $a = \dfrac{v_2 - v_1}{t} = \dfrac{0-38}{3} = -\dfrac{38}{3}\dfrac{\text{ft}}{\text{sec}}$

$v_2 = v_1 + at = 38 + \dfrac{-38}{3}(2) = \dfrac{38}{3}\dfrac{\text{ft}}{\text{sec}}$

$\dfrac{38\ \text{ft}}{3\ \text{sec}} \cdot \dfrac{\text{mile}}{5280\ \text{ft}} \cdot \dfrac{3600\ \text{sec}}{\text{hour}} \approx 8.64$ mph

The speed after 2 seconds was approximately 8.64 mph.

$\dfrac{38\ \text{ft}}{\text{second}} \cdot \dfrac{\text{mile}}{5280\ \text{ft}} \cdot \dfrac{3600\ \text{seconds}}{\text{hour}}$

≈ 25.9 mph $<$ 35 mph

He was not over the speed limit.

How Am I Doing? Chapters 11.1-11.3

1. $f(x) = 2^{-x}$

x	$y = f(x) = 2^{-x}$
-2	4
-1	2
0	1
1	$\dfrac{1}{2}$
2	$\dfrac{1}{4}$

2. $3^{2x-1} = 27$

$3^{2x-1} = 3^3$

$2x - 1 = 3$

$2x = 4$

$x = 2$

3. $2^x = \dfrac{1}{32} = \dfrac{1}{2^5} = 2^{-5} \Rightarrow x = -5$

4. $125 = 5^{3x+4} \Rightarrow 5^3 = 5^{3x+4} \Rightarrow 3x + 4 = 3$

$3x = -1 \Rightarrow x = -\dfrac{1}{3}$

5. $A = P(1+r)^t$

$A = 10,000(1+0.12)^4 = 15,735.1936$

In 4 years Nancy will have \$15,735.19.

6. $\dfrac{1}{49} = 7^{-2}$

$\log_7\left(\dfrac{1}{49}\right) = -2$

7. $-3 = \log_{10} 0.001 \Leftrightarrow 10^{-3} = 0.001$

8. $\log_5 x = 3$

$x = 5^3 = 125$

9. $\log_x 81 = -2 \Leftrightarrow x^{-2} = 81 \Rightarrow \dfrac{1}{x^2} = 81$

$x^2 = \dfrac{1}{81} \Rightarrow x = \pm\dfrac{1}{9}$, pick $+$ since $x > 0$

$x = \dfrac{1}{9}$

10. Let $N = \log_{10}(10,000)$

$10^N = 10,000$

$10^N = 10^4 \Rightarrow N = 4$

313

© 2006 Pearson Education, Inc., Upper Saddle River, NJ. All rights reserved. This material is protected under all copyright laws as they currently exist. No portion of this material may be reproduced, in any form or by any means, without permission in writing from the publisher.

11. $\log_5\left(\dfrac{x^2 y^5}{z^3}\right) = \log_5(x^2 y^5) - \log_5 z^3$

$$= \log_5 x^2 + \log_5 y^5 - \log_5 z^3$$

$$= 2\log_5 x + 5\log_5 y - 3\log_5 z$$

12. $\dfrac{1}{2}\log_4 x - 3\log_4 w = \log_4 x^{1/2} - \log_4 w^3$

$$= \log_4 \sqrt{x} - \log_4 w^3$$

$$= \log_4\left(\dfrac{\sqrt{x}}{w^3}\right)$$

13. $\log_3 x + \log_3 2 = 4$

$$\log_3(2x) = 4$$

$$2x = 3^4$$

$$2x = 81$$

$$x = \dfrac{81}{2}$$

14. $\log_7 x = \log_7 8 \Rightarrow x = 8$

15. $\log_9 1 = x \Leftrightarrow 9^x = 1 = 9^0 \Rightarrow x = 0$

16. $\log_3 2x = 2 \Leftrightarrow 3^2 = 2x \Rightarrow x = \dfrac{9}{2}$

17. $1 = \log_4 3x \Leftrightarrow 4^1 = 3x \Rightarrow x = \dfrac{4}{3}$

18. $\log_e x + \log_e 3 = 1 \Rightarrow \log_e 3x = 1$

$$e^1 = 3x \Rightarrow x = \dfrac{e}{3}$$

11.4 Exercises

1. Error. You cannot take the logarithm of a negative number.

3. $\log 12.3 \approx 1.089905111$

5. $\log 25.6 \approx 1.408239965$

7. $\log 8 \approx 0.903089987$

9. $\log 125,000 \approx 5.096910013$

11. $\log 0.0123 \approx -1.910094889$

13. $\log x = 2.016$

$$x = 10^{2.016} \approx 103.7528416$$

15. $\log x = -0.3562$

$$x = 10^{-0.3562} \approx 0.4403520272$$

17. $\log x = 3.9304$

$$x = 10^{3.9304} \approx 8519.223264$$

19. $\log x = 6.4683$

$$x = 10^{6.4683} \approx 2,939,679.609$$

21. $\log x = -3.3893$

$$x = 10^{-3.3893} \approx 0.000408037$$

23. $\log x = -1.5672$

$$x = 10^{-1.5672} \approx 0.0270894383$$

25. $\text{antilog}(7.6215) \approx 41,831,168.87$

27. $\text{antilog}(-1.0826) \approx 0.0826799109$

29. $\ln 5.62 \approx 1.726331664$

31. $\ln 1.53 \approx 0.4252677354$

33. $\ln 136,000 \approx 11.82041016$

35. $\ln 0.00579 \approx -5.151622987$

© 2006 Pearson Education, Inc., Upper Saddle River, NJ. All rights reserved. This material is protected under all copyright laws as they currently exist. No portion of this material may be reproduced, in any form or by any means, without permission in writing from the publisher.

37. $\ln x = 0.95$
$x = e^{0.95} \approx 2.585709659$

39. $\ln x = 2.4$
$x = e^{2.4} \approx 11.02317638$

41. $\ln x = -0.05$
$x = e^{-0.05} \approx 0.9512294245$

43. $\ln x = -2.7$
$x = e^{-2.7} \approx 0.0672055127$

45. $\text{antilog}_e(6.1582) \approx 472.5766708$

47. $\text{antilog}_e(-2.1298) \approx 0.1188610637$

49. $\log_3 9.2 = \dfrac{\log 9.2}{\log 3} \approx 2.020006063$

51. $\log_7(7.35) = \dfrac{\log 7.35}{\log 7} \approx 1.025073184$

53. $\log_6 0.127 = \dfrac{\log 0.127}{\log 6} \approx -1.151699337$

55. $\log_{15} 12 = \dfrac{\log 12}{\log 15} \approx 0.9175999207$

57. $\log_4 0.07733 = \dfrac{\ln 0.07733}{\ln 4} \approx -1.846414$

59. $\log_{21} 436 = \dfrac{\ln 436}{\ln 21} \approx 1.996254706$

61. $\ln 1537 \approx 7.337587744$

63. $\text{antilog}_e(-1.874) \approx 0.1535083985$

65. $\log x = 8.5634$
$x = 10^{8.5634} \approx 3.65931672 \times 10^8$

67. $\log_4 x = 0.8645 \Leftrightarrow x = 4^{0.8645}$
$x \approx 3.314979618$

69. $y = \log_6 x$

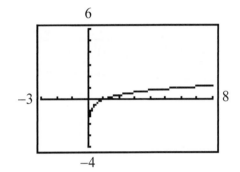

71. $y = \log_{0.4} x$

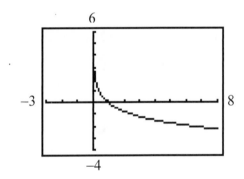

73. $N = 32.82 + 1.0249 \ln x$
$N = 32.82 + 1.0249 \ln 10 \approx 35.18$ in 2000
$N = 32.82 + 1.0249 \ln 20 \approx 35.89$ in 2010
$\dfrac{35.89 - 35.18}{35.18} \approx 0.02$, a 2% increase

75. $R = \log x$
$R = \log 56,000$
$R \approx 4.75$

315

© 2006 Pearson Education, Inc., Upper Saddle River, NJ. All rights reserved. This material is protected under all copyright laws as they currently exist.
No portion of this material may be reproduced, in any form or by any means, without permission in writing from the publisher.

77. $R = \log x$

$6.6 = \log x \Leftrightarrow x = 10^{6.6} \approx 3,981,071.706$

The shock wave is about 3,981,000 times greater than the smallest detectable shock wave.

Cumulative Review

79. $3x^2 - 11x - 5 = 0$

$$x = \frac{-(-11) \pm \sqrt{(-11)^2 - 4(3)(-5)}}{2(3)}$$

$$x = \frac{11 \pm \sqrt{181}}{6}$$

81. Let x, y, z, w, s be the distances between adjacent exits, then:

$x + y + z + w + s = 36$

$x + y \qquad\qquad = 12 \rightarrow$ first eqn

$\quad y + z \qquad\quad = 15$

$\qquad z + w \quad = 12 \rightarrow$ first eqn

$\qquad\quad w + s = 15$

$12 + 12 + s = 36, \; s = 12$

$w + s = w + 12 = 15, \; w = 3$

$z + w = z + 3 = 12, \; z = 9$

$y + z = y + 9 = 15, \; y = 6$

$x + y = x + 6 = 12, \; x = 6$

distance between Exit 1 and Exit 2:
$x = 6$ miles

distance between Exit 1 and Exit 3:
$x + y = 6 + 6 = 12$ miles

11.5 Exercises

1. $\log_7\left(\dfrac{2}{3}x + 3\right) + \log_7 3 = 2$

$$\log_7(2x + 9) = 2 \Leftrightarrow 2x + 9 = 7^2$$

$$2x + 9 = 49$$

$$2x = 40$$

$$x = 20$$

check: $\log_7\left(\dfrac{2}{3} \cdot 20 + 3\right) + \log_7 3 \overset{?}{=} 2$

$$\log_7 \dfrac{49}{3} + \log_7 3 \overset{?}{=} 2$$

$$\log_7 49 \overset{?}{=} 2, \; 2 = 2$$

3. $\log_6(x + 3) + \log_6 4 = 2$

$$\log_6(4x + 12) = 2 \Leftrightarrow 4x + 12 = 6^2$$

$$4x + 12 = 36$$

$$4x = 24$$

$$x = 6$$

check: $\log_6(6 + 3) + \log_6 4 \overset{?}{=} 2$

$$\log_6(9 \cdot 4) \overset{?}{=} 2$$

$$\log_6 36 \overset{?}{=} 2, \; 2 = 2$$

5. $\qquad \log_2\left(x + \dfrac{4}{3}\right) = 5 - \log_2 6$

$$\log_2\left(x + \dfrac{4}{3}\right) + \log_2 6 = 5$$

$$\log_2(6x + 8) = 5 \Leftrightarrow 6x + 8 = 2^5$$

$$6x = 24$$

$$x = 4$$

© 2006 Pearson Education, Inc., Upper Saddle River, NJ. All rights reserved. This material is protected under all copyright laws as they currently exist. No portion of this material may be reproduced, in any form or by any means, without permission in writing from the publisher.

5. check: $\log_2\left(4+\dfrac{4}{3}\right)\overset{?}{=}5-\log_2 6$

$$\log_2\left(\dfrac{16}{3}\right)\overset{?}{=}5-\log_2(3\cdot 2)$$

$$\log_2 16-\log_2 3\overset{?}{=}5-\log_2 3-\log_2 2$$

$$4-\log_2 3\overset{?}{=}5-\log_2 3-1$$

$$4-\log_2 3 = 4-\log_2 3$$

7. $\log(30x+40)=2+\log(x-1)$

$\log(30x+40)-\log(x-1)=2$

$$\log\left(\dfrac{30x+40}{x-1}\right)=2 \Leftrightarrow \dfrac{30x+40}{x-1}=10^2$$

$$30x+40=100x-100$$

$$70x=140$$

$$x=2$$

check: $\log(30(2)+40)\overset{?}{=}2+\log(2-1)$

$$\log 100\overset{?}{=}2+\log(1)$$

$$2=2+\log(1)=2+0$$

$$2=2$$

9. $2+\log_6(x-1)=\log_6(12x)$

$\log_6(x-1)-\log_6(12x)=-2$

$$\log_6\left(\dfrac{x-1}{12x}\right)=-2 \Leftrightarrow \dfrac{x-1}{12x}=6^{-2}$$

$$36x-36=12x$$

$$24x=36,\ x=\dfrac{3}{2}$$

check: $2+\log_6\left(\dfrac{3}{2}-1\right)\overset{?}{=}\log_6\left(12\cdot\dfrac{3}{2}\right)$

$$2+\log_6\dfrac{1}{2}\overset{?}{=}\log_6\dfrac{36}{2}$$

$$2+\log_6 1-\log_6 2\overset{?}{=}\log_6\dfrac{36}{2}$$

$$2+0-\log_6 2\overset{?}{=}\log_6 36-\log_6 2$$

$$2-\log_6 2=2-\log_6 2$$

11. $\log(75x+50)-\log x=2$

$\log(x+20)-\log x=2$

$$\log\left(\dfrac{75x+50}{x}\right)=2 \Leftrightarrow \dfrac{75x+50}{x}=10^2$$

$$100x=75x+50$$

$$25x=50$$

$$x=\dfrac{50}{25}=2$$

check: $\log\left(75(2)+50\right)-\log\left(2\right)\overset{?}{=}2$

$$\log\left(200\right)-\log\left(2\right)\overset{?}{=}2$$

$$\log\left(\dfrac{200}{2}\right)\overset{?}{=}2$$

$$\log 100\overset{?}{=}2$$

$$2=2$$

13. $\log_3(x+6)+\log_3 x=3$

$$\log_3(x(x+6))=3 \Leftrightarrow x(x+6)=3^3$$

$$x^2+6x-27=0 \Rightarrow (x+9)(x-3)=0$$

$$x=-9 \text{ gives } \log_3(\text{negative})$$

$$x=3 \text{ is the solution.}$$

check: $\log_3(3+6)+\log_3 3\overset{?}{=}3$

$$\log_3 9+\log_3 3\overset{?}{=}3$$

$$2+1\overset{?}{=}3$$

$$3=3$$

© 2006 Pearson Education, Inc., Upper Saddle River, NJ. All rights reserved. This material is protected under all copyright laws as they currently exist. No portion of this material may be reproduced, in any form or by any means, without permission in writing from the publisher.

15.
$$1 + \log(x-2) = \log(6x)$$
$$\log(6x) - \log(x-2) = 1$$
$$\log\frac{6x}{x-2} = 1 \Leftrightarrow \frac{6x}{x-2} = 10^1$$
$$6x = 10x - 20$$
$$4x = 20$$
$$x = 5$$

check: $1 + \log(5-2) \overset{?}{=} \log(6 \cdot 5) = \log 30$

$$1 + \log 3 \overset{?}{=} \log(10 \cdot 3)$$
$$1 + \log 3 \overset{?}{=} \log 10 + \log 3$$
$$1 + \log 3 = 1 + \log 3$$

17. $\log_2(x+5) - 2 = \log_2 x$
$$\log_2(x+5) - \log_2 x = 2$$
$$\log_2\frac{x+5}{x} = 2 \Leftrightarrow \frac{x+5}{x} = 2^2 = 4$$
$$x + 5 = 4x$$
$$3x = 5$$
$$x = \frac{5}{3}$$

check: $\log_2\left(\frac{5}{3}+5\right) - 2 \overset{?}{=} \log_2\frac{5}{3}$

$$\log_2\frac{20}{3} - 2 \overset{?}{=} \log_2\frac{5}{3}$$
$$\log_2\left(4\cdot\frac{5}{3}\right) - 2 \overset{?}{=} \log_2\frac{5}{3}$$
$$\log_2 4 + \log_2\frac{5}{3} - 2 \overset{?}{=} \log_2\frac{5}{3}$$
$$2 + \log_2\frac{5}{3} - 2 \overset{?}{=} \log_2\frac{5}{3}$$
$$\log_2\frac{5}{3} = \log_2\frac{5}{3}$$

19.
$$2\log_7 x = \log_7(x+4) + \log_7 2$$
$$\log_7 x^2 - \log_7(x+4) = \log_7 2$$
$$\log_7\frac{x^2}{(x+4)} = \log_7 2$$
$$\frac{x^2}{(x+4)} = 2$$
$$x^2 - 2x - 8 = 0$$
$$(x-4)(x+2) = 0$$
$$x = 4, \ x = -2, \text{ reject, gives } \log_7(\text{negative})$$

check: $2\log_7 4 \overset{?}{=} \log_7(4+4) + \log_7 2$

$$\log_7 4^2 \overset{?}{=} \log_7(8) + \log_7 2$$
$$\log_7 16 \overset{?}{=} \log_7(8 \cdot 2)$$
$$\log_7 16 = \log_7 16$$

21. $\ln 10 - \ln x = \ln(x-3)$
$$\ln\frac{10}{x} = \ln(x-3)$$
$$\frac{10}{x} = x - 3$$
$$x^2 - 3x - 10 = 0$$
$$(x-5)(x+2) = 0$$
$$x = 5, \ x = -2, \text{ reject, gives } \ln(\text{negative})$$

check: $\ln 10 - \ln 5 \overset{?}{=} \ln(5-3)$

$$\ln\frac{10}{5} \overset{?}{=} \ln 2$$
$$\ln 2 = \ln 2$$

318

© 2006 Pearson Education, Inc., Upper Saddle River, NJ. All rights reserved. This material is protected under all copyright laws as they currently exist. No portion of this material may be reproduced, in any form or by any means, without permission in writing from the publisher.

23.
$$7^{x+3} = 12$$
$$\log 7^{x+3} = \log 12$$
$$(x+3)\log 7 = \log 12$$
$$x+3 = \frac{\log 12}{\log 7}$$
$$x = \frac{\log 12}{\log 7} - 3$$
$$x = \frac{\log 12 - 3\log 7}{\log 7}$$

25.
$$2^{3x+4} = 17$$
$$\log 2^{3x+4} = \log 17$$
$$(3x+4)\log 2 = \log 17$$
$$3x+4 = \frac{\log 17}{\log 2}$$
$$3x = \frac{\log 17}{\log 2} - 4 \cdot \frac{\log 2}{\log 2}$$
$$x = \frac{\log 17}{3\log 2} - 4 \cdot \frac{\log 2}{3\log 2}$$
$$x = \frac{\log 17 - 4\log 2}{3\log 2}$$

27.
$$8^{2x-1} = 90$$
$$\log 8^{2x-1} = \log 90$$
$$(2x-1)\log 8 = \log 90$$
$$2x-1 = \frac{\log 90}{\log 8}$$
$$2x = 1 + \frac{\log 90}{\log 8}$$
$$x = \frac{1}{2}\left(1 + \frac{\log 90}{\log 8}\right)$$
$$x \approx 1.582$$

29.
$$5^x = 4^{x+1}$$
$$\log 5^x = \log 4^{x+1}$$
$$x\log 5 = (x+1)\log 4$$
$$x\log 5 = x\log 4 + \log 4$$
$$x(\log 5 - \log 4) = \log 4$$
$$x = \frac{\log 4}{\log 5 - \log 4}$$
$$x \approx 6.213$$

31.
$$e^{x-2} = 28$$
$$\ln e^{x-2} = \ln 28$$
$$(x-2)\ln e = \ln 28$$
$$x = 2 + \ln 28$$
$$x \approx 5.332$$

33.
$$88 = e^{2x+1}$$
$$\ln 88 = \ln e^{2x+1}$$
$$\ln 88 = (2x+1)\ln e$$
$$\ln 88 = (2x+1)(1)$$
$$\ln 88 = 2x+1$$
$$2x = \ln 88 - 1$$
$$x = \frac{\ln 88 - 1}{2}$$
$$x \approx 1.739$$

35.
$$A = P(1+r)^t$$
$$5000 = 1500(1+0.08)^t$$
$$1.08^t = \frac{10}{3}$$
$$\ln 1.08^t = \ln \frac{10}{3}$$
$$t = \frac{\ln \dfrac{10}{3}}{\ln 1.08} = 15.64392564\ldots$$

It will take approximately 16 years.

© 2006 Pearson Education, Inc., Upper Saddle River, NJ. All rights reserved. This material is protected under all copyright laws as they currently exist. No portion of this material may be reproduced, in any form or by any means, without permission in writing from the publisher.

37.
$$A = P(1+r)^t$$
$$3P = P(1+0.06)^t$$
$$1.06^t = 3$$
$$\ln 1.06^t = \ln 3$$
$$t \ln 1.06 = \ln 3$$
$$t = \frac{\ln 3}{\ln 1.06}$$
$$t = 18.85417668...$$
It will take approximately 19 years.

39.
$$A = P(1+r)^t$$
$$6500 = 5000(1+r)^6$$
$$1.3 = (1+r)^6$$
$$\ln 1.3 = \ln(1+r)^6 = 6\ln(1+r)$$
$$\ln(1+r) = \frac{\ln 1.3}{6}$$
$$e^{\ln(1+r)} = e^{\frac{\ln 1.3}{6}}$$
$$1+r = e^{\frac{\ln 1.3}{6}}$$
$$r = e^{\frac{\ln 1.3}{6}} - 1$$
$$r = 0.0446975079...$$
The rate is approximately 4.5%.

41.
$$A = A_0 e^{rt}$$
$$12 = 7e^{0.02t}$$
$$\frac{12}{7} = e^{0.02t}$$
$$\ln \frac{12}{7} = \ln e^{0.02t}$$
$$\ln \frac{12}{7} = 0.02t, \quad t = \frac{\ln \frac{12}{7}}{0.02} = 26.94982504...$$
$$t \approx 27 \text{ years}$$

43.
$$A = A_0 e^{rt}$$
$$2A_0 = A_0 e^{0.02t}, \quad 2 = e^{0.02t}$$
$$\ln 2 = \ln e^{0.02t}$$
$$\ln 2 = 0.02t$$
$$t = \frac{\ln 2}{0.02} = 34.65735903...$$
$$t \approx 35 \text{ years}$$

45.
$$N = 20{,}800(1.264)^x$$
$$N = 20{,}800(1.264)^{13}$$
$$N = 437{,}295.79$$
In 2003 there will be approximately 437,000 employees.

47.
$$N = 20{,}800(1.264)^x$$
$$274{,}000 = 20{,}800(1.264)^x$$
$$1.264^x = \frac{274{,}000}{20{,}800}$$
$$\ln 1.264^x = \ln \frac{274{,}000}{20{,}800}$$
$$x = \frac{\ln \frac{274{,}000}{20{,}800}}{\ln 1.264} = 11.00461354...$$
The number of employees will reach 274,000 sometime in 2001.

49.
$$A = A_0 e^{rt}$$
$$120{,}000 = 80{,}000 e^{0.015t}$$
$$e^{0.015t} = 1.5$$
$$\ln e^{0.015t} = \ln 1.5$$
$$0.015t = \ln 1.5$$
$$t = \frac{\ln 1.5}{0.015}$$
$$t = 27.03111721...$$
$$t \approx 27 \text{ years}$$

© 2006 Pearson Education, Inc., Upper Saddle River, NJ. All rights reserved. This material is protected under all copyright laws as they currently exist. No portion of this material may be reproduced, in any form or by any means, without permission in writing from the publisher.

51. $A = A_0 e^{rt}$

       $1800 = 200 e^{0.04t}$

       $e^{0.04t} = 9$

       $0.04t = \ln 9$

       $t = \dfrac{\ln 9}{0.04} = 54.93061443\ldots$

       It will take approximately 55 hours.

53. $A = A_0 e^{rt}$

       $A = 24{,}500 e^{0.05(13)} = 46930.75031\ldots$

       By the end of 2010 approximately 46,931 people will be infected.

55. $R = \log\left(\dfrac{I}{I_0}\right)$

       $7.1 = \log\left(\dfrac{I_{SF}}{I_0}\right) = \log I_{SF} - \log I_0$

       $8.2 = \log\left(\dfrac{I_{KI}}{I_0}\right) = \log I_{KI} - \log I_0$

   Subtracting the two equations gives

       $-1.1 = \log I_{SF} - \log I_{KI} = \log \dfrac{I_{SF}}{I_{KI}}$

       $10^{\log \frac{I_{SF}}{I_{KI}}} = 10^{-1.1}$

       $\dfrac{I_{SF}}{I_{KI}} = 10^{-1.1}$

       $I_{KI} = 10^{1.1} I_{KI} \approx 12.6 I_{SF}$

   The Kurile island earthquake was about 12.6 times as intense as the San Francisco earthquake.

57. $R = \log\left(\dfrac{I}{I_0}\right)$

       $8.3 = \log\left(\dfrac{I_S}{I_0}\right) = \log I_S - \log I_0$

       $6.8 = \log\left(\dfrac{I_J}{I_0}\right) = \log I_J - \log I_0$

   Subtracting the two equations gives

       $1.5 = \log I_S - \log I_J = \log \dfrac{I_S}{I_J}$

       $10^{\log \frac{I_S}{I_J}} = 10^{1.5}$

       $\dfrac{I_S}{I_J} = 10^{1.5}$

       $I_S = 10^{1.5} I_J \approx 31.6 I_J$

   The intensity of the San Francisco earthquake was approximately 31.6 times greater than the intensity of the Japanese earthquake.

59. Graph $y_1 = 300 e^{0.12x}$ and $y_2 = 750 + 100x$ on the same screen and use the *intersect* feature to solve.

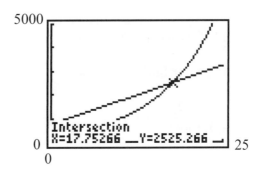

The populations will become equal in approximately 17.8 years.

© 2006 Pearson Education, Inc., Upper Saddle River, NJ. All rights reserved. This material is protected under all copyright laws as they currently exist. No portion of this material may be reproduced, in any form or by any means, without permission in writing from the publisher.

Cumulative Review Problems

61. $(\sqrt{3}+2\sqrt{2})(\sqrt{6}-\sqrt{2})$

$= \sqrt{18}-\sqrt{6}+2\sqrt{12}-4$

$= 3\sqrt{2}-\sqrt{6}+4\sqrt{3}-4$

63. 9 years old: 1 student, given in problem
12 years old: 54 students, also given
13 years old: $54+13 = 87$ students
14 or 15 years old: 80 students, given
10 years old + 11 years old:
$248-80-87-54-1 = 26$ students
Let $x =$ the number of students 10 years
old and $y =$ the number of students 11
years old.

$x+y = 26$

$x+10 = y \rightarrow x+x+10 = 26$

$2x = 16, \ x = 8$ students 10 years old

$y = x+10 = 18$ students 11 years old

Summary:
    9 years old: 1 student
    10 years old: 8 students
    11 years old: 18 students
    12 years old: 54 students
    13 years old: 87 students
    14,15 years old: 80 students

Putting Your Skills to Work

1. $\dfrac{28,349}{3,071,692} = 0.9\%$

2. $\dfrac{13,291}{872,506} = 1.5\%$

3. $0.363(772,185+858,793+872,506)$

   $= \$908,765$ million

4. $\dfrac{x}{908,765} = \dfrac{13,291}{872,506}$

   $x = \$13,843$ million

5. $2005: 65+65(0.17) = 65(1.17)$

   $2006: 65(1.17)+65(1.17)(0.17)$

   $= 65(1.17)(1+0.17) = 65(1.17)^2$

   Online sales(in billions) $= 65(1.17)^n$

   where $n =$ number of years after 2004.

6.

Year	Estimated Online Retail Sales (in billions of dollars)
2005	$65(1.17) = 76.05$
2006	$65(1.17)^2 = 88.98$
2007	$65(1.17)^3 = 104.10$
2008	$65(1.17)^4 = 121.80$

Chapter 11 Review Problems

1. $f(x) = 4^{3+x}$

x	$y = f(x) = 4^{3+x}$
-5	$1/16$
-4	$1/4$
-3	1
-2	4
-1	16

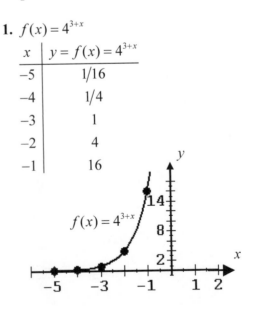

$f(x) = 4^{3+x}$

© 2006 Pearson Education, Inc., Upper Saddle River, NJ. All rights reserved. This material is protected under all copyright laws as they currently exist. No portion of this material may be reproduced, in any form or by any means, without permission in writing from the publisher.

2. $f(x) = e^{x-3}$

x	$y = f(x) = e^{x-3}$
1	0.14
2	0.37
3	1
4	2.72
5	7.39

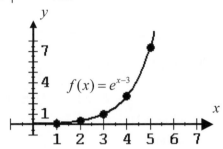

3. $3^{3x+1} = 81 = 3^4$

$$3x + 1 = 4$$
$$3x = 3$$
$$x = 1$$

4. $-2 = \log_{10}(0.01) \Leftrightarrow 10^{-2} = 0.01$

5. $8 = 4^{\frac{3}{2}} \Leftrightarrow \log_4 8 = \frac{3}{2}$

6. $\log_w 16 = 4 \Leftrightarrow w^4 = 16 = 2^4, \; w = 2$

7. $\log_3 x = -2 \Leftrightarrow 3^{-2} = x, \; x = \frac{1}{9}$

8. $\log_8 x = 0 \Leftrightarrow 8^0 = x, \; x = 1$

9. $\log_7 w = -1 \Leftrightarrow 7^{-1} = w, \; w = \frac{1}{7}$

10. $\log_w 64 = 3 \Leftrightarrow w^3 = 64 = 4^3, \; w = 4$

11. $\log_{10} w = -1 \Leftrightarrow 10^{-1} = w, \; w = 0.1$

12. $\log_{10} 1000 = x \Leftrightarrow 10^x = 1000 = 10^3, \; x = 3$

13. $\log_2 64 = x \Leftrightarrow 2^x = 64 = 2^6, \; x = 6$

14. $\log_2 \frac{1}{4} = x \Leftrightarrow 2^x = \frac{1}{4} = 2^{-2}, \; x = -2$

15. $\log_3 243 = x \Leftrightarrow 3^x = 243 = 3^5, \; x = 5$

16. $\log_3 x = y \Leftrightarrow 3^y = x$

$x = 3^y$	y
1/9	−2
1/3	−1
1	0
3	1
9	2

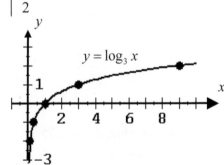

17. $\log_2 \left(\dfrac{5x}{\sqrt{w}} \right) = \log_2(5x) - \log_2 \sqrt{w}$

$$= \log_2(5x) - \log_2 w^{1/2}$$

$$= \log_2 5 + \log_2 x - \frac{1}{2}\log_2 w$$

18. $\log_2 x^3 \sqrt{y} = \log_2 x^3 + \log_2 \sqrt{y}$

$$= 3\log_2 x + \log_2 y^{1/2}$$

$$= 3\log_2 x + \frac{1}{2}\log_2 y$$

323

© 2006 Pearson Education, Inc., Upper Saddle River, NJ. All rights reserved. This material is protected under all copyright laws as they currently exist.
No portion of this material may be reproduced, in any form or by any means, without permission in writing from the publisher.

19. $\log_3 x + \log_3 w^{1/2} - \log_3 2$

$= \log_3 x + \log_3 \sqrt{w} - \log_3 2$

$= \log_3 (x\sqrt{w}) - \log_3 2$

$= \log_3 \dfrac{x\sqrt{w}}{2}$

20. $4\log_8 w - \dfrac{1}{3}\log_8 z = \log_8 w^4 - \log_8 z^{1/3}$

$= \log_8 w^4 - \log_8 \sqrt[3]{z}$

$= \log_8 \dfrac{w^4}{\sqrt[3]{z}}$

21. $\log_e e^6 = 6\log_e e$

$= 6(1)$

$= 6$

22. $\log_5 100 - \log_5 x = \log_5 4$

$\log_5 \dfrac{100}{x} = \log_5 4$

$\dfrac{100}{x} = 4$

$x = 25$

23. $\log_8 x + \log_8 3 = \log_8 75$

$\log_8 (3x) = \log_8 75$

$3x = 75$

$x = 25$

24. $\log 23.8 = 1.376576957$

25. $\log 0.0817 = -1.087777943$

26. $\ln 3.92 = 1.366091654$

27. $\ln 803 = 6.688354714$

28. $\log n = 1.1367 \Leftrightarrow n = 10^{1.1367}$

$n = 13.69935122$

29. $\ln n = 1.7 \Leftrightarrow n = e^{1.7}$

$n = 5.473947392$

30. $\log_8 2.81 = \dfrac{\ln 2.81}{\ln 8}$

$\log_8 2.81 = 0.4968567101$

31. $\log_{11}\left(\dfrac{4}{3}x + 7\right) + \log_{11} 3 = 2$

$\log_{11}(4x + 21) = 2 \Leftrightarrow 11^2 = 4x + 21$

$4x + 21 = 121$

$4x = 100$

$x = 25$

check: $\log_{11}\left(\dfrac{4}{3}\cdot 25 + 7\right) + \log_{11} 3 \overset{?}{=} 2$

$\log_{11}\left(\left(\dfrac{4}{3}\cdot 25 + 7\right)\cdot 3\right) \overset{?}{=} 2$

$\log_{11}(100 + 21) \overset{?}{=} 2$

$\log_{11}(121) \overset{?}{=} 2$

$2 = 2$

32. $\log_8(x-3) = \log_8 6x - 1$

$\log_8(x-3) - \log_8 6x = -1$

$\log_8 \dfrac{x-3}{6x} = -1$

$\dfrac{x-3}{6x} = 8^{-1} = \dfrac{1}{8}$

$8x - 24 = 6x$

$2x = 24$

$x = 12$

© 2006 Pearson Education, Inc., Upper Saddle River, NJ. All rights reserved. This material is protected under all copyright laws as they currently exist. No portion of this material may be reproduced, in any form or by any means, without permission in writing from the publisher.

32. check: $\log_8(12-3) \overset{?}{=} \log_8(6 \cdot 12) - 1$

$$\log_8(9) \overset{?}{=} \log_8(72) - \log_8 8$$

$$\log_8(9) \overset{?}{=} \log_8\left(\frac{72}{8}\right)$$

$$\log_8(9) = \log_8(9)$$

33. $\log_5(x+1) - \log_5 8 = \log_5 x$

$$\log_5(x+1) - \log_5 x = \log_5 8$$

$$\log_5 \frac{x+1}{x} = \log_5 8$$

$$\frac{x+1}{x} = 8$$

$$x+1 = 8x$$

$$7x = 1$$

$$x = \frac{1}{7}$$

check: $\log_5\left(\frac{1}{7}+1\right) - \log_5 8 \overset{?}{=} \log_5\left(\frac{1}{7}\right)$

$$\log_5\left(\frac{8}{7}\right) - \log_5 8 \overset{?}{=} \log_5\left(\frac{1}{7}\right)$$

$$\log_5\left(\frac{1}{7} \cdot 8\right) - \log_5 8 \overset{?}{=} \log_5\left(\frac{1}{7}\right)$$

$$\log_5\left(\frac{1}{7}\right) + \log_5 8 - \log_5 8 \overset{?}{=} \log_5\left(\frac{1}{7}\right)$$

$$\log_5\left(\frac{1}{7}\right) = \log_5\left(\frac{1}{7}\right)$$

34. $\log_{12}(x+2) + \log_{12} 3 = 1$

$$\log_{12}(3x+6) = \log_{12} 12$$

$$3x+6 = 21$$

$$3x = 6$$

$$x = 2$$

34. check: $\log_{12}(2+2) + \log_{12} 3 \overset{?}{=} 1$

$$\log_{12}(4) + \log_{12} 3 \overset{?}{=} 1$$

$$\log_{12}(12) \overset{?}{=} 1$$

$$1 = 1$$

35. $\log_2(x-2) + \log_2(x+5) = 3$

$$\log_2\big((x-2)(x+5)\big) = 3$$

$$(x-2)(x+5) = 2^3 = 8$$

$$x^2 + 3x - 10 = 8$$

$$x^2 + 3x - 18 = 0$$

$$(x+6)(x-3) = 0$$

$x = 3, \ x = -6$, reject -6 since it gives

$$\log_2(\text{negative}).$$

$x = 3$ is the solution.

check: $\log_2(3-2) + \log_2(3+5) \overset{?}{=} 3$

$$\log_2(1) + \log_2(8) \overset{?}{=} 3$$

$$0 + \log_2(2^3) \overset{?}{=} 3$$

$$3\log_2 2 \overset{?}{=} 3$$

$$3 = 3$$

36. $\log_5(x+1) + \log_5(x-3) = 1$

$$\log_5\big((x+1)(x-3)\big) = 1$$

$$(x+1)(x-3) = 5^1 = 5$$

$$x^2 - 2x - 3 = 5$$

$$x^2 - 2x - 8 = 0$$

$$(x-4)(x+2) = 0$$

$x = 4, \ x = -2$, reject -2 since it

gives $\log_5(\text{negative})$

325

© 2006 Pearson Education, Inc., Upper Saddle River, NJ. All rights reserved. This material is protected under all copyright laws as they currently exist. No portion of this material may be reproduced, in any form or by any means, without permission in writing from the publisher.

36. check: $\log_5(4+1) + \log_5(4-3) \overset{?}{=} 1$

$$\log_5(5) + \log_5(1) \overset{?}{=} 1$$

$$1 + 0 \overset{?}{=} 1$$

$$1 = 1$$

37. $\log(2t+1) + \log(4t-1) = 2\log 3$

$$\log\big((2t+3)(4t-1)\big) = \log 3^2 = \log 9$$

$$(2t+3)(4t-1) = 9$$

$$8t^2 + 10t - 3 = 9$$

$$8t^2 + 10t - 12 = 0$$

$$4t^2 + 5t - 6 = 0$$

$$(4t-3)(t+2) = 0$$

$t = \dfrac{3}{4}$, $t = -2$, reject -2 since it gives

$$\log(\text{negative})$$

$t = \dfrac{3}{4}$ is the solution.

check:

$$\log\left(2\cdot\frac{3}{4}+3\right) + \log\left(4\cdot\frac{3}{4}-1\right) \overset{?}{=} 2\log 3$$

$$\log\left(\frac{9}{2}\right) + \log(2) \overset{?}{=} 2\log 3$$

$$\log\left(\frac{9}{2}\cdot 2\right) \overset{?}{=} 2\log 3$$

$$\log(9) \overset{?}{=} 2\log 3$$

$$\log\left(3^2\right) \overset{?}{=} 2\log 3$$

$$2\log 3 = 2\log 3$$

38. $\log(2t+4) - \log(3t+1) = \log 6$

$$\log\left(\frac{2t+4}{3t+1}\right) = \log 6$$

$$\frac{2t+4}{3t+1} = 6$$

$$2t + 4 = 18t + 6$$

$$16t = -2$$

$$t = -\frac{1}{8}$$

check: $\log\left(2\cdot\dfrac{-1}{8}+4\right) - \log\left(3\cdot\dfrac{-1}{8}+1\right) \overset{?}{=} \log 6$

$$\log\left(\frac{15}{4}\right) - \log\left(\frac{5}{8}\right) \overset{?}{=} \log 6$$

$$\log\left(\frac{\frac{15}{4}}{\frac{5}{8}}\right) \overset{?}{=} \log 6$$

$$\log\left(\frac{\frac{15}{4}}{\frac{5}{8}}\right) \overset{?}{=} \log 6$$

$$\log 6 = \log 6$$

39. $3^x = 14 \Rightarrow \log 3^x = \log 14$

$$x\log 3 = \log 14 \Rightarrow x = \frac{\log 14}{\log 3}$$

40. $\qquad\qquad 5^{x+3} = 130$

$$\log 5^{x+3} = \log 130$$

$$(x+3)\log 5 = \log 130$$

$$x + 3 = \frac{\log 130}{\log 5}$$

$$x = \frac{\log 130}{\log 5} - 3$$

$$x = \frac{\log 130 - 3\log 5}{\log 5}$$

© 2006 Pearson Education, Inc., Upper Saddle River, NJ. All rights reserved. This material is protected under all copyright laws as they currently exist. No portion of this material may be reproduced, in any form or by any means, without permission in writing from the publisher.

41. $e^{2x-1} = 100$

$$\ln(e^{2x-1}) = \ln 100$$
$$(2x-1)\ln e = \ln 100$$
$$2x-1 = \ln 100$$
$$2x = \ln 100 + 1$$
$$x = \frac{\ln 100 + 1}{2}$$

42. $e^{2x} = 30.6$

$$\ln e^{2x} = \ln 30.6$$
$$2x \ln e = \ln 30.6$$
$$2x = \ln 30.6 \Rightarrow x = \frac{\ln 30.6}{2}$$

43. $2^{3x+1} = 5^x$

$$\ln 2^{3x+1} = \ln 5^x$$
$$(3x+1)\ln 2 = x \ln 5$$
$$3x \ln 2 + \ln 2 = x \ln 5$$
$$x(3\ln 2 - \ln 5) = -\ln 2$$
$$x = \frac{\ln 2}{\ln 5 - 3\ln 2}$$
$$x \approx -1.4748$$

44. $3^{x+1} = 7$

$$\ln 3^{x+1} = \ln 7$$
$$(x+1)\ln 3 = \ln 7$$
$$x = -1 + \frac{\ln 7}{\ln 3}$$
$$x \approx 0.7712$$

45. $e^{3x-4} = 20$

$$\ln e^{3x-4} = \ln 20$$
$$(3x-4)\ln e = \ln 20$$
$$3x - 4 = \ln 20$$
$$x = \frac{\ln 20 + 4}{3} \Rightarrow x \approx 2.3319$$

46. $1.03^x = 20$

$$\ln 1.03^x = \ln 20$$
$$x \ln 1.03 = \ln 20$$
$$x = \frac{\ln 20}{\ln 1.03}$$
$$x \approx 101.3482$$

47. $A = P(1+r)^t$

$$2P = P(1+0.08)^t$$
$$2 = 1.08^t$$
$$\ln 2 = \ln 1.08^t$$
$$\ln 2 = t \ln 1.08$$
$$t = \frac{\ln 2}{\ln 1.08}$$

$t \approx 9$ years to double money in account

48. $A = P(1+r)^t$

$$A = 5000(1+0.06)^4$$

$A = \$6312.38$ in account after 4 years

49. $A = P(1+r)^t$

$$20,000 = 12,000(1+0.07)^t$$
$$\frac{5}{3} = 1.07^t$$
$$\ln 1.07^t = \ln \frac{5}{3}$$
$$t \ln 1.07 = \ln \frac{5}{3}$$
$$t = \frac{\ln \frac{5}{3}}{\ln 1.07}$$
$$t = 7.550041795\ldots$$
$$t \approx 8 \text{ years}$$

© 2006 Pearson Education, Inc., Upper Saddle River, NJ. All rights reserved. This material is protected under all copyright laws as they currently exist.
No portion of this material may be reproduced, in any form or by any means, without permission in writing from the publisher.

50. $A = P(1+r)^t$

$$A_{\text{Robert}} + 500 = A_{\text{Brother}}$$

$$3500(1+0.05)^t + 500 = 3500(1+0.06)^t$$

$$7(1.06)^t - 7(1.05)^t = 1$$

$$(1.06)^t - (1.05)^t = \frac{1}{7}$$

Solve with a graphing calculator. Graph

$y_1 = 1.06^x - 1.05^x$ and $y_2 = \frac{1}{7}$ and use the

intersect feature.

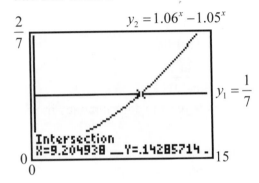

It will take approximately 9 years for Robert's amount to be $500 less than his brother's amount.

51. $A = A_0 e^{rt}$

$$16 = 7e^{0.02t}$$

$$\ln\frac{16}{7} = \ln e^{0.02t}$$

$$\ln\frac{16}{7} = 0.02t \ln e$$

$$t = \frac{\ln\frac{16}{7}}{0.02} = 41.33392866...$$

$$t \approx 41 \text{ years}$$

52. $A = A_0 e^{rt}$

$$10 = 6e^{0.02t}$$

$$\ln 1.\overline{6} = \ln e^{0.02t}$$

$$\ln 1.\overline{6} = 0.02t \ln e$$

$$t = \frac{\ln 1.\overline{6}}{0.02} = 25.54128119...$$

$$t \approx 26 \text{ years}$$

53. $A = A_0 e^{rt}$

$$2600 = 2000 e^{0.03t}$$

$$\ln 1.3 = \ln e^{0.03t}$$

$$\ln 1.3 = 0.03t$$

$$t = \frac{\ln 1.3}{0.03} = 8.745475482...$$

$$t \approx 9 \text{ years}$$

54. $A = A_0 e^{rt}$

$$95,000 = 40,000 e^{0.08t}$$

$$2.375 = e^{0.08t}$$

$$\ln 2.375 = \ln e^{0.08t}$$

$$0.08t = \ln 2.375$$

$$t = \frac{\ln 2.375}{0.08} = 10.81246797...$$

$$t \approx 11 \text{ years}$$

55. $W = p_0 V_0 \ln\left(\dfrac{V_1}{V_0}\right)$

(a) $W = 40(15)\ln\left(\dfrac{24}{15}\right)$

$$W \approx 282 \text{ lb}$$

(b) $100 = p_0(8)\ln\left(\dfrac{40}{8}\right)$

$$p_0 = \frac{100}{(8)\ln\left(\dfrac{40}{8}\right)} \approx 7.77 \text{ lb/in.}^3$$

© 2006 Pearson Education, Inc., Upper Saddle River, NJ. All rights reserved. This material is protected under all copyright laws as they currently exist. No portion of this material may be reproduced, in any form or by any means, without permission in writing from the publisher.

56. $M = \log\left(\dfrac{I}{I_0}\right)$

$8.4 = \log\left(\dfrac{I_A}{I_0}\right) = \log I_A - \log I_0$

$-\left(6.7 = \log\left(\dfrac{I_T}{I_0}\right) = \log I_T - \log I_0\right)$

$\overline{1.7 = \log I_A - \log I_T}$

$\log\dfrac{I_A}{I_T} = 1.7$

$10^{\log\frac{I_A}{I_T}} = 10^{1.7}$

$\dfrac{I_A}{I_T} = 50.11872336...$

$I_A = 50.11872336...I_T$

$I_A \approx 50.1 I_T$

The Alaska earthquake was about 50.1 times more intense than the Turkey earthquake.

How Am I Doing? Chapter 11 Test

$f(x) = 3^{x+1}$

1.

x	$y = f(x) = 3^{x+1}$
-1	1
0	3

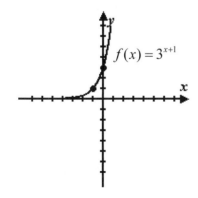

$f(x) = 3^{x+1}$

2. $f(x) = \log_2 x$

x	$y = f(x) = \log_2 x$
$\dfrac{1}{2}$	-1
1	0
2	2
4	2

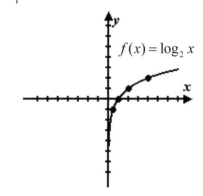

$f(x) = \log_2 x$

3. $4^{x+3} = 64 = 4^3$

    $x + 3 = 3$

       $x = 0$

4. $\log_w 125 = 3 \Leftrightarrow w^3 = 125 = 5^3, \; w = 5$

5. $\log_8 x = -2 \Leftrightarrow x = 8^{-2} = \dfrac{1}{64}$

6. $2\log_7 x + \log_7 y - \log_7 4$

    $= \log_7 x^2 + \log_7 \dfrac{y}{4}$

    $= \log_7 \dfrac{x^2 y}{4}$

329

© 2006 Pearson Education, Inc., Upper Saddle River, NJ. All rights reserved. This material is protected under all copyright laws as they currently exist. No portion of this material may be reproduced, in any form or by any means, without permission in writing from the publisher.

7. $\ln 5.99 = 1.7901$

8. $\log 23.6 = 1.3729$

9. $\log_3 1.62 = \dfrac{\log 1.62}{\log 3} = 0.4391$

10. $\log x = 3.7284 \Leftrightarrow x = 10^{3.7284}$
$$x = 5350.569382$$

11. $\ln x = 0.14 \Leftrightarrow x = e^{0.14} = 1.150273799$

12. $\log_8(x+3) - \log_8 2x = \log_8 4$
$$\log_8\left(\frac{x+3}{2x}\right) = \log_8 4$$
$$\frac{x+3}{2x} = 4$$
$$x + 3 = 8x$$
$$7x = 3$$
$$x = \frac{3}{7}$$

check : $\log_8\left(\dfrac{3}{7}+3\right) - \log_8\left(2\cdot\dfrac{3}{7}\right) \overset{?}{=} \log_8 4$

$$\log_8\left(\frac{24}{7}\right) - \log_8\left(\frac{6}{7}\right) \overset{?}{=} \log_8 4$$

$$\log_8\left(\frac{\frac{24}{7}}{\frac{6}{7}}\right) \overset{?}{=} \log_8 4$$

$$\log_8 4 = \log_8 4$$

13. $\log_8 2x + \log_8 6 = 2$
$$\log_8((2x)(6)) = 2 \Leftrightarrow 12x = 8^2$$
$$12x = 64$$
$$x = \frac{16}{3}$$

13. check: $\log_8 2 \cdot \dfrac{16}{3} + \log_8 6 \overset{?}{=} 2$

$$\log_8\left(2\cdot\frac{16}{3}\cdot 6\right) \overset{?}{=} 2$$

$$\log_8 64 \overset{?}{=} 2$$

$$\log_8 8^2 \overset{?}{=} 2$$

$$2 = 2$$

14. $\quad e^{5x-3} = 57$
$$\ln e^{5x-3} = \ln 57$$
$$(5x-3)\ln e = \ln 57$$
$$5x = \ln 57 + 3$$
$$x = \frac{\ln 57 + 3}{5}$$

15. $\quad 5^{3x+6} = 17$
$$\ln 5^{3x+6} = \ln 17$$
$$(3x+6)\ln 5 = \ln 17$$
$$3x + 6 = \frac{\ln 17}{\ln 5}$$
$$x = \frac{-6 + \dfrac{\ln 17}{\ln 5}}{3} \approx -1.4132$$

16. $A = P(1+r)^t$
$$A = 2000(1+0.08)^5 = 2938.656154\ldots$$
Henry will have \$2938.66

17. $\quad A = P(1+r)^t$
$$2P = P(1+0.05)^t$$
$$2 = (1.05)^t$$
$$\ln 2 = \ln 1.05^t$$
$$\ln 2 = t \ln 1.05$$
$$t = \frac{\ln 2}{\ln 1.05} = 14.20669908\ldots$$
$$t \approx 14 \text{ years to double}$$

© 2006 Pearson Education, Inc., Upper Saddle River, NJ. All rights reserved. This material is protected under all copyright laws as they currently exist. No portion of this material may be reproduced, in any form or by any means, without permission in writing from the publisher.

Cumulative Test for Chapters 1-11

1. $2(-3) + 12 \div (-2) + 3\sqrt{36}$
$= -6 + (-6) + 3(6) = 6$

2. $3mx = 5(mx - y) + 1$
$3mx = 5mx - 5y + 1$
$2mx = 5y - 1$
$x = \dfrac{5y - 1}{2m}$

3. $y = -\dfrac{2}{3}x + 4$

x	y
0	4
6	0

4. $5ax + 5ay - 7wx - 7wy$
$= 5a(x + y) - 7w(x + y)$
$= (x + y)(5a - 7w)$

5. Switch first and third equation
$x + y + z = 2$
$3x - y + z = 6$
$2x - y + 2z = 7$
Add -3 time first equation to second equation and -2 times first equation to third equation

5. $x + y + z = 2$
$\quad -4y - 2z = 0$
$\quad -3y \quad\quad = 3 \Rightarrow y = -1$, from second equation, $-4(-1) - 2z = 0$
$2z = 4 \Rightarrow z = 2$, from first equation,
$x + (-1) + 2 = 2 \Rightarrow x = 1$
$(1, -1, 2)$ is the solution.

6. $(3\sqrt{7} - \sqrt{3})(\sqrt{7} + \sqrt{3})$
$= 3(7) + 3\sqrt{21} - \sqrt{21} - 3$
$= 18 + 2\sqrt{21}$

7. $\quad x^4 - 5x^2 - 6 = 0$
$(x^2 - 6)(x^2 + 1) = 0$
$\quad x^2 - 6 = 0, \ x^2 + 1 = 0$
$\quad\quad x^2 = 6, \ x^2 = -1$
$\quad\quad x = \pm\sqrt{6}, \ x = \pm i$

8. $2x - y = 4 \Rightarrow y = 2x - 4$
$\quad 4x - y^2 = 0 \Rightarrow 4x - (2x - 4)^2 = 0$
$4x - 4x^2 + 16x - 16 = 0$
$\quad x^2 - 5x + 4 = 0$
$\quad (x - 4)(x - 1) = 0$
$\quad\quad x = 4, \ x = 1$
$\quad\quad y = 2(4) - 4 = 4,$
$\quad\quad y = 2(1) - 4 = -2$
$x = 4, \ y = 4; \ x = 1, \ y = -2$ is the solution.

9. $2x - 3 = \sqrt{7x - 3}, \ 4x^2 - 12x + 9 = 7x - 3$
$4x^2 - 19x + 12 = 0 \Rightarrow (x - 4)(4x - 3) = 0$
$x = 4, \ x = \dfrac{3}{4}$ which does not check
$x = 4$ is the solution.

© 2006 Pearson Education, Inc., Upper Saddle River, NJ. All rights reserved. This material is protected under all copyright laws as they currently exist. No portion of this material may be reproduced, in any form or by any means, without permission in writing from the publisher.

10. $\dfrac{3x}{\sqrt{6}} \cdot \dfrac{\sqrt{6}}{\sqrt{6}} = \dfrac{3x\sqrt{6}}{6} = \dfrac{x\sqrt{6}}{2}$

11. $f(x) = 2^{3-2x}$

x	$y = f(x) = 2^{3-2x}$
1	2
2	1/2
3	1/8
4	1/32

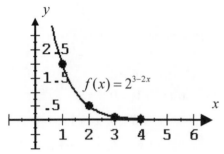

12. $\log_x\left(\dfrac{1}{64}\right) = 3 \Leftrightarrow x^3 = \dfrac{1}{64} = \left(\dfrac{1}{4}\right)^3$

$$x = \dfrac{1}{4}$$

13. $5^{2x-1} = 25 = 5^2$

$2x - 1 = 2$

$2x = 3$

$x = \dfrac{3}{2}$

14. $\log 7.67 = 0.8847953639$

15. $\log_x = 1.8209 \Leftrightarrow x = 10^{1.8209}$

$$x \approx 66.20640403$$

16. $\log_3 7 = \dfrac{\ln 7}{\ln 3}$

$= 1.771243749$

17. $\ln x = 1.9638 \Leftrightarrow x = e^{1.9638}$

$$x \approx 7.1263558$$

18. $\log_9 x = 1 - \log_9(x-8)$

$\log_9 x + \log_9(x-8) = 1$

$\log_9(x(x-8)) = 1 \Leftrightarrow x(x-8) = 9^1$

$x^2 - 8x - 9 = 0$

$(x-9)(x+1) = 0$

$x = 9, \ x = -1$ which must be rejected

since it gives $\log_9$ (negative)

$x = 9$ is the solution.

19. $\log_5 x = \log_5 2 + \log_5(x^2 - 3)$

$\log_5 x - \log_5(x^2 - 3) = \log_5 2$

$\log_5\left(\dfrac{x}{x^2-3}\right) = \log_5 2$

$\dfrac{x}{x^2-3} = 2$

$2x^2 - 6 = x$

$2x^2 - x - 6 = 0$

$(x-2)(2x+3) = 0$

$x = 2, \ x = -\dfrac{3}{2}$ which must be rejected

since it gives $\log_5$ (negative)

$x = 2$ is the solution.

20. $3^{x+2} = 5$

$\ln 3^{x+2} = \ln 5$

$(x+2)\ln 3 = \ln 5$

$x + 2 = \dfrac{\ln 5}{\ln 3}$

$x = -2 + \dfrac{\ln 5}{\ln 3} \approx -0.535$

© 2006 Pearson Education, Inc., Upper Saddle River, NJ. All rights reserved. This material is protected under all copyright laws as they currently exist. No portion of this material may be reproduced, in any form or by any means, without permission in writing from the publisher.

21. $33 = 66e^{2x} \Rightarrow e^{2x} = 0.5 \Rightarrow \ln e^{2x} = \ln 0.5$

$\ln e^{2x} = \ln 0.5$

$2x = \ln 0.5, \; x = \dfrac{\ln 0.5}{2}$

22. $A = P(1+r)^t$

$A = 3000(1+0.09)^4 = 4234.74483...$

They will have \$4234.74.

Practice Final Examination

1. $(4-3)^2 + \sqrt{9} \div (-3) + 4$

$= 1^2 + 3 \div (-3) + 4$

$= 1 + (-1) + 4$

$= 4$

2. $36,250,000 = 3.625 \times 10^7$

3. $3a + 6b - a + 5ab + 3a^2 + b$

$= 2a + 7b + 5ab + 3a^2$

4. $3[2x - 5(x+y)] = 3[2x - 5x - 5y]$

$\qquad\qquad\qquad = 3[-3x - 5y]$

$\qquad\qquad\qquad = -9x - 15y$

5. $F = \dfrac{9}{5}C + 32$

$F = \dfrac{9}{5}(-35) + 32$

$F = -31$

6. $\dfrac{1}{3}y - 4 = \dfrac{1}{2}y + 1$

$\dfrac{1}{6}y = -5$

$y = -30$

7. $\qquad A = \dfrac{1}{2}a(b+c)$

$\qquad 2A = ab + ac$

$\qquad ab = 2A - ac$

$\qquad b = \dfrac{2A - ac}{a}$

8. $\left| \dfrac{2}{3}x - 4 \right| = 2$

$\dfrac{2}{3}x - 4 = 2$ or $\dfrac{2}{3}x - 4 = -2$

$\quad 2x - 12 = 6 \qquad 2x - 12 = -6$

$\qquad 2x = 18 \qquad\qquad 2x = 6$

$\qquad\; x = 9 \qquad\qquad\; x = 3$

9. $2x - 3 < x - 2(3x - 2)$

$2x - 3 < x - 6x + 4$

$7x < 7$

$x < 1$

10. $\qquad P = 2L + 2W = 1760$

$\qquad\quad L + W = 880$

$2W - 200 + W = 880$

$\qquad\qquad 3W = 1080$

$\qquad\qquad\; W = 360$

$\qquad L = 2W - 200 = 520$

The width is 360 meters and the length is 520 meters.

11. Let $x =$ amount invested at 14%

$0.14x + 0.12(4000 - x) = 508$

$0.14x + 480 - 0.12x = 508$

$0.02x = 28$

$x = 1400$

$4000 - x = 2600$

\$1400 was invested at 14% and \$2600 at 12%.

© 2006 Pearson Education, Inc., Upper Saddle River, NJ. All rights reserved. This material is protected under all copyright laws as they currently exist. No portion of this material may be reproduced, in any form or by any means, without permission in writing from the publisher.

12. $x + 5 \le -4$ or $2 - 7x \le 16$

$\qquad x \le -9 \qquad -7x \le 14$

$\qquad\qquad\qquad\qquad x \ge -2$

13. $|2x - 5| < 10$

$\qquad -10 < 2x - 5 < 10$

$\qquad -5 < 2x < 15$

$\qquad -\dfrac{5}{2} < x < \dfrac{15}{2}$

14. $7x - 2y = -14$

x	y
0	7
-2	0

y

$(0,7)$

$(-2,0)$

x

$-8 \quad -4 \qquad 4 \quad 8$

$7x - 2y = -14$

15. $3x - 4y \le 6$

Test point: $(0,0)$

$3(0) - 4(0) \le 6$

$\qquad 0 \le 6,\ \text{True}$

y

$3x - 4y \le 6$

x

$-8 \quad -4 \qquad 4 \quad 8$

16. $m = \dfrac{y_2 - y_1}{x_2 - x_1} = \dfrac{-3 - 5}{-2 - 1} = \dfrac{8}{3}$

17. $3x + 2y = 8 \Rightarrow y = -\dfrac{3}{2}x + 4,\ m = -\dfrac{3}{2}$

$\qquad m_p = -\dfrac{3}{2},\quad y - 4 = -\dfrac{3}{2}(x - (-1))$

$\qquad\qquad 3x + 2y = 5$

18. $f(x) = 3x^2 - 4x - 3$

$\qquad f(3) = 3(3^2) - 4(3) - 3$

$\qquad f(3) = 12$

19. $f(x) = 3x^2 - 4x - 3$

$\qquad f(-2) = 3((-2)^2) - 4(-2) - 3$

$\qquad f(-2) = 17$

20. $f(x) = |2x - 4|$

x	$y = f(x) = |2x - 4|$
1	2
2	0
3	2

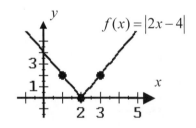

21. $2x + y = 15 \Rightarrow y = 15 - 2x$

$\qquad 3x - 2y = 5 \rightarrow 3x - 2(15 - 2x) = 5$

$\qquad 3x - 30 + 4x = 5$

$\qquad 7x = 35$

$\qquad x = 5$

$\qquad y = 15 - 2(5) = 5$

$\qquad (5,5)$ is the solution.

© 2006 Pearson Education, Inc., Upper Saddle River, NJ. All rights reserved. This material is protected under all copyright laws as they currently exist.
No portion of this material may be reproduced, in any form or by any means, without permission in writing from the publisher.

22. $4x - 3y = 12 \xrightarrow{\times 4} 16x - 12y = 48$

$3x - 4y = 2 \xrightarrow{\times -3} \underline{-9x + 12y = -6}$

$7x = 42$

$x = 6$

$4(6) - 3y = 12$

$-3y = -12$

$y = 4$

$(6, 4)$ is the solution.

23. Solve the system.

$2x + 3y - z = 16$

$x - y + 3z = -9$

$5x + 2y - z = 15$

Multiply first equation by 3 and add to the second equation

$6x + 9y - 3z = 48$

$\underline{x - y + 3z = -9}$

$7x + 8y = 39$

Multiply third equation by 3 and add to the second equation

$x - y + 3z = -9$

$\underline{15x + 6y - 3z = 45}$

$16x + 5y = 36$

Now solve the system

$7x + 8y = 39 \xrightarrow{\times 5} 35x + 40y = 195$

$16x + 5y = 36 \xrightarrow{\times -8} \underline{-128x - 40y = -288}$

$ -93x = -93$

$x = 1$

$16x + 5y = 36 \Rightarrow 16(1) + 5y = 36$

$5y = 20$

$y = 4$

$x - y + 3z = -9 \Rightarrow 1 - 4 + 3z = -9$

$z = -2$

$(1, 4, -2)$ is the solution.

24. $3x - 2y = 7 \xrightarrow{\times 3} 9x - 6y = 7$

$-9x + 6y = 2 \rightarrow \underline{-9x + 6y = 2}$

$0 = 9$

Inconsistent system. No solution.

25. $A =$ number of adult tickets

$15 - A =$ number of children tickets

$8A + 3(15 - A) = 100$

$8A + 45 - 3A = 100$

$5A = 55 \Rightarrow A = 11$ adult tickets

$15 - A = 4$ children tickets

26. $3y \geq 8x - 12$ $2x + 3y \leq -6$

Test point: $(0, 0)$ Test point: $(0, 0)$

$3(0) \geq 8(0) - 12$ $2(0) + 3(0) \leq -6$

$0 \geq -12$, true $0 \leq -6$, false

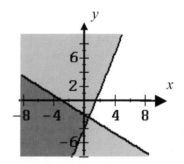

27. $(3x - 2)(2x^2 - 4x + 3)$

$= 6x^3 - 12x^2 + 9x - 4x^2 + 8x - 6$

$= 6x^3 - 16x^2 + 17x - 6$

© 2006 Pearson Education, Inc., Upper Saddle River, NJ. All rights reserved. This material is protected under all copyright laws as they currently exist. No portion of this material may be reproduced, in any form or by any means, without permission in writing from the publisher.

28.

$$
\begin{array}{r}
5x^2 - x + 2 \\
5x+1\overline{)25x^3 + 0x^2 + 9x + 2} \\
\underline{25x^3 + 5x^2} \\
-5x^2 + 9x \\
\underline{-5x^2 - x} \\
10x + 2 \\
\underline{10x + 2} \\
0
\end{array}
$$

29. $8x^3 - 27 = (2x)^3 - 3^3$

$\qquad = (2x - 3)((2x)^2 + (2x)(3) + (3)^2)$

$\qquad = (2x - 3)(4x^2 + 6x + 9)$

30. $x^3 + 2x^2 - 4x - 8 = x^2(x+2) - 4(x+2)$

$\qquad = (x+2)(x^2 - 4)$

$\qquad = (x+2)(x+2)(x-2)$

31. $2x^3 + 15x^2 - 8x = x(2x^2 + 15x - 8)$

$\qquad = x(2x - 1)(x + 8)$

32. $x^2 + 15x + 54 = 0$

$\qquad (x+9)(x+6) = 0$

$\qquad x + 9 = 0, \quad x + 6 = 0$

$\qquad x = -9, \qquad x = -6$

33. $\dfrac{9x^3 - x}{3x^2 - 8x - 3} = \dfrac{x(9x^2 - 1)}{(3x+1)(x-3)}$

$\qquad = \dfrac{x(3x+1)(3x-1)}{(3x+1)(x-3)}$

$\qquad = \dfrac{x(3x-1)}{(x-3)}$

34. $\dfrac{x^2 - 9}{2x^2 + 7x + 3} \div \dfrac{x^2 - 3x}{2x^2 + 11x + 5}$

$\qquad = \dfrac{(x+3)(x-3)}{(2x+1)(x+3)} \cdot \dfrac{(2x+1)(x+5)}{x(x-3)}$

$\qquad = \dfrac{(x+5)}{x}$

35. $\dfrac{3x}{x+5} - \dfrac{2}{x^2 + 7x + 10}$

$\qquad = \dfrac{3x(x+2)}{(x+5)(x+2)} - \dfrac{2}{(x+5)(x+2)}$

$\qquad = \dfrac{3x(x+2) - 2}{(x+5)(x+2)}$

$\qquad = \dfrac{3x^2 + 6x - 2}{(x+5)(x+2)}$

36. $\dfrac{\dfrac{3}{2x} - 1}{\dfrac{5}{2} + \dfrac{1}{x}} \cdot \dfrac{2x}{2x} = \dfrac{3 - 2x}{5x + 2}$

37. $\qquad \dfrac{x-1}{x^2 - 4} = \dfrac{2}{x+2} + \dfrac{4}{x-2}$

$\qquad \dfrac{x-1}{(x+2)(x-2)} = \dfrac{2}{x+2} + \dfrac{4}{x-2}$

$\qquad x - 1 = 2(x-2) + 4(x+2)$

$\qquad x - 1 = 2x - 4 + 4x + 8$

$\qquad 5x = -5$

$\qquad x = -1$

38. $16^{\frac{3}{2}} = \sqrt{16^3}$

$\qquad = \sqrt{16 \cdot 16 \cdot 16}$

$\qquad = 4 \cdot 4 \cdot 4 = 64$

39. $\sqrt{44a^4 b^7 c} = \sqrt{4(a^2)^2 (b^3)^2 \cdot 11bc}$

$\qquad = 2a^2 b^3 \sqrt{11bc}$

336

© 2006 Pearson Education, Inc., Upper Saddle River, NJ. All rights reserved. This material is protected under all copyright laws as they currently exist. No portion of this material may be reproduced, in any form or by any means, without permission in writing from the publisher.

40. $5\sqrt{2} - 3\sqrt{50} + 4\sqrt{98}$

$= 5\sqrt{2} - 3\sqrt{25 \cdot 2} + 4\sqrt{49 \cdot 2}$

$= 5\sqrt{2} - 15\sqrt{2} + 28\sqrt{2}$

$= 18\sqrt{2}$

41. $\dfrac{5}{\sqrt{7} - 2} \cdot \dfrac{\sqrt{7} + 2}{\sqrt{7} + 2} = \dfrac{5\sqrt{7} + 10}{7 - 4} = \dfrac{5(\sqrt{7} + 2)}{3}$

42. $i^3 + \sqrt{-25} + \sqrt{-16} = -i + 5i + 4i = 8i$

43. $\sqrt{x + 7} = x + 5$

$x + 7 = x^2 + 10x + 25$

$x^2 + 9x + 18 = 0$

$(x + 6)(x + 3) = 0$

$x + 6 = 0, \ x + 3 = 0$

$x = -6, \ x = -3$

check: $\sqrt{-6 + 7} \overset{?}{=} -6 + 5$

$\sqrt{1} \overset{?}{=} -1$

$1 \neq -1$

$\sqrt{-3 + 7} \overset{?}{=} -3 + 5$

$\sqrt{4} \overset{?}{=} -3 + 5$

$2 = 2$

$x = -3$ is the solution.

44. $y = kx^2$

$15 = k(2)^2$

$k = \dfrac{15}{4}$

$y = \dfrac{15}{4} x^2$

$y = \dfrac{15}{4}(3)^2 = 33.75$

45. $5x(x + 1) = 1 + 6x$

$5x^2 + 5x = 1 + 6x$

$5x^2 - x - 1 = 0, \ \text{use quadratic formula}$

$x = \dfrac{-(-1) \pm \sqrt{(-1)^2 - 4(5)(-1)}}{2(5)}$

$x = \dfrac{1 \pm \sqrt{21}}{10}$

46. $5x^2 - 9x = -12x \Rightarrow 5x^2 + 3x = 0$

$x(5x + 3) = 0$

$x = 0, \ x = -\dfrac{3}{5}$

47. $x^{2/3} + 5x^{1/3} - 14 = 0, \ \text{let } x^{1/3} = w, \ x^{2/3} = w^2$

$w^2 + 5w - 14 = 0$

$(w - 2)(w + 7) = 0$

$w - 2 = 0, \ w + 7 = 0$

$w = 2, \qquad w = -7$

$x^{1/3} = 2, \quad x^{1/3} = -7$

$x = 8, \qquad x = -343$

48. $3x^2 - 11x - 4 \geq 0$

$3x^2 - 11x - 4 = 0$

$(3x + 1)(x - 4) = 0$

$3x + 1 = 0 \text{ or } \qquad x - 4 = 0$

$x = -\dfrac{1}{3} \text{ or } \qquad x = 4$

Region I: Test $x = -1$

$3(-1)^2 - 11(-1) - 4 = 10 > 0$

Region II: Test $x = 0$

$3(0)^2 - 11(0) - 4 = -4 < 0$

Region III: Test $x = 5$

$3(5)^2 - 11(5) - 4 = 16 > 0$

$x \leq -\dfrac{1}{3} \text{ or } x \geq 4$

© 2006 Pearson Education, Inc., Upper Saddle River, NJ. All rights reserved. This material is protected under all copyright laws as they currently exist.
No portion of this material may be reproduced, in any form or by any means, without permission in writing from the publisher.

49. $f(x) = -x^2 - 4x + 5$

parabola, opening downward

$f(0) = -0^2 - 4(0) + 5 = 5 \Rightarrow$ y-int: $(0, 5)$

$-x^2 - 4x + 5 = 0 \Rightarrow x^2 + 4x - 5 = 0$

$(x + 5)(x - 1) = 0 \Rightarrow x = -5, \ x = 1$

x-int: $(-5, 0), \ (1, 0)$

$-\dfrac{b}{2a} = -\dfrac{-4}{2(-1)} = -2$

$f(-2) = -(-2)^2 - 4(-2) + 5 = 9$

$V(-2, 9)$

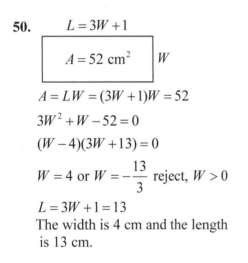

50.

$L = 3W + 1$

$A = 52 \text{ cm}^2 \quad W$

$A = LW = (3W + 1)W = 52$

$3W^2 + W - 52 = 0$

$(W - 4)(3W + 13) = 0$

$W = 4$ or $W = -\dfrac{13}{3}$ reject, $W > 0$

$L = 3W + 1 = 13$

The width is 4 cm and the length is 13 cm.

51. $x^2 + y^2 + 6x - 4y = -9$

$x^2 + 6x + 9 + y^2 - 4y + 4 = -9 + 9 + 4 = 4$

$(x + 3)^2 + (y - 2)^2 = 2^2$

$C(-3, 2), \ r = 2$

52. $\dfrac{x^2}{16} + \dfrac{y^2}{25} = 1$

$\dfrac{x^2}{4^2} + \dfrac{y^2}{5^2} = 1$, ellipse: $C(0, 0)$

$a = 4, \ b = 5$, x-int: $(\pm 4, 0)$

y-int: $(0, \pm 5)$

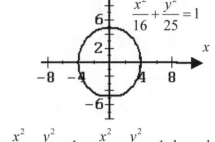

53. $\dfrac{x^2}{4} - \dfrac{y^2}{9} = 1 \Rightarrow \dfrac{x^2}{2^2} - \dfrac{y^2}{3^2} = 1$, hyperbola

$C(0, 0), \ a = 2, \ b = 3$

x-int: $(\pm 2, 0)$

$y_{\text{asymptote}} = \pm \dfrac{3}{2} x$

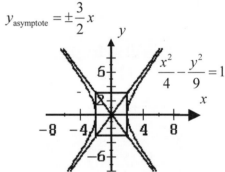

54. $x = (y - 3)^2 + 5$

parabola opening right, $V(5, 3)$

$x = (0 - 3)^2 + 5 = 14$, x-int: $(14, 0)$

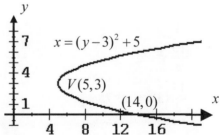

© 2006 Pearson Education, Inc., Upper Saddle River, NJ. All rights reserved. This material is protected under all copyright laws as they currently exist. No portion of this material may be reproduced, in any form or by any means, without permission in writing from the publisher.

55.
$$x^2 + y^2 = 16$$
$$x^2 - y = 4 \Rightarrow y = x^2 - 4$$
$$x^2 + (x^2 - 4)^2 = 16$$
$$x^2 + x^4 - 8x^2 + 16 = 16$$
$$x^4 - 7x^2 = 0$$
$$x^2(x^2 - 7) = 0$$
$$x^2 = 0,\ x^2 = 7$$
$$x = 0,\ x = \pm\sqrt{7}$$
$$y = x^2 - 4 = 0^2 - 4 = -4$$
$$y = x^2 - 4 = (\pm\sqrt{7})^2 - 4 = 3$$
$(0, -4),\ (\pm\sqrt{7}, 3)$ is the solution.

56. $f(x) = 3x^2 - 2x + 5$

(a) $f(-1) = 3(-1)^2 - 2(-1) + 5 = 10$

(b) $f(a) = 3a^2 - 2a + 5$

(c) $f(a+2) = 3(a+2)^2 - 2(a+2) + 5$
$$= 3a^2 + 12a + 12 - 2a - 4 + 5$$
$$= 3a^2 + 10a + 13$$

57. $f(x) = 5x^2 - 3,\ g(x) = -4x - 2$
$$f[g(x)] = f(-4x - 2)$$
$$= 5(-4x - 2)^2 - 3$$
$$= 5(16x^2 + 16x + 4) - 3$$
$$= 80x^2 + 80x + 20 - 3$$
$$= 80x^2 + 80x + 17$$

58. $f(x) = \dfrac{1}{2}x - 7,\ f(x) \to y$
$$y = \dfrac{1}{2}x - 7,\ x \leftrightarrow y$$
$$x = \dfrac{1}{2}y - 7 \Rightarrow y = 2x + 14,\ y \to f^{-1}(x)$$
$$f^{-1}(x) = 2x + 14$$

59. $M = \left\{(3,7),(2,8),\left(7,\dfrac{1}{2}\right),(-3,7)\right\}$ is not one-to-one because two pairs, $(3,7)$ and $(-3,7)$, have the same second coordinate.

60. $f(x) = 2^{1-x}$

x	$y = f(x) = 2^{1-x}$
-1	4
0	2
1	1

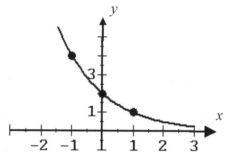

61. $\log_6 1 = x \Leftrightarrow 6^x = 1$
$$6^x = 6^0$$
$$x = 0$$

62. $\log_4(3x+1) = 3 \Leftrightarrow 3x + 1 = 4^3 = 64$
$$3x + 1 = 64$$
$$3x = 63$$
$$x = 21$$

63. $\log_{10} 0.01 = y \Leftrightarrow 10^y = 0.01$
$$10^y = 10^{-2}$$
$$y = -2$$

© 2006 Pearson Education, Inc., Upper Saddle River, NJ. All rights reserved. This material is protected under all copyright laws as they currently exist. No portion of this material may be reproduced, in any form or by any means, without permission in writing from the publisher.

64.
$$\log_2 6 + \log_2 x = 4 + \log_2(x-5)$$
$$\log_2(6x) = 4 + \log_2(x-5)$$
$$\log_2(6x) - \log_2(x-5) = 4$$
$$\log_2 \frac{6x}{x-5} = 4$$
$$\frac{6x}{x-5} = 2^4 = 16$$
$$6x = 16(x-5) = 16x - 80$$
$$16x - 80 = 6x$$
$$10x = 80$$
$$x = 8$$

© 2006 Pearson Education, Inc., Upper Saddle River, NJ. All rights reserved. This material is protected under all copyright laws as they currently exist. No portion of this material may be reproduced, in any form or by any means, without permission in writing from the publisher.